Birmingham Blitz

ANNIE MURRAY was born in Berkshire and read English at St John's College, Oxford. Her first 'Birmingham' novel, *Birmingham Rose*, hit *The Times* bestseller list when it was published in 1995. She has subsequently written fourteen other successful novels. Annie Murray has four children and lives in Reading. You can visit her website at www.anniemurray.co.uk.

ALSO BY ANNIE MURRAY

Birmingham Rose
Birmingham Friends

Orphan of Angel Street
Poppy Day
The Narrowboat Girl
Chocolate Girls
Water Gypsies
Miss Purdy's Class
Family of Women
Where Earth Meets Sky
The Bells of Bournville Green
A Hopscotch Summer
Soldier Girl
All the Days of Our Lives

ANNIE MURRAY

Birmingham Blitz

PAN BOOKS

First published 1998 by Pan Books

This edition published 2010 by Pan Books
an imprint of Pan Macmillan, a division of Macmillan Publishers Limited
Pan Macmillan, 20 New Wharf Road, London N1 9RR
Basingstoke and Oxford
Associated companies throughout the world
www.panmacmillan.com

ISBN 978-1-4472-6815-4

1 3 5 7 9 8 6 4 2

A CIP catalogue record for this book is available from
the British Library.

Typeset by SetSystems Ltd, Saffron Walden, Essex
Printed in the UK by CPI Group (UK) Ltd, Croydon, CR0 4YY

Visit www.panmacmillan.com to read more about all our books
and to buy them. You will also find features, author interviews and
news of any author events, and you can sign up for e-newsletters
so that you're always first to hear about our new releases.

For Mum and Dad,
with love and gratitude

ACKNOWLEDGEMENTS

Special thanks are due to the Birmingham people who generously gave their time to talk to me about 'their war': Elsie Ashmore and Nancy Holmes for their hospitality and frankness, Doris Burke who was a star and prepared to answer any number of daft questions, Rose and Jack Hall with whom I spent a great afternoon (Jack makes the best chips in Birmingham, if not the world), and Eric Langston for his welcome and his memories. A particular thank you also to Joe Mattiello who made himself available at unexpected moments and was a rich vein of information, and to my parents, George and Jackie Summers, who have frequently cast their minds back fifty or more years at a few seconds' notice.

Thanks also to Martin Parsons at Reading University, to Dr Rob Perks, Oral History Curator at the National Sound Archive, to Tony Doe and Concept Creative Productions.

There are a great many excellent books available about the Home Front during World War II and I drew on a variety of them, but none deserves mention more than Angus Calder's comprehensive and humane book *The People's War*. Thanks also go to Birmingham's Tindal Memory Writing Group which convened to produce *Writing It Down Before It's All Gone*, edited by Alan Mahar, which is a repeated source of inspiration.

NOTE TO THE READER

This story was originally conceived round the concept of the new and powerful influence of radio during the Second World War. Each chapter was prefaced by part of a contemporary song which in some way reflected its contents. Regrettably, because of the extremely high copyright costs of reproducing quotations from songs, these have had to be omitted from the finished book. However, readers who are familiar with the lyrics of the time might like to supply a suitable song for themselves as they go along.

A little happiness, a little sorrow,
May be awaiting you tomorrow –
That's what life is made of anyhow.

A little tearfulness a little laughter
And not a care for what comes after
There's nothing to be afraid of anyhow.

For the world rolls on the same old way
Just as night comes after day
And none of us can have a say about it,

So make the most of every minute
And get your sixty seconds in it,
'Cos that's what life is made of anyhow.

Ray Noble
(That's What Life is Made of)

August 1939

'Mom?'

Silence.

'MOM!'

'What?' That was her 'what the hell do you want *now*?' voice.

'Come up quick. It's Lola. She's dead.'

A pause from downstairs. We never usually called her Lola. Granny, Nan, filthy-old-cow, depending on who was talking, who listening. I couldn't call her Granny today somehow, not now she'd gone.

'Hang on a tick – let me put this on the gas. Genie? Sure she's not having you on?'

God Almighty. 'I'll ask her shall I? Lola? You dead, or what?'

'Don't be so cheeky.' I heard her footsteps across the back room. Then nothing. Above the mantel there was an oval mirror with a green frame, faded pink flowers stencilled round it. I realized she'd stopped, actually stopped to look at her reflection, her pale face which looked gaunt and scooped out under the high cheek-bones, thin brown hair twisted in a knot at the back, wisps of it always working out of the pins.

She dragged herself up the stairs eventually, muttering, the martyr as usual. 'She would go on a Sat'dy morning when no one's around and your dad's off playing soldiers. As if I haven't got enough on my plate.

What're we going to do? Oh!' She clapped her hand over her nose at the door.

'She must've messed herself,' I said.

'As if I couldn't tell. In this heat too!'

She hadn't messed like that before as a rule. Not the full works. Just wet the bed, my bed where I'd had to sleep with her every night for three years, pressed up against the bugs on the wall waiting for it, the wet and stink and it seeping across, warm first, then cold.

Not taking her eyes off Lola, Mom backed over and flung open the window with one hand. We could hear kids playing out the back next door. Then she crept forward, face all screwed up, on tiptoe as if she thought Lola was going to explode or jump up and dance a polka. She bent over the bed, keeping her hand on her nose. Long, pointy nose like a pixie, my mom.

Lola's hands were lying outside the covers. They'd barely looked like hands for a long while. Had a hard life. They were red like mutton chops, the knuckles tight and swollen, and she used to nurse them in her lap when they throbbed. Mom picked one up like she would a dead rat (except she never would pick up a dead rat, she'd get me to do it), her face still looking as if someone'd forced a cup of castor oil down her.

'She's not breathing.' One hand was still pegged to her nose, the other groping about round Lola's wrist. 'She's gone.' Dropped the hand and let it fall back on the bed. Finally she loosed her nose, staring at Lola's grey old face. '*Shame.* Looks quite peaceful now, don't she? You'll have to clean her up, Genie, before we get her laid out. Can't let her be seen in that state, can we?' She was over at the door by now. 'I couldn't do it. It'd make me bad.'

*

2

So I washed my dead granny that baking hot afternoon. You have to do your duty to the dead, even though she was smelly and vicious and I hated her. She had disgusting habits. Taking snuff was one of them and she only had two hankies which I always got the job of washing out. They looked as if a dog had sicked on them and I could never get them any cleaner. She sniffed louder than water going down the plughole and gobbed into the fireplace, she soaked me in urine nearly every night and talked a load of gibberish. I'd kneel down in front of her to roll her stockings up her sickly white legs with the bacon-burn marks up them from sitting close to the fire all her life, the smell of wee rising off her. Sometimes she'd slap me, hard as she could round the face. Brought tears to my eyes. She'd squawk, 'Bitch! Common little bitch!' and I knew she meant Mom because she always reckoned Mom wasn't good enough for her darling babby Victor, her youngest and best. Mom wouldn't lift a finger for her so long as I was around to do it.

She was still wearing her corset, the colour of old cement, with bits of whalebone sticking out all over the place. I pushed her over on one side which was an effort because I wasn't much of a size, and skinny with it, and she was heavy for such a scrawny old bird. Shoving my shoulder against her, I managed to get her unlaced. She was trying to roll back on me all the time, with me gagging at the stink. I took off her lisle stockings, the interlock vest and bloomers and saw all the brown mess between her legs and up her back and in her scraggy little mound of hair down there.

While I was going over her with a rag and a pail of water (cold – Mom said, 'What's the use in wasting gas, she's dead, isn't she?') I thought, what would she have looked like when she was fifteen? And how with a name

3

like Lola Mavis she ought to have been in a circus act instead of working factories the length and breadth of Birmingham.

I bent down to squeeze out the rag in the water that looked like stewed tea but didn't smell at all like it, trying not to drip any on my frock.

'Oh my God!' I said, straightening up. My heart was pounding like a mad thing and sweat pricked under my arms because I'd have sworn on my own life she moved and I was out of that room and down the stairs as if my bloomers were on fire.

'Mom – she moved. She's not dead. I saw her titties going up and down!'

'*No.*' Her hand halted a wooden spoon in the air. 'You're seeing things!'

But we both tiptoed up the stairs and peeped into that room, not knowing what we were scared of except we'd both have screamed like billy-o if there'd been one tiny flicker of movement from her. All we could see were the grimy old soles of Lola's feet and the soiled sheet in a heap on the floor and the enamel bucket and there wasn't a sound as we moved closer. She lay quite, quite still.

We stood by the bed and suddenly Mom was tittering away like the Laughing Policeman and set me off. I thought this was a bit of all right, Mom being nice to me, us laughing as if we couldn't stop. But we did stop, very sudden, because we saw Lola's eyes had slid half open and she was watching the pair of us like an old parrot.

'For God's sake get her eyes closed,' Mom said, disgusted. 'I'll fetch you a couple of pennies.'

I pushed Lola's eyes closed and laid a penny and a ha'penny on top, which was all she could find. I covered her, pulling an old sheet up over her twisted feet, the wasted belly which had turned out twelve children, three dead, nine living, her papery old bosoms and her mean, crumpled face. I thought how a dead body isn't just the person who's left it a few minutes ago but a shrine to everyone they've ever been. And I also thought thank God I can have the bed to myself instead of perching on the edge waiting for the deluge.

There was a deluge then, because outside it started to rain like hell and the sky was so low it nearly scraped the rooftops. It felt like a promise of something, like God saying yes, I'll give you a chance, kid. Now you can make things right in your family. Now you can be happy.

Mom chose to name me Eugenie Victoria Josephine Mary Watkins (I don't suppose Dad had any say in the matter). At my christening at St Paul's Church in 1924, he leaned over my pram, a father for the first time, and I imagine his round face pink with pride.

'Look at her,' he said, chucking my cheek. 'She'll go far.'

Nanny Rawson, my other grandmother, stood just behind him, commented, 'With a gobful of names like that she'll need to.'

I don't know how far he thought I was going, but by 1939 none of us had got further than Brunswick Road, Balsall Heath, where we had a back door as well as a front and our very own flush toilet in the garden. I lived with my mom, my dad who was a bus driver, my little brother Eric, seven years younger (Mom's 'other mistake' as she kindly called him), and Mom's brother, Uncle Len. And Lola of course, up until now.

Nanny Rawson lived nearly half a mile away in Highgate, and Len stopped at home with her up until Mom's sister, my auntie Lil, had to move back in there with her kids and Len came to live with us. He wasn't quite the full shilling, Uncle Len. No one'd say why, so I took it for granted he must've been born that way. He was an enormous bloke. Didn't just come into a room, he took up half of it. He was all right. Sweet natured, and loved to hear people laugh. Not that living with Mom and Dad was ideal on that score.

He came to us a few months after Lola'd arrived, so our terraced house started to get crowded. Lola and I had had a room each. Mine was the little one at the end and Eric slept in with Mom and Dad at the front. But when Len arrived everything had to be juggled round.

'Eric'll stay in with us,' Mom decreed. She didn't object to Eric down at the foot of their bed on his mattress. I suppose someone else in the room helped keep Dad off her. 'And you'll have to bunk up with Lola at the end.'

'With Lola! But Mom – there's no room for another bed in there.'

'You won't need another bed. The one you've got now's three-quarter size. You'll have to share. It'll only be for a bit. She can't last much longer.'

This was appalling news. Lola was revolting enough round the house, but to have to share my bed with her! Being an innocent twelve-year-old, I protested, 'Well, why can't I share with Len?'

Mom glowered at me. 'Don't talk so silly. Len's a grown man and he needs a decent room to himself. And besides,' as she was turning away, 'he's not without a few funny habits.'

Typical of her, that was. Never explained things.

'Don't run backwards!' she'd shout at me when I was younger and capering along the pavement. 'I know someone who died doing that.'

I found out about Len's funny habits all too quickly. I barged into his room one day and there he was, kneeling on the floor in front of the chamber pot, unbuttoned, with his willy clenched in his hand, except it wasn't like a willy any more. More like a policeman's truncheon. He didn't even notice me, he had this grin on his moon face and whatever he was doing I could see he was enjoying it. I knew I'd best not say anything to Mom. I carried on sharing with Lola and kept out of Len's bedroom.

Len was no trouble though. I was puzzled to notice Mom'd do anything for him, because she certainly didn't display that attitude to anyone else, not even her pal Stella, and you can at least choose your friends. Len just sat about or went for little walks round the local streets. He played tip-cat and football with Eric and me. He looked through Eric's comics, *Desperate Dan* and *Hotspur*. He sat in the pub and laughed if someone else was laughing, and people were mostly kind to him. He never had a job in those days. Jobs were hard enough to come by for anyone. I grew ever so fond of him. He was more like a big, soft brother to me than a grown up man.

Dad couldn't make a fuss about him moving in because he had Lola there already, transforming Mom into one of the saints and martyrs even though I did most of the skivvying. He liked Len. Besides, he wasn't the sort to make a fuss. Quiet man, my dad. He didn't get up and bang on about anything much. Mom could've got away with murder, and often did. Emotional murder. Poison darts kept flying his way – 'Victor, you're useless, hopeless, no good to anyone . . .'

She made it quite clear to Eric and me that pregnancy and birth had been the greatest trials of her life and that to compensate her for the ordeal of bringing us into existence we had to bother her as little as we could manage. We'd been through the ploys of trying to get her attention by loudness, naughtiness and breaking things, and nothing had worked for long, so we had to learn to put up with it and shift for ourselves.

Mom had days sometimes when she couldn't even seem to move herself, just sat in a chair staring at the walls. Life weighted her to the floor. She was literally bored stiff. Bored with my dad, my solid, reliable dad, who had not an ounce of lightness or fun in him but was all a husband and father should be – except whatever it was she wanted him to be. I know she never loved him – not even when they first got married. Lil always said Mom married him to keep up with her pal Stella.

When I used to hear them talking, Stella and Mom, about their lives, Mom'd say, 'And then of course I went and married Victor.' The way she said it it might as well have been, 'And then I died.'

A lot of women didn't expect more than they got, but she did. She was romantic and full of dreams. I reckon on those bad days, when her face was strung tight and her hair never came out of a scarf and she smoked and snapped and sighed all day, she was looking at her life those last twelve, thirteen, fourteen years and thinking, 'What a waste.'

For Eric and me there was Nanny Rawson. She was always there and always, after a fashion, pleased to see us. When Mom sat listless in her chair and said, 'Oh go out and do summat with yourselves,' we'd often as not shoot up the Moseley Road to our nan's, me holding Eric's little hand to keep him off the horse road. Nanny

Rawson'd give us a piece with jam if she had any and let us play out in the yard with the neighbour's kids. We'd stay until it was nearly time for bed. When we got home, sometimes Mom had cooked for us. Sometimes she was still sitting in her chair, the same cup of cold tea balanced on the arm.

Course, all the family were at Lola's funeral in their glory. Dad got back from his camp with the Territorials two days earlier. He joined the TA a year before, after the Munich crisis, which I suppose made him feel useful and got him out of the house one evening a week after a shift on the buses, and some weekends. Must have been restful for him. They were training him up as a signalman.

Life was barely worth living in our house the morning we buried Lola. Mom had given Dad hell ever since Lola passed on because he hadn't been there.

'I couldn't help it, Doreen,' he snapped at her finally. He must have been feeling guilty enough already. 'But I had to go. The way things are there's going to be a war – soon.'

'There's not going to be a war,' Mom sneered. 'They won't let it happen.' She looked suddenly frightened. 'They won't, will they?'

She'd been up since crack of dawn, a scarf round her curlers, cutting bread for sandwiches, eggs bobbling noisily in a pan of water. Good job it was only sandwiches because she wasn't the world's greatest cook. She got everything too dry or too wet and finished it off by burning it. Her rock cakes spread out into black coins of sponge, charred sultanas bulging out.

'Who's coming then?' I asked.

Mom sniffed. 'Don't know for sure. But some of *them*'ll most likely turn up.'

'Them' were some of Dad's long lost relatives, and she was going to show them what was what. Dad's brothers and sisters were all scattered about, some in Birmingham, some wider still. We weren't sure where and we never saw any of them. But Mom was determined that she was a cut above whoever might turn up so it was out with a tin of salmon and the house had to be spotless.

The coffin was in the front room taking up most of the space between the whatnot in the window with an aspidistra on the top in a brass pot, leaves snagging on the window nets, and the little china cabinet at the back end of the room. The chairs had been pushed to one side, and dead flies dusted out of the vases. Mom liked to keep the front room a bit special so we spent most of our time in the back round the table.

Thing about my mom was, she had dreams of everything all kippers and curtains out on one of the new estates. She'd say names like 'Glebe Farm, Weoley Castle, Fox Hollies' with a special look in her eye, sort of tasting them on her tongue. New houses with bathrooms and neat little gardens front and back. But she wouldn't go. It wasn't Dad stopping her. And we weren't half as hard up as some of the neighbours. Balsall Heath, just a couple of miles south of the middle of Birmingham, may not have been her first choice, but she could at least feel she'd gone up in the world because she had a back and a front room and a patch of garden, and she had a set of willow pattern china off the Bull Ring when many a household in the street were still drinking out of jam jars. And in the end she needed another kind of security – she'd never move too far from her mom, Nanny Rawson, in her back-house in Highgate.

It was Nan who'd arranged everything for Lola: the plot in Lodge Hill Cemetery, registering the death, the hearse. Mom had one of her times of deciding she couldn't cope. But she was the one in charge today, pinner over her nightdress, dispensing orders. The house filled up with shouting.

'Doreen – I need a shirt collar . . .' Dad didn't tend to move when he needed anything, just sat tight and hoped it would appear.

'Here!' she hollered up the stairs from the back room. Could bawl like a fishwife she could, when she forgot she was trying to be respectable. She had a collar in one hand, loaf under the other arm, the top half buttered. 'It's starched.' Course it was. I'm surprised she didn't starch his underpants.

'Genie – I want you out scrubbing the front step before you think about getting dressed up. Eric—' thwack—'get your hands off. Look – the table's all smears now!'

'I daint mean to,' Eric snivelled, clutching his smart-ing ear.

'Genie – just get him out of here. Keep out of my way. And Lenny, sit down, will you? You're getting me all mithered. At least you're ready – even if it is hours before time.'

Len launched himself backwards into a chair so the cushion would've groaned if it were capable. His clothes were too tight and none of us had had any breakfast, but Len still had the grin stuck on his face that had been there since Monday when he got his first ever job, aged twenty-nine. He was going to pack shells at the Austin works, travel out on the bus, the lot, and he was so

11

pleased with himself he'd hardly been able to sit still since.

'You'd best go in the garden for a bit,' I advised Eric. 'I've got to scrub the step.'

'Can't I come and watch you, Genie?'

'All right. If you have to.'

I completed my chore in the morning sunlight, made hazier by all the smoke from the factory chimneys. The smell of manure rose from the horse road and there was a whiff in the air of something chemical. Eric stood leaning against the front wall, sniffing and idly scuffing his shoes against the brickwork.

'You'd better pack that in,' I said, 'or you won't half get it.'

Then I was allowed to get changed. I had one decent dress which Mom had knocked up on her old Vesta machine. First time she'd made me anything. It was a pale blue shirtwaister, and I wore it with a pair of white button-up shoes which were scuffed grey round the toe-tips and pinched at the sides, but I could at least still get them on. I felt awkward in that dress. That was partly because Mom had managed to get the waist too high. And I suppose I didn't think of myself as a girl – not a proper one, like my friend Teresa, and other girls who liked to dress up. I was so skinny, Dad used to say, 'We could use you as a pull-through for a rifle' – elbows and knees sticking out and my socks would never stay up. I was supposed to be a woman by now, getting 'bosoms' and acting grown up. After all, I was out at work. But it was all a flaming nuisance, to my mind. Your monthly coming on, rags chafing in your knickers. I didn't half wish I was a boy sometimes.

Downstairs in the back room I peeped in the oval

mirror. My face looked back at me from the yellow glass, big grey eyes almost too big as my face was so thin and delicate, pointy nose, though not sticking out as far as Mom's. My straight, straight brown hair was parted in the middle and hung thick over my shoulders. Auntie Lil used to say I was prettier than my mom. She may've said that just to rile Mom of course. I gave myself a smile which brought out my dimple, like a little pool by the right side of my mouth.

Dad emerged from the stairs and said, 'You look a picture, Genie. Be nice to see you doll yourself up more often.' I went pink. Dad seemed to be having trouble turning his head. Must've been the starch in that collar.

Mom'd been fussing on the way. 'Victor, your tie's not straight. Genie, you take Len into church and make sure he behaves himself. Eric, for pity's sake stop sniffing.' Poor Eric. Very snotty, my little brother. Whatever the time of year there was always a reservoir of green up his nose.

They were all waiting outside St Paul's Church in their Sunday best, a line of desperately polished shoes, and coats even though it was the middle of summer, giving off a smell of mothballs. Nanny Rawson had on a navy straw hat and her mud-coloured coat which she'd bought off a lady second-hand, saying you could get away with brown on any occasion. She was a wide lady, walked rocking from foot to foot the way you might shift a full barrel of beer. She had an ulcer on her right leg so it was thickly bandaged, and round, muscular calves as if someone had dropped a couple of cricket balls down inside her legs. To match her hair she had a bit of a black moustache, which is more than my grandad had. Bald as a pig's bladder he was. But of course he'd been dead ten years by 1939.

There were a group of four people in shabby clothes and down-at-heel shoes who I thought looked ever so old, and when Dad went to them, red in the face, sweat on his forehead, I realized these were some of the uncles and an auntie we never saw. He shook each of their hands or slapped their shoulders, said, 'Awright are you?' and couldn't seem to think of anything else to say. Mom was looking down her nose at them, and they shifted about on their feet and looked embarrassed. I went and shook hands too, and one of the men looked nice and kissed me, and they said, 'Hello Eugenie,' the woman with a sarky note in her voice. I don't think she was my proper auntie. She just married someone.

Lil was there with her kids. She had a wide black hat on with a brim which we'd never seen before. Mom sidled up to her nodding her head like a chicken at the hat. 'Cashed in your pawn ticket in time, did you?'

Dad was saying, '*Doreen*,' pulling her arm. 'Remember who we're burying today, please.'

'I'm hardly likely to forget, Victor,' brushing his hand off. 'Since I was the one left to deal with it all while you were off playing soldiers.'

Dad's cherub face was all pink now, his voice trembling. 'How many times do I have to tell you, the Territorial Army does not play soldiers. Don't you realize just how serious . . .'

Lil started putting her threepence ha'penny in too, her lovely face puckered with annoyance. In a stage whisper she started off, 'Don't forget, you stuck up cow, that some of us do a job of – Patsy!' She broke into a yell, catching sight of him leaping gravestones like a goat. 'Get here – now!' That was our Lil for you. Scarcely ever got through a whole sentence without having to bawl out one of the kids.

'Pack it in, the lot of you,' Nan hissed at them. 'They're staring at us.' She tilted the straw hat towards the aunt and uncles whose eyes were fixed on us. 'Doreen – go in,' Nan commanded, still through her teeth. 'And see if you can keep your gob shut.'

'Come along, Eric.' Mom flounced off in her mauve and white frock, yanking Eric along in his huge short trousers which reached well below his knobbly knees.

Dad seemed flustered, not knowing who to sit with, and ended up following me in with Len. I took Len's hand. 'Come on – I'll look after you.'

He came with me like a little kid. No one wanted to sit in the actual front row so we filed into the second lot of pews. Len's knees were touching the back of the pew in front, his enormous thighs pressed against mine. It wasn't that he was a fat man, he was just built on a huge scale. He kept looking round at me, pulling faces and grinning.

'S'nice this, Genie, in't it?' I think he liked the candles and the coloured glass. He pointed to his fly buttons and said loudly, 'What if I need to go?'

'You just tell me,' I whispered. 'I'll take you out. Try and keep your voice down, Len.'

He heard Cathleen, Lil's three-year-old, laughing behind us, so he started laughing too – hor hor hor – hell of a noise, shoulders going up and down.

'Len.' I gripped his arm, nervously. 'You're not s'posed to be laughing. Lola's in that coffin up there.' I pointed at it, flowers on top, the lot.

'In there?' He pointed a massive finger.

I nodded. 'She's dead – remember?'

15

But that set him off even worse and I had to start getting cross and say, 'Now Len, stop it. You mustn't.'

Along our pew Mom was frowning across at Eric for pulling snot up his nose too loudly. Then there was a bawl from behind. Cathleen must've pulled Tom's hair and made him whimper and Lil had smacked him one low down on the leg hoping no one'd see. He blarted even louder and Cathleen was grinning away to herself under those angelic blond curls, the mardy little cow. Nanny Rawson, next to the aisle in our pew, swivelled round and gave them all the eye from under that hat.

A train rattled past at the back of the church. At last the Reverend started in on his prayers. 'We brought nothing into this world and it is certain we carry nothing out . . .'

I started to feel sorry for old Lola now I couldn't smell her. Dad was a bit upset and blew his nose a lot. He'd tried to do his best for her. After all, she was his mom, even if she was a miserable old bitch. He was forever telling us it was just her age. She wasn't always like that. Mom'd say, 'Oh yes she flaming well was.'

But I sat there and thought what a rotten life she must've had. Terrible poverty they lived in when her kids were small. A slum house, not even attic-high, two up, one down on the yard, with nine children in the house and never enough to go round. Didn't make her a kind person. Her husband did his best, from what Dad said, but he was a bit of a waster. My father was her little ray of sunshine. Bright at school and had always held down a job. The other kids drifted away and mostly stayed away.

I looked across at the coffin as we stood up and started in on 'Abide With Me'. I thought about her old wasted body in there. How she'd climb out of bed very quick and pull her clothes up to sit on the chamber pot. Sometimes I'd get a glimpse of something hanging down there, like an egg, white and glistening. She'd sit for an age, grunting and cursing, willing urine to flow the way you will a late train to come. Sometimes she'd put her hand up her, try and push it back and relieve herself, and she'd give a moan. Soon as she lay down again it'd all come in a rush and I'd be clinging to the edge of the mattress trying to keep as far from her as I could, almost crying at the smell.

Poor old Lola. Thank God she'd gone.

'I hope they don't notice I've eked the salmon out with milk,' Mom whispered, stirring the teapot in the kitchen at the back. 'Here, take these through, will you Genie?'

I carried the sandwiches to the front room, Mom's willing slave as ever. Willing because I'd have done anything for her if only she'd be glad I existed. She was being quite pally-pally with me today because she needed my help.

Everyone was crushed into the front room except Lil, who'd taken the kids out to let off steam in the garden. Eric and Little Patsy, a year his junior, were brawling on the grass like puppies.

It went all right, just about. Dad's brothers and sister were either silent or very very jolly and the uncles loosened their threadbare ties, asked each other for a light and stood about smoking and sweating. There wasn't the room to sit down. The auntie spent a lot of time peering in Mom's china cabinet. They ate all they could and went out saying, 'We'll have to do this again,' but all knowing the truth was that it'd be at the next funeral, and departed even more awkward than when they arrived.

So that left our family with the curling egg sandwiches and nubs of Madeira cake to get on in our usual affectionate way. I stuck with Len and brought him more helpings of food because he could eat for ever, his mouth churning away like a mincer.

Lil had brought the kids back in. She was a stunner, our Lil, and like a flypaper to men. Like Nanny Rawson she looked as though she had a touch of the tar-brush: she had tresses of black hair, almond-shaped brown eyes and olive skin, and today she'd got a dab of colour on her lips. Before she had the kids she sometimes used to put curl papers in her hair, and it hung in shiny black snakes down her back. Wild as the wind she was then, all high heels and make up. She worked as a french polisher in a toy factory, on gun handles and little carpet sweepers.

Mom'd always been jealous of her. Lil's looks of course, for a start, even though she was worn to the bone nowadays with the kids. Lil was chosen as the May Queen when they were kids at school and Mom's never forgiven her for that. But I think another part of her jealousy was Lil moving back in with our nan after her husband died. Well, I say died. Patrick Heaney was his name. Cheerful Big Patsy. Mom never liked him. Doesn't like the Irish full stop, and his other crime was to make Lil happy. Patsy got into a fight one night – more of a friendly by all accounts – but the other bloke knocked him over on the kerb and he had a nasty bang on the head. He was never the same after. Turned to the booze, had fits, couldn't get out of bed of a morning.

Next thing was they were dragging him out of the canal. It was a shame. Lil was in pieces. But at least while he was alive she really had something with Big Patsy that Mom'd never had. You could see it in their eyes. She'd sit in his lap, even after Little Patsy was born. Popped out a couple of kids in as many years.

But she couldn't cope on her own, what with holding down a job and the kids and their third child Cathleen being only a titty-babby. Poor Lil.

Cathleen sat on Lil's lap and started pulling at her waves of black hair.

'Leave off, will you?' Lil snapped. 'Never get a second to yourself with kids, do you? Can't even fart in peace.'

'Give 'er 'ere,' Nan said. She took the little girl on to her enormous lap and bounced her until she squealed.

Lil sat back, tired as usual. Her mouth turned down more nowadays. 'How about another cuppa tea, Dor, now that lot've gone?'

'You know where the kettle is,' Mom said with her usual charm.

'I'll get it.' I went to the kitchen and made tea, not that I expected any thanks for it, and when I got back they were arguing. Mom and Lil that is. Len was shuffling a pack of cards. He never played anything, just shuffled. He and Dad usually just sat waiting for the wenches to burn themselves out.

Our nan had a look in her eye I didn't quite like. She was sat forward. Cathleen had got down and was on the floor waving her legs in the air, showing off her bloomers.

'Because,' Nan was saying, 'it's the practice run Sat'dy, ain't it?'

'I'm not sending my kids nowhere,' Lil said, scraping at egg on Tom's face with her nails. 'Whatever Adolf bloody Hitler's planning.'

Hitler this, Hitler that, all we ever heard nowadays. I put the tray down, pushing plates aside. Everyone was keyed up about the thought of war war war.

'Your mom'll need you at 'ome,' Nanny Rawson said to me. 'You can look after your dad.'

'Why?' Lil looked at Mom. In a nasty tone she demanded, 'Where're you off to then?'

'With Eric.'

Eric looked from one to the other of them, mouth full of cake and a hopeless expression on his face. He knew he wasn't going to get a say.

'You mean you're sending him? To live with complete strangers?' Lil was on her high horse. She caught hold of Cathleen and cuddled her tight, doing her best impression of the Virgin Mary.

'That's what we're supposed to be doing, isn't it? Or d'you want your kids bombed and gassed like they say they will be?'

'But just sending him off ... Poor little thing.' Eric looked about as depressed as anyone would be faced with the choice of bombing and gassing or being sent away to live heaven only knew where. 'Anyhow,' Lil said. 'You don't need to go to the practice. Not as if you're going with him, is it?'

Mom was silent for a split second. Everyone stared at her. She stuck her chin out. 'I thought I'd go.'

Dad sat up then. News to him, obviously. 'But Doreen...'

Nan was scandalized. 'You mean go off – leave Victor and Genie?'

'Not for good. I thought I could just deliver him. Have a look over where he's going.'

'But you're not allowed,' Lil argued. 'I'd be allowed to go, with Cathleen so young, but you're not – not unless you're a helper or you're . . .' Lil looked ever so suspicious all of a sudden.

Mom stared back at her, brazen, nose in the air.

'You're never going to tell them . . .' Lil started laughing a real nasty laugh. 'Oh I get it. Well it wouldn't be the first time, would it? After all, you were "expecting" when you got Victor to marry you, weren't you? Longest pregnancy on record that one. What was it? Fifteen months?'

Dad had gone nearly purple in the face, to the roots of his hair. Mom stabbed her knife into the last piece of Madeira cake as if she wanted to kill something. 'You bloody little bitch.' I thought she was going to slap Lil but Nanny Rawson was on her feet pushing them apart.

'That's enough from the pair of you.' She stood with her arms outstretched between them.

'She only said she was pregnant so she could beat Stella to the altar!'

'Well at least I've still got a husband – I'm not dragging my kids up in the slums.'

'But you don't give a monkey's about sending Eric off to live with Christ only knows who . . .'

'That's why I'm saying I'm expecting you silly cow – so I can get on the train with him . . .'

I went and sat by Eric, who no one seemed to have given a moment's thought to.

'Take no notice,' I said, putting my arm round him.

'Is she going to send me away?' He had tears in his eyes. 'Where am I going?'

21

'Somewhere nice I expect. In the country. See the cows and sheep. It'll be all right,' I told him, though I hadn't the foggiest whether it would or not. 'Here – want a game of snap?'

Eric nodded, picture of misery.

'Right, now sit yourselves down,' our Nan was saying. 'As a mark of respect to Lola, since we 'aven't seen much of that yet, we'll 'ave a song.'

'I'm not singing with her,' Mom said.

'That's what you think.' Nan got her squeeze box out from the corner and sat with it on her lap, legs apart, skirt pulling tight across her knees.

'She's wearing red bloomers,' Eric whispered to me, distracted for a moment.

'Doreen, Lil, stand up. You sing along too, Len,' Nan urged him.

I got the cards off Len and played with Eric, and Dad sighed with relief that they'd all stopped carrying on and the two loving sisters started on a song. Nan was fantastic on the accordion. She'd picked it up off her dad and she could play the piano too. Just about anything you asked in the way of songs. A gift that, that ran in the family until it got to me, apparently. Mom could have a go too, given the chance. She, Lil and Nanny Rawson all had good strong voices. People called them the Andrews Sisters, and they did a turn in the pub now and again. Times when they sang were mostly the only occasions when they weren't arguing.

So they stood in our front room with the sunlight fading outside and Dad lighting one fag after another to calm his nerves. They sang 'The Rose of Picardy' and 'Ta-ra-ra-boom-de-ay', blending their voices, and then that new song, 'The Lambeth Walk' everyone was mad about. Lil looked so pretty and not tired suddenly, Nan's face was softer than usual and Len was swaying from side to side in his chair, face split by a smile, in heaven.

Mom looked almost happy while the music was going on. I saw Dad watching her and there were tears in his eyes. Shook me a bit, that. I wondered whether he was thinking about Lola, or about the fact that he might soon have to go away, or whether he was wondering the same as I was: why Mom couldn't find it in her to be happier with him – with all of us.

Come the end of that week we were in for a surprise. I was working in a pawn shop in Highgate, which disgusted Mom, but it was one of the best jobs I'd had so far. That week, as we stood in the little shop on the Moseley Road, we watched a crowd filling sandbags to shore up the factories opposite. Every day there were changes. That Friday I walked home after work and saw the last evening rays catching the bloated shape of a barrage balloon, a silky light coming from it. Some people, Mom among them, were still saying, 'Oh there's not going to be a war.' But if there was to be no war, what was all this for? Digging trenches in the parks, blackout curtains downstairs, and sending the kids away.

We'd had the gas masks months. One day when I got home Mom'd said in a grim voice, 'Look what's arrived.' There was a pile of boxes by the door. The masks were most off-putting. They looked a bit of a joke with their mouse faces until you put one on. When I pulled it over my face it was so tight, and the smell of rubber made you heave. The leaflets told us there'd be wardens round with rattles if we had a gas attack.

'I couldn't wear that,' Mom said, shuddering. 'Make me sick that would.'

Dad, standing in shirtsleeves at the door, remarked, 'I don't s'pose being gassed'd make you feel all that marvellous neither.'

I didn't really understand about war. Everyone was forever on about 'the Last One' but I wasn't born till nearly six years after it finished. All I knew was that everyone was living on their nerves. Mom was on at Dad because he might have to go away. 'What did you have to go and join the TA for? Other men of your age aren't being called up. How d'you think I'm going to manage without you here?' she'd wail. Tears turned on as well. There was a feeling about, excited and deadly serious at the same time, building up like the tension in a dog waiting to spring.

When I walked through the front door that evening I knew something was different. It was quiet, much more so than usual, but I could hear a voice in the back room. A man's voice. Posh. I didn't know who it was. I pushed the door open and before I'd had a chance even to open my mouth they all said, 'Ssssh!' without even looking at me. There they were, all sat round the table: Mom, Dad, Eric, Len. And in the middle of the table, shiny and new and absolutely gorgeous, there she was.

'Blimey! Whose—? What—? Whose is it?'

'Sssssh,' they said again. Len was making gleeful sounds, bouncing up and down in his seat.

The man's voice went on for a moment longer, then music started to trickle out into the room. I tiptoed closer and stared. It was a beautiful thing, almost a couple of feet long, encased in veneered wood with a dark grain across it as if it had been washed by the sea. On one half of the front was the speaker, the overlaid wood cut into a sunburst. On the other half, set into a metal surround, was the dial, with little ebony knobs underneath it. Out from it, louder now, were coming the sounds of violins and trumpets and other instruments all pitching in together, and it gave me a queer feeling. Made me want to cry suddenly though I didn't know why. Even Len went quiet.

I didn't get any sense out of anyone until Mom got up to put the kettle on.

'So – whose is it?'

'Len's. He bought it. First wage packet.' She moved her mouth close to my ear. 'We made up the extra for him – saw he had enough.' Her little brother. The one person in the world she'd kill to protect.

'Is that yours then, Len?' He looked as if he was going to burst, head nodding up and down like crazy.

'Pleased as punch he is,' Dad said. As if he needed to.

I squeezed Len's shoulder. 'Aren't you lucky? It's really smashing.'

Next day, Mom dragged Eric off to school for his evacuation rehearsal. The schools opened specially, even though it was the summer holidays. Mom had put away her ideas of being able to wangle a passage with him now it had dawned on her that Dad might have to go sooner than she'd realized. Eric had to go off with a small holdall for his clothes and a little bag for his 'iron rations' and his gas mask.

It was a peaceful morning in one way. Dad sat and read the *Sports Argus* and we didn't clear away breakfast for a good hour. Len settled himself down by his wireless and kept twiddling the dial, catching torn up bits of sound until he heard something he fancied.

I was supposed to be cooking lunch, but I sat down for a bit too, feeling that without Mom around I could leave my hair loose and straggly and no one would tick me off for the grubby stains on my frock. I stretched my legs out in front of me, seeing how skinny and pale they looked, and wished I didn't have a figure like a clothes-horse. But all the time worries about Eric kept flickering through my mind and I had a queasy ball of tension inside me. I thought about my family all being split up and suddenly they didn't seem so bad any more and I wanted things to stay as they were.

'Dad?'

'Mm?'

'If there's a war will you have to go straight away?'

He laid the paper down in his lap and looked ahead. Outside someone was having a fire and rags of smoke kept drifting past the window. 'Could be any time now, love.'

'Oh.' The music carried on quietly behind us.

Dad turned his head to look at me. 'I know I'm not all your mother would want ...' He couldn't seem to finish that bit. 'You will look after her for me, won't you?'

I nodded and he looked away again. 'You're a good wench.'

That morning, while we were waiting and wondering, I heard a singer who was to become one of my favourites. Her voice came from the wireless strong and dark as gravy browning. We sat quite still while she was singing. The second she'd finished, Len pointed at the wireless and said, 'Gloria.'

'What you on about, Len? They said her name was Anne Shelton.'

He shook his head hard and pointed again. 'Gloria.'

I realized he meant the wireless itself, and I saw how

much it suited her. Glorious Gloria. From then on she was never known as anything but Gloria.

One Wednesday night we were all listening to *Band Waggon*, all in stitches at Arthur Askey, Len laughing at us laughing – hor hor hor – out of his belly. We had Gloria turned up high and I thought she was the best thing that had ever happened because before that I never ever remember us all sitting laughing together. Even Mom looked happy, and I saw Dad watching her, all hopeful.

And then she stopped. Right in the middle of it, no more Gloria. Len was out of his chair, wild at the knobs. 'Gloria ... Gloria ...' Not listening to Mom, who was trying to say, 'Lenny, it's OK, it's just the accumulator ...'

Len sank back on his chair and blubbed, fat slugs of tears rolling from his eyes and his shoulders shaking as if there was an earthquake. 'Gloria ... Gloria!'

'LEN!' Mom bawled down his ear. 'GLORIA WILL BE ALL RIGHT. WE NEED TO TOP UP HER ACCUMULATOR!' To the rest of us, she said, 'Listen to me. *Gloria*. Getting as bad as he is.'

She got through to him in the end and he stopped crying, but his face was dismal. He spent the rest of the evening with Gloria in his lap, lying across his thighs as if she was an injured cat.

I took the accumulator in on my way to work the next day. There was a cycle shop on Stoney Lane would top them up for you. I'd never given much thought to what was in them before, but I soon found out because the aroma of spilt acid in that shop made my eyes water. It was eating into the floor.

'You got a spare?' the bloke asked.

We hadn't, though I thought we'd better get one so's not to have this performance every time.

'I'll be back for it after work,' I told him.

So, come the evening I handed over threepence, and it would have been worth a shilling just to see Len's face when I walked in with it. Gloria was on again straight away in time for *The Six O'Clock News*.

Those last days of August we still waited and waited. It was like being held under water.

The groups of people gossiping in Nan's shop were saying, 'Let's get it over with if it's coming. Just let us know one way or the other.'

It was a time full of instructions. Leaflets through the door, the papers, and of course Gloria, who took our hands and led us into the war, giving out advice and information as we went. Hearing the voices which came from her was like someone sat right there in the back room with you. And she gave us relief from it, letting our minds slip away into plays and stories and songs.

The newspapers were different. On 31 August Dad brought home the *Birmingham Mail*. There was the banner across the front, stark in black and white:

EVACUATION TOMORROW . . . BRITAIN AWAITS
HITLER'S REPLY.

September 1939

'Genie? can I come in with you?'

It was before dawn. I could just see Eric's outline in the doorway of my room.

'What's up?'

He came silently up to my bed. 'She's sending me away, ain't she?'

I pulled the bed open. 'Here – hop in.'

'Ain't she?' His toes were chilly against my leg.

'She thinks it's for the best. You don't want that nasty man Hitler dropping bombs on you, do you, Eric?'

His tousled head moved from side to side against my chest. I put my arms round him, scrawny little bit that he was, and pulled the sheet close round us.

'Little Patsy's not going.'

'But the Spinis are – Francesca and Giovanna and Tony – even Luke.' My friend Teresa's brothers and sisters.

'They'll all be together . . . I'll be all on my own.'

'You never know – you might be able to go with them.'

But he was already crying, snuffling like a kitten, a hand pressing on one of my titties, such as I had.

'Don't wanna go. I don't wanna.'

'Now Eric – it won't be for long,' I kept telling

him. 'It'll be for the best. Mom only wants the best for you.'

I lay holding him, hoping that was the truth.

Mom stood by the open back door with a packet of Players, blowing smoke across our thin strip of garden. I went out to use the privy. There were cobwebs under the roof, cut out squares of the *Gazette* on a string, and no seat. I sat on the cold white enamel feeling a breeze under the door. When I came out, a bird was singing. A thin mesh of cloud covered the sky but the air was growing warm. It was about six-thirty.

Mom stood with one arm wrapped round the waist of her cotton nightdress, her bit of stomach pushing out from under it, other hand holding the cigarette in front of her face. Her skin looked pasty, nose shiny with night sweat. She was often like that, miles away, but this time her expression was drawn and frightened. I didn't even think she'd seen me, until she said, 'What're we going to do?'

I stared at her. I was angry at her for sending Eric away, and angrier because I knew she was right: there was going to be a war and none of us knew what would happen, and we were all confused and frightened.

'How d'you mean?'

'I don't know if I'm doing the right thing.'

You're the mom, I thought, not me. What you asking me for?

'Mrs Spini's got four to send,' I said, stepping past her.

'Thought she wasn't going to.'

'Changed her mind.'

'Typical.' Tutting. 'Italians.'

I filled the teapot. Mom turned, slit-eyed, smoke unfurling from her nose. 'I'm only doing what I'm told, you know Genie.' She pointed in, towards Gloria. 'She – I mean they – say that's what we've got to do. This is an evacuation area. So we're s'posed to evacuate.'

'Well that's all right then, isn' it?'

'What are you looking at me like that for then?'

'I don't know.' I could feel the tears coming on. I turned away.

We heard my dad coming down. The stair door pushed open into the back room.

'It's right, in't it Victor?'

'What is?' He was stood there in his shirt and underpants.

'Sending Eric out of harm's way.'

Dad looked in some amazement into Mom's pinched, foxy face and saw that for the first time any of us could remember she was actually asking his advice. He pulled his shoulders back and stroked the reddish stubble on his chin. 'I should say so. If that's what they're saying.'

'Where is he, anyhow?'

'In my bed. Still asleep. He came in in the night, crying.'

'Shame.' Mom stubbed out her cigarette, grey ash dirtying a white saucer. 'Better get him up. It's an early start.' She went to the bread bin and fished out the stub end of a loaf. 'I'll make him a piece. He'll need summat on his stomach.'

Eric had to leave as soon as he'd had breakfast. His little bag and his gas mask stood forlornly in the hall. He clung to me, bawling his eyes out, and I was in tears myself. Hadn't thought how much I'd miss him, even though he'd been stuck to me like my shadow all his life. There'd be no more Eric sneaking out after school with jam jars to sell for a ha'penny each, or driving us mad with that clattering go-cart of his with the back wheel falling off. No more walks to Cannon Hill Park to 'get him from under my feet' with a stale crust for the ducks. He suddenly seemed the most precious person I knew, my baby brother.

'Can't you come with me, sis?' he sobbed, already in his little gaberdine coat.

'I've got to get to work, Eric. Mom'll look after you. We'll see you soon.' Someone had their hands round my throat. 'Won't be for long.'

Mom didn't say much, couldn't. I did my best to hide most of my tears until they were away down the road. I stood waving him off, him turning, cap on his head, silver streaks of dried tears on his cheeks and new ones coming. He was twisting round, trying to wave, right the way to the corner. Then they were gone.

I had a proper cry then, upstairs. Dad had gone out the back. I suppose he was upset too. After, I blew my nose, pulled myself together and hurried to work. I thought of Eric all the way there, wondering where he'd end up, what it was like outside Birmingham, and what an unknown family somewhere would make of the arrival of my snotty-nosed brother, Eric Rudolph Valentino Watkins.

Palmer's was on the Moseley Road, its golden balls hanging outside. It was a dark little shop and stank a bit inside of course, of frowsty clothes and camphor, of the gas lamp that was kept burning most of the time so we could see to write out the tickets, and of Mr Palmer's fags.

He was already in when I got there. He was ever so old – seemed it to me – fifty-something at least, with half-moon glasses, a paunchy stomach and grey hair greased flat to his head. The whites of his eyes had gone yellow, maybe from smoking, like his fingers. He was a shrewd operator, Mr Palmer, but well capable of kindness.

'Ready for the Friday rush, Genie?' he said as I walked in, shivering in the dank shop in my cotton dress.

I liked Fridays. Payday – everyone coming to redeem the Sunday outfits they'd pawned on Monday for a bit of extra to see them through the week, and many would stop for a chat. We'd see them all back in the next Monday.

''Ere I am again,' one lady used to say. 'In out, in out, quick as me old man on a Sat'dy night.' Took me a minute or two to work out what she was on about.

'You get busy then,' Mr Palmer said. He was half way through a fag and didn't seem to be planning on shifting himself. I started tidying bits and bobs, dusting the crocks. He'd told me he'd never seen the place so organized before I came along.

That was my trouble with jobs. If I wasn't kept on the run I got bored. And not just a bit yawning bored, but screaming and running round the room sort of bored. I'd done all sorts: sticking Bo-Peep stickers on babies' cots, taking calls for a taxi firm where I got so fed up I gave the windows a going over in my spare time . . . Soon as it got too slow my head filled with fog and my legs went heavy as brass weights. That was when it was time to look for something else.

33

As I was tidying I heard a click, and a voice said, '... we're on number twelve platform at Waterloo Station ...'

My head jerked up. 'A wireless!'

Mr Palmer nodded, pleased with himself. It was at the end of the counter, a little box with a curved top and nothing like as grand as Gloria, but the reception was quite clear.

'Thought I'd bring it in,' he said, through a cloud of blue smoke. 'Didn't want to miss anything. Funny times these.'

'... the train's in,' the voice was saying, 'and the children are just arriving ... the tiny tots in front ... they're all merry and bright, we haven't had a single child crying and I think they're all looking forward to this little adventure ... The whistle goes, the children are looking out ... and in a moment this train moves out to an unknown destination ...' We heard the sound of the train chugging hard and loud, finally dying away. I thought of Eric sobbing his little heart out. Was he the only child in England not 'merry and bright'?

'You all right?' Mr Palmer asked. He twizzled the knob and the wireless went off.

I started to fill up a bit then. 'It's my brother Eric. He's eight. He's gone today.'

Mr Palmer tutted and shook his head. 'Terrible,' he said. 'They said they had it all sorted out the last time. Mind you, wench, it's for the best. They say this one'll start with bombing. If my kids were young I'd want 'em right out of it. Anyhow—' he winked at me— 'they reckon if anything happens it'll be finished by Christmas.'

The rush started, with all the Sunday best going out again, as if it was going to be just any old normal weekend. Then we heard Mrs Wiles coming. She lived round the corner on Balsall Heath Road and she'd bring in bundles for the neighbours. You could hear her coming from half way up the road, pushing the rottenest old wheelbarrow you've ever seen.

Mr Palmer turned to give me a wink. 'Oh – 'ere we go.'

The first we saw of her was her behind because she turned and shoved the door with it, too hard, so it flew open and the bell almost turned itself over ringing. She pulled the barrow down over the step with a loud 'thunk' so I wondered if that would be its last time, and stood blinking for a second or two, in her old man's cloth cap, a sacking apron and man's boots tied with string. She can't have been much different in age from my nan, but her face looked like an old potato.

'Mrs Johnson wants two shilling for this,' she said, picking up Mrs Johnson's bundle of washing.

Mr Palmer looked her in the eye over his glasses. 'One and nine.'

'Two shilling. She wants two shilling.'

'One and nine.'

Every week it was the same, and the look she gave him, I was laughing that much bent over the counter that I could barely write out the tickets.

'Oh you bloody fool,' she said, screwing up her leathery face. 'Oh, you old miser.'

They went through this with every bundle on the barrow. She counted and recounted the coins Mr Palmer gave her, and pushed them into a little pouch which she had tucked into her waistband.

This was all part of the normal performance. But what wasn't part of it was that this week she looked a lot more agitated than usual, couldn't seem to find her waist at all and was pulling at her long skirt as if she thought something might drop out of it. Then she started making funny noises like a guinea pig. Mr Palmer glanced anxiously at me.

'You all right, Mrs Wiles?' He pulled up the flap in the counter to get through and then just stood there while Mrs Wiles suddenly clutched at her chest, fingers clenched and head back pulling the chicken skin under her chin tight, and then dropped to the floor, pawn tickets fluttering from her.

'Oh Lor',' Mr Palmer said, looking down at her. 'Genie – what do we do?'

'Her pulse.' I ducked under too and knelt by Mrs Wiles's slumped body. 'I'll feel for her pulse. You go and get help.'

Mr Palmer charged out of the shop, probably faster than he'd moved in thirty years, and I found myself alone once again with a dead old lady. Because she was dead. I felt the faint pulse flicker, then disappear in her wrist. I folded her hands together over her chest, except one of them kept dropping off. Other customers started coming in.

'What's Mrs Wiles doing down there?' the first woman asked.

'She's dead.' My knees were shaking.

'Oh you poor kid! Did she just ...? Where's Reg Palmer?'

I shrugged. 'Gone to get help.'

By the time Mr Palmer came back with Mrs Palmer, who was fat and usually jolly but not at the moment as someone'd just died, there was quite a crowd in the shop, waiting with their tickets and standing round the walls because Mrs Wiles was taking up such a lot of the floor.

'Her son's coming,' Mrs Palmer said after tutting. 'He's arranging transport. In the meantime . . .'

Since we couldn't leave Mrs Wiles where she was, the Palmers and I stowed her behind the counter. Mrs P found an old sheet on a shelf.

'No one'll be wanting that back now,' someone remarked.

Course, there was barely room to move behind there, and I had to work with one foot on either side of her legs.

When things had settled down a bit Mr Palmer said, 'Oi – it's news time.' It was ten-thirty. He switched on the wireless.

The customers in the shop stood stock still as we heard it. Afterwards, everyone was coming in with their lips all in position as they got through the door to say, 'Have you heard? I suppose you'll have heard by now?' It was on everyone's face. 'They've gone into Poland. The Germans have invaded Poland. We're for it now.' One lady was crying. Her son was twenty and she hadn't forgotten the last war, lost two brothers.

What about my dad? I wondered. The air crackled with goings on, with nerves. I knew everything was changing and everyone thought it was very serious, that the kerbstones on the Moseley Road had been painted black and white for the blackout, that my brother had been taken from us.

It wasn't until the afternoon that Carl Wiles turned up to pick up his mom, and then not with very good grace. I saw Mrs Wiles carted out to his van like a sack of onions. I wondered if anyone had ever really loved her. And I thought, surely, surely there's got to be more to existence than slaving your fingers to the bone all

37

your life and then dropping dead in a pawn shop and no one really caring whether you do or not?

The thought of Mom in a soggy heap was too much for me straight after work so I went to my nan's, which felt just as much like home. I knew I could tell her about Mrs Wiles passing on in front of me and she'd listen.

Belgrave Road was a wide, main street sloping down from the Moseley Road to the Bristol Road. Nan lived almost at the top, had done for years, in one of the yards down an entry behind the shops. As you went down the hill the houses gradually got bigger and bigger and at the bottom end there were some really posh ones. Nanny Rawson started her working life in one of those, in service to a family called the Spiegels, soon after the turn of the century. She didn't get paid in money, they gave her bits of clothes and food instead. She'd lived in three different houses in Belgrave Road, and, as Mom was forever reminding us, Nan brought up her three surviving children at about the same level of poverty as everyone else in the back-to-back courts of houses. Poor as grinding poor back then, after the Great War, not knowing from one day to the next if my grandad would be in work or out of it, drunk or sober. Their clothes shop was the heap tipped out in the yard by the rag and bone man.

'We couldn't shop three days ahead in them days,' Mom'd say (oh, here we go). 'It was hand to mouth. Your grandad was out of work and your nan in the factory, until she got that shop ... You got an ounce of jam at a time in a cup, if you was lucky. Your nan was up in the brew'us at five in the morning doing other people's washing to make ends meet.' Mom'd never forget it, scrubbing at the top of shoes with barely any soles on them, never knowing a full stomach, coats on the bed and the house lousy and falling down round their ears. Nan had struggled to give her kids better and Mom knew to hold on tight to what she'd got.

The road was full of the smell of hops from Dare's Brewery and the whiff of sawn wood from the timber merchant's down opposite Hick Street. On the corner stood the Belgrave Hotel, and Nan's huckster's shop was across the road with a cobbled entry running along the side of it which ran into the yard. The shop's windows had advertisements stuck to them for Brasso, Cadbury's, Vimto and such a collection of others that you could hardly see in or out. Her house, which backed on to the shop, was attic-high – three floors, one room on each, and in the downstairs you could walk through the scullery, lift up a little wooden counter and you were in the shop.

I was almost there when Nan's shop door flew open, bell jangling like mad, and two girls tumbled out shrieking and spitting like cats. One had a heap of blond hair and long, spindly legs pushed into a pair of ankle-wobbling high black patent heels. The other had crimpy red hair and a skin-tight skirt, scarlet with big white polka dots, and showing a mass of mottled leg.

'You mardy old bitch!' the blonde yelled into the shop at the top of her lungs. As she did so, she caught her heel in the brick pavement and fell over backwards, white legs waving. 'Now look what you've made me do, you fucking cow!'

The redhead was helping her up. 'You wanna watch it – we can have you seen to, grandma . . .'

Nanny Rawson loomed in the doorway, enormous in her flowery pinner crossed over at the back, face grimmer than a storm at sea. Bandaged leg or no, she was out of that door in a jiffy, giving the redhead a whopping clout round the face that nearly floored her. The girl set up a train-whistle shriek, as much from wounded pride as from pain, which brought people out of the shops to stare and grin.

'All right, Edith?' someone shouted. 'That's right – you give 'em one!' Nanny Rawson ignored them.

'Get this straight,' she barked at the girls. 'You may be Morgan's latest tarts but while you're in my shop you behave like proper 'uman beings and keep a civil tongue in your 'eads. Don't come in 'ere showing off to me. And if you want to come through and up my stairs—'

'They ain't your stairs, they're Morgan's,' the redhead retorted, hand pressed to her cheek. 'And there's bugger all you can do about it. 'Cept move of course, and do everyone a favour.'

Nan bunched her hand into a fist and the redhead quailed. 'Don't hit me again!' she pleaded, backing off.

The blonde had got to her feet by this time. Now I was closer I saw she had pale, pitted skin, thickly caked in powder, and can't have been that much older than me. If she'd been thinking of having another go at Nan she changed her mind, knowing she'd more than met her match, and turned on me instead. 'And what d'you think you're gawping at, you nosy little bitch?'

Nanny Rawson suddenly saw me too, and she didn't like her family getting involved with Morgan and his women. She rounded on the girls. 'Get inside there quick. For my own state of health I'm going to forget I ever saw you.' As they teetered back in through the door she shouted after them, 'Coming to him two at a time. It's disgusting!' There was a cheer from the bystanders which Nanny Rawson, on her dignity, completely ignored.

Her run-ins with the landlord Morgan and his endless parade of 'young trollops' had been going on since she started renting the place nigh on sixteen years ago, and she and Morgan, a scrawny, over-sexed weasel of a man, were growing old together. When Nan first got the shop she was desperate to keep the lease and was beholden to Morgan for keeping the rent low. Now she'd been here this long she wasn't going anywhere for anyone and Morgan knew he'd never get a better tenant. It had developed into a contest – who could hold out there the longest. But the fact that the only way to get to the upstairs was through the shop meant that Nan had had her nose rubbed in his preoccupations week in, week out, and even after all this time there was no chance of her accepting it.

As soon as the girls disappeared it was as if nothing had happened. Suddenly her face was full of doom. Hitler. Poland.

'What you doing 'ere?' she demanded.

'Come to see you, what else?'

'You don't look too good – seen your mother, 'ave you?'

'No. Why?'

She jerked her head towards the door. 'You'd best come in.'

Nan's shop had seemed like a magic palace to me when I was a kid. You couldn't see across the room much better than you could through the windows, there was that much stuff in there. She sold everything you could think of: sweets, kids' corduroy trousers, balls of string, gas mantles, mendits for pots and pans, paraffin, safety pins, scrubbing brushes. There were glass-fronted wooden cabinets where I used to bend down and breathe on the glass, see my ghostly eyes disappear into mist. Inside, rows of little wooden drawers held all sorts of bits and bobs, spools of cotton, hooks and eyes, ribbons. There were flypapers, brushes and paraffin lamps from the ceiling, and shelves round the sides and across the middle.

Nan folded her arms and stared at me. 'You'd best get home. Doreen'll need you. It's your dad. Soon as the news came out this morning they started calling up the territorials – 'e's already gone.'

'Gone?' I couldn't understand her for a minute. 'Where?'

'Into the army, Genie.' She softened, seeing the shock on my face. It was all too much in one day. Eric, Mrs Wiles, and now this. 'He's not far away. He'll be back to see you. Come on—' She led me by the shoulder, through the back into the house. 'Your mother'll cope while you have a cup of tea. It's just as much of a shock for you as for 'er, though no doubt she won't see it that way.'

I sat by the kitchen table which was scrubbed almost white. Nan's house was always immaculate, even with Lil's kids living there. She still prepared all her food on the old blackleaded range which gleamed with Zebo polish. She rocked round the table from foot to foot, rattling spoons, taking the teapot to empty the dregs in the drain outside. I looked at her handsome, tired face. Always here, Nan was. Always had been, with her hair, still good and dark now, pinned up at the back. She'd always been the one who looked after everyone: Doreen this, Len that, Lil the other. Slow old Len always here, round her, until he came to us. And now she was half bringing up the next generation.

I watched her pour the tea into two straight, white cups. There was shouting from the yard outside, getting louder, rising to shrieks. The sound of women bitching. Nan eyed the window and tutted. 'Mary and Clarys again.'

'You all right, Nan?'

'As I'll ever be.'

I went and looked out of the door into the yard. Two of Nan's neighbours, Mary and Clarys, were up the far end by the brewhouse, Mary with her red hair, hands on her hips, giving Clarys a couple of fishwifey earsful. Little Patsy, Tom and Cathleen had been playing round the gas lamp with another child. Usually there'd have been a whole gang of them out there. They'd stopped to watch, Tom, my favourite, swinging round the lamp by one straight arm.

'Wonder what's got into them two,' I said.

'Be summat to do with Mary's kids again,' Nan said. 'Right 'andful they are.'

The bell rang in the shop. Nan stood still, teapot in hand, listening as the door was pushed carefully shut. There were furtive footsteps on the front stairs. Morgan had arrived. His life was strung between his mom, who he lived with over his ironmonger's shop in Aston, and his bolt-hole here. Nan carried on with what she was doing, which nowadays was exactly what she would have done if Morgan was in the same room. It was the girls who could still get under her skin, but Morgan, so far as she was concerned, was invisible, like a tiny speck of dirt. He crept in and out with an ingratiating smile on his face, and what was left of his streaks of greasy hair brushed over so they lay across his head like something fished out of a river.

I sat back down and within minutes we heard Lil.

'Awright, awright,' she was saying to the kids. 'Let me at least get in through the sodding door.'

'I see them two are at it again,' she said, flinging herself down on the horsehair sofa, in the worn cotton dress she wore to work at Chad Valley Toys. She put a hand over her eyes. 'She wants to keep them kids in order she does. My head's fit to split.'

Nan handed her a cup of tea and stood in front of her, hands on hips. 'You having second thoughts?' There was silence. ''Bout sending the kids?'

'No I'm not!' Lil sat upright quick as a flash, then winced at the pain in her head. 'I'm not having anyone else lay a finger on them. Sending the poor little mites off to fend for themselves.'

At that moment the three 'poor little mites' roared in through the door at full volume. 'Mom! Mom! – what's to eat? We're starving!'

'Out!' Lil yelled over the top of them. 'Stop "Momming" me when I've only just got in. You can push off out of 'ere till your nan says tea's ready!'

The room emptied again. The voices had quietened down outside but Lil's boys started drumming a stick on the miskin-lids down the end of the yard. Lil groaned, then sat up and drank her tea, pulling pins out of her hair so that hanks of it hung round her face.

'That foreman won't leave me alone again. I'm sick to the back teeth of it.' Lil was forever moaning about men chasing her. It was such a nuisance, the way they wouldn't leave her alone . . . None of us believed a word. She loved every minute of it.

Nan ignored her. 'Victor's gone you know. Dor was up here earlier in a state. Called 'im up straight away.'

Lil stared back at her. 'Bejaysus.' She often said that. It was one of Patsy's sayings and she clung to it. 'I didn't think it'd be so soon. They haven't said there's going to be a war yet. Not for sure.'

'Looks mighty like it though.'

'Poland,' Lil said with scorn. She lit a fag and sat back. 'Where the hell is Poland anyhow?'

Nan sat on the edge of her chair, sipping tea. 'I've cleared out the cellar.'

'What for?'

'What d'you think for? I'm not going out in those public shelters with just anyone. There's not much space down there but we can fit and it'll have to do. I've given it a scrub.'

'Charming. Reducing us to sitting in the cellar.'

'Want some bread and scrape, Genie?' Nan said.

'No, I'm all right, ta. Nan?'

'What, love?'

I told her about Mrs Wiles.

'Well, what a thing,' she said. 'I thought you was looking a bit shook up. Poor old dear.'

'Shame.' Lil took a drag on her cigarette. 'Be much nicer to die in Lewis's, wouldn't it?'

'Better not tell Doreen,' Nan said. 'She'll only say that's what you get for working in a pawn shop up 'ere.' Mom put on a show of thinking people in Highgate were common, which was rich considering she grew up there herself. When I got the job I didn't tell her for days.

'You'd better be moving on,' Nan said to me. 'Got to see to this blackout palaver tonight. Your mother never got it done for the practice, did she? She won't want all that on 'er own.'

'She's all right – it's light yet,' Lil said. She seemed to be coming round a bit now she'd got some tea inside her. 'Eric get off all right, did he?'

I nodded, miserable at the thought. Lil sat forward, her old sweet self for a moment. 'You'll miss him, won't you Genie love? But he'll be all right. He's a good boy.' She smiled at me prettily. 'You'll have to come round and see my lot when you want some company.'

I found Mom in tears of course, with Len taking not the blindest bit of notice. It wasn't that he lacked sensitivity. He'd most likely just given up by now. Soon as he got in from work he usually sat down by Gloria without even washing his hands unless we nagged him, and that was that.

'My boy!' Mom was carrying on behind her hanky. There was no sign of tea on the go. 'My poor little Eric. How will we ever know if they're looking after him properly?'

I felt impatient, although all day I'd had nothing but the same thought in my mind. 'Oh, I expect he'll have a grand time,' I said bitterly. 'Forget we exist.'

'But that's what I'm worried about!' Mom wailed. She flung herself up out of her chair, dabbing at her red eyes. 'First I've got no son, and now I haven't even got a husband!' She clicked the stair door open and disappeared upstairs, slamming it behind her.

'She's crying,' Len remarked.

'You don't say, Lenny.'

I was really fed up with her. Sometimes I'd have liked to be the one who could flounce about and cry and behave like a child. I got sick of being a mother to my own mom. I wanted someone to sit down and put their arm round me while I cried because my dad and my brother had gone away.

'I s'pose this means I'm cooking tea, does it?' I

snapped at Len, since he was the only person left to snap at, though I got no answer anyway.

There was liver in the kitchen. I started chopping onions. Len fiddled with Gloria until music came streaming from her. I felt a bit better. Len beamed. 'S'nice this, Genie, in't it?'

There was a voice kept coming on as I was cooking, saying we had to retune the wireless. Len was taking no notice, didn't understand.

I wiped my hands and went over. 'Len, the man says we've got to turn the knob to a different number.' Len stared blankly at me. I went and fiddled with Gloria's dial and Len got a bit agitated.

Just as I was dishing up, this voice said, 'This is the BBC Home Service.' I'd just called Mom down and we looked at each other expecting something else to happen.

'The what?' Mom shrugged and stepped over to look at herself in the mirror – 'What a sight' – then, as the light was waning outside, went round the windows, pulling all the black curtains she'd made. 'This should've been done earlier,' she said accusingly, pulling the ordinary curtains over them. 'I'll have to do upstairs tomorrow. Well this *is* going to be jolly I can see. Feels like the middle of winter.'

My liver and onions wasn't out of this world, though no worse than Mom would've managed, but she still turned her nose up at it.

'Gravy's lumpy. And how did you get the liver so hard?'

We waited, tensed up as the nine o'clock bulletin came on, but there was nothing new, nothing definite, except that Australia had said she'd support the Allies if war broke out.

'Who are the Allies?' I asked.

'Us of course.'

When we turned Gloria off, finally, to go up to bed, it was eerily quiet. There wasn't a sound from outside. Wasn't something supposed to be happening?

'I wonder what Victor's doing,' Mom said, turning all soggy again. 'How could he do it to me?'

Saturday 2 September. The day of waiting.

It had been a golden afternoon, the city's dark bowl lit by autumn sun. Two blokes whitewashing the entrance to an ARP post whistled at me on the way home. The balloons sailed in the sky, tugging gently on their lines.

What's up now? I wondered, stepping in from work that evening. The house was quiet again but I could hear music in the distance. They were out in the garden, Gloria too, on a paving slab with her accumulator. Someone was playing 'Somewhere Over the Rainbow' on the organ with twiddly bits.

At the end of the garden, next to the wizened lilac tree, its mauve flowers now brown, stood Mom, Len and Mr Tailor from two houses along. They were all looking at a big, grey loop of corrugated iron and two other flat bits which were leant up against the fence. The Anderson shelter had arrived.

''Ullo Genie!' Len boomed across at me. The others didn't seem to notice if I was there or not.

Mom was all worked up. 'Isn't this just the limit?' She lit one cigarette from the stub end of another and sucked on it like a sherbet dip. 'Isn't it just like Victor to go away the day before the shelter gets here. How am I ever going to cope with all this?'

'Look, love, you're awright – I've said I'll do it,' Mr Tailor said. He was always the philosopher, Mr Tailor. Maybe because he had a grown up son whose testicles had never come down. Nan said with something like that in the family there was no point in getting worked up about anything else. He'd most likely be there on his own deathbed in the same grey braces saying, 'Yer awright, bab – things'll look better in the morning.'

'I'll sort it out for you, soon as I've finished my own. I'm not going anywhere, am I? Too long in the tooth for that caper. Look – you just have to dig down and put this bit in the ground—' He pointed to the big curved bit which I saw was two sheets of metal bolted together at the top. 'Then you put the soil back over the top, these bits are the front and back, and Bob's your uncle.'

Len had already got the spade and was all for starting off.

'He could do it if I show him,' Mr Tailor went on. 'Big strong lad.'

Mom was hugging her waist. I could see the shape of the Players packet in the pocket of her pinner. 'Looks more like a dog kennel. I certainly don't fancy sitting out in that of a night.'

'It's tougher than it looks,' Mr Tailor said, slapping his thick, hairy hand on the side of it. 'I'll come and give Len a hand finishing it tomorrow – how's that?'

Mom nodded. 'Look, I've got to get in and finish these flaming blinds. Been queuing half the morning for the material . . .'

The organ music which had gone on and on stopped suddenly. 'Sssh,' I said. 'Listen!'

We walked back over the toasted daisies and stood round Gloria.

'This is the BBC Home Service ... Here is the six o'clock news ...'

Everyone stood still. Mr Tailor raised one hand in the air, flat as if he was pushing against an invisible wall.

The government had given a final ultimatum to Hitler. Withdraw from Poland or we declare war. They'd given him until the next morning.

When it was over, another voice said, 'This is Sandy MacPherson joining you again on the BBC organ ...'

'Not again,' Mom said. 'That bloke must be exhausted. He's been stuck on that flaming organ all day.' As she disappeared into the house she added, 'Why does that Hitler have to do everything on the weekend?'

The sun went down slowly, though not slowly enough for Mom, who was still toiling away on the Vesta, the reel of black cotton flying round on the top, cursing to herself.

Without being told, I picked up the idea pretty quick that I was cooking tea. I saw there was a rabbit hanging by its hind legs in the pantry. Mom said Mr Tailor had got it somewhere. Don't ask, sort of thing. 'That's for dinner tomorrow,' she said. 'Do summat with eggs tonight.'

When I'd got the spuds on, I went and stood out in the garden. Len was working like mad digging out turf and soil, dry though it was. He was droning some kind of tune and he didn't look back or see me.

I took my shoes off, felt the wiry grass under my feet and wondered what it'd be like to live in the country with nothing but grass and trees. I wondered about Eric. The street was so quiet. Usually it was full of kids playing, in the gardens and out the front.

And I thought this evening was like no other I'd ever known. Not even the night I left school when I knew I was going to a job next week and everything else would be the same, not like Christmas Eve, even though there was the same sort of quiet. Everything was shifting, you could feel it all around you, those balloons filling in the sky. No one had a clue what was going to happen tomorrow.

I didn't know whether to be excited or frightened.

Mom still didn't manage to black out the whole house by sundown. 'Cotton kept breaking,' she complained. She wasn't very good at sewing either.

We ate scrambled egg and potatoes. Len ate astonishing heaps of mash. It was a queer feeling sitting there with the windows all muffled. Made you feel cut off, as if you were in prison. And Mom decided for reasons of her own that we had to have the windows tight shut as well and nearly suffocated the lot of us.

None of us could settle to anything. Mom said she couldn't stand the sight of any more sewing. So we sat round Gloria and listened in. She was our contact with the outside world: Sandy MacPherson, records, news. Parliament had sat in emergency session. Len slouched, picking his nose.

'Don't, Len!' Mom scolded.

We sang along with 'We'll Gather Violets in the Spring' and 'Stay Young and Beautiful, If You Want to Be Loved.'

We wondered what tomorrow would bring. There was a storm in the night and I barely slept.

The Prime Minister was due to speak at eleven-fifteen. Mom was in the front at her machine again, tickety-tick, and I, who seemed to be cook for the duration, was stuck at the sink. Len was out digging, the ground softened by the rain.

It dried out to a perfect, calm morning, though the air was humid. I could hear church bells early on, then they stopped.

Our dinner was going to be late.

'I can't touch that thing,' Mom said, pointing at the rabbit, its legs rigid against the door. 'Make me bad, that would. You'll have to skin it, Genie – we'll have stew this afternoon.'

What a treat. Didn't she always find me the best jobs?

I spread an old *Sports Argus* on the kitchen table. There were a couple of knives that needed sharpening and the kitchen scissors. It was a wild, brown rabbit with a white belly, and heavier than I expected. Its back legs were tied with string and it was sticky with a smear of blood where I touched it on one side. Its eyes looked like rotten grapes.

Before I got started I went and switched Gloria on and heard a band playing.

'What time is it?' Mom called through.

'Five to eleven.'

There was a ring of blood like lipstick round the rabbit's mouth. The ears felt very cold and there was a pong coming off it like fermented fruit.

It was a hell of a job to get the head off. Our knives sunk in deeper and deeper but wouldn't break the pelt. In the end I snipped at the neck with the scissors, but it took so long it made me feel panicky, as if I was fighting with it.

The news came on on the hour. There was a knock at the front door.

'Get that, will you Genie?'

'Can't – I'm all in a mess.'

I heard her sigh, like she always did if I asked her to do anything. Peeping into the hall I saw Molly and Gladys Bender from across the road. I knew Mom'd be thinking, oh my God. They both stood there with big grins on their faces, each of them the size of a gasometer, still in their pinners. Gladys was Molly's mom and by far the sharper of the two. They lived together and both did charring and you almost never saw them without a pinner or an overall. They both wore glasses and both had their hair marcelled and probably had done since it was fashionable sometime round the year I was born. Molly looked the image of Gladys except that Gladys, being twenty years older, had hair that wasn't exactly grey, but dusty looking, and Molly's cheeks weren't full of red wormy veins.

They were beaming away like a couple of mad March hares. 'We was wondering,' Gladys said in her blaring voice, 'Mr Tailor said there's to be an announcement – only, we haven't got a wireless . . .'

So all Mom could really say was, 'Why don't you come in then?' and called to me, 'Genie – get the kettle on, love.'

Love? That was a sign we had company.

'Don't mind Genie,' Mom said. 'She's doing our dinner.'

I caught a whiff of Molly and Gladys. There were grey smudges down their pinners and they always reeked of disinfectant and Brasso and sweat. Especially sweat, but it was always mixed in with all these cleaning fluids and polish. They sat down, filling the two chairs. Molly craned to see out to the garden.

'Oooh,' she said. 'Your Len's busy, in't he? We could do with borrowing him.'

They chattered away to Mom, who was as polite as she could manage. I got into the rabbit by snipping up from under its tail with the scissors – tricky with me being left-handed – along the soft white belly. With the first cut a round hole appeared like a little brown mouth and the smell whooshed up and hit me. Lola. I opened it up and there was a pool of muck inside, and round it, holding everything in, a glassy film of pink, grey and white, tinged with yellow. The kettle whispered on the stove. It was ten past.

'Shall I call Len in for you?' Molly asked eagerly.

'You stay put,' Gladys bossed her.

I called down the garden. Len dropped the spade and loped up to the house. I don't know if he knew why he was hurrying but he'd caught the atmosphere, something in my voice. He stamped his feet on the step outside.

'It's all right – nothing yet.'

I pushed my knife into the thin, tough film of the rabbit's insides. There was blood everywhere suddenly. Soft jelly shapes slumped into my hand, cold trails of gut like pink necklaces, rounded bits with webs of yellow fat on them, green of half-digested grass when I pulled on its stomach and it tore. I knew which bit the liver was, rich with blood, four rubbery petals like a black violet.

When I'd got everything out it had gone quiet next door. Nice of them to call me, I thought, washing my hands. Mom, Molly, Gladys, Len and I all stood or sat round, everyone's eyes fixed on Gloria.

'I am speaking to you from the Cabinet Room at Number Ten Downing Street,' the Prime Minister said. Words we'd never forget. The announcement of war.

'Now that we have resolved to finish it, I know you will play your part with calmness and with courage.'

When Mr Chamberlain had finished they played the National Anthem. Molly and Gladys struggled grunting to their feet. Then church bells pealed from Gloria, filling the room. We drank tea. None of us spoke for a time. No one knew what to say. Molly and Gladys weren't grinning any more.

'So it's finally happened,' Mom said at last. 'Len – you'd better go out and finish off. Mr Tailor's coming later.'

Len wasn't listening and nor was Molly, because they were staring hard at each other as if they'd never seen one another before, with great big soppy smiles on their faces. He walked backwards out of the room, tripping up the step into the kitchen.

'I'll have to watch him,' Mom said when Molly and Gladys had departed, thanking us endlessly. 'He may be soft in the head but he's all man, our Len.'

'I know,' I said.

Her head whipped round. 'What d'you mean, you know?'

I finally finished the rabbit, pulling back the skin from over the front legs like peeling a shirt off. The inside of the pelt was shiny and covered with hundreds of wiggly red veins like Gladys's cheeks. When I got the skin off it looked small and helpless like a new-born babby. Tasted all right though, come three o'clock, with a few onions.

We waited for the peril that was supposed to fall from the clouds. That's when people started staring up at the sky, heads back, eyes narrowed. The night war was declared I went out into the garden after it was dark. Mom was despondent because they'd announced in the afternoon that all the cinemas were going to close.

'Life's not going to be worth living!' she kept on. I wanted to get out of our muffled rooms.

I leapt out of the back door closing it as fast as I could so's not to spill any light. I walked down the garden. It was dark as a bear's behind out there. Everything was quiet, deathly quiet I thought, really eerie.

At the bottom of the garden I could just make out the hunched shape of the Anderson which Mr Tailor had put in for us that afternoon. Len had heaped the soil back on top. It was odd seeing it there. A web of searchlights danced in the city sky, but down in the garden you could barely see a hand in front of your face. No lights from the street, the houses, the cars. Nothing.

I stumbled on a hummock of grass. Then there was a sound. Must've been a twig scraping the fence but it set me thinking, and my heart was off thudding away.

No one knew when the Germans would come. We'd expected them down the street straight away. Maybe they were here already. Was that what I'd heard, someone moving about in the garden next door? Or maybe there was someone in the Anderson ... Someone just behind me with a gun ...

Panic seized me tight by the throat and I was across that scrap of lawn and struggling with the door handle so mithered I could hardly get it open. I landed panting in the kitchen.

'What's got into you?' Mom called through. There was a laugh in her voice.

*

One Sunday in the middle of September Mom was having one of her wet lettuce sessions. Lunch had been cooked by yours truly (I was getting a lot of practice). I'd done a piece of chine and Mom said, 'This isn't up to much, Genie. How d'you manage to make such a mess of it?'

So I said, 'Cook it yourself next time if you're so fussy.' She slapped me for that, hard, at the top of my arm. Sod you too, I thought.

I knew what was wrong though. Partly the feeling of anticlimax.

'You only have to strike a match out there at night and someone jumps on you,' Mom moaned. 'But there's nothing cowing well happening, is there?' You could tell she was under strain when her language started slipping.

Earlier in the week Dad had come home to tell us that his short period in Hall Green was finished and that they were being transferred for training outside Birmingham. He didn't know where. Before he went, suddenly younger-looking in his uniform, I saw Mom go to him, and they held one another. He stroked her hair and she clung to him.

'I can't stand it,' she sobbed into his chest. 'Can't stand being here on my own. I won't be able to cope.'

'You've got Genie,' Dad said. 'I'm sorry, love. I hadn't realized it would all be so soon.'

She seemed to have more respect for him now he had an army uniform on. And I hadn't seen Mom and Dad cuddling before, not ever. Made me cry too. And then Dad did something he'd not done since I was a tiny kid. He came and took me in his arms too and I saw there were tears in his big grey eyes.

'Goodbye, Genie love. Eh, there's a girl, don't cry

now. You're going to help your mom out, aren't you? I s'pect I'll be back before we know it.'

Len was starting to blub too, watching us all, and Dad gave his shoulder a squeeze and then he was gone. I dried my tears. Didn't like crying in front of Mom. It didn't feel right.

She'd been all right up until Sunday. Even though we had a letter from Eric:

Dear Mom,
    Ime well and I hope you are to. And Genie and Dad and Len. I was at one ladys and now Ime at annother. Shes qite nice. Shes got cats.
    Love Eric.

It was from Maidenhead. Mom sniffled a bit when she read it – 'Not much of a letter, is it?' – but then carried herself along being busy and was quite cheerful. She even had a mad cleaning session and the house was spotless. But finally she fell over the edge into gloom and sitting for hours in chairs without her shoes on.

So I left, and went to see my pal Teresa. She'd always been my best pal, ever since we were kiddies, although we were never at the same school. The Spini kids traipsed all the way over to the Catholic School in Bordesley Street. Teresa, who was always up to something the rest of the time, could dress up demure as a china doll on a Sunday with a white ribbon in her hair and go off to Mass at St Michael's with Vera's – Mrs Spini's – family, who all lived in the streets of 'Little Italy' behind Moor Street Station. It was like stepping right into Italy down there, with them all speaking Italian and cooking with garlic. I used to go with Teresa and see her granny sometimes. Nonna Amelia was a wispy old lady with bowed legs and no teeth who always wore black and spoke hardly any English. She used to suck and suck on sugared almonds from home and spit the nuts out because she couldn't chew them.

They had a back-house in a yard just along from my nan's, though not behind the shop as they'd tiled that part white like a hospital and turned it into their little ice-cream factory. The door of the house was almost always open, summer or winter, and usually there were kids spilling in and out. When I got there I could see the back of Micky, Teresa's dad, sat at the table in his shirtsleeves. He wore belts, not braces like my dad. I could hear their voices, loud, in Italian.

'Genie!' Teresa called, spotting me. Soon as I got there they switched to talking in English.

Their house was much like any other in area inside, with a couple of small differences. Near the door was a black and white engraving ('my photograph' as Vera called it) of Jesus, and over the mantel hung a tile, in a thin wooden frame. On its deep blue glaze was a handpainted figure of the Madonna and child, and beneath, the words AVE MARIA. I'd asked Teresa about it once, years ago.

'My nan in Italy gave it to Dad before he came here,' she said. 'She didn't want him to go, and she gave it to him as she kissed him goodbye. She said "If your own mother can't watch over you, remember that the mother of God is always near to catch you when you fall."' Micky had never seen his mother again after walking out with that lovingly wrapped tile at the age of twenty.

'Anyway,' Teresa'd said. 'He met Mom his second day in Birmingham, so someone was looking out for him.'

Teresa pulled a chair out for me at the table between her and Micky.

''Bout time,' she said. 'We haven't seen you in ages.'

'Some of us work for a living you know.' Now I was at the pawn shop I worked most Saturdays. 'No time for gadding into town to try on hats in C&A. Come to think of it that might be a good reason for moving on!' I glanced nervously at Micky. You never quite knew what mood he was going to be in.

He frowned. 'I thought you were at that pie factory?'

'I was – for a week. There was this bloke opposite me with a great long dewdrop in 'is nose. I reckon there was more snot than meat in some of them pies. One week of that and I was off.'

The others groaned and laughed, even Stevie, Teresa's older brother who was usually either in a daydream about shiny new Lagondas or being a self-righteous pain in the neck. I saw Teresa looking nervously at her father for his reaction and I wondered if I'd walked into the middle of something. 'You wouldn't want your seat getting too warm anywhere, would you?'

'I have to be kept busy.'

'You've practically done the lot already!' Teresa said. She sounded envious, and her eyes strayed once more over to Micky. He was holding a hunk of bread in his strong hands, pulling off pellets and half throwing them into his mouth.

I looked round the table. 'It's quiet, isn't it?' And then wished I hadn't said the one thing they were all most likely trying not to think about. Vera's eyes turned to pools of misery.

But God, it was quiet. Normally when I went in there eight pairs of dark brown eyes turned to look at me, but now the four younger ones were missing and I felt the loss almost as if they were my own brothers and sisters. In terms of noise you barely noticed Eric being gone because he was such a mouse most of the time. Micky and Stevie weren't all that vocal, but those Spini women were LOUD. Even Giovanna at seven had a voice on her like a foghorn, and Teresa was about the noisiest of the lot. Great blast of a voice and sandpaper-rough as if she'd smoked forty a day since birth.

'I can hardly look at Teresa in that dress for wondering how they are and what they're doing.' Vera's homely face was crumpling.

The dress was crimson with a white lace collar and Vera had made three to match, so other Sundays Francesca and Giovanna had been turned out in theirs too, matching and all lovely with their dark hair, Teresa's long and loosely tied back, Francesca with plaits and Giovanna's in a pert, swinging ponytail.

'Will they be able to go to Mass where they've gone?' I asked.

Tears started running down Vera's cheeks. She shook her head and shrugged. 'Don't know, love. I told Francesca to ask, but with them down Wales . . . Don't know that they're all that keen on Catholics down there. I can't stand thinking about it. At least they've been kept in twos – Francesca's got Luki, and Tony and Giovanna are together. I s'pose I should be thankful for that.'

'They'll be all right, Mom,' Teresa said, putting her hand on her mother's plump arm. She was such a happy woman usually. You'd see her in the shop even in the depths of winter, blowing on her hands to keep warm, songs billowing white out of her mouth. And she hugged and kissed those kids like no one had ever done to me in my life.

'I don't know why I sent them,' she went on. 'Nothing's happening. Only I kept on thinking about what they did bombing Spain and I thought it'd be the same here. Every day I have to stop myself going to fetch them back.'

'No good thinking like that,' Micky said more gently. 'The war's only just started and we don't know what's coming. Francesca'll see they're all right. She's nearly grown up now.'

I looked at Micky timidly. He was a moody so-and-so – tough as anything on his kids, though he'd barely ever said a harsh word to me. 'How's the Fire Service, Mr Spini?' I asked.

'Dad 'ad a bit of a shock this week, didn't you?' Teresa said cautiously.

We waited for a split second to see the reaction. And Micky's face broke into a grin, as did Stevie's. 'Oh God yes, the jump!' He blew smoke at the ceiling, smoothed a hand over his wiry black curls. He'd done his first two weeks in the Auxiliary Fire Service. 'They got us doing sheet jumps. That means you 'ave to go up the drill tower in the station. Everyone else is standing at the bottom holding out a sheet to catch you. If you're holding it you have to brace yourself to take the weight.' He clenched his fists, the hairy backs of his hands turned towards the floor. 'So you're up the top of the tower, sitting on this window-sill and the instructor's told you "Don't jump off, just step off." You're thinking Christ Almighty—'

'Micky!' Vera interrupted, eyes fierce.

'Sorry. But I was, I can tell you. I was thinking to myself, that's not a sheet down there, it's a pocket handkerchief.'

'So you jumped?'

'Didn't have no choice. My insides followed me down about five minutes later!'

'You should just thank your stars you don't have to jump out of aeroplanes!' Vera said.

'Well at least they have a parachute!' We all laughed at his head-shaking indignation.

Vera got up, clearing dishes already wiped clean with bread, scraping bones and wrinkles of fish skin on to the top one. She was not a tall woman, but rounded and comfortable, and Teresa looked very like her, although Vera Spini's long hair was blond – out of a bottle Mom said – but it suited her, even though her eyebrows were jet black.

Already it was half way through the afternoon. They could make meals last an age, the Spinis. Eating was a pastime as well as a necessity. Sometimes, Sundays, they were all still sitting round the table at four o'clock, spinning the meal on into cups of tea.

'Who wants ice cream?' Vera called from the scullery.

'Oooh!' I said. 'Yes please!'

'I didn't need to ask you, did I?' She smiled, bringing the basin of homemade ice cream to the table. 'You'd eat it until it came out of your ears.' She leaned forward and pulled my cheek affectionately between her finger and thumb.

'Only my ice cream,' Micky teased.

Vera faced him indignantly, hands on her shapely hips. '*My* ice cream? Listen to him. Who makes all the ice cream around here Micky, eh? Whose family has been making ice cream for three generations?'

'Yours, my darlin'.' Micky looked mock humble.

'I should think so.' Vera dug in the spoon. 'We had a few punnets of strawberries over so I put them in too.'

That set my mouth watering. Vera's mom and dad,

the Scattolis, were part of the community from Sora in the middle of Italy, one of the ice-cream families, and you came across Scattoli ice-cream cycles all over town. When Vera married Micky, a newcomer and a southerner, the family accepted him and helped set them up in their own shop. Old Poppa Scattoli gave his blessing not only on the marriage, but also on their using the family's ice-cream recipe for another string to the Spinis' business bow – provided they used the Scattoli name.

The ice cream was delicious. I was just sitting there relaxing, thinking how nice it was to be eating food that might've been made by angels, in a proper family with a mom and dad there and no rows, when Teresa had to go and say, 'I wish I could get a job.'

Micky's eyes swivelled round to her angrily and Vera and Stevie sighed. Teresa always had a way of offering the red rag straight to the bull. You didn't argue with Micky – except Teresa did – and the Spinis' ding-dongs had a way of blowing up on you sudden and harsh as a summer storm.

'We need you here,' Micky decreed, jabbing a stubby finger towards her. 'And first you got to learn 'ow to behave yourself before you go anywhere out of my sight on your own.'

'I am behaving myself.' Teresa was on the boil already, voice booming. 'He was a customer. I was only talking to him. What's wrong with that?'

'Talking to him!' Micky's voice was mocking. He sat back, waving one thick, hairy arm, his Brummie accent laid over his Italian one. 'You think you're just talking but I can see what he's doing with his eyes. And what you're doing with yours too. You make yourself cheap, girl, behaving like that. You give him ideas about yourself. If I see you doing that again . . .'

He stopped because for once he couldn't think of anything to say and Teresa stared back brazenly. She never went out anywhere, except to Mass, and she knew she was an asset in the shop. The customers loved her, listening to their moans, her big laugh ringing down the road behind them.

'Don't keep on, Micky,' Vera interrupted. 'You've said enough already.'

'But she don't take any bloody notice!' Micky roared. 'What do you want – eh? You got no respect!'

'You got my respect,' Teresa bawled. 'But how come it's always me?' She pointed at Stevie, who was watching her across the table with his heavy-lidded eyes. 'You don't say anything when he's going about with that lunatic Fausto. Or is it awright now to invite a mad man into the family and one who still thinks he's a Blackshirt as well – eh?'

'You've got Fausto wrong,' Stevie said with contempt.

Micky waved the air dismissively. 'The boy's a hot-head, a fool . . .'

'It's not fair!'

'Teresa!' It was Vera's turn to try and calm her down.

'But I'm sick of it! The men in this family do just what they like and expect us to stay at home and wait on them hand and foot.' She pushed her chair back and marched off outside, saying, 'It's like a prison here . . .'

Micky slammed his spoon down and left as well. I thought he was going after her but we saw him move past the window and head for the street.

Vera sighed. 'When will Teresa ever learn to keep her mouth shut?'

*

Teresa and I sat out on the back step, frocks over our knees.

'I s'pect Dad's gone over Park Street to the pub. I really hate him sometimes.' She squinted up at the sky. 'Wish they'd come if they're coming. We could do with a bit of action round here.'

'You're awful,' I said. 'Any rate, I didn't think that was the kind of action you were interested in nowadays.'

She stuck her tongue out at me as far as it would go.

'Come on then, tell us. Who is 'e?'

Teresa stuck a finger urgently against her lips and peeped round the door. Vera was washing up, had said Stevie should help so he was wiping, with his altar boy face on.

'Come over here.' Teresa pulled me to my feet and over towards the brewhouse and we stood with our faces to the wall. Her whisper tickled my ear.

'He keeps coming in the shop – from that sheet metal place opposite Frank Street. I'm sure he's taken a fancy to me.' Even at this distance she kept looking back nervously at the house. Micky and Vera thought Teresa was far too young to be thinking about boys.

Although we'd left school we were still treated as kids, weren't allowed out dancing, nothing like that. Teresa was barely allowed to set foot outside by herself. But the boys went for her. It wasn't that she was pretty exactly. She was shorter than me, small and round, whereas I was bony and boyish; she had Vera's looks, a snub nose, and her complexion wasn't all that marvellous. But what she had was a lot of life and a lot of laughs in her. And what's more she was ripe and ready to be swept off her feet, even though she was innocent as a day-old child, and looked it in that Sunday dress.

'He keeps coming in – I've never known anyone buy

so many apples – 'cept he comes and gets them one by one!' She burst into her infectious giggle. 'Ooh, sometimes I feel like taking off just anywhere, just for a bit of excitement!'

'So he's Prince Charming then, is he?' I couldn't help sounding sarky.

'He's all right. Nice enough. Bit skinny. I like 'em with a bit more brawn on them than that!'

'Brawn or brains – make your choice.'

'And he's got this great big Adam's apple – wobbles around when he's talking as if he's got a plum stuck down his throat . . .' The giggle turned into her loud, exuberant laugh. 'No, I'm being unkind. He's got a nice way with him. Oi – what's up with you?'

'Nothing.'

'Don't just say nothing—' She elbowed me but I pulled away, staring stubbornly across the yard. From the top-floor windows the Spinis' bedding was hanging out to air as usual, an Italian habit the neighbours still weren't sure about.

'B for Boys. B for Boring.'

'Well, you wanted to know!'

'Yeah, and you told me,' I snapped, crosser with myself than her because I was mucking up the afternoon. But God she didn't half go on. I wanted her to be happy – she was my best pal. But I wanted her all to myself as well. She was so restless and impatient. Even now she was tapping her feet against the grey bricks as if she wanted to be off and none of us were good enough for her.

'I don't know what you're always moaning about—'

'Who says I'm moaning?' she interrupted my outburst.

'If I had a family like yours I'd think I was in clover. You should try living with my lot.'

'Oh don't you start getting on your 'igh 'orse with me!' Teresa's temper had a shorter fuse than a banger on fireworks night. 'You're not the one stuck in the shop and minding little kiddies all the time . . .'

'Nor are you now, 'cause they're not here, are they?'

'And your dad doesn't come down on you like a ton of bricks every time you even open your mouth to talk to a boy . . .'

I was getting ready to say that's because he never noticed anything much I did but she was getting well warmed up now. 'Family this, family that. You can't get away from them ever – and if it's not them it's the sodding church.'

'Well how come Stevie doesn't mind?'

She made a big, irritated puffing sound through her lips. 'Because Stevie's pain in the backside little Stevie. He's like a policeman round the place and all he ever thinks about are cars and football.'

She relented and looked round at me. 'All I want's a bit of excitement. We'll be pals whatever. Boys don't make any difference.'

'I know,' I said, face all red.

Just then we heard footsteps charging along the entry. The Spinis' yard was a 'double knack' which meant there were two ways in, and there was an entry running along by the brewhouse. When I saw who it was my face blushed to my ears. Walt Eccles, Stevie's pal. I was scared stiff every time I saw Walt, by the way my knees turned wobbly and my heart went like the clappers and my insides churned with frightened, helpless adoration. An adoration I'd rather have jumped from the spire of St Martin's than let him know about. After all, Walt was two years older than us, which seemed like centuries, and why should he be interested in a gangly scarecrow like me?

The sun shone on his shock of gold hair and there was the usual cheeky grin on his freckled face as he came panting up to us, looking gorgeous.

'In a bit of a rush, are we?' I said, tart as I could manage, while Teresa smiled sweetly at him, as she would at anything in trousers.

Walt gave me his best ingratiating smile which filled me brimming over with panic. 'Nice to see you too,' he said. 'How're you then?'

'None the better for seeing you.'

He pulled a face at me. 'See you're full of charm as ever. Stevie in?'

'Somewhere,' Teresa said, waving into the house.

A moment later the two of them came out, off up to the park to kick a ball around. The blush rose in my face again, and I turned crossly to the wall. Teresa was giving me a really close, squinty look.

'You're sweet on 'im, aren't you?' Her face was full of devilment.

'I'm not!'

'Oh yes you are!' she bawled in her big husky voice, and jumped about triumphantly clapping her hands. Luckily the yard was quiet. 'Genie's sweet on Walt. Genie likes boys after all!'

I went all tight inside. Only half joking I pushed her up against the wall of the brewhouse, gripping her shoulders.

'One word to Stevie, or *anyone*,' I said between my teeth, 'and you won't live to see another day. And that's a promise.'

We were bored with the so-called war already. Every night we sat round the wireless, windows blacked, waiting. Mom hadn't been to the pictures for three weeks. It was Bore War. Sitzkrieg instead of Blitzkrieg. We wanted something to happen, and not just in the Atlantic. Something we could see.

Gloria kept handing out announcements. Keep off the streets. Carry your gas mask as at all times, etc. In fact recently she'd been a bit of a bore herself.

The proper programmes were back on now at least. *Band Waggon* now on a Saturday night, Len with his cup and saucer jigging about as they sang, 'Come and make a trip upon the Band Waggon – skiddeley-boom,' until Mom'd say, 'For goodness' sake give me your Bournvita, Lenny. It'll be in your lap, else.'

She was still low. Blackout, no pictures, supposedly in charge of the house, the uncertainty of it all getting on her nerves. Said she was scared to be out at night. Her so-called pal Stella had moved across town with her husband and hadn't troubled herself to come back and visit so she wasn't around to have a moan to. Mom did crack her face at Tommy Handley sometimes.

One evening she got out of her chair and said, 'I've had enough of this. There aren't going to be any air raids. Let's have the last of the light before we all die of asphyxiation, never mind the flaming bombs.'

She threw open the blackout curtains and the waning light lapped across the room. We all took in a deep breath, thought something would happen. Nothing did.

The weeks passed. Poland surrendered. We clung to the music and wondered what was happening. We waited.

October 1939

'Well, that's that,' Mom announced. 'I'm not stopping in like this. I've had more than enough already.'

Mr Churchill had just announced that the war would last three years. How he knew that we didn't understand, but something about him made you believe it. And that did it for Mom.

'There's no knowing when your father'll be home for good.' That thought seemed to rouse her out of the depressed stupor into which she'd kept dipping.

Lil had just moved jobs, though she hadn't escaped the factory. She was learning welding at Parkinson Cowan, in overalls and with a snood over her hair, and kept on about how useful she was being to the war effort and humanity in general despite having three young children. She put on a good show of being irritated by a new set of admirers.

Mom decided that for the first time in fifteen years she'd get herself employed. She fixed herself up with a job on the telephone exchange, second shift of the day.

'But Mom – you'll have to come back from town on the bus late at night. You won't even go out as it is now.'

Apparently this didn't matter. 'I'll just have to manage.' She was excited all of a sudden, cheeks pink. 'You'll have to stop in and keep Len company.'

This was all quite a turn about for the woman who'd

refused even to go up to our nan's of an evening because she was too scared to come back in the blackout.

'I could be knocked down in the street and robbed,' she'd kept saying. 'There's a lot of it about you know.'

'So who's going to cook? And shop and clean?'

'Genie!' She laughed, looking back over her shoulder at her reflection in the mirror. 'You sound like an old woman. We'll get by. I'll be home mornings, and you know what to do by now, don't you? It's not as if we've got your father to feed.'

On the strength of the vast fortune she was about to earn she went out and kitted herself up with a couple of frocks and a pair of shoes with T-bars and a chunk of heel, and started on her new working life. The rest of us, who'd been at it for some time with no red carpet laid out, had to stand aside.

She went off at dinnertime, hair knotted low in her neck, in one of her new dresses and her small black bag over one arm, and came home at about half ten at night off the bus. She was full of it. The work, the people. It was fast, busy. And she was needed suddenly.

'They even have special gas masks for us with a little microphone at the side so we can carry on working.' She laughed. 'After all, in a gas attack the telephones would be essential.'

I could just imagine her putting on a posh telephone voice. She stood more upright now, strutted about as if she owned the place, and didn't sit in chairs and stare at nothing any more. Nor, from the first day, did it seem to cross her mind that there was such a thing as housework to be done.

I decided to have a go at something else myself. I was getting restless with all this change around me, and I needed a job which allowed me to start early and finish early, what with the shopping and cooking to do and often washing thrown in as well. Mom was at home all morning but she was barely ever up until gone eleven. She needed the time to recover, she said.

There was a job going at a firm in Cheapside called Commercial Loose Leaf. I walked through the sand-bagged entrance up a gloomy staircase smelling of glue, to a cluttered little office above the shop floor. The gaffer was a middle-aged man with a tired, worried-looking face, thin hair and blue eyes like a little boy's.

'D'you know your numbers properly?' he asked.

'Oh yes,' I said airily. 'I was good at arithmetic at school.' Once again I showed my certificate and reference from the school.

He just glanced at them, not really interested. 'Just so long as you can count.' He gave me a quick look up and down. 'Table hand. You can start Monday.'

Well, that job nearly did me in. The company produced trade books and ledgers. To start with they put me to collating piles of paper covered with print about technical things I couldn't make head or tail of. The second week I was put on numbering. So this was the reason I needed to be able to count. The blue-tinged papers were all numbered by hand. You had to concentrate enough doing it so's you didn't lose your place and that meant you couldn't talk to anyone, but it didn't take up anything like the whole of your mind. The second night I dreamed of nothing but numbers.

We got used to a new routine at home. Suddenly we were a family where everyone had a job. I was working from eight in the morning until half past four. So after work I'd walk home and pick up any shopping on the way. Len came in soon after from Longbridge, so muggins here would cook the meal and wash up (Len wiping) and we'd sit in the rest of the evening until Mom came in. Occasionally Teresa would come down to keep us company.

'You're the one person who cheers me up,' I told her one night. 'It's an endless round of drudgery otherwise, and no one notices what I've done anyway.'

'Why don't you say something to your mom?' Teresa said, not being one to sit down under anything.

I shrugged. 'She'll only play the martyr. She's got her head so high in the clouds I don't think she even notices the rest of us exist any more.'

Teresa sat back with her legs stretched out, playing with a lock of her hair. 'You'll make someone a lovely wife,' she teased. 'With a flock of kids.'

I scowled. 'I'm not getting married. Not ever. I'm going to work as hard as I can and get rich and buy a cottage in a field next to a river, where there's no chimneys and no factories and no people, and I'm going to live there on my own for the rest of my life and grow flowers. Well – Len could come too if he wants.'

'Oh, I want to get married,' Teresa said. 'I think it's sad seeing a woman left on the shelf.'

'Sure you're talking about marriage and not just a white dress and a veil?'

'Oh Genie! You're such a flaming misery you are!' She laughed, exasperated.

'I just think you're better off on your own. I mean, look at my family. Who'd want to get hitched after seeing them lot?'

'Lil had a decent husband.'

'Yes, but what's the good of a decent husband if he's just going to throw himself in the canal?'

Teresa found this mighty hilarious for some reason. 'Genie, you're awful you are!' She sat up again. 'Guess what?' Then she was off again, giggling so much she set Len off and then I started laughing too, which came as a relief, although in the end none of us knew what the hell we were laughing about.

'My love life is about to begin,' she got out in the end.

'No,' I said. 'Not him? The Adam's apple?'

'That's the one,' Teresa managed to get out between guffaws of laughter. 'We're going out for a walk – Sunday. In Highgate Park.'

My eyes widened. 'Does your mom know?'

Teresa shook her head. 'I'll tell them I'm coming to yours.'

'But that's lies! How many Hail Marys is that, Teresa?' It wasn't like her to tell fibs, even if she was a bit wild.

'It is not as if we're going to do anything. Not real mortal sins or anything.'

'What's a mortal sin?'

'Having a babby when you're not married and killing someone and – you know, bad things. But I just want summat to happen. Some excitement. I get sick of being under Mom and Dad's noses all the time. Anyway, his name's Jack and he's seventeen.'

Determined not to look impressed I said, 'Well keep me posted. Don't go giving sweets to any strange men. And Teresa – don't make me lie for you.'

Why did I do it? I asked myself, cheeks aflame at the memory. Something made me. Something called living in hope. I'd been at Commercial Loose Leaf for a couple of weeks. Already I was half mad with boredom. We needed something for our tea and I had to shop on the way home. Sausages would be easiest for Len and me. Mom had a meal in the works canteen.

I went home via Belgrave Road, along to Harris's the butchers where Walt worked. It was a detour, but it made perfect sense to go there, didn't it? Because after, I could pop in and see my nan.

Walt was standing behind the counter in his striped, bloodstained apron, a pencil behind one ear, bright red against the shorn gold of his hair. I could see through the window that most of the stock had gone by this time of day. I walked into the tiled shop, my feet almost silent on the sawdust-covered floor, though the bell on the door gave me away with a loud tinkle. Walt was sharpening a knife and whistling as if he had not a care in the world.

'Can I help you, madam?' He half caught sight of me, then looked up properly, his freckly face spreading into a grin. The grin was laced with mischief that at first I was too blind to see. ''Allo, Genie! What're you doing here?'

'Come for a pound of sausage, what d'you think?' I said, my cheeks pinking up, to my extreme annoyance. 'This is a butcher's if I'm not mistaken.'

I didn't know exactly why I was like that whenever I saw Walt, but I couldn't help myself. I lay in bed thinking about him, daydreamed about him for a proportion of my time that I would rather die than admit, but I simply couldn't let him know I liked him. I wasn't going to set myself up for being kicked in the teeth. What I was too stupid to realize was that he could see it as clear as day.

'I was only asking,' he said, pretending to be hurt.

'Sausage? There's a few left.' As he was weighing them out he said, 'Seen Teresa?'

'No I 'aven't. Not in a week. Don't get time for anything, do I, what with Mom working, Len working . . .'

Walt flung the sausages into the scale with a flourish, eyes fixed on the needle, which swayed back and forth. 'Just over,' he said. 'Seeing as I know you. How's the new job then?'

I gave him a sideways look. 'If you're looking for a new exciting life, don't go to Commercial Loose Leaf.'

Walt grinned again. 'Don't go on. You're making me jealous.'

As I handed over the money he closed his fingers over mine and held them. I managed to look into his eyes. 'You'd be nearer Jamaica Row there, wouldn't you?' he said.

It was true. We were a stone's throw from the meat market where I could easily have chosen to shop if I'd wanted. Feeling his warm hand on mine I blushed like mad and realized that was exactly what Walt had been aiming for.

I yanked my hand away. 'I'm allowed to shop where I want, aren't I? I've come up here to see my nan. If that's all right with you.'

I flounced out of the shop. Half way along the road I stopped, cursing. I'd taken off without the sausages. I stood there for almost a minute trying to decide what to do. I had to go back. I was going to look a right idiot whatever I did. Summoning what dignity I could, I pushed the shop door open. Walt stood there with my bag of sausages held out in one hand, with the kind of teasing smile on his face that made me want to curl up somewhere dark and never come out. I couldn't look him in the eyes. I grabbed the sausages, said 'Ta' in a sarky voice, and took off to the door as fast as I could.

'Genie.' His voice was soft suddenly, sweet, with a kind of longing in it.

I turned back, my pulse speeding up, and for one split second my silly little heart told me Walt'd been hiding his feelings. I was special to him ... As I looked round at him he must have seen it, my need and hope spraying out like sparks across the room.

And he was grinning, a mean, triumphant smile which made me shrink and buckle up inside. 'You still haven't got your change.'

I snatched the tuppence from him, dropped the sausages, had to fumble to pick them up and finally slammed out of the shop, cheeks ablaze.

'Bye bye beautiful,' he shouted, his mocking laughter following me along the pavement.

'You bastard, Walt Eccles,' I fumed, storming along the street. I was in too much of a state even to go and see my nan.

Life was peaceful in its way without Mom around. Len'd roll up his sleeves and get a fire going in the grate after work while I got the tea and we'd listen to Henry Hall or some other show. Then *The Nine O'Clock News*, after that old 'Jairmany calling, Jairmany calling' Lord Haw-Haw. He gave me the creeps at first, just the sound of his voice, but then we all just used to listen for the daft things he came out with. Then there'd be music and I'd do mending or tidying or hand washing – whatever else was needed – until Mom came in like the conquering hero and we'd have a cuppa with bread and butter. Then bed. That was our day, every day.

One night while Len and I sat waiting we heard the front door open and Mom's voice, high and animated in a way I'd almost never heard it before.

'Goodnight then – and thanks ever so much!'

The door slammed shut. She was in the hall taking her coat off and humming to herself. I went to look and she turned round and smiled at me. Which was all pretty unusual. She was unknotting a woollen scarf from round her neck.

'Brr, s'getting cold out nights now. Awright?' she said. 'Everything OK?'

'Who was that at the door?'

'Oh ...' She kept her tone casual, hanging the scarf on the hook behind the door. 'He's a copper – seen me home a couple of times off the bus after I said I was scared in the blackout. He's very helpful.'

'That's nice.' I stood watching her, her lit up expression. I'd seen my own face in the mirror not long before, pale, with dark grooves under my eyes from exhaustion like an old woman. I felt wrung out and lonely, and I wanted her to look after me and be my mom.

'Got the kettle on? Hallo, Lenny love.' He nodded amiably at her. I went and lit the gas. Mom stood by the hearth, back to the fire. She rubbed her hands, started telling us about the 'girls' at work, jokes, things that'd happened. I sank into a chair. 'Aren't you making tea?' she asked eventually.

'I'm tired out. Can't you make it?'

Her eyes narrowed. She looked spiteful. 'You're tired? Huh. I get in from work in the middle of the night and you tell me you're the one who's tired.'

I was near to tears with weariness. After all, who was running this house with no help or thanks from anyone?

Sometimes I wish she'd just go, then there'd be just me and Len. Things were all right until she came home. But I wasn't going to show how miserable I felt in front of her.

She sank down by the fire in a martyred fashion and twiddled bits of her hair round her fingers as I got up to make the tea.

'Mrs Spini does the house and the shop,' I said. 'Always has.'

'I've got quite enough on my plate with your father and Eric away,' she snapped. 'Vera Spini.' She put all her energy into that sneer. 'Hair out of a bottle.' The way she said it dyeing your hair might have been crime of the century.

Then she turned plaintive again. 'It takes getting used to going back to work again and working shifts. I think I deserve all the help I can get.'

November 1939

Strikes me it's about time someone told Teresa the facts of life, I thought to myself. And who else is going to take the trouble but me?

Teresa was one of those girls who could give men the wrong idea. Too friendly, too vivacious, too downright appealing, but with barely the first idea of what it was all about, for all her talk of mortal sins. Of course most of us girls were innocent as morning dew until we strayed into marriage or trouble, but what with the trollops coming and going I'd long started asking questions, and Lil made it her business to get a few things straight with me when I left school.

'Your mother'll never be able to bring herself to do it,' she said. 'God knows, she spends enough time with her head stuck in a pile of sand as it is. But you ought to know, Genie. The factory's no place for an innocent kid like you. Specially with your pretty face.'

We were in Nan's house. Lil had chased the kids out to play.

'You're 'aving me on!' I said when she explained. 'Not with his willy!' My mouth hung open for minutes after.

Lil's cheeks went rose pink all of a sudden. 'I know it don't look much of a thing as a rule, but when they come on to you and get the least bit excited, it . . .' She gave me a vivid demonstration with her index finger. 'That's how they put the babbies inside.'

I sat there goggling at her. Her brown eyes smiled mischievously. I had so many questions I couldn't think what to ask first. 'But doesn't it feel – *funny* – them doing that?'

'Feels a bit funny at first of course. But you get used to it. Can be ever so nice . . .' Her face took on a dreamy look. I got the definite feeling this was something she liked talking about. 'Best feeling on earth at times, that's if you love 'im. But Genie . . .' She leaned forward solemnly and lowered her voice to a whisper. 'What I'm saying is, you don't want to do it with any old dog who comes along. Keep yourself nice for someone special. And make sure 'e's going to marry you before your knickers get below your knees.'

'Lil!'

'I'm giving you good advice, Genie, believe me. It's not nice to be a tart, and anyhow, you don't know quite where else they've been dipping it if they're that way inclined.'

Things were beginning to make a bit of sense, quite apart from the trollops. Len, for a start. That enigmatic smile that used to come over Big Patsy's face when Lil sat on his lap. And Lil was right. I couldn't for the life of me imagine Mom coming out with any of this information. For a second I thought of Walt and blushed to the roots of my hair.

Since, according to Lil, men were only after One Thing, I thought it was time Teresa knew. Which she didn't, I was sure. Her Mom and Dad treated her as a child and she was still safe in the bosom of home – or so they thought. Course they didn't know she was walking out late some Sunday afternoons now with Mr Sheet

Metal, supports-the-Villa Jack, using me as her alibi. Lil had given me such a vivid account of the male sex drive that I thought Teresa was in immediate danger of losing her virtue in Highgate Park.

I went to the Spinis' in the middle of Sunday afternoon when I guessed the marathon meal would be over. In any case, with only half of them there the heart had gone out of it. Only Vera and Teresa were in and Vera was sat at the table touching up the roots of her hair from the bottle of peroxide which Mom had been right about.

'Micky's pumping water out of air raid shelters,' Vera said, squinting at the little oblong mirror. Her dark eyebrows looked startling set against the bleached-out hair. 'That's all they seem to have to do in the Fire Brigade. S'pose I shouldn't be complaining though, should I?'

Teresa had on her red dress from Mass and she'd dolled up her hair with a matching red bow. 'We were just going out, weren't we?' she said, looking meaningfully at me.

'S'pose so.' I didn't take too kindly to being treated as a decoy in place of some bloke.

'What're you doing here?' she hissed at me as soon as we were in the street. 'You know I'm meeting Jack.'

'All right, all right, I'm not going to forget, am I, the way you keep on?' Jack this, Jack that. The minute he'd come along he'd become far more important than I was. I didn't seem to be important to anyone nowadays.

We cut past the closely packed lines of houses and factories along Stanhope Street.

'Don't walk so fast.'

'I'll be late. I told him half past three.'

'But I've got summat to tell you.'

I suddenly felt like the guardian of Teresa's virginity, my imagination running riot about what she and Jack were getting up to.

'Hang on a tick.' She pulled me into an entry. 'Hold these for me a minute.' I found I was holding a handful of pins.

'What the hell are these for?'

Skilfully Teresa made a thick tuck in the red skirt, pinning it up round her bit by bit and shortening the drop of the church-length dress by a good six inches.

'You can't go around like that!' I laughed at her. 'You'll get them sticking in you!'

'Wanna bet?' She did her coat up round her with a grin, hiding the clumsy lump of material. 'There. That's better. Come on.' She pulled me along the road again. 'What you got to tell me?'

Once I'd blurted it out Teresa stood stock still on the pavement and just stared at me, brown eyes popping. I thought for a horrible moment she was going to come out with something like, 'Oh Genie, how could you think I didn't know? Jack's already had his evil way with me and I'm expecting twins . . .'

Instead of which she erupted into her huge laugh, bending backwards, then leaning forward doubled up. I ended up in stitches too just watching her. People were staring.

'Oh no!' she cried when she could speak. 'No, that can't be right, Genie. Where in hell did you get that from? That's the most horrible idea I've ever come across!' And she was off again, tittering away. 'You don't half come up with some barmy notions, you do.'

'But it's true!' I insisted. 'How else d'you think . . .?'

She moved closer, aware of ears flapping along the

street. 'A man kisses you a special way and then the Holy Spirit gives you a babby. That's what really happens. Come on,' she said, stepping out again. 'He'll be waiting. You keep out of sight, eh?'

'Charming.' I was stung by jealousy again. 'Don't believe me then. I just hope you don't live to regret it.'

'All he's ever tried to do is hold my hand,' she said smugly, disappearing round the corner. 'Which is more than anyone does for you.'

'I've got more bloody sense, that's why!' I felt like tearing her eyes out, the stupid cow.

Her voice floated round to me, mocking. '*Ciao*, Genie.'

I peeped round the corner. Standing by the gate to the park, waiting for her, was one of the tallest, gangliest blokes I'd ever seen. His hair was curly and a bright carroty red as if his head was on fire. I couldn't spot the Adam's apple, but it would've been hard to miss the great big daffy grin on his face as Teresa walked up to him. She'd forgotten all about me, that was for sure.

When I couldn't stand any more of Commercial Loose Leaf I got myself another new job in a little factory in Conybere Street, staining bunk beds which they made for the forces and the shelters. It was a small, dark place, all one room. On one wall there was a poster in big red letters which read: 'FREEDOM IS IN PERIL. DEFEND IT WITH ALL YOUR MIGHT. YOUR COURAGE, YOUR CHEERFULNESS, YOUR RESOLUTION WILL BRING US VICTORY.'

On one side a few fellers were knocking up the beds, then they came to us to be stained before the webbing was put on. It wasn't too bad. If it ever got a bit slack I went round and swept up or kept my hand in cleaning windows again.

'I've cleaned that many factory windows,' I told them, 'I'm starting to think I ought to set up in business as a window cleaner.'

'You're like greased bloody lightning you are,' one of the lads said to me. He had black curly hair, uneven grey eyes and his name was Jimmy. 'Don't you ever let up?'

'No,' I said. 'Not if I can help it. Gets boring. I like to be on the go.'

'I can see that.' He kept watching me dashing about, throwing me the odd wink.

The other girl working with me, a stodgy blonde called Shirley, said, ''E fancies you. See how 'e keeps on looking over here? You're in there, you know.'

'In there? What's that s'posed to mean?'

Shirley looked at me pityingly. 'Don't you want a bloke? I'd do anything to 'ave a bloke of my own.'

It was odd the way she said it. She might just as well have said she'd do anything to have a dog, a budgie, a house ... But I can't say I wasn't flattered by his attention. I pulled the belt tight round my overall and kept my hair brushed. I couldn't help thinking about what Lil had said about men and their willies. But then I'd go and look at a real live man – let alone these boys around me – and I couldn't quite put the two together. I thought maybe Lil was having me on after all. It really was beyond imagining.

Every week we had a letter from Dad, who was down south, somewhere with a funny name. He said he'd started off being billeted in a barn with rats running round his head of a night, the food was abominable and he seemed to spend most of his life digging – trenches, latrines, holes . . .

He said he missed us and hoped he'd be back for Christmas, though the war showed no more sign of being over than it did of getting going.

Mom seemed a bit shaken by this news. 'It's funny, isn't it?' she said. 'Feels as if he's been away such a long time. I've got sort of used to it. As if he was never here.'

Eric wrote every so often and told us not a lot except that he was all right and Mrs Spenser was a very nice lady, and thanked us for the letters we sent him.

'Can he come home at Christmas, Mom?' I asked. 'We can't just leave him down there – not then.'

'Oh, I should think so,' she said vaguely. I had this feeling when I talked to Mom nowadays that most of her mind was out to graze somewhere else.

'Couldn't he stay home? Lots of other kids have - come back. There's nothing happening, is there?'

'What?' Her attention snapped back to me. 'Oh no – I don't think so, Genie. Not while there's any danger of bombs. I mean, they keep telling us to leave the children where they are. And in any case, there's no one at home to look after him, is there?'

I didn't dare ask why she couldn't just give up work. Was it that the country needed her or that she was enjoying herself far too much? After all, as she'd kept reminding us one way or another, we'd been getting in her way for the past fifteen years.

One night after work I got so fed up with doing bits of hand washing, and had a bit of extra energy for once, so I stoked a fire with slack under the copper and had a good go at it, pounding it with the dolly. When it came to mangling it I called Len to come in the kitchen and give me a hand. We just fitted into the room and he turned the handle for me.

'Things all right at work?' I asked him. 'You managing still?'

'Yes,' he said in his slow, thick voice. 'I like it. S'nice.'

'Good.' I pulled a snake of wet washing from the wooden rollers of the mangle. 'I'm glad you're happy, Len.'

He nodded enthusiastically, looking across at me, his eyes always appealing, somehow innocent. 'You OK, Genie?'

'Oh . . .' I sighed. 'Yes. I'm OK, Len. Ta.'

There were shirts and underclothes, the lot, draped all round the room by the time Mom got in. We heard the front door and felt its opening jar all the other doors in the house.

'Come on through,' I heard her say.

Len and I looked at each other. Her voice was so smooth, soapy bubbles of charm floating from it.

I saw the shock in her face as she came into the back, catching sight of her drawers hung out to dry by the fire. But she recovered herself quickly. Over her shoulder I could see his face – dark brown hair, swarthy, handsome and young – quite a bit younger than her actually. The shoulder of a copper's uniform. He was looking nervous.

'This is Bob,' Mom started babbling. 'He's just popping in for a bit. He's been very kind and escorted me home from the bus a few times and his shift's finished so I thought a cup of tea was the least we could do.' She gave a tinkly laugh. 'This is my brother, Len. Shake hands, Len.'

Len said, ''Ullo,' and did as he was told, dwarfing Bob's hand in his. Bob coughed and nodded at him.

Now he'd got himself into the room I could see he wasn't much taller than Mom, with a stocky, muscular body.

'Len's not quite – you know . . .' Mom was saying. She slid over that one. 'And this is my daughter, Eugenie. I had her when I was very young of course. Much too young,' she threw in quickly.

'Eighteen,' I added, pretending to be helpful. 'And I'm fifteen.' Mom glowered at me. PC Bob nodded again, even more nervously.

'Genie,' Mom said between her teeth. She gave a little jerk of her head. 'The washing – couldn't you just . . . Until we've finished . . .?'

'I've just hung it all out,' I said stubbornly. 'I've spent the whole evening doing it.' My hostility wasn't lost on her. 'You could go in the front.'

'It's icy cold in there.'

'Never mind,' PC Bob said quickly. He gave a stupid little laugh. 'I take people as I find them in my job. And I have got a family of my own, after all.'

'Bob's got two kiddies,' Mom said, seeing him to a chair. She turned up the gaslight, peeling back the shadows. 'Kettle on, Genie?'

'No.'

She clenched her teeth again. 'D'you think you could put it on?'

We all drank tea while Len and I sat quiet and Mom chattered on about her job, my job and about Eric being away. She didn't talk about Dad. I watched her. She was like another person from the one we saw every day – alight, talkative, a bit breathless.

I had a good look at PC Bob. He knew I was staring at him but he couldn't do much about it. It's not that I dislike people on sight as a general rule, but I couldn't stand him. I could sense it with them. What was between them. And I didn't like it.

He didn't say much. Smiled in the right places when Mom laughed. He had a heavy-set face and dark, mournful eyes which hardly ever looked anywhere but at her. I knew she could feel it, that stare. I'm not sure he was more than half listening to what she was saying, and she was making less and less sense because of the charge his look had set up in the room. His eyes travelled over her as she talked. I think they were a sludgy grey but it was hard to tell in the gaslight. I wanted to get up and shout stop it. Stop staring at her like that. He was following her shape and she talked all the more as if to fight off the magnetic intensity of those eyes.

When he'd drunk up and left, at last, the force of his presence left a hole in the room, like the sudden silence when we switched Gloria off for the night.

Mom was in a dither, cheeks flushed. 'You didn't have to be so short, Genie,' she said. 'All he came for was a cup of tea.'

'Just make sure the house is tidy when I come in,' Mom instructed me at least once a day. 'Just in case.'

And he was soon back.

I made tea and sat watching them. No one was saying anything much and all you could hear were spoons in the cups and the fire shifting. Mom looked down at the peg rug by the hearth, at her feet, then up at Bob. He was sat forward on the edge of his chair in his dark uniform, sipping the tea, giving Mom soulful looks. When their eyes met she giggled.

God Almighty.

'What about some music?' Mom said in the end. 'No Gloria tonight, Len?'

'I told him to turn her off when we heard you come in,' I said.

'Oh, there was no need.'

PC Bob was giving a quizzical sort of frown. 'Gloria?'

'Our wireless.' Mom tittered again. I'd never seen anything like the way she was behaving. 'Len calls her Gloria. Go on Lenny – switch her on.'

Len lumbered to his feet and in a second there was music, something soft, violins. Bob sat there dutifully for a few minutes, pushing the fingertips of each hand against the other.

'Better be off home,' he said. At last. He put his cup on the floor.

'Oh yes.' Mom was sparkly still. 'Back to your little family. Never let you loose for long, do they?'

They both went into the hall, snickering like a couple of monkeys. It went quiet for a moment. I wondered what they were doing. I thought about walking through to the front just to annoy them, but then I heard her letting him out.

When she came back she saw me staring sullenly at her. Oblivious to this, she gave me a wide smile. 'He's such a nice man, isn't he?'

A week later when she was due home from work, I left Len shuffling a pack of cards in the back with Gloria on, and went to the front room. I left it dark, pulled back the corner of the blackout curtain and slid the window open just a crack. There were no lights in the road of course and I knew I shouldn't be able to see them coming from far. But the room was very dark as well, and my eyes were settling to it.

Not many minutes later I heard them. I couldn't make out the shape of them in the sooty darkness, but I could see the burning tips of two cigarettes, and I knew Mom's tone. Their voices were low and I couldn't make out any words at first.

They came and stood on the front step and I was scared stiff they'd see me or notice the open window. I felt it must be plain as daylight I was there. But even if they could have spotted anything much out in the cold damp of the evening, the only thing they were interested in seeing was each other. They came and leaned up against the window where I was sitting. Mom perched on the sill, so if I'd wanted I could have pushed my fingers through the slit and touched her coat.

'Least we don't have to worry what the neighbours are thinking in this,' she said, giggling.

Silence. Kissing. The blood pounded in my ears.

'Bob . . .' Her voice was wheedling now. 'You are going to be able to sort out your shifts, aren't you?'

'For this week,' he said, impatient. His mind was on other things. 'What about your kid? She giving any trouble?' His voice was a low growl. There was something hypnotic about it.

'Nah – she hasn't got a clue about anything. Anyroad – we said you'd got a family, didn't we?'

'Oh yeah.' He thought that was very amusing apparently. 'My family. My two kids! Come on Dor—'

Mom said 'Oooh' and gave a little squeal. Then it went quiet and I knew they were kissing again. After a bit Bob pulled away, giving an impatient sigh. 'I need more than this, Doreen. I can't wait for ever, you know.'

'Oh, I don't care what anyone thinks!' Mom

squeaked at him. 'I know I shouldn't, but I want it too –
if only there was a way we could get on our own . . .'

Silence.

'You do love me, don't you Bob?'

Lord above, I didn't want to hear any more of this. I
let the curtain drop, reminding myself I'd have to come
back later to shut the window.

I was all tight and squirmy inside. As I sat with Len,
waiting for her to come in, I thought of my poor old
dad in a barn full of rats, of the way he looked at Mom,
always wanting, always hopeful.

Cow! I thought to myself. You horrible selfish cow.
I felt like killing her.

I didn't say anything. I started to think I was the only
sensible person left around the place, what with Mom
and PC Bob and Teresa going doolally over Aston Villa
Jack and telling fibs to her mom and dad.

'Len,' I said to him one evening, 'at least I've got you.
You've got more common sense than the rest of them
put together.'

'Yeah.' Len swayed and grinned. 'You and me, Genie.
You and me.'

The winter set in and our days of limbo crawled past.
Work, work, work, was all life consisted of now. All
day painting woodstain on the rough bunks with Jimmy
the Joiner, as I called him, winking away at me across
the small factory floor as he bashed the frames of the
bunks together. I started smiling back. What the hell.

Then there were the evenings of enthralling drudgery
and Mom fluttering in late, her brains gone AWOL for

the duration. The war was still not showing any signs of getting off the ground so far as we were concerned, but we still had to live with all the disadvantages: creeping about in the dark, staying in, and food costing a bomb.

The only thing that cheered me up in the evenings now was Gloria, and when Nanny Rawson and Lil paid us an occasional visit, usually on Mom's day off. The kids'd erupt into our house, glad of a bit of extra space round them, and I'd always try and have something nice laid on for them – a bit of cake or some sweets, with the best one saved for my soft, brown-eyed Tom. Nan'd bring her squeeze box and we'd sit round the back room and drink endless cups of tea and talk about how much better things were 'before the war' – barely three months ago.

At the end of the month they came, full of news.

'Have you heard, Dor?' our nan said, plonking the accordion down on the table. 'There's bombs gone off in town.'

'Oh Lor,' Mom said with the kettle in her hand. 'Has it started? Are they over here?'

'They reckon it was the IRA again,' Nanny Rawson said. 'Blew a couple of phone boxes to bits. No one killed I don't think.'

'That's just what we need, isn't it?' Mom was climbing up on her high horse already. 'Them coming over here making trouble.'

Oh no, not the Irish again. That usually set Lil off and then they'd be at each other's throats . . . But Lil wasn't even listening. Sometimes, especially when she was feeling low, she went off into another world. She was pulling the kids' boots off to dry by the fire. Cathleen was moaning on about something. Patsy'd brought a comic with him.

'Orrible night out,' Lil said absent-mindedly. Her face was pale with exhaustion, the dark hair scraped back. She struggled with the knots in Tom's laces, and I knelt down beside her and worked on the other foot.

'We're in for a hard winter I reckon,' our nan said.

'Got your torch?' Mom stood watching in her pinner, hands on hips.

'Course.' Lil sounded impatient. 'It's like looking up a bear's arse out there. And the flaming paper got wet through.'

Torches and the batteries to go with them were like gold dust. Nowadays you could use a torch so long as the light was dulled down with a sheet of tissue paper. Lil laid the crumpled sheet of paper on the tiles by the fire to dry out.

'We had about three people following us down the Moseley Road, all in a line.' Nan laughed. 'Just for one bleeding little torch.' She was wiping the accordion down. 'That won't've done it much good. Still – it's had worse in its time. Come on – let's have a cuppa before we get started.'

Mom beat me to the kitchen. She seemed mighty eager to please. Guilty conscience, I thought.

She came back in again with a few Rich Tea on a plate, and offered them round, hovering round her sister like Nurse Cavell. 'How're you bearing up, Lil?'

Lil looked round at Mom as if she'd just been spoken to by some barmy person. 'Awright, ta. What's got into you?'

Mom couldn't hide it, try as she might. The new look, the glow, the vivacity. She was lighter altogether. 'I wouldn't mind a bit of whatever it is you're on,' Lil said wearily. 'Patsy – leave Tom alone.'

'Here.' I pulled out a bag of aniseed balls. 'This'll

keep you lot quiet for a bit.' The kids' cheeks soon had satisfying bulges.

'Ta, Genie,' Lil said, then announced out of the blue, 'Any rate – I've put my name down for a council 'ouse. I'm sick to death of living in a rabbit warren. I want the kids to breathe in some clean air for a change.'

'But how'll you cope if you get one?' Mom asked, with a snidy edge to her voice. Glebe Farm, Turves Green, Weoley Castle . . . Was Lil going to get the little dream house Mom had always fancied? 'You couldn't cope last time.'

Lil stuck her chin out. 'I was in a state, what with Patsy's – accident. And Cathleen was only a babby. Not long now and she'll be at school. I'll cope. I'll just have to, won't I?'

'Well, that'll remain to be seen.'

'Doreen,' Nan said, warning.

Mom, remembering she was the perfect hostess all of a sudden, poured tea, spooned in the condensed milk and offered round biscuits which the kids had to take the aniseed balls out of their mouths to eat, the red outsides already sucked white. Len chomped away, eating two biscuits at once.

'Ah – nectar!' Nan smiled, sipping the tea. 'That's better. Let's 'ave a bit of a sing-song now.'

Patsy lay by the fire with his comic and we fished out a few of my old crayons for Cathleen to scribble on some paper.

'You come and sit with me, Tom,' I said. Stuck between an elder brother and his temperamental baby sister I could see he was always hungry for affection. He came readily to sit on my knee.

'That's it – you go to Genie, she'll look after you,' Nanny Rawson said, sitting forward on her chair and settling the accordion on her knees. She smiled across at me as I hugged Tom tight, her dark brows lifting. 'Hey, Genie—' She frowned suddenly. 'You look all in. Is she sickening for summat, Dor? She's as thin as a stick, and ever so pale. Don't you think she looks peaky?'

Mom looked at me properly for the first time in weeks. Tears came into my eyes and my cheeks burned red. 'You're awright, aren't you Genie?'

I glowered back at her over Tom's head. If I was exhausted she ought to know the reason perfectly well, the way she was carrying on.

'You ought to take better care of her,' Lil said. 'After all, it's not as if you've got any others to worry about now, is it?' That was another of Lil's hobby-horses – she'd got more kids, more problems. I waited for the fight to begin but, to my amazement, Mom said cheerfully. 'Oh, she's all right. Just needs a bit of sun on her face like the rest of us, that's all. Come on, Lil – I feel like a real good sing tonight.'

They sang the rest of the evening away with their strong voices. It was a miracle because we got through that night without a fight, even though the fuse was lit more than once. Cathleen fell asleep on the floor among the crayons while they were singing 'When They Begin the Beguine', and Tom dozed on my lap. All the old favourites which Nan could pump out with an ease that never failed to impress me, never once looking down at her fingers.

I watched Mom as we went through 'An Apple for the Teacher', walking her feet on the spot in time with the music and snapping her slim fingers. Tonight she looked so vivacious, almost prettier than Lil. There was a spark in her eyes so that somehow you didn't notice the hard angles of her face. I thought of Dad watching her with that 'Love me – please' look in his eyes. And I knew it was only through his going away that she'd been able to come to life again, come out from under it all, the years of wife and mother and nothing else and not really wanting it. Maybe she really couldn't help herself. But neither could I help my deep, burning anger at seeing her so carefree, so disloyal.

December 1939

It was evening and I was lying talking to Teresa up in the 'girls'' bedroom in their house which she now had to herself. There were two beds in there and nothing else – the big one which Francesca and Giovanna shared and Teresa's next to the wall. We had a bed each to lie across as we talked. Teresa's hair was loose, laid out in a dark swathe one side of her head.

'You shouldn't tell fibs to your mom and dad like you do,' I said to her. 'They've always been so good to you.' The Spinis would've been broken-hearted if they knew Teresa was deceiving them. Both of them looked so worn and tired at the moment.

'But they'd stop me seeing Jack. Dad's a bully. You just can't see it.'

'He's strict all right, but . . .'

Teresa half sat up. 'He's not just strict. He's not fair. Like last week – it was Nonna Spini's anniversary, my nan in Italy. We all had to go to Mass because that was the day she died and none of us have even met her. And he belted me one because I said I didn't want to go. And it's only because he feels guilty because he always said he'd go back to Italy and see her and he never did.' She lay down again with a thump. 'He just pushes things on us that are nothing to do with us.'

I sighed. We'd been having a bit of a laugh until she

got on to the inevitable Jack. She leaned over to me, tight-faced. 'You'd better not tell 'em.'

'Don't worry – I won't.'

Teresa was changing. I felt old and disappointed, as if such childhood as I'd had was dead and buried overnight. Even though the war had barely affected us in terms of fighting, we had all changed. It was as if we'd had a layer of something scraped off us and we acted more on our impulses than we used to. I watched my mom and my friend and felt like a disapproving old spinster.

Teresa couldn't talk enough about Jack. She was droning on about him again, leaning up on one elbow. 'He's ever so good looking when you get up close – lovely eyes. And so grown up. He's got a real cigarette lighter and he likes football. It's a great game, you know. He said he might take me to see the Villa play one day.'

'For God's sake, Teresa, you hate football!'

'I don't. It's just I've never had the chance to see it played properly – that's what Jack says. He says—'

'I couldn't care less what he says!' I exploded at her. 'It's all a bloody waste of time. Boyfriends. Getting married. All of it. It's stupid.' I found myself nearly in tears.

'You're just jealous.'

I hated her. I wanted to smack her smug face. 'Well, bugger you, Teresa. That's all I can say.' I climbed down from the bed. 'I'm off.'

I ran downstairs and shot through the room where Micky and Vera were sat by the table.

'Hey!' Micky said, as I was going to open the door. He was leaning forward on a chair pushed back from the table, cleaning his boots. Vera sat across from him with a darning mushroom pushed into a stocking, squinting in the gaslight. 'Going already?' he said. 'You just got here. Stay for a cuppa tea with us, eh? Kettle's on.'

I shook my head, choked up inside, looking down at the floor. I couldn't open the door and I couldn't speak.

Micky stood up. 'Genie? Hey darlin' – what you unhappy about?' At that, I burst into tears. Micky stood there at a loss and Vera came quickly over to me, making comforting noises, and pulled me into her arms, pressing my head against her soft body.

'Come on – you can tell your Auntie Vera. What's got into you? You and Teresa had a bit of an argument?'

I couldn't tell them. Not about Mom and Bob or Teresa and Jack, and how I was feeling inside. I was too ashamed. And I felt so silly blarting in front of Micky. When I looked across at him though, I saw such unexpected kindness in his eyes. But I just nodded, let them think it was just over me and Teresa squabbling.

'Teresa!' Micky shouted upstairs grimly. '*Vieni qui – subito!*' Teresa clattered down the stairs right quick. 'What you said to Genie to make her cry like this?' He turned to me. 'She's got a terrible temper on her, you know. You should take no notice.'

I was beginning to feel really stupid about this and I didn't want to get Teresa into trouble, but I just couldn't stop crying now I'd started, blubbering away like a little kid. Vera looked really concerned.

'You feeling all right?' She looked down into my face with her dark eyes, which made me want to cry again. 'Not sickening for summat, are you?'

Teresa was looking pretty scared. I suppose she thought I might've given the game away about Jack, but it soon became clear to her that I hadn't. 'Come on, Genie,' she said. 'What's got into you? I hardly said a word,' she told her father. 'Honest.'

The three of them all gathered round staring at me, so I felt obliged to cheer up and start smiling just to stop them looking so blooming worried. Vera fed me a cup of tea with a heap of sugar in it and Teresa kissed me. 'Pals?' she said.

I sniffed, nodded. 'Yep.' And felt a bit better.

As Christmas drew nearer I thought, at least Dad'll be home. Maybe he'll be able to knock some sense into Mom. Not literally of course. He was never violent. I just thought him being there might bring her to her senses. Can't really imagine what made me think that but I had to have something to cling to.

That day the week before Christmas had started off badly in the first place. I was already feeling run down, so much that even Mom noticed enough to say, 'What's up with you?'

At work a couple of days before, a whopping splinter speared into the thumb of my left hand. I thought I'd got it out, but found my hand swelling up enormously.

'That's a full-blown whitlow,' Mom told me. 'Looks bad that.' I'd made a linseed poultice to try and bring it on but my thumb was still throbbing like mad, felt about ten times bigger than it should have done and was making me turn feverish and light-headed.

Breakfast time wasn't improved by a letter arriving from Eric's foster mother, Mrs Spenser. I watched Mom read it. The letter had got her out of bed unusually early.

Behind her Gloria was pumping out *Up in the*

Morning Early, a new exercise to music programme. Mom's face was stony.

'. . . across . . .' the woman's voice chirped on. '. . . to the side . . . the left arm . . .'

'The cow!' Mom erupted, reaching the end. 'Who the hell does she think she is, telling me what to do about my own son? The nerve!' I took the letter off her.

'I have told Eric that you require him to be sent home for the Christmas holiday,' Mrs Spenser had written. 'I felt obliged to do so, naturally, but to be frank with you I am not sure that moving him again at this stage would be advisable. Eric seems most reluctant to go through the process of uprooting himself again, and I wonder whether it would not be better to surrender your own desires on this occasion and let him remain here until it is deemed safe for him to return to you permanently.

'I shall, of course, abide by your final decision.'

' "Require him to be sent . . ." I ask you.' Mom ranted on for a bit about Eileen Spenser: stuck up, condescending bitch, and a few other choice terms. Then the doubts sneaked in.

'Eric wouldn't not want to come home, would he?' Her face looked pinched and anxious. 'This is his home. Not with some woman in Maidenhead.' She was pacing around our little room. 'Of course he wants to come back. Doesn't he, Genie?'

'Course he does,' I said, feeling, in my sick state, as if the inside of my head was lunging around. I couldn't believe Eric wouldn't want to see us, even though it sounded as though he had a cushy number down there with this Mrs Spenser.

'I'll write and tell her what's what,' Mom said,

searching for a pen to do just that. All she could find was the wooden handle of one of my old dip pens from school with no nib and no ink.

Work didn't go too well. I couldn't use my left hand so tried to hold the brush with my right and I was slow and clumsy. I tried to keep busy, keep my mind off the pain, and crack jokes with the lads in the factory, but even Shirley noticed I wasn't myself. 'You sure you're awright?' she kept saying, and I thought how it was strange that everything Shirley said sounded like a moan.

Come dinnertime I was feeling rotten. I went to stand up from my work place and the next thing I knew I was on a chair with my head between my knees and people fluffing round me. My right ear was hurting me now as well. Must've caught it when I went down.

'You'd best get 'ome,' Jimmy was saying, his face topped by black curly hair, swaying in front of me as I tried to focus again.

'You've gone green,' Shirley complained.

I groaned, sick and dizzy.

The gaffer said I should get off as well. It was a while before I cooled down and the inside of my head stopped throbbing and swimming about. After that I went cold and shivery.

I headed out into an overcast, freezing afternoon, hugging my hand up against my chest as if it was a kitten needing protection. It felt so swollen and sore I'd have screamed if anyone had tried to touch it. I cut through on to Belgrave Road and up to my nan's, thinking that if I came over faint again I could at least go in there for a rest. I thought about home, about curling up under the blanket on a chair with a hot cup of tea and the wireless on. The house to myself. Bliss.

And then I saw them, across the road. By the

doorway of Harris's, where of course I couldn't help my wretched eyes turning. They were standing just outside, Walt leaning one elbow up against the glass and her facing him sideways on. Some girl. She had copper-coloured hair, a sweet pretty face with an upturned nose, and was laughing away at something he'd said, the cow. He was smiling, talking, liked her a lot, I could tell.

He had to go and catch sight of me across the road, and in that split second I saw a vicious smile sneak across his face. He moved deliberately closer to the girl and shouted across at me, 'Awright, are you Genie? Nothing I can get for you today then?'

The girl frowned up at him, hearing the taunting in his voice. Yes, you just be warned, I thought.

'Found a better class of shop, ta,' I shouted back, then pulled my collar up round my face with my good arm and hurried past with my nose in the air and Walt's mocking laugh again to speed me along.

It gave me new strength to get home. All the way I was saying to myself, you're so stupid. You're such a stupid little cow, Genie. Why would Walt be interested in you? You've no looks like that other girl and you can't open your mouth to him without coming out with something tart or horrible. You deserve everything you've got. And after all, you don't care anyway, do you?'

But as soon as I was in the house I couldn't pretend any more and the tears came. I couldn't even find the crocheted rug I'd dreamed of sitting under. I sat in the cold back room hugging my throbbing hand and Janet, my old worn-faced rag doll I hadn't touched in years, feeling frozen and ill and as sorry for myself as it's possible to feel.

The next two days disappeared down a long dark

pipe full of confusion. Tossing from side to side in bed, conscious of nothing much except the agony in my hand and arm and unable to lie in certain positions because it hurt so much. Sometimes I knew there were people in the room. Len bringing me drinks of Beefex cubes which I sometimes drank and sometimes not. Mom's face, her voice – 'Genie? Can you hear me?' – trying to get me to take a spoonful of some stuff or other. Nanny Rawson knitting by the side of my bed on the hard chair, knowing her mainly by the rough black wool of her sleeve or her singing. A patchwork of dreams, cooking smells, bits of talk: Walt, the girl, 'bomb . . . IRA . . . doorway of Lewis's . . . mess . . . Eric . . . Victor . . .' Walt, *her*, that girl . . . Christmas carols and band music coming from Gloria downstairs. The lumps in the hot mattress swelled under me into molehills.

By the time I could sit up and eat oxtail soup and hold a cup of tea myself, Eric was there perched on my bed.

'You look bigger!' I told him.

'I get lots to eat. She's got chickens and a vegetable patch. And I got a nice comfy bed and she uses table napkins. And you don't have to go down the garden to spend a penny.'

He'd also grown a couple of new teeth since he left.

'Sounds a bit of all right then.' I noticed Eric was talking a bit different, putting his aitches on. 'You glad to be back?'

Eric looked down at the old blanket with a bleak expression and shrugged. Then he met my eyes and managed a bit of a smile. 'Yes. S'pose so.'

'Aren't you pleased to see me?'

He'd gone stiff and shy.

'Come on – come 'ere.' I pushed the soup bowl aside

and gave Eric a cuddle which he submitted to. He wasn't just skin and bone any more.

'Cor, Genie,' he said, pulling away. 'You don't half pong, you do.'

'Oh.' I was hurt. 'Well I've been stuck here for a bit.'

'You been bad?'

'I had a bad hand.' I pointed to the dressing on my thumb. 'It's getting better.'

'Mrs Spenser says, whatever happens, there's no excuse for not keeping clean.'

'Oh. Does she?'

Eric was looking round my room as if he'd never seen it before. I had a bedstead, an old rickety cupboard and a chest of drawers, a mirror that hung on the wall by a nail and a couple of old squares of carpet on the floor. Suddenly he got up and started kicking the chest of drawers with his boots, hard, until he splintered the front of the bottom drawer. 'Cheap!' he shouted. 'Everything's cheap and old and rotten.' His face was red and furious.

I started crying but he took no notice, just stood there with his fists clenched.

Eventually I said, 'Dad's coming home Sat'dy.'

Eric looked at me for a second, then turned and ran back downstairs.

Mom managed to wangle herself some time off work the night before Dad came home.

'I'm having an evening out,' she said, touching up her hair in front of the mirror in the back room. She had it hanging loose at the back and pinned up in a roll away from each side of her face at the front. 'Wish the dratted mirror was bigger.' She had to go right up to it to peer down and see if her dress looked all right. 'You'll be OK, won't you Genie? You got Eric for company now.' She was putting lipstick on, so it was mostly the vowels we heard.

I sat watching: Len was peeling spuds at the table and Eric was playing Shove Ha'penny, nudging at me to join in. Apart from his outburst to me, he'd just been quiet since he got home and Mom hadn't seemed to notice any difference in him.

'This is one of the things you don't want me to tell Dad about then, is it?'

She whipped round and gave me a really nasty look, eyes like slits. Then she tried to soften her expression. 'Now Genie, there's no need to be like that. It's just better if you don't say anything about Bob – your father'll only go and get the wrong idea.'

'Will he?'

She stared hard at me. 'Bob's just a pal of mine. Someone to have a chat to – bit of company. I'll just have to hope he doesn't . . .' She jerked her head in Len's direction but he was well taken up with his potatoes.

Come seven o'clock Bob arrived, in a suit this time, not his uniform, five o'clock shadow shaved off and a hanky dangling from his breast pocket. Smoothy bastard, I thought.

'D'you tell your wife you're on a late shift then?' I asked him. I wasn't going to act polite to him. He should've known better. They both should.

'Genie!' Mom snarled. 'Not in front of Eric. Say you're sorry.'

I didn't say anything, just walked off into the kitchen. 'Come on,' Bob said. 'Let's get out of here. Bringing your gas mask?'

'Nah,' Mom said. 'No point, is there?'

When they'd gone Eric said, 'Who's he then?'

'Just someone Mom knows. They go out sometimes. He's a copper.'

'Bob,' Len said.

'That's right, Len. Now let's just forget about them, shall we?'

'Mrs Spenser says—'

'Will you shut up about that cowing Mrs Spenser!' I yelled at Eric, finding my hand raised ready to hit him. He cowered in front of me which made me feel even worse.

We passed the evening, ate our meal, had Gloria on. I played games with Eric, trying to make up to him. Make him want to be my brother again. Come nine I put him to bed and waited for Len to go. I wanted to have a good wash and brush up for the next day with Dad coming home, especially after Eric's charming comment, but I wasn't going to do it with them about. I still couldn't find the yellow and green crocheted rug which I wanted to put on Eric's bed. Normally it was kept folded over the back of a chair.

I heated up two kettles full of water on the stove and filled a basin. The house was very quiet except for the clock ticking on the mantel. I switched Gloria back on low, so as not to disturb the others.

I wanted to wash my hair, which was limp and greasy and smelt sour as I hadn't washed it since before I was ill. I thought of Mom's rainwater bucket outside. Why shouldn't I have nice hair as well? God knows, I had little enough time to spend on my looks.

I opened the back door and let a wide slice of light fall on the garden, trying to see the bucket. Blackout – what blackout? Couldn't see it. I stepped outside. It was a freezing night. The air almost cut your face and I could see stars clear as anything. The bucket was down by the privy, but when I found it of course the water inside was frozen solid. Just my luck. I'd have to use the water I'd already got.

Then I heard the noise. It didn't scare me. Wasn't that sort of sound. It was a giggle and it was coming out of the Anderson. I crept down there and stood outside, breathing very light little breaths. There wasn't much to hear. Long bits of silence, whispering, then a burst of giggling. Mom's giggling. I'd heard enough. Shaking with anger, I went back to the house. I thought of bolting the side gate on the outside to spite them but I didn't want them traipsing through the house with me about to strip off.

Bugger the both of you, I cursed to myself, tipping water wildly over my hair. At that moment I hated the whole world.

'Long film was it?' I asked Mom next morning.

She'd stayed in bed late and came down yawning. She gave me a startled look, hearing the hate in my voice. 'We went dancing. At the . . .' She trailed off. Couldn't think of a porky-pie fast enough. 'It was really lovely.'

When I said nothing and just kept looking at her, she said between her teeth, 'If you dare breathe a word . . .'

When Dad got home she was all over him. Poor Dad was as pleased as punch. Thought she'd missed him so bad she'd decided she loved him after all.

He'd even brought a box of eggs from the farm where he was billeted.

'You brought those all the way back on the train?' Mom laughed. 'That's just like you, Victor – and look, only one broken.'

'Lovely and fresh too,' Dad said. 'Laid this morning I expect.'

When he saw our dad, Eric showed the first real signs of positive emotion we'd seen since he got back. Dad squatted down and Eric flung himself into his arms, face against the scratchy khaki uniform.

'That's a lad,' Dad said. After a moment he held Eric away from him and looked at him. 'You're bolting! Must have grown six inches since I last saw you!'

'It's the country. Mrs Spenser seems to be looking after him a treat,' Mom said smoothly.

'We'll play some football while I'm at home, shall we?' He gave Eric a playful punch. They'd never played football together before. Eric's face was a picture, lifted with delight. Dad looked younger and thinner in the face, with more life in him than I'd remembered. He looked over Eric's shoulder. 'Genie, you're growing up too.'

Shy suddenly, I went to be taken in his arms. Relief seeped through me and even my anger with Mom stopped bubbling and lay calm and still. Everyone was back. We could now at least pretend things were normal, that we were a proper family again.

'Here – I've got summat for you.' Dad pulled a little folded piece of paper from a pocket of his kitbag. 'Not much, but I thought they'd suit you.'

Inside were three ribbons, red, white and blue.

'Patriotic too,' Mom gushed. 'What d'you say, Genie?'

'Thanks Dad, they're smashing.' And they were. I

was so chuffed, not just with the gift but because he'd thought of me. A smile worked its way across my face and settled there.

'We're having Christmas here,' Mom said. 'Our mom and Lil and the kids can come over. We'll make a real celebration of it.'

Dad put his arm round her. 'That's my wench. It's good to be back where I belong.'

The Spini household was alight with celebration. The kids were home!

'And they're not going back, neither,' Vera vowed from behind one of the lines of washing strung across the tiny room due to the rain outside. 'Never again.' She poked her head out from behind a row of the damp children's clothes which she'd washed as soon as they arrived home. Her face looked shaken out and softer, the tension gone from it. 'Whatever happens, if anything ever does the rate we're going, at least we'll all be together.'

The tiny back-house seemed to have shrunk even further now it was full of children, all bigger than they had been when they left. The two younger ones, Giovanna and Luke, who was now nearly five, came home and settled in as if they'd never left it. Francesca, who was twelve, was glad to be back with Teresa and her mom and dad, although she seemed more moody and far more grown up than before. It was Tony who was finding it hardest to settle back.

'He keeps saying the house is too small,' Vera said dismally. 'The family he went to had a rabbit hutch not much smaller than our house.'

'He'll be OK – give him a chance,' Micky said. He

was happy now, sat at the table in the heart of the family, all his kids around him. 'Another three months and he won't remember he was ever there.' He gave Giovanna's cheek a playful pinch. 'Who's my beautiful girl, eh?' And she went pink and said, 'Gerroff, Dad!' the little ponytail swinging at the back.

It was Christmas Eve and I'd brought a few sweets for the Spini kids. They were all home after the rush in the shop, customers clearing the shelves of Brussels and chestnuts and potatoes. There wasn't room for a tree, but Francesca, who was now used to being in charge, was organizing the younger kids, making streamers, so they were up to their ears in strips of paper and flour and water paste at the table and squabbling over the scissors. Luke was sat on the floor smearing paste down his legs as if he was embalming himself. They fell on the sweets, jelly babies and fruit drops – 'Cor – thanks Genie!' through hardworking mouths.

Stevie was hooking bits of holly over the mantel, adorning a picture he'd got hold of of a shiny Lagonda. There wasn't room for Teresa and me to sit so we stood around watching. Vera was stirring pots on the stove and the room smelt of stew and was steamy with boiling spuds.

'What about a bit round here?' Stevie said to Micky, pointing to his Italian tile.

'Yes – go on. Put it there, put it everywhere!' Micky waved his hands, ready today to decorate his house, his life, everything.

Vera gave us all a cup of Tizer. Teresa was in a good mood too.

'Must be lovely having Eric and your dad home,' she said. 'Proper family again.'

'Ummm – 'tis,' I said. I hadn't told her about Mom

113

and Bob of course. I just couldn't. Even if I'd wanted to she hadn't had much time for listening lately.

Amid the chaos I whispered, 'How's Jack?'

Teresa's face clouded over for a second. 'OK – I think.'

'Haven't you seen him?'

'He's busy.'

'Take a hint then. He's had enough of you.'

'That's just like you, ain't it?' She managed to snarl in a whisper, which isn't easy. 'Making me think the worst. I knew you were jealous.'

'I'm not,' I lied. 'I just don't want to see you get your feelings hurt.'

'They won't be,' she said haughtily. 'I know what I'm doing.'

'You reckon?'

'Oi – you two aren't falling out, are you?' Vera scolded. 'You staying to have a bite with us, Genie? There'll be enough.'

'Can't, Mrs Spini, thanks very much. Got too much to do at home.' In fact that brought me up sharp. 'Blimey. I've got to go.'

All the family kissed me and wished me a happy Christmas. Vera pushed a small packet into my hand.

'That's for you, love. You deserve a little summat. And these are for the family.'

She sent me off with a bag of fruit and a warm happiness fizzing inside me.

That night I tucked Eric up in bed. Now I was better he was sharing my bed, which I didn't mind at all. I quite liked it. After all, he wasn't Lola. I sat on the bed beside him.

'Look – I've put you this old stocking here for Daddy Christmas.' I laid it at the foot of the bed. I was puzzled he hadn't asked for one. Last year he'd been on about it for days. 'You need to get to sleep quick – he won't come if he knows you're awake.'

'There's no such thing as Father Christmas,' Eric retorted. 'Mrs Spenser says. She says it's just a story made up by grown ups and I'm too old for it now.'

'Mrs Spenser's got a lot to say for 'erself, hasn't she?' I snapped. Then I was sorry and patted him. 'You just get to sleep and see what happens.' There wasn't much to put in it but I'd gathered up a few bits and pieces.

As Eric dozed off to sleep I sat there feeling very low in myself. Damn you, Mrs Spenser, I thought, for nothing like the first time. Even if my childhood seemed to have long vanished, I'd still wanted to share what was left of his. To have something pretty and magical and more than real life to believe in. Reindeer on the roof and bells and a white world when it wasn't really snowing. I still half believed in it all myself. But now even that was gone.

Mom did us proud over Christmas. She put on such a good show that even I was lulled into forgetting what a deceiver she was. She adorned the house with a tree in the front room, mistletoe (of all things) in the doorway of the back room so Dad kept bashing his head on it, and tinsel all along the mantel, which Len loved. He kept going and stroking it.

We had turkey and trimmings. Len and I sat and peeled spuds, scraped carrots and put criss-crosses on the stalks of sprouts. Mom took over the main cooking for once and did her best to get it all the right consistency and a colour other than black. She filled the turkey's behind with sage and onion and the craw with a cooking apple. She was like another person, bright and chirpy and singing carols along with Gloria and the rest of us, stirring the gravy, pink-cheeked and happy looking. Dad was allowed to go in the kitchen and put his arm round her waist. I watched from the back room.

'Love you, Dor. You know that, don't you?' This, by Dad's standards, was an outburst fit to be put on stage.

She said, 'Oh Victor,' in a half-reproachful voice but she turned and kissed him and he touched her hair.

Before lunch Nanny Rawson and Lil brought the kids over and they all came in singing, 'Ding Dong Merrily on High' out of time with each other and laughing, and Patsy was shouting with excitement. Tom came straight over to me. Nan had brought her accordion. She had a bad chest but was cheerful. Eric seemed happy enough to see his cousins.

'You're looking very pleased with yourself,' Lil said to Mom, and she didn't sound spiteful about it for once.

Mom was feeling so well disposed to the world in general that she even invited Gladys and Molly over after dinner to listen to the concert on the wireless put on for the boys in France. They had taken their pinners off and wore flower-print dresses in the same material and had dabs of rouge on their cheeks.

'This is ever so kind of you,' they kept saying. They'd brought over cake with a scattering of dried fruit and a little packet of butterscotch.

Molly made a beeline for Len who was sat at the table and plonked herself down right next to him, smiling away like mad. Most of the butterscotch went by Molly's hand straight into his mouth, which was definitely the way to Len's heart.

116

It was grey and cold outside but cosy in the house. We listened to the concert, opened our few presents and drank ruby port, the scraped turkey bones still jutting up on the table. Vera's present to me was a pretty hairslide, Mom had talc from Dad and there were chocolates. Gracie Fields was singing 'The Biggest Aspidistra in the World' as Gladys fell asleep in the armchair with her legs apart. Molly barely took her eyes off her until she was letting out little snores. Then she shifted her chair even closer to Len's, giggling and peeping round into his eyes. Their two hands crept together and lay there like ham joints on the pale blue tablecloth. Mom pretended not to notice. Molly slipped the last square of butterscotch into Len's mouth.

Dad was due to leave in the New Year. It'd been a happy week, the happiest I could remember in a long time, since way before the war ever started. Lots of singing and talking and people being nice to each other. I kept trying to forget it was a lie. That the glow on Mom's face was put there by a stocky copper called Bob several years younger than both her and my dad.

On New Year's Eve we joined in 'Auld Lang Syne' along with the people singing on Gloria. We listened to the King's stumbling voice: 'I said to the man who stood at the gate of the year, "Give me a light that I may tread safely into the unknown." And he replied, "Go out into the darkness and put your hand into the hand of God. That shall be to you better than light and safer than a known way."'

We looked over the year's dark rim into the unknown of 1940.

January 1940

Once Christmas was over we came down to earth with a crash. Dad had to go and so, apparently, did Eric.

'D'you want to go back to Mrs Spenser?' I asked him.

Mom was watching us like a hawk. 'He's got to go, there's no two ways about it. "Leave the children where they are." That's what they're saying.' For a moment she squatted down next to Eric and looked into his face. 'You do understand, don't you love? It's for your own safety. It's not 'cause we don't want you. I wish you could stay.'

Fortunately I had the wisdom to keep my mouth shut about the Spinis. 'But d'you *want* to go?' I asked again.

Eric shrugged. 'Dunno.'

'Oh Eric, spit it out!' I nudged his arm impatiently. 'You must know whether you want to or not.'

'Don't mind going,' Eric said. 'Mrs Spenser's all right.'

'I've told you,' Mom snapped, straightening up again. 'He's going.'

Ten whole days of Bob deprivation had left her nerves properly frayed. The sugary act she'd managed for Dad was beginning to wear off too and she was being short and snidy with him again. Now Christmas was over there was nothing to look forward to but being back where we were with more work, more blackout, more drudgery. Mom at least had a grand reunion with Bob to look forward to, so she was better off than the rest of us.

Dad knew he was bound for France and he was a bit emotional. I didn't see Mom shed any tears for him, although she was smoking her fags end to end the morning he went. He set off very early so he could take Eric on the way and meet the dreaded Mrs Spenser. So the two of them got togged up, Dad in his uniform, which suddenly made him stand up straighter, his kitbag over one shoulder, and Eric as before with the gaberdine, little case and gas mask. Mom and I weren't yet dressed.

Dad came and gave me a big tender hug and I felt like bawling and saying, don't go because everything's going to be terrible once you've gone. But I didn't, I just hugged him back and swallowed on the lump in my throat as I felt his newly shaven cheek against mine. He stroked my head like I'd seen him do Mom's. 'Tara, Genie,' he said, looking into my eyes, and I saw his were watery. Then he hugged me again. 'Be a good girl now.'

All I managed to get out was, 'Bye Dad.'

Eric clung to me and I tried to talk in a normal voice, still sounding as if I had a bad cold. 'Be a good boy for Mrs Spenser, won't you? I s'pect you'll be 'ome again in no time.'

Len gave Eric a bear-hug and Mom, Len and I stood out the front as the two of them walked off down the street into the pale dawn, hand in hand, Eric swinging the gas mask from its string. At the corner they turned and waved a last time.

Mom let out a big breath, said, 'So . . .' and went indoors.

That very evening Bob was round again. Must've

been psychic. Later on in the night I had a dream about the pie factory and the bloke with the leaking nose. In my dream, Bob had fallen into a gigantic mincing machine and scraps of blue uniform kept turning up, pressed tightly into the pies. I woke feeling quite happy the next morning.

Teresa managed to tear herself away from Jack long enough to come with me into town one Saturday. Big of her.

'It's blooming freezing, isn't it?' she said as we cut down Bradford Street to the Bull Ring. She pulled the collar of her old blue coat close round her. Our cheeks were pink and raw.

'S'going to snow. Gloria said.'

The sky looked grey and full.

'Jack said too.'

'Oh well – must be true then.'

'Cheeky cow.' She decided not to take offence, which made a welcome change. 'Here, what you going to get? I'm going to Woollies to buy a lipstick.'

'Lipstick?' I'd had in mind some new knickers from off a stall in the Bull Ring. 'You can't wear that!'

'Who says?'

'You'll look like a tart. What'll your mom say?'

'She won't see. I'll put it on when I'm out. Jack can kiss it off again.'

'Yeeurgh! Thought you said you got babbies if you kissed.'

'Hasn't happened so far,' Teresa said smugly. 'Anyhow – I've decided you were probably right about what really happens. Now I've got a bit more – experience.' She went ever so red in the face all of a sudden.

'What experience?'

'Never you mind.' Her cheeks aflame.

'You *haven't*, have you?'

She was shaking her head like anything. 'Course not. It's just—' She put her mouth by my ear. 'Once when we were having a kiss and cuddle he pulled me close and I could feel it there against me. As if it was waiting.'

'So what did you do?'

'Nothing! What d'you take me for?' We both got the giggles a bit then. We turned up past St Martin's Church.

'When are you going to let me meet wonder boy then?' I practically had to shout over the din in the Bull Ring.

'Oh – sometime,' she said, casual like. 'Don't want him running off with you, do I? You and your big soulful eyes.'

I was still recovering from this remark as we made our way through the bustling and pushing and shoving in Spiceal Street. There was a tight bunch of people round a bloke stood on a box who was throwing socks into the crowd.

'Here y'go – three pair a shilling. I'm practically giving 'em away. Don't for God's sake wear 'em and then bring 'em back, will yer?' Lots of laughter and repartee from the crowd. There was the usual collection of people hanging round the statue of Nelson and someone playing a trumpet, a melancholy sound, and all the stalls of fruit and veg and cheap clothes and crocks and some people getting a bit scratchy with the crowds round them. There were some uniforms mingling in with the rest, on their way up and down to the station, and kids crying and stallholders yelling and smoke from cigarettes curling into your face on the freezing air. The sky was so dark and heavy that some of the stalls already had naphtha flares burning on them.

We went to Woolworth's, catching whiffs of fish from the market next door. Teresa bought herself a sixpenny lipstick called 'Lady Scarlet' and put some on straight away.

'It does make you look like a tart.'

'Ta very much.' She preened in front of a little round mirror in the shop. 'I just want to grow up. I'm fed up of being treated like a kid.'

I sighed and she looked round. 'What's up with you?'

'I wish I was a kid still. A little tiny babby who doesn't know about anything.'

Teresa saw my downcast face. 'D'you want to do your bit of shopping?'

'Nah. Shan't bother.' Couldn't face the idea of buying camiknickers now somehow.

'Let's go to the Mikado then – have ourselves a cake?'

On the way round there we passed one of the emergency water tanks ready for all the fires this war was supposed to set off. Some clever dick had stuck signs on saying 'NO BATHING   NO FISHING'.

The Mikado was a lovely café and was packed as usual. It was a big place with an upstairs, did lunches and teas, and the windows full of cakes invited you in. You walked into a warm, fuggy atmosphere of steam and the sweet smell of all sorts of cakes, people with bulging cheeks wiping cream from their lips with rough little paper napkins, and cups and saucers chinking.

Teresa and I took our trays upstairs after we'd passed through the agony of choosing a cake. This was just before things were rationed and we'd come to appreciate it even more later. What to have? Chelsea buns you could unroll into a long, currant-spotted strip, flaky

Eccles cakes dark inside, chocolate éclairs squirting cream at every bite? I settled for a cream doughnut and Teresa had a custard slice which erupted with yellow gooiness every time she stuck the dainty little fork into it.

We hung our coats on a proper coatstand and took a table by the window, looking out over the Saturday bustle of Birmingham's Martineau Street. Everywhere people were milling about with bags of shopping.

Teresa and I grew drunk on the sweetness of the cakes and got the giggles. I tried to forget everything at home and we sat and laughed and reminisced. Teresa was her old jolly pre-Jack self, and I looked at her dancing eyes and lipsticky mouth which had faded in the onslaught of custard and thought, she really is my best pal and that'll never change. And I was in a quite good mood until suddenly Teresa said, 'Seen Walt?'

'No.' I couldn't help sounding sulky. 'Why would I have done? You're the one whose brother's pally with him, not me.' I slammed my fork down too hard on the tea-plate and a lady stared at me.

'Come on, Genie. You know you like Walt. You're your own worst enemy, you are. You're not going to like this but I'm going to say it—'

'He's walking out with another girl. I know, ta.'

'How?'

'Seen 'em.' I kept my eyes fixed on my plate.

'Oh Genie.' Teresa was all sympathetic in a superior 'I'm so lucky to have gorgeous Jack but poor old you' sort of way which got right under my skin. She leaned forward. 'She's not reliable that one. I've heard things about her.'

'So what, anyhow,' I said savagely.

'He does like you, you know he does.' Teresa was

grinding on at me. 'If you didn't do everything you could to put him off. Why can't you be nice to him instead of eating him alive every time he speaks to you?'

'I don't like him now anyway. He's a pig.'

'How come then?'

I wasn't going to tell her about him making a fool of me. Twice.

'What's her name?'

'Lisa.'

'Bully for her.'

'Well you asked.'

I didn't want to know any more. Didn't want to think about it any more either. The afternoon was spoilt.

'Fancy going to C&A?' Teresa said when she'd drained her teacup.

I shook my head, staring at the endless movement of people outside. As my eyes focused on the faces, I noticed one shambling along who was nearly a head taller than everyone else, gangly, head aflame with red curly hair.

'Isn't that . . .' I said, before I had time to think.

'Who?' Teresa craned her neck, following the direction where I'd been looking. I saw her eyes widen. 'It is,' she said. I could hear the hurt in her voice. 'It's Jack.' Her cheeks went red, clashing with the fading lipstick. 'He told me he had to work this afternoon. Was doing an extra shift. That's why I came . . .'

'With me?' I finished for her, pushing back my chair. 'Well thanks a lot, Teresa. It's always nice to feel second best to some carrot-top who doesn't give a monkey's about you in any case.'

She was peering round the window-frame, following him as he disappeared. 'Was he with anyone? Did you see?'

'No, I didn't as a matter of fact. But it proves one thing. You can trust your beloved Jack about as far as you can spit.'

'It's just a misunderstanding,' Teresa said, lower lip trembling. 'Course it is. He wouldn't lie to me. Not Jack.'

But I couldn't help a guilty feeling of triumph at the sight of Teresa's crumpling face.

Next time I saw her of course, Jack had wormed his way out of it. Fibs? Him? Downright porky-pies? No – it had slipped his mind, he wasn't working after all, and being a model son he had to run some urgent errands for his mom.

His devoted, starry-eyed girl told me this in all seriousness, face ashine. 'I knew it'd all be all right! He's explained everything.'

'Teresa,' I said, 'if you'll believe that, you'll believe anything.'

The thing I hadn't told Teresa was that I did have an admirer in Jimmy the Joiner.

I paid him a bit more attention. Smiled sometimes. After all, I wanted someone to want me. In fact I pretty desperately wanted someone to want me. Number one on the list would have been my own mother. But I wasn't going to show it or go begging for it from anyone. I managed, me. I could cope. Didn't need anyone. That's what I wanted to say to everyone. Scared the life out of me, all that wobbliness every time I saw Walt. And the terrible stabbing jealousy when I saw him with Lisa or whatever the hell her name was. I didn't dare think what would happen if I gave in to feelings like that. But Jimmy was different. Apart from the fact he wasn't unpleasant as such, I had nothing in the way of actual attraction towards him at all. Except for being a bit flattered. It gave me a warm, stroked sensation that anyone was taking an interest.

Since I didn't feel anything except a helping of curiosity, I wasn't worried enough to be nasty to him. In fact I started to get a thrill saying 'Hello Jimmy' when I came into work and seeing I had the power to make a red flush spread over his pale, underfed-looking face.

'Rationing starts today,' Mom said, though I could hardly have missed the fact since Gloria had been on and on about it. The week's ration was to be: bacon, 4 oz.; butter, 4 oz.; sugar, 12 oz. We were already registered with all the right people. Thank heavens we were with another butcher and not Harris's, I thought with a shudder. Didn't need my nose rubbed in it.

'We'll have to make sure we don't have that Molly over every five minutes, living off our ration,' Mom said. She was ironing at the table. Now there was an unusual sight. I should've had a photographer in. 'She seems to be coming over here a lot.'

She didn't know the half of it. Molly was over just about every evening when Mom was out at the telephone exchange. She seemed to have got out of Gladys's clutches, and instead of being dragged into premature old age had decided to *live*. The dabs of rouge got thicker. She brought boiled sweets. She had a cousin worked over at Cadbury's and got her cheap chocolate so she brought that along as well and saved all the best bits for Len, even some with nuts in. Once Len was home from work he and Molly parked themselves in front of Gloria for the evening, enormous in their chairs, sucking and champing away on barley sugars and Dairy Milk with serene smiles on their faces. They never said much to each other. Barely a word in fact. Whatever was on, they listened. *The Nine O'Clock News*, they tuned into Haw-Haw, concerts, records, *ITMA*. They cheered the house up no end, chuckling away when anyone laughed on the wireless, Molly's titties heaving up and down. I thought how their dimensions suited each other.

And Gloria had just given us a new treat: the Forces Programme which was put on for the lads in France, but we could tune into it at home as well. I wondered if Dad'd hear it and felt cheered by the thought that he might. It was like a link with him. Gloria's music was the one thing that could lift my spirits on these chill, dreary days. All those bandleaders, their music like shiny sparkling trails through the house, making you want to sing, to move your body – Geraldo, Joe Loss, Ray Noble, Glenn Miller. I was in love with them all, though I had no idea whether any of them looked like the Hunchback of Notre Dame. And my Anne Shelton, and the Mills Brothers with those sweet, melancholy voices. I wanted to be tucked into bed by 'Goodnight Sweetheart' and dance till I was drunk on happiness to 'In the Mood'. They did what they did for me, for Len, for Molly, and for countless other people. They made life worth living.

It started snowing. I say snowing. It was snow such as I'd never seen in my life before. Heaps and swathes and layers and banks of it clogging up the town and blown across the parks. The old'uns were all saying, 'Can't remember snow like this since . . .' – though each of them seemed to recall a different date. Gloria said it was turning into the worst winter for forty-five years. Everything was muffled and the sky seemed to sink lower as if it was creaking under the weight of it all. Buses, already crawling along in the handicap of the blackout, were now going so slowly they were almost going backwards. Everyone was even friendlier than usual and Mom had to buy herself a new pair of boots to get to and from work.

'Feels safer somehow, doesn't it?' Mom said, when the snow had been falling for some time. 'As if they couldn't get at us with all this wrapped round.' She stood staring out of the back window.

'It's so cold though.' I was crouched by the fire, turning this way and that to try and feel the warmth on every bit of me. 'I was frozen in bed last night. Where's that crocheted blanket of Nan's gone?'

Mom picked up her bag and started fiddling inside it. 'What blanket?'

'You know. The yellow one.'

Mom shrugged and made a show of checking through her coins. 'It's so flaming dark on the bus you can't see what change they're giving you . . . Maybe Len's got it.'

Since Len had already gone I couldn't ask him, but there was no sign of it on his bed.

'That strip of baize we had in the front room's gone too,' I told her.

Mom frowned. 'D'you think that Molly's light-fingered?'

'No, I don't.' The thought hadn't crossed my mind.

It was hard to imagine Molly being light-anythinged. 'I s'pose it'll turn up.'

One night Len and Molly started kissing. After some sign between the two of them which I must have missed, Len knelt down on the floor in front of her. Molly spread her legs apart to let him come near and they locked their lips together. And that was that. For ages. I was ever so embarrassed. Seeing people kissing like that's enough to make you jump out of a window even from the top floor, and they didn't care whether I was there or not. They didn't even notice.

But what could I do? Len had his eyes shut and Molly's brawny hands were clamped behind his back, so I went into the kitchen and did the washing up. Mom would've had a fit if she'd known about them. But then who was she to complain? Everyone else seemed to be at it, so why shouldn't Molly and Len have a go, even if they were both as thick as butter? So I just left them to it.

When I crept back in later Molly was sitting on Len's lap. She beamed at me, her red face pressed against Len's, and he was in some sort of dreamy trance as well.

'Awright, Genie?' Molly said. 'Don't mind us, will you?'

'D'you want a cuppa tea?'

'Ooh yes,' Molly gasped, as if she'd just run ten times round the block. She lurched off of Len's knee. 'I made a few biscuits – 'ere.'

She handed me a paper bag containing four crumbly biscuits. 'Two for Lenny,' she said, planting herself opposite him.

Soon after there was a loud hammering at the front. The three of us looked at each other.

'Stay in your own chairs,' I said, running to answer it.

Lil was in a right state. Her coat collar was pulled up round her throat and her hair and shoulders sparkled with snow.

'It's taken me a bleeding age to get here,' she panted, steaming in past me. When we got into the back her eyes looked darting and scared. 'It's your nan. She had a fall earlier and they've taken her up the hospital. She's done summat to her leg. Where's Doreen?'

'Work.'

'Course. I'd forgotten you're on your own every evening.' She nodded at Molly. 'Len – our mom's hurt her leg. Fell on the ice.' She spoke slowly so he'd take it all in. Molly made some sympathetic noises and then, surprisingly, seeing she'd be in the way, took herself off home.

'I'll wait and tell Doreen,' Lil said.

It was ten o'clock. 'She should be half an hour or so.'

Lil went and stood by the fire. 'Jaysus, my legs are shaking.' After a moment she burst into tears and sank into a chair. 'I've never seen Mom like that,' she sobbed. 'She was on the corner of Moseley Road. She'd been to see Mrs Briggs – the one who's got pleurisy – and she fell on the way back. When they came to get me she was lying there making this horrible noise. I can't get it out of my mind. It was the pain – she sounded like a dog whimpering. Someone from the hotel got her an ambulance and it took ages and ages to come. Mom went quiet and I thought she was dead.'

I went and knelt down by Lil and watched her,

130

wondering if I should take her hand. I was scared. Len sat, looking stunned.

'It's all right.' Lil looked quickly across at him. 'She's not dead. She'll be OK. She's done summat to her knee. But when they put her on the stretcher to go in the ambulance, someone shone a torch in her face and she looked so old and her eyes were full of fear. I've never seen her like that before.'

She was sobbing even harder now. I felt so sorry for her and for our nan I nearly started crying myself. I went and poured her a cup of tea. She hadn't even taken her coat off and was still hunched up in its grey, prickly warmth.

'You said Nan's going to be all right, didn't you?' I asked cautiously. I felt very young suddenly. I wasn't exactly sure what was up with Lil but I put it down to shock. Len leaned forward and took her hand and Lil suddenly threw herself into his arms, laying her head on his big strong chest.

'I hate being on my own,' she cried in a desolate voice. 'I want my Patsy back. I want him so bad. Why did he have to do it?' She tried to say a few more things that got lost in sobs and gulps. Len rocked her back and forth. 'I can't stand it,' Lil said. 'I can't go on. I need someone to be with. I hate sleeping in a lonely bed every night and doing all the worrying for all of us on my own. It's too much, day after day. How'm I going to manage now?'

When she'd calmed down a bit I said, 'Who's with the kids?'

'Mary, from next door.' That was a sign of how bad things were if she'd entrusted her kids to Mary Flanagan.

Lil suddenly seemed to lose all the energy that had

131

driven her here in such a state. She sniffed, sat quiet back in her chair and drank her tea. But it was still all going round in her mind because after a while she said, 'Mom won't be able to manage. I'll have to give up work and run the shop.' She sighed. 'I hate that bloody factory, but I'm making better money now than I've ever done in my life.'

'Or I could,' I said. It sounded like a nice idea to me. There was no point in suggesting my own dear mother. I knew that just wasn't going to happen.

'I can't move out now,' Lil said gloomily, only half hearing me. 'Not even if they offer me a council house. I'll be stuck in Belgrave Road for ever.'

'No you won't. Nan'll get better.'

Lil looked at me, dark eyes filling again. 'When she was laid there in the road I saw what it'd be like without her at home. And I thought how she's had it hard, what with me coming back to live and Len ... And Doreen and me not getting on. I wanted to make it up to her. She's been a good mom to us ...' And she was off again.

The mantel clock said ten twenty-five. 'Mom'll be in soon,' I said, desperately.

But she wasn't. We all sat and waited. Lil was tapping her foot on the tiles round the hearth. By a quarter to eleven I had this nasty suspicion turning round in my mind.

'Probably the weather,' I said.

Ten more minutes passed and I was getting in a panic. How could she, tonight of all nights? She had to be somewhere with PC Bob, but I couldn't tell Lil that because the most God Almighty amount of shit would hit the fan if she was to find out about that, specially the state she was in tonight. I sat tensed with terror at the thought of hearing the front door and Mom, in her flirty voice, asking Bob in for a drink.

Once it reached ten past eleven Lil stood up. 'I'll have to go and let Mary get home. What the hell's happened to her? Is she often this late?'

'Oh, sometimes she is,' I said quickly, praying Len wasn't going to say anything.

'Will you be all right?'

'We'll be OK, just as normal,' I said. I was nearly laughing with relief that Lil was going. 'I'll tell her, soon as she gets in.'

When I opened the door to let Lil out Mom was standing on the other side of it with a kind of smirk on her face which she wiped off right quick when she saw us.

'What's the matter? What're you doing here?'

When Lil told her, Mom was about as upset and flustered as she deserved to be. We all stood crushed into the hall.

'I'll go straight up the hospital and see her tomorrow,' Mom said. She hadn't taken her coat off either.

'Visiting's afternoons,' Lil told her in a chilly voice.

'Oh – well, Genie can go after work, can't you love?'

I was going anyhow. Didn't need her sending me.

Lil disappeared along the road, her muffled torch playing on the icy ground. I shut the door carefully and turned round and stared at Mom. She had guilt not just written, but carved in massive gullies all over her face.

Eventually, with a shrug, she said, 'We just went out for a drink.'

I kept staring really hard at her eyes. How could she? How could she?'

'What, Genie?' Her face went all sharp and spiteful.

'I didn't know, did I? How could I know what was going to happen? Don't barge past me like that . . .'

I'd heard enough of her already.

'I have too much of your cheek sometimes . . .' she shouted up after me.

I didn't say another word. Just went up and shivered myself to sleep in bed wishing to God I could have a new life, new family, new everything.

The next morning brought a blue sky without blemish, grey clouds wiped away and the sun brilliant on the snow. Before Mom was up I opened the back door and went out. From the kitchen to the privy the snow had been well stamped down by us tramping back and forth. No one, so far as I knew, should have walked on the thick pie crust of snow towards the bottom of the garden where the Anderson sat smooth and rounded as an igloo. But of course I found footprints, not filled in by any night snow, leading from the side gate to and from the shelter. Two sets. I followed them, pressing my feet into the bigger ones with their rugged prints. Round the door of the shelter it'd all been stamped down. There was a cleft in the snow at the edge of the roof as if someone had rested their hand there.

I pulled the door away and looked inside. In the confined space a piece of thick canvas had been laid out to cover the frozen floor. On top of it were a Tilley lamp, a variety of covers and materials: a thick grey blanket I'd never seen before, the strip of green baize, a couple of pillows and the yellow, orange and green crocheted blanket of Nan's which had long been missing from the back room.

February 1940

Life got a bit better after that because Lil took up my offer and I said goodbye to Jimmy the Joiner and Shirl, and went to look after my nan and help run her shop.

She was properly laid up and Lil was earning better money than me. I was happy. Nan let me come and go as I needed to. She understood about Mom. Not Mom and Bob of course – I hadn't said a word to anyone about that. Just about the way Mom used me.

'She don't deserve you,' she said to me, laid back on the horsehair sofa with her leg, rigid in its plaster cast, stuck out in front of her. She'd done some horrible thing to her knee.

'Summat to do with cart-lidge they said up the 'ospital. They say it'll take weeks to heal. Flaming nuisance.'

It'd knocked the stuffing out of her. Her face looked thinner and more lined. Sometimes I found her asleep, head lolling back on the sofa, which was unheard of for her as a rule. But she was always on her dignity. She'd never come down in her nightclothes. When I arrived in the morning she was always dressed. I suppose she must have hoisted herself up off the bed to put her dress on, rolling a stocking up her good leg – good except for the ulcer dressings. She always sat and pinned up her hair.

'I've taken to coming downstairs on my backside,' she said. 'I'm not up to hopping at my age.'

I looked after her as if she was a queen, which she was in my eyes, as she'd never been anything but good to me. I wasn't the only one who thought so – the neighbours drifted in and out of the back door like flies, wanting to know if she needed anything. Hot-tempered, red-headed Mary Flanagan came almost every hour trailing an assortment of her seven kids behind her. She'd tried evacuating them once but they'd all come home.

'You awright there, Edith?' she'd say. 'You shout me if you need anything.'

And in the shop it was always, 'How's Mrs Rawson?' and then they'd say, 'I bet she's glad of your 'elp, bab. I couldn't borrow you for a bit, could I?'

'You're golden,' Nan said to me sometimes, watching me work. I scrubbed her quarry tiles on my hands and knees. I blackleaded the grate, did her washing in the brewhouse when it was our turn, and hung it steaming across the freezing yard. I cooked for her, I ran errands, I scuttled back and forth to the shop whenever we heard the click of the door opening and the bell ringing out.

I felt grown up. I'd just turned sixteen after all, even if that hadn't been much of an event. I served in the shop. I sorted stock, arranging jars of sherbet lemons and throat drops – there were still sweets to be had then – and bars of Lifebuoy and blue Reckitt's powder in packets and piles of enamel buckets. It was peaceful in there most of the time, except once or twice a week when Morgan made his forays through to the upstairs with a selection of trollops in tow. Once the girls arrived there were bangs and squeaks of the floor and giggles and thumps from the bug-ridden rooms upstairs. It was no good suggesting to Nan that she move. There was a time when I just didn't understand this attitude. But it was so much part of the fabric of life at her house I barely gave it a thought now. There was Nan, and there was Morgan. That's how it was. Nan would roll her eyes to the ceiling and tut a bit at the louder noises, but we mostly just had to ignore them. Besides, people being the nosy so-and-sos they are, the trollops were surprisingly good for business.

I adopted Nan's policy towards Morgan, that he was like a mote of dirt passing through, unseen under my nose. That is until he started coming in a bit early – before his girls – and fixing his pale eyes on my chest.

''Allo my dear,' he'd say, wiping his sweaty forehead with a hanky. The strips of hair hung down like pondweed. 'You are growing up fast, aren't you?'

'Nan, he keeps talking to me,' I reported.

'Right,' she said.

Next time he turned up, sneaking in and pussyfooting about instead of going upstairs, grinning at me with yellow smoker's teeth, Nan's voice roared through from the back.

'You filthy bastard, Morgan!' He actually jumped. It had more impact her being invisible, like God's voice out of a cave. 'You as much as speak to my granddaughter again and I'll 'ave your bollocks twisted round the back of your neck!'

'No offence intended, my dear,' Morgan said to me, retreating hurriedly to the stairs.

I kept the place immaculate, took people's money or filled in the strap book so they could pay later. I checked with Nan. She knew them all and trusted most of them. She'd been known to land a punch on the jaw for bad debts. I tore round the place like a whirlwind and I loved it. I was doing it for my nan and I could decide what I wanted to do and when and do it as fast as I liked. I had a fierce mixture of anger and love inside me and I was like a fury.

Sometimes Cathleen trailed round after me, or Nan tried to keep her amused. There were the other kids to deal with when they got home from school. They came and sat by the hearth, hands blue from the cold walk home, and I gave them each a cup of tea and cut them a piece to eat so they were in a good mood by the time Lil got home. I got high marks from Lil because I saved her a lot of chores.

Nan was none too happy though. She wasn't fed up with me, who she couldn't find enough praise for, but because sitting about on her backside wasn't exactly her style. She tried to teach Cathleen to knit but the kid was too young and flew into a tantrum and was happier with a bag of clothes pegs. But Nanny Rawson was bored, so I asked Len if he'd be very very kind and let her borrow Gloria for a bit while she was poorly? It took a bit of persuasion of course, because Gloria was meat and drink to him. But he did love his mom, and in the end he nodded his heavy head when I said we could all have our tea over at Nan's of an evening so he could hear Gloria too.

One morning I trudged over to Nan's through the slush, water seeping into my old boots, carrying Gloria, with the accumulator hanging from one arm in a hessian bag. Nearly flaming killed me. I had to stop every few yards to rest because my muscles were aching so bad, balancing Gloria on people's front walls and switching the accumulator from arm to arm.

I was standing by St Paul's churchyard with Gloria resting on the wall when a voice said, 'Need a hand?'

I nearly dropped the thing.

'Er – oh, hello,' I said. 'Yeah. Ta.'

Walt took Gloria off me with ease and the accumulator suddenly felt light as a sparrow on its own. I rubbed my arms as we set off.

'Where you off to with this?'

'My nan's.'

'I 'eard about her accident. She bad?'

'She'll be all right. Bust up her knee. She's fed up not being able to get about.'

'I'll bet. You brought this to cheer 'er up?'

Why the hell was he being so chummy all of a sudden?

'It's Len's – my uncle. I nearly 'ad to put a gun to 'is head to get 'im to borrow it 'er.'

I gave a laugh, to show I could be light and joke. He was nothing to me now. I didn't care. I'd seen Walt in his true colours, putting me down the way he did, and now he was walking out with that Lisa girl I found it perfectly easy to be civil to him and show I didn't care. I wasn't out to waste my affection on someone who'd taunt me and put me down. That'd be a sign of things to come all right. So talking was easy all of a sudden. Walt was even laughing at my jokes as we walked to Nan's house.

When we got to the shop I said, 'All right, Walt, ta. This'll do.'

'Might as well take it in for you,' he said. 'Not much further is it, and I can't put it down in the wet.'

But he stopped me before we went in.

'Genie—' He was the one blushing now. 'We got off on the wrong foot, didn't we? I was wondering. D'you fancy going to the pictures – with me?'

I could feel my face taking on a wide-eyed innocent look. 'But Walt, you've got a girl to walk out with. Lisa, ain't it?'

Walt looked at the ground, embarrassed. 'Not any more. I'd rather go with you.'

Oh, would you now.

'Sorry. I can't go out. Mom's working evenings and I'm busy.'

'What about a Sat'dy matinée?'

'No ta,' I said, ever so politely. 'To be truthful I wouldn't go out with you if you were the last man on earth.'

He decided to stop helping me after that.

Nan of course was up and dressed. She was amazed. 'Is that Len's wireless?'

I nodded, a smile spreading ear to ear. She looked ever so pleased and I knew I'd done something good. 'He said you could have it while you was laid up. I'll set it up, shall I?'

Between us we wired it to the accumulator and Gloria was off, jollying the place along no end. Nan cheered up straight away. 'Isn't it marvellous?'

By the end of the day, during which Gloria was barely switched off, Nan said, 'I think me and Lil ought to see about getting one of these.' She nodded at the kids who were sat next to *Children's Hour* sucking bulls' eyes. 'And it doesn't 'alf keep them quiet.'

I was tingling from more than one sense of triumph.

Soon after, I popped into the Spinis' one dinnertime and walked slap bang into a family row. The Spini family's disputes had two things which outdid even the most ferocious yard fights in the area: one was fluency, the other was volume.

I could hear it coming when I stepped out the front of Nan's, voices all the way down the street, and there was a gaggle of people gawping in the Spinis' doorway to watch the fun. Their rows seemed to work better in Italian, so none of us could understand a word, and even if we could the four of them were all yelling at once.

I went and pushed through the nosy parkers until I was just inside. Vera was holding her ground on one side, arms waving in the direction of Micky, who was wagging an infuriated finger mainly in the direction of a box heaped with turnips, and I couldn't tell who he was actually shouting at. Stevie, in a white apron, his sleeves rolled up, was framed by the back door leading into the ice-cream-making room where he had presumably been interrupted churning the 'Scattoli's Outstanding Ices'. He, like the others, was shouting and wore a heavy scowl, although that wasn't unusual.

Close by was the tall young man with a drooping black moustache, a nose curved and slender as a knife blade, who Teresa had such scorn for. Fausto Pirelli. He was watching, wearing a superior kind of expression, saying nothing.

And in the middle of them all stood Teresa, between two sacks of carrots as if they were protecting her, like sandbags, from the blast coming from all around. But she was doing her fair share of shouting too.

They must have found out about Jack, I thought, and I wasn't quite as sorry as I should've been.

But no. Teresa was off again, hair hanging down, hand out in front, slapping at the air with the back of her hand. In the midst of all the Eyetie I heard the words 'war effort'.

Suddenly catching sight of me standing there, she yelled in English, 'Ask Genie, since you think she's such a model daughter. Go on, tell 'em, Genie. She goes out to work in factories and there's no trouble. Nothing. All

141

the time you treat me like a child and I'm sick to death of it. Sick of it!'

The row suddenly switched into English. 'We just want to protect you,' Vera said. She didn't seem on the boil as much as Micky and Stevie, who were doing their injured male pride bit. 'We want to keep the family together.'

'Well that didn't stop you sending the kids half way across the country, did it? You soon did that when you decided it was the right thing. So what's wrong with me just going out to get a job up the road somewhere?'

'No one's going anywhere unless I say so,' Micky decreed. His face was thunderous. 'I'm not having you going off behind my back. You stay here, you work here and that's an end of it – finish.' He swiped his hand across as if cutting his own throat and made as if to walk off, but found the door blocked by all the gawping passers-by, so he turned and had another go. 'That's the trouble with you young people. You got no respect for your families now. You got to keep respect – do as you're told.'

'You're stupid, Teresa,' Stevie started up. 'You're being selfish. You should act more responsible instead of being so childish.'

'I'm not childish!' Teresa shrieked at him, arms waving. 'I'm just sick of you all running my life for me. "Teresa you can't go here . . ." "Teresa you've got to do this . . ." And anyway, Stevie, what's all this got to do with you? Why don't you shut your trap and take your bloody ice-cream cart out? It'll give us all a rest.' She waved an arm at Fausto Pirelli. 'And take Mussolini here with you!'

That did it, they were all off then, Fausto too, who

was totally enraged all of a sudden, and no one could get a word in edgewise for minutes at a time.

Then, in a tiny chink of quiet, Teresa said, 'But they've given me the job!'

'Tell them you can't do it—'

'Go on – let 'er get a job,' some woman shouted from the doorway. 'It's all for the war effort.' No one took the blindest bit of notice of her.

I could see they were going to start off all over again. This one could go on for hours. So I pushed my way out and slipped back to Nan's, their voices following me down the street.

'What happened?' I asked Teresa, tiptoeing back in later.

'My daughter, she wants to just go,' Vera said, one hand scooping through the air like a plane taking off.

'She got her own way – as usual,' Stevie said, grumpy sod that he was.

Teresa put her thumb up and grinned. 'I'm going to have a go. It's Green's, over in Sparkbrook, making army uniforms.'

'You'll be kept busy then.'

She waited till Stevie had moved out of earshot, then hissed at me, 'The factory's right by Jack's house.'

'Oh,' I said. 'Bully for it.'

Jimmy the Joiner walked back into my life one freezing Saturday with a ring of the shop bell. I ran through, ducking under the dividing counter, and there were Jimmy and Shirl.

'Genie!' Shirl greeted me as if I was her long lost, best ever pal, and I found I was really pleased to see her. I'd quite missed her voice droning on down my ear.

Jimmy was giving me a shy smile and his squiffy eyes were warm and friendly. I wasn't sorry to see him either. 'We thought we'd come and see how you was getting on,' he said. 'T'ain't the same at work without you, Genie.'

This was gratifying to hear. 'Come through and meet my nan,' I said.

Nan was friendly, as she was to people she expected to approve of. 'Sorry I can't get up and do anything for you,' she said. 'It's not me at all, sitting about like this.'

'Oh no, you must rest,' Shirl said.

Shirl's pale hair was soft and curly and she had thick pink lips and enormous blue eyes. Everything about her was round, her behind, the shape of her legs, her cheeks, her big heavy titties. She was another of those that made me feel scraggy and boyish. But there was something very comforting about Shirl. Cathleen was hovering by her and Nan seemed to feel it at once.

'Come and sit by me,' she said to her. 'Genie'll make us a nice cuppa tea.'

'Lovely place you've got 'ere, Mrs Rawson,' Shirl said in the sort of voice most people put on to tell you someone's died. Nan knew perfectly well her house was just like thousands of other back-houses, if perhaps more spick and span, but she seemed chuffed all the same.

Jimmy sat quiet. He'd hardly taken his eyes off me since they arrived. I kept looking at him out of the corner of my eye, not sure whether I liked him or not. There was something awkward about him, his very pale skin, dark hair curling at his white neck, and when he looked at you he almost squinted in a way which made my flesh creep a bit. But on the other hand I'd seen worse. And he'd come specially to see me, and not many people ever did that.

'She's a good girl, our Genie,' Nan said, nodding across at me as I lit the gas. 'She's been a right little gem to me.'

'We miss her,' Shirl said, taking Cathleen up on to her lap and stroking her plump hands. 'It's not the same at the factory without her buzzing about.'

They sat and drank tea while Nan gave Shirl a blow-by-blow account of the fall, the doctors, the hospital where she'd spent four days.

''E said 'e didn't like the look of my knee at all,' she was going on. ''E said, "I shall 'ave to consult with my colleague." Those are the exact words he used.' Shirl gave every sign of loving it all, and cuddled Cathleen. I could picture Shirl with loads of kids.

Jimmy kept sneaking looks at me. Once he winked and I smiled back. Yes, he was all right Jimmy was, I thought. I'd missed his attention.

Outside in the yard when they were going, Cathleen still clung to Shirl's hand.

'Jimmy's got something to ask you, Genie,' Shirl said.

Jimmy shuffled his feet. 'D'you fancy coming out with me, Genie?' Then, thinking he'd been a bit short, he added a quick, 'To the pictures or a walk or summat?'

I thought about Walt. Stuff Walt.

'I would, Jimmy,' I said. 'Only it's hard for me to get away, what with my nan and my uncle and my mom.'

His face dropped.

'You two go,' Shirl said. 'I'll come and sit with your nan Sat'dy afternoon, that's if she's no objection. And I can play with little Cathleen here.' She pinched Cathleen's cheek. 'I'd like that. We got on ever so well.'

We consulted Nan and she looked pleased. 'It's time Genie 'ad a bit of life of her own for a change.' She turned a sterner eye on Jimmy. 'As long as you both know 'ow to behave yourselves.'

Next week Jimmy and I walked down the Cannon Hill Park. I wore my best green winter frock and huddled in my coat. Truth to tell I wasn't feeling at my best. I had a cold and a blocked nose and it had been an effort to come out. But I decided to think positive, to like Jimmy's loping walk and his voice, which came out sounding deeper than you'd expect from the size of him.

Almost as soon as we were on our own he grabbed my hand, which took me aback. Bit pushy, I thought, when he'd always seemed a timid sort before. But he turned and smiled at me and said, 'Don't mind, do you? I've been wanting to hold your hand ever since I first saw you.'

Course, if someone says something like that you don't resist, do you? And it was a nice feeling, special, having someone close. His hands were warm even in the cold. The snow was thawing slowly and there was wet everywhere.

'You're ever so pretty, Genie.'

'Me?' I laughed, pleased as punch. Sometimes I just wanted to be a proper girl. 'Go on. I'm not.'

'You are. Your eyes are like – like – well, they're – nice. And the way you get that dimple when you smile.'

We walked round watching the ducks on the small lake. The park stretched wide around us, sloping down to the swimming baths at the bottom, full of leaves now, and chunks of ice. It was a shock to see green again after all the days of white. There were still hard mounds of snow with grey crusts on top melting slowly down the slope.

Jimmy told me he had four sisters and a brother and his mom was deaf, had to lip read.

'What about your dad?'

'Oh . . .' he said, almost as if he'd forgotten about him. 'He's reserved occupation – Heath's, the foundry.'

'Mine's away,' I said, suddenly proud. 'In France.'

'Wish mine was,' Jimmy said with feeling. 'He's a bugger – pardon me.'

I wasn't sure what to say to that. There are such a variety of ways of being a bugger and I wasn't sure I wanted to know the particulars.

And Jimmy said, 'I don't want to talk about 'im. What d'you like doing best?'

I had to think hard about that one. 'I don't seem to get the chance to do anything much these days. I like going to see my friend Teresa. When she's got the time,' I added gloomily.

'I like football.'

Oh Gawd, not another one. 'You don't support the Villa, do you, by any chance?'

'Nah – never. Blues.'

That was something, although whether he was going to carry on about Aston Villa or Birmingham City wouldn't make much odds to my passing out with boredom in the long run.

When he got me up by the trees at the quiet, top end of the park, he caught hold of me and kissed me like I'd seen Len and Molly doing. I had a bit of trouble with that because I didn't think to breathe in before he started and my nose was all stuffed up. His big slimy tongue popped into my mouth and he was sucking away at my lips and I found myself thinking Jaysus – like Lil would have said – is this right, us getting on to kissing so quick? I couldn't do anything back except cling on to his shoulders struggling for breath as he pushed his body against me. In the end I had to pull away and take in a big gasp, which Jimmy took to mean I was so overcome with emotion I couldn't stand any more. Which was pretty near the truth, only not quite how he thought.

When I turned round again after fixing some sort of smile on my face, he was giving me a grin brimming over with triumph. 'You're my girl now, Genie.'

Len was coming to Nan's straight from work now, early evening, so I could cook for all of us with Lil, and get it all over in one go. It also meant he could have a good old listen to Gloria before we had to go home. It was much nicer this way, sharing some of the chores with Lil. She was being as nice as pie to me as I gave her so much help with the kids, dunking them in the tin bath by the fire for her once a week, clearing up the mess after and keeping them entertained. She taught me a few tricks to help the cooking go better, like taking the custard off the heat to start stirring it so it didn't heave up into lumps like it usually did. Mom never told me anything useful like that even though she'd once worked in the Bird's factory in Digbeth, and you'd think she'd at least have picked up how to make the stuff.

That night we had stew with loads of dumplings. Lil showed me how to make them really nice with suet. We all squeezed round the table, except for Nan who couldn't get her leg under it. It was cosy with the fire and Gloria and the dim gaslight and we all ate hungrily.

'Feels a bit like Christmas, doesn't it?' Nan said. 'Shame Doreen's not here as well.'

My eyes met Lil's. We couldn't bring ourselves to agree with Nan on that one. My feelings of fury at the way Mom was carrying on had grown worse and worse.

Len and I walked home together after, holding hands for safety: the street was so dark and it was beginning to freeze again. We had our torch but didn't bother carrying the gas masks any more.

'I'm glad you're here, Len,' I said. 'I'd be scared stiff else.' He was so big and slow and solid.

One hint of sound from outside our house brought Molly to her door. 'You're back then?' she called across the street.

Couldn't really disagree with her there. Sometimes it got on my nerves a bit, her pouncing on us like that. But you couldn't dislike Molly. She was inoffensive and as generous as she could afford to be. And she made Len happy.

'Doesn't Gladys mind?' I asked as she came over. I was struggling to find my key in the dark.

I just saw Molly put a finger to her lips, rather coyly. 'She's asleep. Didn't see me go.'

As I went to the front door I heard a faint knocking noise from the side of the house. There was a breeze and the entry gate was unfastened. Anger twisted in me, and dread.

'You go in,' I said to Len and Molly, unlocking the door. 'I'm just going to shut the side gate.'

They weren't listening to me anyway, so wrapped up were they in each other.

I tiptoed down the little alley between our house and the next into the back garden and slid across the wet grass. I knew it. Noises from the Anderson. Even more blatant noises than before. It was horrible. Molly and Len, Jimmy, now this. Something exploded inside me.

I pelted back round and in through the front door, steaming in past Len and Molly who were in each other's arms but still alert enough to look round in amazement at me.

'Len!' I commanded him from the kitchen. 'Get in 'ere a minute.'

I had an enamel pail in the sink, the tap full on so water was rushing into it at the full strength of the old plumbing. Len stood watching. When it was three-quarters full I dumped it on the floor in front of him.

'I want you to do a piddle in there. The biggest one you can manage.'

Nice thing about Len was, he never asked questions. Just unbuttoned his flies and obliged, with Molly watching, eyes on stalks, over his shoulder.

I flung open the back door and stomped down the garden, leaning well over to one side to balance the pail. On the way I stopped and scraped what dirt I could from the top of the flower bed, hurting my hands on the icy ground, and chucked that in too.

From inside the Anderson I could still hear loud, indecent sounds. They wouldn't have noticed if the whole bloody Luftwaffe had come over that night.

I could barely see a thing but it was so small I couldn't possibly have missed. I yanked the front aside and sloshed the bucket of wee-wee stew in on top of them.

'Bob's your sodding uncle!' I yelled. And left them in a wet, shrieking, effing and blinding heap inside.

Mom's rage knew no bounds. To begin with. She called me every name under the sun, once PC Bob had dripped off down the road refusing to stay another moment to be treated like this, etc. etc.

'You *stu-u-upid*—' she screeched, dragging the word out long, '—selfish, evil little cow!' She was shivering in the back room, lank strips of hair hanging on her shoulders and her red dress daubed with soil, clinging to her. 'I wish I'd never – never even *seen* you in my whole life. I'm cowing frozen – and Bob could catch his death . . .'

'There was wee in there as well.' Thought it best to tell her. Otherwise she'd never know, would she?

'WHAT?'

She'd stormed into the house without even noticing Molly sprawled on top of Len in one of the chairs, the top buttons of her dress undone. They hadn't wasted any time. Molly strugged to her feet like an upturned beetle and skedaddled, right quick.

'Who in the hell d'you think you are?' Mom ranted on. Quite a bit of pacing up and down the room went on, except being such a small room any pacing turned more into pigeon stepping. 'Interfering. Passing judgement. What's Bob going to think, me having a daughter like you?' She was working herself up. 'He might never come back and it'll be all your fault.'

'GOOD!' I shouted. 'I hope he dies. I hope he catches pneumonia or falls under a bloody bus. He shouldn't be here at all. He's not my dad, and you shouldn't be carrying on behind Dad's back. You're a disgusting tart, that's what you are.'

That was when she started hitting me, the bitch, stinging slaps round my face again and again until Len had the wit to grab her arms and stop her. I bit my lip until it bled. I wasn't going to cry for her. I hated her.

151

It was she who burst into tears then, sobbing and snivelling and carrying on while Len and I just stood there staring at her. I put my hands to my smarting cheeks and my heart was completely hardened towards her.

Until suddenly she said, 'You don't understand, Genie.' She looked up, sharp face all raspberry blotches, appealing to me. For the first time trying to tell me something she truly felt. 'You don't know what it's like to find someone you can really love. To be lifted out of years of feeling dead and buried, and scared stiff you might lose it again. You've seen how he looks at me. I've never in my life been wanted like that before – ever.' She was sobbing again at the thought of it.

'Dad wants you.'

She looked down and I knew she was ashamed. 'But I don't want him. God knows, I've tried. I just don't. He makes me feel buried up to the neck. Always has.'

I started crying then. Didn't know where it came from, all of it. Frightened Mom a bit I think, the way I howled. Scared me too. It was like a pain pushed down so far I didn't know it was there, all gushing out. I didn't want to hate her. She was my mom. Your mom's the one person you can't hate or it eats you inside. She's like the North Star and you always need that right direction.

And for once she forgot herself and put her arms round me, and I sobbed and bawled and couldn't stop. Len came and hugged the both of us together like a gorilla.

'I'm sorry, Genie,' Mom said in the middle of it. I could feel her tears dropping on the top of my head. 'I can't help it. I just can't help myself.'

March 1940

My Dear Doreen and family,

Well at least the weather's warming up slowly and we wake with the birds now – they've started singing at last! We can still see clouds of our breath on the air first thing too. Roll on spring proper. So now my only complaints are that I still haven't found a pair of boots that fit properly and that I wish I could be at home with you. We're still here waiting to find out what proper soldiering, as the lads call it, is all about.

One new thing – they've issued us with special day passes to go into——. I went, Saturday, with Dickie, the pal I told you about who comes from Stechford. It was an experience. Very smart and pretty with flowers at the windows and people sit out and drink on the pavements. We tried some of the wine they sell. It's some rough stuff – I'd rather have a pint of Ansells!

I've read so many books since we've been here. The lads pass them round. Otherwise it's card sharping and letters. Thank Genie for the chocolate – a proper taste of home. How is Gloria doing? The wireless in our billet stops us feeling too blue. Today I heard Vera Lynn singing 'Somewhere in France with You' and it made me pick up my pen to tell you, my Dor, how much I miss you.

Glad to hear Edith's knee is on the mend. I'll write again soon. In the meantime, try and keep in good spirits, won't you?

Your loving husband, Victor.

I liked letters from Dad, knowing he was safe and hearing about new places he'd been. Mom always read the letters of course, but she'd put them down on the table without a word. After, she'd be scratchy and short for a bit.

Bob stayed away for a week after our little set-to. Don't know whether she told him to or whether he was in a huff or scared I might go for him with the carving knife. Whatever the reason, he kept his distance and all was rosy. We had Gloria back – Nanny Rawson and Lil had bought a little set of their own – and Mom was being extra specially nice to me. She ran me up a new dress on her machine and it actually fitted me. It was navy with white polka dots and a little matching scarf to go in the neck. She visited our nan twice a week. She even did some cleaning. I found her up early one morning sweeping out the back room.

'I know I've been a bit neglectful, Genie,' she said a couple of days after our fight. 'And your nan says you've been a proper treasure to her.' She even brought me up tea in bed, which was an unheard of luxury. Suddenly I felt like someone's daughter.

One morning she sat on the edge of my bed, her hair loose, and said with a coy little smile, 'So who's the lad courting you, Genie?'

Can't say I'd thought of it as courting exactly. But Mom was trying to be my friend and I wasn't getting much change out of Teresa nowadays.

'His name's Jimmy Davis. He was at the factory in Conybere Street.'

'Nice then, is he?'

''E's all right.'

'Bring him home to meet me, Genie.'

As I nodded she put her head on one side so her hair fell in a fine, straight sheet. 'You're not getting up to anything you oughtn't, are you?'

What a question. 'No,' I said, thinking, no more than anyone else round here anyhow. Jimmy was keen on kissing. Ever so keen.

'What about Len and Molly?' she asked suddenly.

'What about them?'

'Are they behaving themselves? I don't want any trouble on my hands from them two.'

'They're all right.' She may have been my pal all of a sudden but I wasn't going to go and spoil things for Len. 'They keep each other company in the evenings.'

'So long as that's all they're doing.'

'Mom?'

She raised her eyebrows.

'Is Bob ever coming back?'

'Genie – I've told you.' She gave a big sigh. 'I love Bob. He loves me.'

'But what about my dad?' My voice turned squeaky and tearful. 'What're you going to do?' It felt as if the world was falling apart.

She got up and went over to the window, stood with her back to me in her white nightdress. 'I don't know. Can't seem to think about it. I keep hoping it'll just sort itself out, one way or another.'

I was crying quietly behind her. 'But what about when Dad comes home?'

155

'I've told you—' She turned to me again, half angry but near tears herself. 'I don't know, do I? This has never happened to me before. Don't think I don't feel badly about your father. He's a good man and he don't deserve it, I know. But I can't throw away what I've found. Bob's come along and I feel as if he's saved me – saved my life.'

''E hasn't really got a wife and kiddies, has 'e?'

'No.' She at least looked ashamed of this lie. 'He hasn't.'

I pushed my face down into the prickly blanket, hugging my knees, rocking back and forth. 'I want my dad. I want him home. I want things to be all right again.'

She sat by me, even stroked my back. 'I'm sorry, Genie,' she said eventually. 'But Bob's the man I love.'

After his short bout of quarantine, Bob was back and I was faced with an offensive of charm.

'Hello Genie,' he said when he first came back one Saturday morning, his tone sounding as if I, not Mom, was his long lost love. He produced a bunch of daffs from behind his back like a conjuror with a rabbit. 'These are for you. To make friends.' He stuck a really sick-making smile on his brawny face.

'You'd better give them to Mom. Flowers make me sneeze.' I flung the bright yellow blooms on the table as if they were dog muck.

Bob clenched his teeth but he didn't say anything. He stood in the back room with his hands in his trouser pockets. I didn't remember inviting him in but he seemed to be there anyhow.

'All right are you, Len?' he said in the stupid, jolly

voice people seemed to think they'd got to put on with Lenny just because he was a bit simple, as if he needed humouring. Len grinned obligingly. But then Len'd have grinned at Adolf Hitler if he'd happened to pop in. He was like that. Bob turned round and about, jingled coins in the pockets of his loud checked suit. I stood watching him, po-faced.

He tried again: 'That's a right pretty frock you're got on there, Genie.' Then he coughed. 'Very nice.' I glowered at him. 'Your mom knows I'm here then, does she?'

'No.'

'How about telling her then? There's a good girl.'

'Mom!' I yelled up the stairs without shifting myself. '*He*'s here.'

She looked ever so nervous when she came down. She had her hair up and was wearing a pretty, tight dress which hugged her waist and her small bosoms. Bob's eyes swept up and down, devouring her, dirty sod.

'I've got to go,' I said. Nan was expecting me.

'We'll all have to go out together one day, won't we Bob?' Mom said brightly. 'To the pictures or something. Get to know each other better. You'd like that, wouldn't you Genie?'

I didn't even bother answering that one.

Teresa was rather full of herself. Working outside the family business had turned her head.

'Don't know what you see in it,' I told her, since for the moment I was finding more freedom working in my family's business than out of it. 'Clocking on, and at someone's beck and call every minute of the day.'

'Yes, but it feels like a real job. And I feel as if I've grown up.'

'And you get to see Jack? When am I going to meet lover boy then?'

Teresa hesitated. Even with her olive skin she blushed easily. 'Yes – I see Jack,' she said, very offhand.

What was going on here then? 'I thought that's just what you wanted?'

'I did – do. Only . . .' In her eyes I could suddenly see a funny little gleam. 'Oh Genie – there's the most gorgeous feller at the factory. It's mostly girls there of course – but he brings all the supplies in and he's forever stopping for a chat. Specially with me.' I could well imagine. I could hear Teresa's wonderful, life-giving laugh echoing out across the factory floor.

'But Teresa, I thought Jack was the be all and end all, your one and only—'

'Oh, I'm still walking out with Jack,' she said hastily. 'Only I can't help liking Clem. He's got the most beautiful green eyes.'

Oh yes, green eyes? I didn't believe in green eyes. I mean I couldn't put my hand on my heart and say I'd ever in my life seen anyone whose eyes were truly green.

I was hanging on to what I had with Jimmy. Which wasn't much. But I needed someone. Truth was, after his opening outburst of affection and that first breathless kiss Jimmy hadn't poured out much in the way of feelings. In fact he never said very much at all.

A typical date with Jimmy went like this. We usually went out on a Saturday. Shirl came to be with our nan, even though Nan was better and hobbling about with a stick.

Jimmy and I would meet, him grinning away in anticipation. He'd take my hand and sometimes we'd go to a matinée at the Carlton, or if it was fine we'd walk in the park. And I'd try to get him to talk. I told him my nan was better.

'Oh well – that's good.' End of that conversation.

'I might look for another job soon.'

'Oh ah.'

Another attempt. 'D'you still like me, Jimmy?'

'Course. Wouldn't be 'ere else, would I?'

I was even forced to ask about football. Problem was, we just hadn't got anything to say to each other. Was this something I was supposed to mind, I wondered? I thought about married people I knew. Mom and Dad had never had a lot in the way of conversation, other than what was needed to get by. Lil and Patsy had at least had a laugh together. But what I wanted to know was, was this the very best you could expect? I'd hoped for something a bit more like being friends with Teresa. Getting on, feeling the warmth and excitement of seeing her, laughing together. Was it normal to find your mind wandering when a man kissed you and to be thinking up a shopping list in your head, or wondering why it was Jimmy's mouth often tasted just a bit of rhubarb when it wasn't even in season?

After he thought we'd indulged in enough pleasantries, Jimmy set to with the real business of the date so far as he was concerned. It'd be back of the cinema as the picture flickered on high above us (I'd try to twist into a position so I could at least watch it as well, over his shoulder). Or in the park, or a doorway on the Stratford Road monkey run while near us, girls snatched handkerchieves out of the boys' breast pockets – you name it, Jimmy took his chances. Blimey, the hours I spent locked, more than half bored, in Jimmy's grasp. Sometimes he got bold and tried to worm his fingers into my coat, inside my dress, but I wasn't having that.

'Oi – you can get out of there.'

He'd give me a sheepish grin and those lips would come close again. So far none of it was like Lil said. Certainly not the best, dreamiest feeling in the world. Frankly I'd rather've had a more tasty sort of gobstopper like a bag of Brazil nut toffees. Except that he was there and he wanted me and kept coming back for more.

Maybe I'm not normal, I thought. Teresa seemed to get a lot more of a thrill out of a man than I did. Perhaps all my housewifery and careworn life and all that was going on at home had made me old too soon?

Bob, like the proverbial rash, was back with a vengeance. Our house was nothing short of a knocking shop and it was getting me right down. First of the evening shift was Len and Molly. They didn't seem to be pushing the boat right to its full limits with sex, but having those two snogging in front of me half the evening was a disturbing enough sight. Didn't know where to put myself. If we'd had a proper coal shed I'd have gone and sat in it.

I did as many things to distract them as I could. I got them playing rummy, gave them things to eat, made endless cups of tea, switched Gloria on. I was cooking our meals back at our house by now, but sometimes I went out to my nan's, prepared to brave the walk back later through the black streets rather than face the canoodlings of Len and his Moll. After all, he was thirty now. I was just in the way.

Second shift, on nights they could manage it, were

the other two love birds. Now they'd moved into the house, the Anderson shelter not being the ideal place to carry on a romance, particularly because as the ground was no longer frozen it was sometimes ankle deep in water. I saw the first signs of trouble when the crocheted blanket appeared again, folded over the back of a chair like it had always been before.

Thing was, Mom was still being uncannily nice to me. She did the ironing and brought me the odd treat when she could: sweets or bits of clothes, some new black shoes with a bow on the strap. I knew perfectly well it was hush money, bribes to keep me sweet, but at the same time I couldn't bear to lose it. The price was knowing she took Bob up to my father's bed while I sat and cried downstairs and Len, alone by this time of night, comforted me.

'S'all right Genie, s'all right.'

'It's not sodding well all right,' I'd sob, cringing in myself at the slightest sound from upstairs. But they were quite quiet, I'll grant them. Len and I put Gloria on loud as we dared and tried to drown out even the slightest sign that they were there. I did a lot of that in those days – blocking things out, closing my eyes, my ears and my very heart.

Some nights when I thought Bob was coming, sickly sweet as he was to me these days, I just stayed over at Nan's and slept on the prickly horsehair sofa by the dying heat from the range and the ticking of her clock.

It didn't take Nan long to catch on. 'I'm not a fool, you know, Genie. What's going on with Doreen?'

I couldn't meet her eyes. 'Nothing, Nan.'

She sat quiet for a minute, the stick resting by her leg, her breathing loud, wheezy on her chest. 'Is she carrying on behind your dad's back?'

I couldn't tell her a real lie. Not Nan. I just sat there, wanting to die of shame.

'Genie?'

'She's got a – friend.'

'Thought so. She'd been like a bitch on heat since Christmas. I noticed it then but I gave her the benefit of the doubt.' Nan pursed her lips, face grim. 'Selfish little cow. Always been the same when it came to riding roughshod over everyone else.' The extent of her anger took me by surprise.

I was relieved Nan knew, but frightened to death at the same time. Mom'd never forgive me for letting it slip and if she found out I'd lose her again, just when we were getting on so well.

'She says . . .' I began timidly. 'She's never been happy with my dad.'

'Happy? *Happy*.' She turned the word round and about like someone looking for the chip at the edge of a saucer. 'You show me someone who thinks they are happy. A marriage is a marriage and that's that. Wasting time dwelling on whether you're happy or not is a sure way into trouble.'

I looked at her tough, lined face. Mom had told me that Grandpa Rawson used to bash her about till sometimes her face was almost unrecognizable. I wasn't sure whether her missing teeth had dropped out with each child born or whether they'd been knocked from her gums by his fist. He didn't restrain himself any better when she was carrying a child. She'd miscarried two on account of his violence. But even when she managed to lease the shop, when she had more money and could've got shot of him, she carried on, steadfast, in a marriage she'd chosen. 'Where would leaving 'im have got me?' And then he died. If there was anyone,

Mom always said, who deserved heart failure, old man Rawson was the one.

'Don't say anything to 'er, will you?' I begged. 'Not at the moment. Things are all right really.'

'Are they?' Nan's voice was sarky as it ever got. 'So what're you doing sleeping here on my couch?'

I saw Teresa now and then. I wasn't sure about the latest of what she was up to and at the moment I didn't really care. I presumed she was thinking up all the backhand ways she could manage to meet Jack or Clem or whoever the hell it was. Good sodding luck to her.

One night though, she came round to Nan's.

'I was hoping you was still here.' She looked a bit down. 'Fancy coming to ours for a bit?'

I suppose I wasn't very gracious greeting her. My mind was back in Balsall Heath, wondering anxiously what might be going on in our house.

'You go on,' Nanny Rawson said. She was standing ironing at the table which was swathed in an old, singed blanket. 'Do you good to have some young company.'

At the Spinis' I found Teresa's Dad in a bad state. He was downstairs, in a chair by the hearth, but his face was very pale, his skin clammy, and he seemed only able to talk in a whisper. Opposite him sat Fausto Pirelli, the young man who'd been in the shop that day they were all yelling at each other. His shadow fell on the wall beside him, nose like a hawk's beak. He was talking, on and on in Italian in a soft, earnest voice, with a frown on his face. Micky seemed agitated, kept trying to interrupt, but when he tried to speak it ended in a bout of agonized coughing.

Vera, standing by Micky's chair, looked worried to

death as well, and exhausted. 'Micky was called to a factory fire yesterday,' she whispered to me. 'It was over Bordesley way, some chemical place, and he said the fumes and smoke were evil – choked him. He only just managed to get out. It's done something terrible to his chest.' Her eyes filled with tears. 'I hate seeing him like this. Micky.' She leaned down and touched his hand, 'please go to bed.'

'Later,' he managed to say, trying to smile at her, and indicating with an angry nod of his head that the other man was still talking. The anger was directed at him.

'Fausto,' Vera implored the man, and the rest was in Italian, but I could see she was begging him to go, to let Micky rest. He flapped his hand impatiently at her, saying, 'Subito, subito . . . straight away,' and not moving.

The smaller children were in bed but Stevie and Francesca were at the table, not doing anything but listening and watching. Stevie's eyes were absolutely intent on Fausto's face.

'Brew up, Teresa,' Vera ordered quietly. I could see how tense she was.

'What's going on?' I asked, following her into the scullery.

'That stupid idiot.' She jerked her head. 'His family comes from the same place as Dad's in Italy. They're talking about what's happening there – Mussolini . . . Fausto still reckons he's a Blackshirt, even though he can't find many to agree with him. They don't like all that round here. He doesn't even really know what it means – he's all hot air. But Stevie looks up to him – thinks it's big talk. Fausto hasn't got a father of his own, he's dead, so Dad feels responsible for him. He's worried he's going to get into trouble.'

'Trouble?'

Teresa shrugged. She seemed distracted, stood with the empty kettle in her hand as if she couldn't think what to do with it, so I took it off her and went out across the yard to fill it and set it on the gas.

'You worried about him?'

'Who?'

'Your dad.'

'Yes – but the doctor said he should be all right. Needs time to let his lungs clear again. It's not that, it's – Jack found out about me and Clem.'

'What was there to find out about you and Clem?'

Teresa looked down at the floor in shame, face hidden by her dark hair. 'We started to get a bit keen on each other and I went out with him a couple of times. And with Jack living so close to the factory and that, I knew I was going to have to tell him and he was so angry and said he never wanted to see me again.'

'Well what d'you expect? Anyway, that's all right, isn't it, if it's Clem you want to see.'

'But I don't know if I like Clem very much any more. He's ever so cocky.' She sounded very sorry for herself. 'And I'm going to end up with nobody.'

A wave of great weariness came over me. What a load of stupid rubbish it was. All of it. Men, women, girls, boys, love, romance. It was all a silly story put out at the pictures and in sixpenny romances to make us think such things were possible and then cast us in the deepest blue depression when we were brought nose up against real life.

'Oh Teresa,' I said. 'For God's sake just pull yourself together.'

I went out and sat with Vera Spini, watching Fausto

as he talked on urgently. He seemed very strange, as if something was burning him up inside. And I listened to Vera's worries, which at least had some proper substance to them, leaving Teresa to sulk in the scullery.

April 1940

The spring was here with all its usual fevers enhanced, worse luck for me. And then the Flanagans' roof fell in, two houses away from Nanny Rawson's. I was out with Mary Flanagan, hanging out my nan's washing and basking in a little thread of sun which had managed to reach in and light up the far side of the yard. One minute there was the Flanagans' house, large as life, in tightly squeezed back-to-back line. The next, there was a massive great crash and glass shattering and, for what seemed an age afterwards, things groaned and shuddered, tinkled, smashed and finally settled, and sworls of thick dust rose up choking us. Minutes later, when the dust finally sifted down out of the air, we could see through to the street outside and there were people standing looking. My washing, needless to say, was black again.

'Jesus, Mary and fecking Joseph!' Mary was gasping over and over. 'My house – will you look what's happened to my house!'

Then panic set in. 'Where's Geraldine?' Mary laid her hands on each of the other two of her small children who were still at home, reassuring herself. 'Eamonn, where was Geraldine? Was she in the house now, was she?' She was screaming at the boy, shaking him. There was plaster and dust all over her red hair.

All the neighbours were out of their houses. They

stood round, numbed. No one seemed able to move. The thought that six-year-old Geraldine might be trapped under the weight of the house was too terrible to take in. Then people started saying 'What about Mr and Mrs Griffin?' and everyone wondered whether the elderly couple who lived in the front-house had been crushed under it, until Mr and Mrs Griffin were spotted out in the street with a crowd round them.

A small bang was heard from the end of the yard and Geraldine, a child with hair as bright a red as Mary's, emerged unconcerned from the privy saying, 'Mom, what was that noise?'

Mary dashed to her and whacked her one soundly round the ear. 'You eejit of a girl! What did you think you were doing in there? Sure I thought you were dead.' She clutched the bewildered girl against her great big chest, clinging to her while Geraldine bawled from the walloping she'd had. 'Where's our house gone, Mom?' she sobbed over Mary's shoulder.

Mary stood up again slowly and turned to face the fact that she had seven children, a husband away in the RAF and no house. The slum houses in that area were built back in Queen Victoria's day to give the worker bees who manned the factories a place to live, or at least exist. They were jerry built – the state of some of them was so bad it defied description – and Mary's, after the harsh winter, the weight of the snow and then the thaw, not to mention the landlord swiping slates off the roof every time the rent was overdue, had finally given up the ghost.

Mary was silent now and deathly white in the face. As everyone in the yard normally did in a crisis, she turned to my nan.

'Edith – what in the name of heaven am I going to do?'

Nan hobbled over and took command. 'For a start what you'll have to do is go to the Corporation and get on the list for another house. With seven kids they'll have to get summat sorted out for you. In the meantime . . .' She looked round the yard with the kind of expression on her face no one would dare disagree with, even Mary's next-door neighbour and sparring partner, Clarys. 'We'll all make sure you're all right, won't we?' There were nods, some more doubtful than others. 'We can fit some of you in,' Nanny Rawson went on.

Where on earth? I was thinking, listening to my nan setting example by what I thought of as rash promises.

By the evening it was sorted out. Lil's kids stayed on in Nan's attic bedroom. Nan persuaded Lil to move in with her and freed up the second bedroom for Mary Flanagan and her two youngest kids. Geraldine and one of the lads were taken in by another neighbour, the other kids by a third. And so, the teeming yard at the back of Belgrave Road, already overcrowded, ramshackle and insanitary, managed to redistribute itself with one less house to go round. The only person driven completely barmy by it was my auntie Lil, who already thought her own kids quite enough to cope with, ta very much, without having extras foisted on us.

'How about a trip to the Lickeys?' Jimmy said, and at the time I couldn't think of anything better. It was a gorgeous spring, the skies powder blue, sun warm, any last nip on the air long gone now, and the trees uncurling their leaves to the spring air looked like a miracle after the winter we'd had. Even the yard behind our nan's seemed a less drab place with sunlight streaming off the newly washed windows.

Course, just as the world seemed the most precious and lovely the spring can make it, Hitler's troops started to move across Denmark into Norway and we sat round Gloria waiting to hear the latest. In the newsreaders' solemn voices we heard names which were strange on our lips, ones we'd never heard before – Narvik, Trondheim – bringing the world in on us. You could feel suspense in the air.

Jimmy and I rode the 62 bus out to the Lickeys. The Lickey Hills are a beautiful, wooded ridge on the south edge of Birmingham where the trams and buses terminated after the long, tree-lined swoop along the Bristol Road. This was the place where hordes of factory-pale, work-weary Brummies would congregate on holidays and weekends to escape the claustrophobic closeness of the city's walls and alleys, to feel they were in the country and picnic with the sun on their faces if they were lucky.

Jimmy started trying to kiss me on the bus.

'Oh, gerroff, will you,' I said irritably. 'Not in front of all these people.'

Jimmy leered at me. Love, or at least a shortlived infatuation, is blind, I thought. His wonky eyes had given him charm and appeal at first. Now they looked as if they were squinting at me all the time, full of unwelcome lust.

'No one's looking.' There were loads of kids on the bus which kept stopping to pick up more passengers until it was crammed full. People were clinging to each other in the aisle and there were shrieks of laughter when we swung round a corner.

'I don't care. You should behave yourself when there's people about.'

'What – so I don't 'ave to when we're on our own?'

'Don't you ever think about anything else?'

It was well warm enough for my summer frock and Jimmy only had on trousers and a grey shirt that had once been white. We had a bag with bread and butter and cake, apples and a few lumps of cheese and bottles filled with cooling tea. I was excited. A trip to the Lickeys was a really special day out.

We passed through Northfield, Longbridge, to the terminus at Rednal where the bus disgorged us all. Mothers in hats yelling at gaggles of kids, all with too much to carry, headed off in excitement for the paths to Lickey Hill or Cofton Wood.

I'd have liked to go to the park with its ornamental pool, swans riding their reflections in the glassy water, and peaceful, dreamy paths and flowers. But no. Jimmy had other plans. Grabbing my hand, he said, 'Come on – let's get shot of all this lot, shall we?' and dragged me off to the tracks that led off through the woods. It wasn't that difficult to get away from the other day trippers. The Lickeys had paths winding all across them and through the trees. Many of the families out for the day walked as short a distance as possible and settled on the grassy hillside with a sweeping view of the surrounding counties, picnicking and lazing while their kids played round them, and hardly shifted all day.

Truth to tell, I was already wishing I could have come on my own. I could feel coming over me the bored restlessness I felt more and more with Jimmy, making me want to tear about shrieking or thump someone, preferably him.

'Come on.' I pointed to a place on the grass with

rings of families in view. 'This is a nice spot. Let's have our picnic here, eh?'

'Nah.' Jimmy pulled me on further and further, into the woods. 'Don't want to be surrounded by people, do we? This way . . .'

He dragged me right out to the edge of the place somewhere, finding a spot in the woods which no one else apparently thought was the great beauty spot of the Lickey Hills because no one else was there. It was pleasant enough, light darting in through the leaves, never still, and leafmould and twigs on the ground. But it wasn't exactly the scenic view I had in mind. And I knew what he wanted. God, I was fed up at the thought of wasting a day in the Lickeys stuck to the end of Jimmy's lips.

'Now I've got you all to myself, 'aven't I?' He chuckled. 'Come 'ere . . .'

I saw those lips coming towards me again, a light stubble on the white skin above them.

'Will you just lay off and let me eat my dinner in peace,' I snapped.

'Well, you're not much company, are you?'

'Can't you think about summat else for a change? Or don't you have anything else in your head at all?'

'What I've got's all 'ere,' he said, patting his crotch.

'So I've sodding well gathered.' I shifted away from him and opened the packet of sandwiches. Boredom perched on me like a gigantic bird. I wished Teresa was here. Not that she was better at the moment, but with a bit of work you could get her mind off men.

At least he let me eat for a bit.

'Find you were hungry after all, did you?'

Jimmy grinned. 'Nice cake of your nan's.'

'She's a good cook.'

'My mom's cooking's terrible.'

'So's mine.'

We laughed together. He was talking to me, which made a change.

'I bet yours has never cooked a hen with the feathers on like mine did once.'

'She never! What the hell'd she do that for?'

'She was the worse for it – the drink, you know.'

'She drink a bit then, does she?'

'Yep. Don't blame her. If I was married to a bastard like my dad I'd get kalied all the time as well.'

'What's he like then?'

Jimmy dug a dirty thumbnail into his apple. 'Our mom relies on him, see, not being able to 'ear. And he treats her like the lowest form of life. Brought the clap 'ome to her once – never been the same since, she 'asn't. She was expecting a kid at the time too. She lost that one.' Jimmy took a big bite of the apple. 'If he died I'd cheer.'

I watched him, glad at least to feel something for him again, even if it was only sorry. Some fellow feeling. And I was hoping at last here was someone who would understand what was on my mind.

'My mom . . .' It was costing me to speak and I wasn't even sure he was listening. 'She's going with another bloke. Brings him to our house. I hate him.'

Jimmy said nothing, just munched on the apple.

'It's horrible, isn't it?' I persevered, watching his pale face.

Jimmy hurled the apple core away over into the trees. 'Come on. Let's do it.'

'What?'

'The whole thing. Fucking. Properly.'

'Jimmy!' The very word gave me the heebie-jeebies. It sounded so *rude*. 'You don't use words like that.'

He was shuffling closer to me. 'Sorry.'

'Should think you are. It's not nice.' I was sitting clenched up tight, knees against my chest.

Jimmy slunk his arm round my back. 'What d'you want me to say instead?'

'Something nice and romantic. Say how you feel about me.'

'Well, you're all right, you are. I've told you. I like you, Genie.'

'But d'you feel anything more than that? D'you love me, Jimmy?' It felt important that he did, that it wasn't just One Thing he was after.

His face loomed closer. 'Yeah, OK Genie. I love you. Now give us a kiss.'

I gave a big sigh. What price affection. He kissed me for some time, then undid a couple of the buttons on the front of my dress and wriggled his fingers inside.

'Don't,' I tried to say, but he wasn't having it. He squeezed until I squeaked with pain. I was mortified. Didn't want his hand down my dress. His eyes had started rolling about and he looked so queer with his white face close to me and his body rocking up and down beside me as if he had a horse under him.

There's got to be more to it than this. Lil hadn't had those dreamy eyes on her just for this. And how long'd we got to sit here doing it for? What a complete waste of the afternoon when we could've been out in the sun. And then I started thinking about home, Mom and Bob doing this. I felt sick.

Jimmy started fumbling about in his clothes. ''Ere,' he said, ''ave a feel of this. This is 'ow much I want you.'

174

He yanked at my hand, rubbed it against him.

'No!' I said, pulling away. It felt hot and sticky. 'Don't be dirty.'

He scowled. 'All right then. If you're going to be like that, we'll do it another way.'

Hands on my shoulders, he shoved me back so my head was in a pile of leaves and twigs. He pulled my dress up and got his hand down my knickers, poking around hard and clumsily. Lying along me, half on, half off, he ground his body up and down, faster and faster. It didn't take long. He tensed up, eyes squeezed shut, hurting me with his hand and I called out in pain.

When he got off, my blue dress was all wet and sticky.

'You pig,' I said. 'You horrible, disgusting pig.'

'Go on.' He half turned away, buttoning himself up again. 'That's what you wanted. Next time I'll give it to you proper.'

I felt very cold suddenly, and shivery, sat huddled up, clutching my knees tight. The world was a nasty mean place.

'Let's go. You wanted a walk, didn't you? Bit of sun on your face?'

I spread out the skirt of my dress, all gluey and wrinkled. 'What's my mom going to say?'

Casually, Jimmy picked up one of the stera bottles we'd brought our tea in. It was a third full still, and he poured the rest of it in my lap. The blood-warm tea seeped through and trickled between my thighs.

'There y'are. Now she'll never know the difference, will she?'

*

'There's no need for you to keep my nan company no more,' I told Shirl. 'I'm not going to be seeing Jimmy again.'

'Oh.' The smile dropped off Shirl's face but I was too wrapped up in my own mortification to take in how downcast she looked.

'Got fed up of 'im, 'ave you? Thought you would. Not got a lot going on upstairs, 'as 'e?'

I shook my head.

'So – you don't need me round then? I mean I don't mind . . .'

'No,' I said, very short with her. 'There's no need to put yourself out any more.'

She took me at my word and walked out of our lives again. I didn't give it a lot of thought then because it was absolute mayhem up at Nan's, with Lil's lot and the Flanagans roaring in and out. Nan was getting better. She was taking over from me again day by day and I knew I'd soon be booted back out into the working world. She bore the Flanagans with her usual stoicism – 'The Corporation'll sort them out a place soon enough.'

But it was Lil who was doing her nut. The price of fags had gone up by a ha'penny a packet, the government was behind the factories to up production (especially aircraft – Len was on extra long shifts) and to cap it all the house was nearly full to bursting.

'Your life's never your own,' she moaned regularly. 'At work you don't have time to turn round hardly and when I get home I can't see across the room for mad bloody kids.'

And the Flanagans were wild. After all, we only had two of them, but the mess they made was indescribable. The boys were bedwetters, so there were smelly sheets to be dealt with every day, dirty clothes left in heaps, Patsy, Tom and Cathleen's things all turned upside down and scattered round the place, and the constant noise of them charging in and out. Mary seemed helpless to control them, try as she might. How the hell did she cope normally? we wondered. They started to make Lil's kids look like angels with haloes.

It was getting Lil down and I felt sorry for her. She was growing sourer by the day and I thought she deserved better.

I went to see Vera Spini one day. The shop was quiet and she was out the back making ice cream, her face sagging with exhaustion. She wore a white cap on her head to keep her hair out of the way.

'Let me help, Mrs Spini,' I said, going to the churning handle.

They boiled the ice-cream mixture in the copper until it was like custard, which stood overnight covered with muslin cloths to keep any flies out. The next day it'd go in the churning machine, a long cylinder which was kept cool by electricity. There were blades inside to turn it round and it got paler and paler yellow, smelling sweet and turning into food from heaven when you were used to lumpy tapioca.

'How's Mr Spini?'

'Not too good.' She stopped turning and pulled the cap off. Her pale hair was dark at the roots as if it was planted in soil. 'He hasn't managed to do anything much for the past two weeks. I'm ever so worried about him, Genie.'

She wiped her dry, workworn hands on a cloth and

tried to force a smile. I'd never seen her do that before. Not force it. But there were no songs on her lips today, no hymns or Santa Lucia.

'Here, come and see him. He'll be glad to have a bit of company.'

'Me?'

Vera looked at me in surprise. 'Course. He'd love to see you. He's got a real soft spot for you, Genie. Always has had.'

This was news to me all right and it didn't stop me feeling scared. I'd hardly ever seen Micky without Teresa around.

'Stevie!' Vera shouted into the yard. 'Come up front for a bit, will you? I'll not be long.'

In the house, Micky was sitting by the fire huddled in his coat, watching Luke push an old wooden horse with rough little wheels along the floor. His body looked thinner, his face was drawn and sick looking and he had several days' worth of greying stubble on his cheeks. There was a newspaper on the table and a cup with tea dregs in it.

'Genie!' He really did look pleased to see me and I felt warmed by it. In fact he looked nothing like as stern as usual. 'Come and have a sit down with me. I'm stuck here, useless to everyone at the moment.'

'You're telling me,' Vera mocked him.

'Feeling any better, Mr Spini?' I asked, perching on the edge of a chair by the table.

'A bit.' He ran a hand over his wavy, pepper and salt hair and nodded insistently at his wife. 'I do. She don't believe me. Makes you think though. I don't know what was in that smoke but it nearly did for me, I tell you.' And he was off, coughing again. He didn't sound well, whatever he said.

Vera stayed long enough to brew up a pot of tea, sugaring a cup for Micky and placing it tenderly on the table beside him before going back to the shop.

'You got time to sit for a bit?' Micky asked.

I nodded.

'It's very nice. Long time since you sat and had a chat. Now you're a working girl.' He laughed, then coughed. I couldn't say I ever remembered sitting having a chat before, but I wasn't going to argue. But what in heaven were we going to talk about?

'You OK, Genie? Everything all right at home?'

'Yes,' I lied.

He looked into my eyes with his dark ones for a moment then stared at the back of the door which Vera had closed for once.

'I've been sat here all this time – so I've been thinking. Never get the time on a normal day.' He stopped. I waited for him to keep talking, not sure if I was meant to ask, and then I saw he was struggling to keep from coughing.

'I remembered something from when I was a little boy in Italy – about seven or eight. I had a special place for myself. No one else knew about it.' He stirred the tea and took a sip, slurping it. 'Of course everyone knew about it – but no one except me knew it was special. Our village was outside Castellamare, and the church where we said Mass was high on the cliff and the land round it looked out over the water – that's the Mediterranean Sea. Beautiful blue it is. There were a few trees on that piece of land and one was an olive tree with a very old, twisted trunk where I used to go and sit. It was at the far end, away from the church, so the old ladies who came in and out to clean the church or say their rosary couldn't see I was there. I used to feel the trunk of the tree behind my back and the land in front of it sort of dipped down towards the sea. There'd be salamanders – little lizards – running up the tree and there were crickets in the grass. You ever heard the noise crickets make, Genie?'

I shook my head.

'The grass was a dry, wiry kind that scratched at the back of your legs. Sometimes I sat there as long as an hour, hoping no bigger boys would come and find me. The sky was always blue – that's how I remember it, and you could smell salt on the wind. And because I was alone and all I could see was sea and grass and sky it gave me room for all these dreams to pass through my head. I felt very big sitting up there, as if I owned all the world and I could do anything I wanted.'

He laughed again suddenly as if he'd said something daft, because he never talked like this normally. Certainly wouldn't have done to his own kids. The laugh ended in a long bout of coughing and his lungs sounded as if they were half full of liquid. Each breath was a strain for air and his face went red. Luke stared up at him. When it'd passed he said, 'D'you have a place like that, Genie?'

I shook my head. 'There's no room for that here, is there?'

Micky tapped his head with one thick finger. 'There is in here.'

I thought of my house all for me, by the river with fields and trees and flowers. 'I s'pose I do then, yes. Only it's not real.'

'It don't matter. When I want to dream of something outside all these houses so close together I can go back to my tree. So you're looking at a crazy bloke who spends his morning sitting under a tree thousands of miles away!' He seemed embarrassed now, after saying all that. Luke jumped up and pulled at his father's leg and Micky lifted him up on to his lap, Luke watching him with a finger in his mouth.

Seeing the newspaper on the table, Micky picked it up and handed it to me. 'Here – another good reason for sitting under a tree.'

It was the *Mirror*. With a black-rimmed nail, Micky pointed to one column:

> There are more than twenty thousand Italians in Great Britain. The . . . Italian is an indigestible unit of population . . .
> Even the peaceful, law-abiding proprietor of the back street coffee shop bounces into a patriotic frenzy at the sound of Mussolini's name . . .

'In Italy we have the *Fascio*,' Micky explained. 'The Fascist Party, pretty much like the German Nazis. So they think that because we are Italian we must support Mussolini . . . I can't think of anyone now who is a supporter – well, except young Pirelli, or he likes to think so anyhow . . .' Micky shook his head.

I read the last part of the newspaper column: 'We are nicely honeycombed with little cells of potential betrayal.'

'But what does it mean?'

He must have seen the worry on my face because he reached over and patted my arm. 'I hope it don't mean nothing. I've been here far too long to worry about.

'Come and see me again if you get time, eh?' he said, as I got up to leave. 'I'll be on my feet soon. Oh – and by the way, Genie. Teresa. She getting up to anything she shouldn't be?'

I shook my head, panic stricken. Why did people have to keep asking me such blooming awkward questions?

'Not that I know of.'

He looked into my eyes for a moment, then smiled. 'All right, love. Thanks for coming to see me.'

I wanted to say something nice but couldn't think of anything. In fact what I really wanted to do was go and put my arms round him for being kind, for making me feel special. I didn't do it, but I knew I'd never see Micky Spini in the same way again.

'Tara,' was all I said. 'Hope you get better soon.'

Mary Flanagan's kids were not the easiest to get to bed. I'd thought of Mary as someone intimidating, forever yelling and carrying on, until she moved in with my nan and I saw her trying to control her kids. It was pitiful.

One night when I was round there the tension of having two families living under one roof was reaching breaking point and although the Corporation had promised to rehouse Mary 'at the earliest possible opportunity' so far there was no date.

'Get up there and stay where I put you or you'll be feeling my hand across you again,' Mary was bawling up the stairs in her deep, throaty voice for about the tenth time. Downstairs I was trying to deal with the devastation the kids had caused while they were still up.

Lil sat on the couch chewing her nails as if she'd like to gnash someone's head off. I could tell she was bubbling inside like a boiler about to explode. She was a stickler for getting her own kids to bed in good time, and once they were there, that was where they stayed, and no messing.

Not long after, despite Mary's threats and pleas and bribes, we could still hear feet padding back and forth upstairs, then the clattering and squeaking of the bed-frame as the two boys bounced on and off it like little rubber acrobats.

Nan and I exchanged glances in the scullery.

Lil suddenly snapped. 'Christ Almighty, would you listen to them! They'll be waking Cathleen again if they carry on like that. What's the matter with them? Why the hell can't you get them to do as they're told? They're like bloody animals.'

'I'm doing my best,' Mary snapped from the bottom of the stairs. 'Don't you talk about my kids like that. Eamonn, Colm – I'm coming up to give you a hiding so I am!'

'They're unsettled,' Nanny Rawson said. She was washing up, I was wiping. 'Poor kids've been split up. They're not used to it.'

'I don't bloody well care.' Lil was on her feet, brown eyes darkened further with fury. 'I've had enough of it. If they come to live in our house they should do as they're told. We want some peace, no sodding kids running round the place all evening. Some of us have a job of work to do as well you know!'

Suddenly there were wails from upstairs. 'That's it!' Lil exploded. 'That's Cathleen. Move, will you.' She pushed past Mary who was at the foot of the stairs. 'They've really done it now.'

'Don't you touch my kids!' Mary spat at Lil's back, following her up the stairs.

'I wouldn't touch your poxy kids if they were the last ones on earth. I'm going to see to mine now they've cowing well gone and woken her up.' But as she passed through the boys' room we heard her bawl at them,

'GET INTO BED AND STAY THERE YOU LITTLE BASTARDS' at the top of her voice as she went up to Cathleen.

We could hear Cathleen's weary, half-awake screams downstairs, and it took Lil some time to get her settled again. Eventually she came back down, but the Flanagan boys were still up there tripping the light fantastic with Mary yelling helplessly at them.

'At least Cathleen's gone off again,' Lil said through clenched teeth. 'I just can't stand any more of this, I really can't. Come on, Genie, I'll take you home.'

'It's hardly even dark,' I protested. 'I'll be all right.' My mind was doing gambols over and over, trying to think what time it was and what exactly might be going on at home.

'It's only nine.' Lil glanced at the clock. 'I can take you along and sit with you for a while. Have a bit of peace out of this madhouse.' Lil was already walking out into the spring evening.

'Just drop me at the door,' I said. 'I'll be all right – really. I've walked back much later than this.'

'Do I smell or summat? I've told you – I'll come and keep you company. See Len. Wait till her in there's got her act together.'

My mind was racing madly ahead. What the hell were we going to find if Molly was over at our house? And then I remembered. How could I have forgotten? They wouldn't even be there. Len and Molly had gone to the pictures – big excitement – and wouldn't be back until after ten. Thank you sweet Jesus.

Lil was carrying on down my ear, sorry for herself, her voice hardly changing tone. Moan tone. 'I'm that tired I can hardly get about these days. If it's not work it's the kids. Sometimes I ask myself why I go on with it all. Why I don't just go and do the same as Patsy did and jump into the canal?'

'Don't say that. You don't mean it, do you Lil?'

'I do. Some days I really do. I mean what's there ever going to be for me now? My life's over. Only you can't do a thing like that to your kids, can you?'

I didn't blame her really. Only I was so relieved, after those moments of outright panic, to think the house would be empty when we got back, I was almost ready to dance down the road.

'Things'll get better, Auntie Lil. You'll get a nice new house and move out – have a garden for the kids.'

'At the rate Mary's getting hers it'll be the turn of the century before they find me one,' she said despondently. 'And I'll be dead by then anyway.'

The house was dark. Blacked out of course, but there were no lights on inside when I opened the front door, finding myself grinning like an idiot with relief.

'Come on in,' I said. 'I'll put the kettle on.'

'Doreen got anything stronger? Drop of port?'

'Dunno. I'll look.'

I lit the gaslight in the back room with a spill and found a tipple for Lil. I'd put the kettle on as well and was trying to poke some life into the fire when we heard it from upstairs. Clear and loud and horribly unmistakable.

'Jesus,' Lil said. 'What the . . .?'

I couldn't answer her. I went straight to a chair, pushed my burning face into it and pulled the cushion over my head as my mother's cries upstairs reached fever pitch. Knees tucked up on the worn seat of the chair, I curled tight into the smallest speck I could manage.

But Lil was at me, poking my back.

185

'Genie . . . Lift your head up. Genie!' She yanked me out of the chair by one arm. I wouldn't look at her, just covered my face with my hands, squinting out between my fingers. Lil hissed at me. 'Who is that up there?'

'It's Mom.' What an admission, my mom behaving like that.

'I know. I can hear that much. But who the hell is that with her?'

'Bob.'

'Who's Bob when he's at home?'

'A copper.'

Lil mouthed air like a fish. 'Well how long's this been going on?'

I shrugged. Couldn't think. I couldn't think of anything. The noise had calmed down upstairs.

'The little bitch.' Lil advanced on the door to the stairs.

'Lil no, don't! You can't!' But it was like shouting into an avalanche.

My legs were trembling so much as she stomped upstairs that I had to sit down, waiting for all hell to break loose above me. I kept thinking over and over, what are they doing here? They're not supposed to be here. How could they do this? How could they?

The fight Mom and Lil had that night outdid anything I could ever remember before. Lil was fit to burst with outrage, righteous indignation, fury at being related to such an obvious trollopy bitch of a sister and, though she'd never have admitted it, pure, grass-green jealousy. And Mom – also outrage at being burst in upon while she lay stark naked in candlelight, her head lifting in panic off Bob's King Kong hairy chest when she heard feet on the stairs. And anger and mortification at being caught in the act of complete, undeniable adultery.

The shouting, sobbing, cursing, slapping and recriminations went on and on. Some time, at about the eye of the storm, Bob slunk downstairs, half dressed in socks, drawers and shirt, looking like an ape in clothes. He pulled on the other bits, the trousers, jacket, even tie, as I sat crying. His shoes came flying down the stairs on the force of Lil shouting, 'Take these with you, you filthy bastard, and don't ever come back!'

Bob never said a word to me. Didn't even look at me. He let himself out and left them to it.

May 1940

It was soon after that Mom started being sick. Course, not having had a babby myself, the sight of someone heaving over a bucket every morning didn't automatically make me suspicious.

'My cooking's not that bad, is it?' I said to her.

All I got in reply was a lot of groaning. Some mornings she'd say finally, 'Oooh, I can't go to work in this state. I feel terrible.' And she'd crawl back up to bed and stay there until the middle of the afternoon. She did a lot of crying as well. A real lot.

I started to get worried. 'Shall I get our nan?'

'No!' She found the strength to push herself up on one elbow. 'Don't you dare say a word to anyone. D'you hear?'

'But you look terrible.'

She did too – face greeny white and clammy, hair in greasy strips. The room smelled stale and sweaty.

'I'll be better in a while. Just get me some water, and don't breathe a word to anyone.'

By the evening she'd dress and come downstairs, unsteady on her feet, eat a little bit and sit, silent most of the time. This went on for days. The time that for the rest of us was really the beginning of the war almost passed her by. Suddenly Gloria's news bulletins were once more the most important notches on which we hung our day. We listened in to *The Nine O'Clock*

News in the evening like religious fanatics, shutting up anyone who dared open their mouth to interrupt.

Hitler invaded the Netherlands. More names of places we'd never heard of. More realization that there was a world out there where things were happening. Bombs fell somewhere outside Canterbury. And Mr Churchill became Prime Minister. I liked him. Nearly everyone did, I think, with his way with words. Made you feel carried along and full of strength, not like the others, all muttering away.

'We have before us,' he said, 'an ordeal of the most grievous kind.'

But he made you feel noble, chosen in some way to do it, as if the fate of the world rested on us, each of us. Even Lil, the great sceptic, was impressed. ''E makes you feel it might all be worth it, doesn't 'e?'

Life was beginning to gleam a bit brighter for Lil. Or at least it was going to revert back to what it was before. Mary Flanagan and her kids were to be rehoused in Stanley Street.

'A front-house too, if you please!' Lil said. But she didn't really care whether the Flanagans were being moved into Buckingham Palace so long as they were well out of her hair.

Mom finally admitted one morning, between bouts of sickness, that she was going to have a babby. She was crying when she told me.

'I can't keep it to myself any more, Genie. You're my daughter' (she'd noticed!) 'and I've got to tell someone.' She lay back weakly sobbing into the pillow.

I was right out of my depth here. 'Is it – er . . . is it Bob's babby?'

'Course it's Bob's!' she wailed. 'How many men d'you think I've been with the past few months?'

I felt sorry for her. I did, really. Because I knew she didn't find having babbies any joy, and to cap it all this one was a little bastard and it wouldn't take the neighbours long to work that out for themselves.

'Are you going to tell 'im?'

Mom sobbed even louder. I sat down on the bed and touched her shoulder. 'D'you want a cuppa tea?'

'No, I don't want a cuppa tea! How's that going to help anything?' Then she softened. 'Sorry, Genie. No ta.' She looked bleakly across at the window. I saw dots of white light in her eyes. 'I want to tell him. I want everything to be all right – for him to want it. But after what happened . . .'

Since the Big Fight with Lil, neither she nor Bob had been near the place. 'I'm scared he won't ever want to see me now . . .' And off she went all over again.

'D'you want me to find 'im for you? Where does he live?'

'You can't go to his house,' she said, wiping her eyes. 'He still lives with his mom and her sister, and he says they're both proper tartars. Look, he works at Moseley Police Station – if you could take a note?'

The note said, 'I've got to see you. D.' I made a detour on the way to my nan's, going to Moseley first.

That night we heard the Germans had bombed Rotterdam. Everyone thought thousands and thousands of people had died, the doom-laden faces were back in my nan's shop – 'We'll be next' – and everyone started dusting off their gas masks again. Len had to take a cactus in a pot out of his and we sent him off with it again every morning. It was a shock. It was near, and getting nearer. The Dutch capitulated and the next thing was they were moving into France, into Belgium, Antwerp, Liège, Brussels, names falling like ninepins.

'They're saying at work,' Lil told us, 'that all the Germans've got to do is fly over. Some of 'em might even be here already. You got to be careful who you talk to.'

Straight away I had a mad, beautiful daydream that 'Uncle Bob' was really a Fifth Columnist spying for the Nazis who would soon be unveiled as the traitor he was, humiliated and tortured in public, then strung up in the Bull Ring to meet as slow and agonizing a death as possible.

Shame life isn't that simple. When he finally turned up I let him in, still in his uniform.

'Awright, Genie?' He was very short with me, pushed past into the hall. We'd had no warning of him coming. Len was still at work at one of his endless shifts at Austin Aero. Luckily Mom was up and dressed and had managed to get some soup down her. She was wearing an old dress, and had dragged a comb through her hair. I didn't get a chance to warn her, what with old Charmschool barging in like that. I heard her say 'Bob!' startled. She struggled weakly to stand up and held on to the back of the chair, smiling so sweetly at him, really trying hard.

'What d'you want?' I couldn't quite make out his tone. It wasn't angry or abrupt, more cautious and slippery.

'I er, didn't get a chance to say sorry. About what happened. My sister . . .' She gave a little laugh. 'Can't ever get away from your family, can you? One way or another?'

Bob didn't look particularly amused. 'Is that it? I haven't got a lot of time tonight.'

'Bob, please.' Mom's eyes filled with tears. 'Don't be like that. It was our fault. We shouldn't have been there

191

– not then. Genie wasn't to know ... Look, Bob, stop—' He was starting to turn away. 'I've summat to tell you. Genie – leave us alone, will you? There's a good girl.'

I went upstairs, feeling sick at everything that was happening. I didn't want PC Bob anywhere within shouting distance of our house.

It didn't take her long to tell him. Didn't take him long to get to the front door either. Within minutes I heard it slam, and Mom's howls of despair from downstairs. I found her lying along the hall on her front, arms stretched out as if she was heaving on an invisible rope, trying to pull Bob back.

'Oh please, *please* ...' she moaned, until the words gave out to sobs with no sound coming at all.

Then there was a great banging on the door. I stepped over Mom. There was Molly, a big grin on her pork pink face. 'Is Lenny in yet?'

'No, he sodding well isn't!' I yelled at her, guilty for it before I'd even finished. 'Sorry, Molly. No, he'll be back later tonight.'

Molly peered in between my legs at Mom's head on the floor behind me. 'Everything all right, is it Genie?'

'No, Molly, it's not,' I said savagely, and slammed the door in her simple face.

'Nan, there's summat you're going to have to know.'

Mom told me to tell her and Auntie Lil, because she couldn't face doing it herself. I told our nan first. Didn't want Lil there ranting and raving.

We had a few quiet moments in the shop. Nan was

sorting through sugar coupons. She looked round at me. I could see she was sort of steeling herself for something she half dreaded already.

'It's Mom. She's expecting.' My cheeks were aching hot. I couldn't look Nan in the eye. 'The babby's Bob's.'

Nan bent her head and pushed the coupons into her battered tin cashbox, her fingers working fast and nervously. I watched her strong profile, dark hair swept round, half covering her ears. 'Nan?'

'What?'

'Did you hear me?'

She bent to push the cashbox under the worm-riddled counter. 'I may be a lot of things, Genie, but I'm not deaf.'

'I just thought you'd say something.'

Nan stood up. She looked tired. 'What d'you want me to say? That she's a fool? That she's throwing away a perfectly good marriage? Your father may not be a Rudolph Valentino if that's what she was after, but 'e's been a good husband to her. 'E's a worker. 'E's never laid a finger on 'er and 'e's looked after you and seen you all right. What more does she want?' She passed a hand back over her forehead. 'I don't know.'

She let herself through into the house at the back. I heard her moving the kettle on the range and wondered where it was Nanny Rawson kept her feelings about all the horrible things that happened. She must have had a hump hidden somewhere where she could store and absorb them like a camel.

I followed her through. 'Mom's bound to ask what you said.'

Nan didn't even turn to look at me. 'No point in me

killing the messenger is there? Tell 'er she knows where 'er family are. We ain't going nowhere.'

'Is there any news, love?'

Vera had run up to Nan's shop in a pair of battered old slippers for a packet of fags.

'I didn't know you smoked.'

'I do today.' She bought matches too and lit up straight away.

'The last letter we had was all wiggly,' I told her. 'He said he was writing in the wireless truck while they were moving along. Said he'd seen German planes dropping bombs and a great big crater where they'd blown up a farmhouse.'

Vera grimaced. I wasn't sure if it was at what I'd said or the cigarette. 'I bet your mom's worried ain't she, poor thing? If there's anything I can do to help . . .?'

'Ta.' I couldn't think of anything at all I could say about Mom's state of mind at that moment. When Dad's letter came she cried and cried.

'Poor Victor. My poor Victor.' Tears of remorse. She'd almost forgotten he existed over the past months and now she could see he wasn't so bad after all.

I changed the subject quickly. 'Mr Spini any better?'

'He's awright – it's taking time.' Vera shrugged. 'Teresa's the one who's trouble – always wanting to be somewhere else away from us. She doesn't do as she's told and she makes Micky furious.' Vera was starting to wave her arms. 'We don't know what she's getting up to. She won't listen to us. She and Micky had a set-to the other night because he tried to make her stay in and she disobeyed him. If he was in better health she'd'd've more than felt his hand across her.' She sighed heavily.

'As if there ain't enough to worry about. What she needs is to find a Catholic boy like her – one of the lads from St Michael's. Mixed marriages only cause trouble.'

'Oh, I'm sure she's not thinking of getting married!' I laughed. Vera's mind always ran on to the worst possible. Teresa marrying a Protestant!

She smiled suddenly, sheepish. 'You think I'm stupid. But she don't tell us what she's doing or where she is. It's not right. I wish she could be more grown up and sensible like you, Genie. D'you think you could have a word with her?'

Mom was managing to pull herself together by dinnertime these days, have a bit to eat and get to work.

'The babby won't show for a bit yet, so I'm not going to get asked any awkward questions. If I don't get out I'll only sit here feeling sorry for myself.' This came as a bit of a surprise to me because I'd thought that was exactly what she would do. What with Bob taking off and his bun in the oven I thought she'd be about ready for the canal herself. But after a few days of pure misery while she mourned her rejection by PC Bob and leaned on me as if I was an iron doorstop, she became almost cheerful. I was baffled. She started going on about my dad.

'I've never given Victor enough credit for what he's given all of us,' she said one evening. 'He's been a good husband and father – not like some. And he's given me you and Eric. It's time I acted like a proper wife to him.'

I was so relieved she wasn't in the depths of despair at this point that I didn't think to ask her what she imagined Dad was going to say when he came home to find this little cuckoo in the nest. Surely she wasn't going to con him again with one of her record pregnancies?

Lil, who'd already had her say in no uncertain terms, came to the conclusion that that was exactly what she was going to do. 'He was here December,' she said in her sarky voice. 'And the babby's due about next December. So it'll be a good three months shorter than the first time, any rate. Poor old Victor, he must love her, God help 'im.'

'Well don't you go interfering,' Nanny Rawson told her. 'We've enough trouble already without you letting fresh air in your gob out of place.'

In the meantime, I got myself a new job. Nanny was recovered, barring a stiff knee. 'You want to get out and earn yourself some more wages,' she said. 'I'm all right 'ere now.'

Lewis Broadbent's foundry was an old family firm with a good reputation in the back streets of Highgate. In peacetime they made brass plumbers' ware – taps and sink bases, washers and screws, but for the war effort the firm had gone over to making caps for shells and petrol cans, and other small parts.

A middle-aged woman called Doris with jet-black hair and watery brown eyes showed me round the factory, which was hot from the furnaces where they heated the brass, and noisy with the clank of metal and the chunking of the pressing machines.

I was taken on in the warehouse at the back as a checker. It was a wide, not very well lit area with rows of women working at long tables. Doris slotted me into a work place at the end of a table and showed me how to look over the parts, searching them for mistakes or rough bits.

'See this one—' She showed me the inside of a petrol cap. 'The thread's not taken properly. You'd never be able to screw that up.'

After checking, we had to wrap the parts in tissue paper and a layer of brown paper and string and pack them in tea chests to go to other factories needing the parts.

It kept me busy enough, that did. We were all working flat out and quite honestly it was nice to get away from my family for a bit. I began to see Teresa's point. Out in the warehouse I was almost the babby of the place. There was just one other girl anywhere near my age, a year older, very pert, called Nancy. She had little freckles on her nose and auburn eyebrows plucked to a thin line. The other women were mom's age and older. They treated me very well and looked after me in a motherly way. In between chat about the job I learned about their families, those with good husbands and bad, those with none at all, who was in a reserved occupation, who'd signed up, and about their children, mothers-in-law, landlords. And about the Broadbent family who owned the factory. Everyone seemed agreed that Lewis Broadbent was second only to God, that his wife Betty was a scheming hypochondriac, his two daughters no better than they ought to be and his son, who was in the RAF, had the sun shining out of various bits of his anatomy. Nancy went silly at the very mention of Joe Broadbent's name.

''E's all set to take over the factory when this lot's over,' one of the women said, waving her hand over the petrol caps as if they were the war itself.

''E's got no airs and graces though, Joe, has 'e? Comes in and knuckles down to any job 'e's given. Knows how the place works backwards.'

'You'd hardly believe 'e was related to the two sisters, would you?' Nancy said bitchily.

'Ooh, she's got her eye on 'im all right,' someone teased and Nancy looked round coyly.

'Just hope they look after 'im in the airforce . . .'

The talk turned, and then one of them said to me, 'You got yourself a nice fella, 'ave you, Genie?'

I shook my head, not looking up.

'Go on – why not?'

'Don't tease her – she's only young yet,' a voice said.

I thought with a pang of Jimmy, and of Walt. I'd messed up my chances good and proper with both of them. Oh well, I thought, giving a shrug inside myself. So what. Who cared anyway?

When it came to Dunkirk it was everyone's news, everyone's war suddenly, and for those last days of May no one could talk or think of anything else. Gloria was on for every news bulletin whenever anyone was in. Mom, still sick, was in a shocking state.

One evening when it was all going on, Auntie Lil turned up. She came to bury the hatchet and not, for once, in the back of Mom's head.

'You still bad, Dor?' she asked, sweet as jam.

Mom was sitting writing to Eric, and Lil's sympathy sent her all weepy. 'I've not been into work I feel that terrible.' Her appearance had gone all to pieces. She was gaunt, her skin the colour of porridge.

'Come on now,' Lil said. 'Genie and I'll help you, won't we love?' She pushed Mom back down into a chair. 'You need some company – get Stella over for a chat.'

'She don't care. Never seen her for dust – some friend that one,' Mom said despondently.

'Never mind. You just stay there and we'll see to everything.'

'I thought you hated me!' Mom sobbed.

'What's done can't be undone,' Lil said. 'Here – I brought you a bottle of stout for later. Buck you up.'

Lil was a busy sort. Spun round the place doing housework as if it was a race. She'd always been like that. Patsy and Tom, who'd come down with her, were out in the garden playing in the evening sun. Before I could blink hardly, Lil had brewed up tea, dusted and tidied downstairs, rinsed and hung out a bucket full of washing and was all for setting in on the cooking.

I watched her as I worked on carrots and parsnips for our tea, her sleek body bending and straightening in the garden as she pegged out, shouting to the boys now and then. Her life had been the same for so long, I thought, and wondered if it'd ever be any different for her, for any of us.

'How is Eric?' she called to Mom as she came in with the empty washpail.

'He's all right.' We could hear the emotion in Mom's voice. She was never more than a breath away from tears these days. They seeped up into her eyes at the mention of all sorts of things: Dad, Eric, the babby, the war, going to work, sometimes even the thought of getting up in the morning. 'He doesn't write much. That Mrs Spenser's got her claws into him – Victor said when he took Eric down there she had ever such a nice house and she nearly jumped on Eric as if he was her own.' She gave a little wail. 'It's not right. I feel as if I've lost him.'

Lil pulled a grim face at me and went in to her. 'Never mind,' she soothed. 'You know he's safe, and at least he's happy where he is. You've no worries on that score.'

'But he shouldn't be happy – he doesn't belong there. You wouldn't send yours off, would you?'

I took them another cup of tea, then retreated into the kitchen. Patsy and Tom were playing down round the Anderson which was now sprouted over with dandelions. Some had already gone to seed and the boys were blowing dandelion clocks. I had a peculiar feeling for a minute which was so strange it took me a while to work out what it was. I was happy. Just for a little flash of time. Seeing the boys there looking carefree like kids should be in the last of the sunshine on these calm, clear-cut days of spring, and Auntie Lil here and people being nice to one another.

But then I heard Lil say, 'What are you going to do, sis?' and the little spark of harmony which lit those few seconds was snuffed out because Mom was crying again and trying to speak and Lil was saying, 'Ssh . . . ssh . . . there.'

'I've been so bad,' Mom was pouring out to her. 'Such a fool. But I loved him. Really loved him, and I've never had it before like that, you know . . . But he never loved me. Not really, properly. It was all a lie . . .'

'Yes.' Lil's voice was desolate. She knew only too well what it was to be left alone. 'He was using you, sis.'

'I want to get back to what we had – me and Victor. I mean it wasn't all I've ever wanted but it was good enough. If I lose that I'll have nothing.'

'But Doreen, the babby. It's not just going to go away.'

I held still in the kitchen listening.

'No, but . . .' I heard her hesitate. 'He might be away ages and the babby'll be born in seven months. I could hand it over. There's people would take it off me – adopt it. And he'd never know. Nothing would have changed then, would it?'

'Doreen!' Lil was dreadfully shocked. 'You can't go on like that, deceiving him. He's your husband!'

'But what else can I do?'

'The truth'll find you out, Dor. The neighbours aren't blind and deaf, are they? Some bloody busybody's bound to say summat even if it ain't out of spite – although the chances are it will be. What about Gladys and Molly for a start? They've not enough sense between them to keep their mouths shut. You're just going to have to tell him the truth.'

'No. Oh no, I couldn't do that!'

I pictured Dad's face if he knew, the twisted hurt in it, and she must've seen it the same way.

We heard Len at the door then and they had to stop talking.

'Awright Len?' Lil said. 'Been at it since the crack of dawn, have you?'

I heard Len making pleased-sounding noises. Then a click and Gloria was on. There was news due. 'Ssssh,' everyone said.

The Germans had reached the Channel coast. The British Expeditionary Force as well as Belgian and French troops were surrounded in a small pocket of ground inland from Dunkirk.

The days as we waited were so beautiful. So lovely it hurt. It looked all wrong for disaster and dread and knowing great calamities were happening somewhere far away. By 24 May the BEF was completely cut off. Those of us who had people there could think of nothing else. What was happening to my father? Were they safe? What was going to happen next? Even for those who could look at the thing less personally, the fact was, the Germans were only twenty or so miles away from the south coast, looking at us across a tiny vein of water.

Over that weekend, when they began the evacuation of Dunkirk, the skies were clear and lovely and people watered their vegetable patches and sunned themselves in the park, wore cotton frocks and held cricket matches. That was the oddest part of the whole thing, trying to hold together in your mind that these things were happening in the same world.

The nights were horrible, broken, patched with bad dreams, and waking it hit you, thoughts coming in a rush – 'Oh God, oh no!' – like black water filling a drain.

On the Monday the Belgians capitulated. They were bringing troops out of France by the thousand every day. Mom was in such a state of agitation she scarcely knew where to put herself. She managed to carry on working most days, which helped keep her mind occupied. But at home she paced the floor, couldn't keep still.

'I feel as if I'm going mad,' she cried. 'I wish they'd get it all over with. This waiting's worse than anything.'

She'd got all the options worked out by now with the clear-cut selfishness of a true survivor.

'If he gets killed I'm going to be a widow on my own. And if he comes back he's going to find out about the babby and everything'll be ruined anyway. He can't come home now. He just can't!'

June 1940

There was no other conversation in those days. Nothing else on anyone's lips. Walking home from work I'd hear the muffled sounds of wireless sets through open windows. The women at the factory were marvellous to me. 'Any news, Genie?' every day. Ever so kind. ''Ow's your mother?' People who saw Mom thought she was jumpy with sleeplessness on Dad's behalf, desperate for him back. I couldn't tell them it wasn't quite like that.

I loved being at work, away from her. She wasn't feeling well still, wasn't sleeping. 'What if Victor comes back? What if he doesn't?' I found it a strain being with her when I was in a state of nervous exhaustion myself. I felt sick almost all the time.

We all sweated it out. The weather was boiling. Every day Mom shrunk a bit thinner. She carried on confiding in Lil and I'd never seen them so close. As for Len, we barely saw him. When he wasn't at the Austin he was off somewhere with Molly. Nanny Rawson was a pillar of strength as ever.

'Come over to ours and have a sing-song,' she insisted to Mom. 'Take your mind off it.'

'Oh no, I couldn't,' Mom said. 'Not singing. Not now.'

'You should,' Nan said. 'Works wonders for you.' She and Lil still played in some of the pubs round and about.

I went anyway, and sat singing with Nan and Lil on an evening that felt like the middle of summer with the door open so some of the neighbours stood round in the yard and chimed in with us. And Nanny was right, a bit of 'Knees up Mother Brown' and other old favourites did take your mind elsewhere for a bit.

But we were still being swept along with the fleets of Dunkirk. All the little vessels, fishing smacks, tramps, paddle steamers, shrimpers and tugs that had gone to support the naval ships and channel steamers to get the boys home. It made you nearly boil with pride inside. Made defeat seem like victory, although really now we were right up against it and we knew it clear as anything. But all I wanted to know then was, are they bringing my dad? I was praying all the time, 'Please God, please . . .'

They started trickling home. Gloria told us how in the Kent gardens along the railway, people stood waving them back. By 4 June the evacuation was over. They'd done all they could and the Germans were getting too close. No more ships were going.

When the men started coming in from the coast, there were heroic stories about their welcome, the programmes of washing and feeding and entertaining them all. We heard of arrivals in Birmingham. We waited and waited, Mom like someone preparing to be fired from a cannon.

'Mom asked if there's anything you need?' Teresa said when she appeared on our doorstep.

It was my mom's day off from work and she was slouched in an old dress with a pinner over the top and her hair all over the place. Teresa looked really taken aback at the sight of her, and seeing Teresa, Mom straightened up and tried to pull herself together. 'Nothing you can do,' she said. 'Waiting's the only thing – ta.'

Teresa, in contrast to Mom, was looking lovely. The sun had only to come out for her skin to light up brown and the days had been tropical. She had on a bright yellow dress with big orange flowers dotted across it and her black hair was hanging loose.

'You look nice,' Mom told her. 'Haven't seen you in ages.' She had to pretend with Teresa. It seemed to do her good, having to act like the pining, faithful wife. 'Sorry I'm such a mess. Got other things on my mind.'

'You must be ever so worried, Mrs Watkins,' Teresa said, sitting down opposite her, dark eyes full of concern.

'Oh I am,' Mom was saying demurely. 'But we're still hoping. There's more coming back all the time.'

She was being a model Person Taking It Well. 'How's your job?' she asked Teresa.

'Boring. Wouldn't mind a change to tell you the truth. Stevie says it serves me right.'

Stevie would, I thought.

Teresa told us about some of the antics they got up to to liven the place up. Her voice rang round our house. Must've shocked the walls. They weren't used to happy sounds.

'Hope you don't mind me having a laugh, Mrs Watkins,' Teresa said.

'No, you go on,' Mom urged. 'Good for us to hear you.'

When Len came back he joined in at the sound of her. Said that after tea he was going out with Molly.

Teresa being there kept Mom together all evening.

We ate boiled beef and spring cabbage – 'Hope you don't mind our sort of cooking,' Mom said – listened to Gloria's music and news bulletins and talked and joked. Teresa even made Mom laugh with her infectious energy. After dark, Len came in looking pleased with himself. Mom gave me a look full of meaning and I tried to ignore her.

'Where've you been, Lenny?' she asked him.

'Out,' was all she got in reply, while he twiddled Gloria's knobs as he had no doubt just been twiddling Molly's.

Teresa ended up staying over. 'Mom'll know where I am.' It was like the old days, before Lola, when she used to come and sleep the night, weekends some-times, when there was no school the next morning. The more we'd been together that night the more I felt we could be close again. She hadn't even mentioned blokes all evening. But there was this great lie and pretence going on in front of her and it made me really uncomfortable.

She bunked up with me on the bed in my room. It took her ages to get ready. I lay down in my thin white nightdress, watching her. She peeled off the sunny yellow dress and laid it over the chair. Underneath she had on a cotton petticoat, old but still surprisingly white, or it seemed so in the candlelight, and her skin looked dark against it. She stood facing me, using my hairbursh to brush her hair forward, first over one shoulder, then the other, then holding it up luxuriously with two hands and letting it fall down her back, bosoms lifting as she raised her arms. Her body tapered down to narrow hips. She smiled at me, eyes dotted with little candles, and laughed her chesty laugh. She's beautiful, I thought. Not pretty, but beautiful.

'Haven't done this for a long time, have we?'

I shook my head, shy of her suddenly. She looked so grown up.

'Hope I'll fit in.'

'You will. You're nothing like the size of Lola. Here—' I pulled the covers back.

She half lay in bed, leaning over on one elbow to blow out the candle on the chair beside her, hair falling forward. It was very dark then, with the windows blacked out. I couldn't even see her outline, only feel the warmth of her next to me. I smiled in the dark.

'I feel like a little kid again,' she said.

'Just what I was thinking.'

I wouldn't want to be though, would you? A kid I mean. Not for anything.'

I was still wondering about this when she said, 'Sorry I behaved like such an idiot over Jack.'

'And Clem.'

'All right. And Clem then.'

'S'all right.'

'Genie? What about Walt – d'you still like him?'

'Haven't seen him.'

'But if you did?'

'No.'

'Never mind, there'll be someone.'

I thought about Jimmy, his body pushing down on mine. The tea hadn't all come out of my dress and Mom had been livid.

'I don't think I care all that much.'

'We just haven't met anyone good enough for us.'

'That must be it. Anyway, there's always us. Pals?'

'Pals.' After a moment she said, 'Your mom's being ever so brave. If it was my dad away I can't imagine how Mom'd cope. Or me.'

'It's a case of having to.'

'Course. All the same, I think you lot are tougher than us. All too emotional, Italians.'

I couldn't lie to her any more, not being there so close to her. And I wanted to stop feeling so alone. But my heart was pounding so hard at the thought of bringing it all out that I couldn't speak and I was shaking.

'What's up with you?' Teresa said.

'I want to tell you summat . . .' Then I was crying so much I couldn't get it out.

Teresa turned on her side and wrapped her arms round me and I hugged her back, feeling her full chest against my skinny body. She felt lovely. She kissed my cheek and I kissed her too.

'Go on – you can tell Teresa. What's got you worked up into this state all of a sudden?'

'It's Mom. None of it's how it looks. She doesn't really want my dad back because she's having a babby and it's not his.' I told her all about it then, spilt it out, about Bob coming to our house in the winter and how he took to his heels as soon as he knew she was expecting. 'Mom's scared about my dad coming home and him finding out. She's been in a state for ages . . .'

'I'm not surprised,' Teresa said. 'Oh my God, Genie, that's terrible. Your poor, poor dad.'

'Promise you won't say anything to anyone,' I begged her. 'I shouldn't be telling you really, only I couldn't help it. You won't, will you?'

'Of course not. On my life.'

She let me cry myself out and eventually we settled down to sleep, with her curled round behind my back. She felt warm and comforting and she wasn't bossing me, wasn't after anything like Jimmy. Lying there with her was the best, warmest feeling I'd had in a long time.

I was at work the morning Mom saw a man in army uniform move into view in front of our window, then stop, looking up at the house. Her legs turned to jelly. She was sure at once it was Dad. 'Even though I could see it wasn't,' she said later. 'I couldn't move. I was convinced it was him. I mean who else would it be? But he was the wrong height and everything.'

Another person stepped into the picture, a neighbour, who spoke to the man, who then came to our front door. Mom opened it, shaking. She saw a face with thick black eyebrows and a grubby khaki uniform.

'Are you Doreen Watkins?' To her nodding he announced, 'My name's Dickie Carter. Army pal of your 'usband's.'

Mom asked him in, gibbering questions. She made tea and sandwiches.

'Didn't know if I'd find him 'ere,' Dickie said. 'We promised each other, whoever got home first, we'd go and see each other's missis and let 'em know.' He ate the bread ravenously. 'I ain't got back over to my missis yet but I sent a message, and she knows I'm on my way.'

'So – Victor's coming home?' Mom asked. Dickie must have seen a white, stricken face in front of him.

He nodded, chewing away. 'Last time I saw 'im 'e was about a mile from the beach. Not far at all. But see, it was chaos at the time – pandemonium. All sorts of stuff blocking the road, lorries and that, things going off all round us ...' Dickie carefully didn't give us all the details he might have done about the bodies of men and horses in the road. We heard about that later. 'Any rate, I never saw 'im after that. Thing was though, we was so close. We 'ad to walk a couple of miles along the beach. Bloody 'ard going across that soft sand and we was all in after the miles we'd come already. There were lines of blokes everywhere so it'd have been easy to miss 'im. Somehow we never caught up with each other again. I reckon 'e'd've got to a boat though. Not much doubt about it. There was all sorts of stuff coming in to get us out.'

'You haven't see him though – over here?'

'No, I ain't, but that don't mean 'e's not 'ere. There's blokes being sent about all over the place. I came through Reading but 'e could've gone anywhere else. But I reckon 'e'll be back.'

When he'd eaten and drunk as much as was on offer, Dickie set off to go back to his missis. 'Don't you worry, Mrs Watkins,' he told Mom. ''E'll turn up sooner or later.'

'I don't understand it, Genie,' Mom said to me. 'If he was back over here, he'd've got a message to us, wouldn't he? Or written a letter. He was always writing letters.'

She was like a Jumping Jack. The slightest sound and she was at the front door to see if it was him coming. There was nothing could be done to set her mind at rest. She didn't turn up for work again and they were already getting browned off with her being so irregular. She was a bag of nerves. Seeing Dickie, a real live returner from Dunkirk, she was now convinced Dad must be on his way.

When I got home from Broadbent's and heard the news I was excited. I wanted my dad home, whatever

210

mess Mom had got herself in. I wanted him fair and square. By the time I got in she'd obviously been at the port bottle and wasn't quite steady on her feet.

'I can't stand this waiting,' she said. Her cheeks were an unnatural, shiny pink.

'Let's go to Nan's.' I couldn't cope with her here on my own all evening.

'What if he comes back when we're out?'

'He'll guess where we are. It's got to be better than just sitting here.'

On the way she insisted on calling in at the Outdoor for ale. 'Mom and Lil'd like a drink I s'pect,' she said.

Nanny Rawson and Lil were all agog hearing about the appearance of Dickie Carter. Another Dunkirk survivor had come home to Belgrave Road, everyone crowding round to hear the tale he had to tell, and we were still waiting for our family hero. Mom had to repeat the details at least three times.

'Is Uncle Victor coming home then?' Tom asked.

'We hope so,' I said.

Mom was already the worse for drink by the time we got there and she kept on tipping it back as the evening wore on. Nanny Rawson was full of an indignant tale about an unusual customer she'd had in the shop that day. She sat with her stocky legs stretched out, leaning down to rub her injured knee as she spoke.

'She stopped outside in a great big car. Come in 'ere with five pound wanting to buy up all the sugar. Told me she came from Henley-in-Arden if you please.' Nan laughed. 'Voice like a glass chandelier.'

'D'you give it to her?' Lil asked.

'Hadn't a lot to give her. But she was prepared to pay well over the odds.' Nan shook her head, laughing suddenly. 'She was wearing a fox fur stole. Beautiful it was. Must have wondered where the 'ell she'd found herself when she came in 'ere.'

'The nerve though,' Lil said. 'They think they can just buy anything, some of 'em.'

Mom was knocking back the beer and Len was eyeing up Nanny's little wireless set. 'Can we 'ave it on?' he said hopefully. It may not've been Gloria, but in his eyes it was better than nothing.

'No,' Nan said. 'We'll make our own music tonight. Lil and I did a spot down at the Eagle last night and it cheered us up no end. Run up and get my squeeze box, Patsy. Otherwise we'll forget how to do it.'

Patsy clomped up the bare wood of the stairs in his heavy Mail charity boots and hairy socks to Nan's bedroom where she kept the squeeze box. We all sat round, the house seeming almost spacious now there were no Flanagans hurtling about. Tom sat close to me on the couch, Lil next to us with Cathleen asleep across her lap, looking angelic enough now her eyes were closed. Len joined in the singing with unpredictable shouts. All Nan's old favourites.

'I wish you could come and live with us, Auntie Genie,' Tom said to me. 'Here – d'you want to see my marbles? I swapped 'em with Wilf at school.'

'Go on then.'

Tom showed me five scratched marbles. He was pleased as anything. 'He collects cards so I give him the ones I had off Auntie Doreen.'

Mom gave her cigarette cards to Tom now Eric wasn't here. Mrs Spenser was paying for Eric to have piano lessons. He lived in another world.

I cuddled Tom to me as Nan's fingers leapt across the keys of her squeeze box, oom-pa-pa, oom-pa-pa.

Mom got up, said she was going to the lav. Her face

was sickly white and she couldn't walk in a straight line. Lil was saying, 'Steady on, Dor. How much've you had tonight?'

She got as far as the door and leaned up against it, faint, saying, 'You'd better get me a bucket,' but it was too late and she was bent over pouring her guts up into the yard, making little moaning sounds in between.

Lil and Nan got her inside and sat her on the couch with a bowl.

'Len!' Nanny ordered. 'Get a bucket of water and wash down the yard.'

'What's the matter with Auntie Doreen?' Tom asked me, and at the same time Lil was on at me saying, 'How much did she have before you came out?'

'I dunno exactly,' I said. 'She had a bit of port I think.'

'More than a bit by the looks of it.' Mom was lying back on the couch now, head lolling.

'I'll make her a cuppa tea,' Nan said. 'The state she's in I don't know as you'll get her home tonight.' She went over and put the kettle on the heat. We could hear Len sloshing water about outside.

Clarys' face appeared round the door. 'Everything awright, is it Edith? Only I saw Doreen looking ever so poorly.'

Lil marched over to the door. 'Everything's tickety-boo, ta, and if it wasn't, you poking your nose in wouldn't make it any better, would it, so why don't you just go in and get on with your knitting?'

Clarys retreated in a huff.

'No call to be so rude,' Nan said, spooning tea. 'We've still got to live with her tomorrow.'

'Nosy bitch,' Lil was muttering.

Len came back in and switched the wireless on as if

to say he deserved it after that charming job. Music streamed out. Glenn Miller, 'In the Mood'. Mom was asleep, snoring. I was ashamed of her.

'She been bad again this week?' Nanny asked me.

I nodded.

'She's bound to be, what with the babby and the worry,' Lil said. 'And if Victor's coming home any minute . . .'

'She's not going to be able to keep it in the family much longer,' Nan said, advancing on Mom with a cup of black tea. 'She always shows early.'

'Let her sleep it off,' Lil suggested. 'She can stay here.'

'She needs summat on her stomach.'

I felt frightened watching my nan sit Mom up, saw her flop as if she was dead, head rolling forwards, unable to open her eyes.

'Give us a hand.'

Lil went over as well. Patsy, Tom and I stood watching, the other side of the table. Lil held Mom's head as Nanny tried to force some of the tea down her. She spluttered and dribbled and murmured, 'Hot.' Eventually, after tipping tea into the saucer and back a few times, they got her to drink some before she subsided back on to the couch. She looked terrible. I felt tears come into my eyes. My life felt like a mirror that had been shattered. I just wanted my dad to come back and make everything all right.

No sign of him. It was a terrible week. The women at Broadbent's tutted round me, and about me.

No one spoke the worst but I knew they were

thinking it. If he's not home by now he must be dead. Surely. It couldn't have taken this long?

At home the strain of living with Mom took its toll. She was falling to pieces and I wasn't far from it myself.

'It's not knowing,' she sobbed one evening. 'I just can't stand not knowing whether he's alive or dead. I just want to get it over with one way or the other. But they'd tell me if he was dead, wouldn't they? There'd be a letter or a telegraph.'

I still clung to my hope that he was alive, maybe in hospital.

She couldn't get through the days without drinking. She still managed to get to work – slept it off in the morning. But as soon as she was home she'd go straight to it. She started on what she had in the house – that bottle of port. But it wasn't long before that was gone and she had to buy more, gin this time, downing it quick, with tears, not pleasure. But at least she was still drinking it nicely then, out of a glass. She'd say, 'Oh – that's better,' and plonk herself down, half gone with drink and tiredness, and just sit there until it was time for bed.

It was a lonely life, even with the kindness of the women at work, of the Spinis. Len was barely ever in in the evenings now, either because of work or Molly. He'd slope in and have his meal, and on these warm, sultry evenings he and Molly took off until after dark. Never said where. They must have gone and walked in the parks, gas masks and all. I found myself missing Len's presence even though it was a relief not having him and Molly in the house together.

I was left with Gloria for company. *Hi Gang! Garrison Theatre, Band Waggon.* Without them I might have gone off my head in those days when part of my mind was always listening for a bang at the front door, for Dad's voice in the hall.

But it didn't come. Still didn't come.

A few little notices started to appear in the *Birmingham Mail*. They tore at your heart. Did anyone have information about ...? Know the whereabouts of ...? People's sons, brothers, husbands, who had not, as hoped, walked in off a train from the coast and Dunkirk. Mom put one in. It was peculiar seeing his name, Victor James Watkins, in the paper like that. As if he was just another name, nothing to do with us.

While we were waiting, a whole new lot of trouble broke out. On 10 June, Italy declared war on Hitler's side and suddenly no one was supposed to like Italians any more. The papers had already stirred that one up, as Micky had shown me. Now the headlines were screaming, 'INTERN THE LOT!'

I went straight to see them that evening. The house was full of people, the older ones sitting on the available chairs, the others all standing round. Vera's family, except for her mom, two other elderly men, a woman with thick black hair swept back in a bun, her arm round Vera's shoulder, and some younger men including Fausto Pirelli. All the talk was in Italian. Bottles of Micky's wine and tumblers stood on the table.

'You all right, Genie?' Teresa asked.

I nodded.

Vera took my hand for a moment and squeezed it. Her face looked strained. 'Any news?'

The other woman was watching me, her dark face serious. 'Her father's missing in France,' Vera told her.

The woman tutted, shaking her head. 'A terrible thing – I 'ope you have better news soon, darlin'. Don't lose 'ope. You must always have 'ope.'

It was hot and airless in the room. Normally they'd have kept the door open but that night it was closed, maybe because they felt safer that way. The air was full of cigarette smoke and loud talk. Stevie was over by Micky looking solemn and grown up. Teresa and I stood by the door.

'Should I go?' I whispered to her.

'No, course not. You're all right.' She put her mouth closer to my ear. 'They're worried. They think people will be arrested.'

'But there's no one here who'd do any harm, surely?'

She shrugged. 'Even today at work someone made a nasty remark about my name. I suppose I'm Italian now whether I like it or not.' She sounded bewildered more than upset.

Suddenly Fausto leaned over the table, raising one of the thick glasses half full of red wine. His sharp-featured face looked quite bonkers, I thought, eyes blazing with fanaticism and the effects of the drink. The men round him, Micky included, all started shouting at him at once, telling him, so far as I could make out, to shut up.

But Fausto wasn't going to shut up. He lifted the glass even higher, slopping some of the wine on the head of a bloke sitting next to him. '*Viva l'Italia!*' he shouted. '*Viva il Duce!*'

Two of the younger men, one an uncle of Teresa's, moved in and took Fausto by the shoulders, forcing him towards the door.

'What did he say?' I hissed at Teresa.

217

'Long live Mussolini,' she said without turning her head, too busy watching what was going on. 'Dad's not going to have that. Fausto's such a bloody idiot. Doesn't spare a thought for anyone else.'

Micky pushed his chair back and stood up. He talked so well with his hands that I didn't need to understand the rest. Get him out of my house. Out. Now. D'you want to get us all arrested?

Fausto was led out of the house by two of the men. As they stumbled past the window we could see his mouth was still going.

That night, Teresa told me, there was a loud hammering on the Spinis' door. Micky went down, pulling on his trousers. The rest of them listened, frightened, at the top of the stairs.

'Micky?' It was a neighbour. ''Fraid you got some trouble out the front, mate. Someone's broke your windows.'

They all went out, except Giovanna and Luke who stayed asleep, and stood in the street in their night-clothes staring at the shattered front window of the shop, the big hole in the glass with jagged splinters round it. Stevie was cursing, Francesca crying. Vera stood with her hands on Tony's shoulders in silence.

'We should have stayed in the Quarter,' she said, shaking. 'Then at least we'd all have been together.'

Micky didn't say much, just kept running his hand through his hair.

'It might have been someone trying to break in?' Teresa suggested. 'Or kids?'

'No. We know why it is.' Micky's voice was quiet, but angry. 'I don't know what to think. I suppose we get it glazed again tomorrow. But maybe now this is going to happen every night? We're in the wrong camp, even if we have spent most of our lives here. We're the enemy all of a sudden.'

There were to be no more church bells. No more of the usual pattern of chimes across the Sunday city. Only if we were invaded. That was to be the warning.

The Germans were closing in round Paris. It was over a week now since the evacuation of Dunkirk ended and we hadn't heard anything. Our newspaper clipping about Dad was starting to go yellow at the edges.

Mom was having to wear her loosest clothes already, though she could still easily get by as not being pregnant. But being a skinny woman she did show early. She put her hand to her stomach a lot. Her face was permanently sullen and sulky as if life had cheated her. Of everything.

The day after Italy declared war, she went out into the garden in the evening. She'd only had one glass of port so far. That performance at Nanny Rawson's had brought her up a bit sharp. 'I'll have to watch myself.' I went out and found Mom staring at the sky, the last bronze light on 'our' barrage balloon. From inside we could hear Gloria playing 'When You Wish upon a Star'. Mom was standing sideways on to me and I thought I could see the little bulge of the baby growing inside her.

'Victor's dead.'

I didn't say anything. I didn't want to hear those words.

'He's dead. I know he is.' She whipped round. 'Genie – whatever am I going to do?'

We stood there, both in agony, but not touching each

other. I wanted my dad so badly, wanted the solid, sensible bit of our family. Mom blew about like a feather and I couldn't trust or rely on her. Everything was breaking up. No Dad, no Eric, and now she was going to bring a babby into the house whose father I could murder with a smile.

'At least he'll never know,' she said, all wrapped up in herself as usual. 'He'll've died thinking I was a good wife to him. I can keep Bob's babby.' Then, voice going high, she went on, 'But how on earth am I going to manage? We'll have no money, and another babby and no man to look after us . . .' That old bogeyman poverty, the cold, aching, eking-out struggle she remembered from her childhood, leered up over her shoulder.

'You've got me, Mom. I can earn money now, don't forget. And Lenny.'

She squatted down on the grass suddenly, hands over her eyes, head bent. 'I've messed up everything, Genie. Every single thing I've ever done I've made a mess of it.'

'Mom . . .'

She didn't look up.

'He might not be dead . . .' I still hoped that, prayed it. Until we had some sign or letter we'd never properly believe it.

She got up suddenly without another word and went into the house as if someone had called. They had. The gin bottle.

On the Wednesday that week, in the evening, the police moved into Park Street, Bartholomew Street and the others which made up Birmingham's Little Italy, arresting a man from every house and carting them off to the police station. Among them was Vera's elder brother, Teresa's uncle Matt Scattoli.

'They thought it was a bit of a joke at first,' Teresa told me. 'Some of the lads anyway. A group of 'em went down there all full of themselves and the police said if they didn't get off home they'd arrest them as well.'

'Have they let them go now?' I asked.

'Oh no. No one knows what's happening. They haven't got themselves sorted out.'

'Well what about your dad?'

'God knows. They haven't come down our way. He's in the Fire Service, Mom keeps saying. What would they want to arrest him for?'

The Germans moved into Paris and the French surrendered. The newsreader's voice was very sombre, seeming to come out of a big echoing silence behind him. After the news they played trumpets.

The heat and breathless calm made the atmosphere electric. Waiting. Rumours all the time. They've landed on the coast at Margate! No – they hadn't. Planes overhead! They were ours. Leaflets came fluttering through our doors again, 'Don't give the invader anything'. Strangers were remarked on, even invented. Previously normal behaviour seemed suspect and all sorts of tales spread based on hearsay. They might parachute in dressed as nuns. Look out for hairy-knuckled nuns!

Even the newsreaders started telling you who they were. 'This is the — o'clock news, and this is Frank Phillips [or Stuart Hibbard or Alvar Liddell] reading it.'

The rumour-mongering reached such a pitch that the government released a whole collection of posters to try and keep us quiet: 'Careless Talk Costs Lives'. This was our turn now. Us. We were next in line now the French had gone. Would we have Germans marching down our street, kicking down our door with their jackboots?

Lil said, once France had fallen, 'Well at least we know what we're up against now.'

But we didn't. Not really. That was the trouble, and our imaginations were on fire.

'Have some dinner with us, Genie – there's enough,' Vera said.

It was Sunday and the Spinis were all squeezed round the table as usual, except for Stevie who was out with the ice-cream cart. Mom was at work, trying to redeem herself by turning up regularly, and so was Len, so I'd come looking for company.

The door to the yard was open and it was quiet, everyone in having dinner. I could see the tap across the way, shining drops falling fast into the blocked drain. The Spinis' yard always stank of drains.

Micky Spini seemed relaxed enough, his health improving by inches. He sat at the table in his shirt-sleeves, in one of his quiet moods, just staring ahead at the table as if he had things on his mind. He smiled at me though, when I came in. Vera had cooked beef, pink in the middle, liver-coloured at the edges, and there were potatoes and peas. It was nice to be in a proper family again with a dad, and a mom who could see further than the bottom of a glass.

'Sorry to hear about your windows,' I said to Micky. 'You had any more trouble?'

He shook his head. 'Not so far.' They kept talking about Uncle Matt and the others still held by the police. Everyone was edgy.

'No news, Genie?' Vera said to me as usual.

'Mom doesn't think he's coming back. He'd've come by now if he was coming, wouldn't he?'

Vera stared at me wide-eyed and tried to make comforting noises but I could see she'd been thinking the same. What else was there to think?

'What about Eric?'

'He still writes. Sometimes. Seems to like it down there. His handwriting's come on a treat.' I sniffed and Teresa reached across and squeezed my hand. 'Can't see him wanting to come home after all she's done for him down there.'

'Course he will!' Vera said indignantly. 'Home's home. You're his family. Not Mrs Whateverhernameis down there.'

I didn't contradict her but I wasn't sure any more. About anything.

'And how's your mother bearing up?' This was always Vera's conversation. Family concerns. She knew Mom hadn't got any time for her but close family ties were what she'd been brought up on.

Teresa's eyes met mine. I couldn't tell Vera about Mom's other predicament. She was kind all right, but sins were sins and she wouldn't have had any cotter with what Mom had been up to.

She brought in ice cream flavoured with vanilla pods.

'It's made with unsalted margarine. There's nowhere near enough butter about.'

'It's not the same,' Teresa said. 'Doesn't have the creaminess.'

223

'No, it's OK. You're imagining it,' Micky said, sliding it over his tongue.

'I'm not. D'you think I can't tell!'

Already the argument was growing heated. Micky splayed his stubby hands, palms up. 'You put two plates side by side. You'd never be able to tell the difference.'

'I can't tell the difference,' Francesca said.

'You see?'

'She doesn't know!' Teresa was shouting by now. 'She can't tell if she's eating lemon drops or bulls' eyes. She's got no sense of taste at all!'

All the kids were tasting now, making their own comments at full volume. Personally I thought Teresa was right but decided to keep my trap shut about it.

'My tongue must be more sensitive,' Teresa said. 'It tastes of margarine. It tastes cheap.'

'Cheap!' This caused uproar. One of the Spinis' full-blast ding-dongs was just getting warmed up, Luke banging his bowl on the table since he couldn't manage anything loud enough with his mouth to enter the competition.

'What d'you think, Genie?'

'I can't remember what it used to taste like,' I was saying, when we all realized there was a shadow across the doorway. Two shadows. Men in dark suits with bowler hats. One red-faced and fat, everything about him round, even his nose, the other tall and gangly. Laurel and Hardy to a tee. But their faces weren't anything to laugh at at all. Their coming slashed into the afternoon. The shouting switched off.

Micky stood up, nervously rubbing his hands on his trousers. 'Can I help you?'

Without being invited they stepped in, and looked

round the tiny room at the ice-cream-smeared faces of the children and at the Spinis' tidy few belongings: the shelf with their remaining bits of chipped crockery that weren't on the table, the worn pieces of brocade draped over the mantel, Vera's 'photograph' of Jesus. They wore sneers on their faces. Considering how hot it was they had ever such a lot on, and the fat one's face was perspiring. It seemed a long time before anyone spoke again and it all felt bad before they'd even opened their mouths.

Eventually the fat one said, 'Are you Michele Spini?'

Micky nodded.

'I am instructed to arrest you under Regulation 18B as an enemy alien to this country.'

Vera let out a gasp and put her hand over her mouth.

'But for God's sake, I've been here eighteen years!' Micky protested. 'My wife was born here, and my children. I'm in the Fire Service.' The agitation started him coughing again.

'That's as may be. But you haven't been here *twenty* years or more, have you?' The thin man stood up very straight and recited pompously, 'We are given leave to take into custody anyone believed likely to endanger the safety of the realm.'

The two of them went to Micky and took him by the arms. 'So let's not waste any time about it, eh?'

'No!' Vera cried, standing in front of them, barring the way. 'You can't do this. It's all wrong! You've already arrested all the wrong people. My husband loves this country. He'd fight if he was the right age. You're making a mistake.'

'Vera,' Micky said quietly. 'It'll be all right. We'll get it sorted out.'

'You've been consorting with known members of the Italian *Fascio*,' the thin one said. He pronounced it '*Fasho*'. 'We have Mr Fausto Pirelli in custody already.'

I heard Teresa make an explosive noise of outrage.

'But it's Sunday today,' Vera carried on. 'You can't arrest him on a Sunday!'

'I'm afraid we can, Mrs Spini,' the fat one said. He nodded at his colleague as if they were about to set off and then said, 'Norman, we haven't searched the house.'

'Ah yes,' said the one called Norman. 'The house.'

Vera sank to a chair as they released Micky and started going through their few possessions. The fat one went and peered up the stairs.

'You ain't going up there!' Vera said. 'There's nothing there.'

'Is that so?' Next thing was his fat arse climbing up to Micky and Vera's room, feet clomping on the floor above. Vera covered her face with her hands.

The thin one was pulling drawers open and shut, and yanked one so hard that it came out and fell on the floor. The side fell off the drawer and Micky and Vera's small collection of papers slid out in a heap. Giovanna started to cry and set Luke off. Teresa picked him up and cuddled him on her lap and Giovanna ran to her mother. Tony sat staring.

'Hoi,' Micky called out. 'Watch what you're doing. What you looking for anyhow?'

'We'll know when we've found it,' the thin one called Norman said. He had squatted down and was rifling through the papers, a look of disgust on his face.

Teresa suddenly erupted from behind the table, still holding Luke in her arms.

'What the hell d'you think you're *doing*?' she bawled at him. Luke was so startled he stopped crying for a moment. 'Coming here, scaring our family, breaking things and insulting us. Who the bleeding 'ell d'you think you are?'

Micky hurriedly laid a hand on her arm. 'Teresa, be quiet. Now!' he ordered, the exertion making him cough again.

'D'you know why he's coughing like that?' The man just stared at her with a flat expression. 'He was in a fire, trying to save a factory, and his chest'll never be the same again. How many times've you done summat like that, eh? You smug bastards. He'd die for this country my dad would. And yes, we do know Fausto Pirelli – he's an ignorant jumped up little shite with a bleeding great chip on his shoulder and anything he thinks or does is nothing to do with us. So why don't you just get out of our house and leave us alone? We haven't done anything.'

The fat man appeared from the stairs. What with Teresa yelling and the kids bawling the racket was getting pretty overwhelming.

'What on earth's going on?'

Teresa turned on him. 'Satisfied now you've had a good nose round, are you?'

'Can't someone shut this wop tart up?' the fat one said and I saw the blood of fury pump into Teresa's cheeks. He jerked his head at the other policeman. 'Come on. Let's get out of here. Mr Spini—' They went and caught him by the arms again. 'You'll be coming with us.'

'No!' Teresa roared. 'No – you can't do this!' Vera watched helplessly. Teresa shoved Luke at her and went to her father, gripping his arm.

Micky's face was grey. He spoke calmly. 'Teresa, *cara*, it's a mistake. I'll go with them and get it cleared up.'

'What – like all their other mistakes?' Teresa retorted. I heard the strain of tears in her voice but she wasn't going to let herself go in front of them.

They ignored her and started to take Micky from the house. He turned his head at the door. 'Don't worry, Vera. It'll be OK.'

We saw them as they took him past the window, his ashen face turned down towards the ground.

Churchill said this was going to be our finest hour, but it didn't feel like my finest hour at all. It felt like the worst time of my entire life.

My mom was only just holding together and I was strung between her and the Spinis. Stevie had returned home to find his father gone and went straight down to the cop-shop only to be banged up as well. They'd be able to see them in a day or two, Vera was told.

A week passed. Vera and Teresa were down at the police station in Steelhouse Lane every day. Eventually they were allowed one visit and they saw Micky, Stevie and Uncle Matteo for a few minutes. None of them had a clue what was happening. Vera said they were all trying to be cheerful, but no one would tell them anything. She was getting more distraught by the day.

Then she found out they'd been moved and they wouldn't say where. The house swarmed with Italians, many in the same position, others offering sympathy or just coming for a nose. Vera was up and down to her mom's. Her eyes were sunken with lack of sleep and she looked as if she'd lost pounds in days.

Teresa gave up her job and came home. 'Mom needs me – and the little 'uns.' So she was back among the fruit and veg, keeping up an amazingly cheery front with the regulars who didn't desert them because they were Italians and suddenly on the wrong side of the war. And I saw a new Teresa, one who was even stronger than I'd thought. Her face looked as sleepless as Vera's, but she pinned her hair back, dressed as nicely as she could and accepted everyone's sympathy.

'They've got to find out sooner or later that Dad shouldn't be there,' she said. 'We've got to keep going for 'is sake.'

She gave me strength. I had to do the same for my own dad. And I noticed a new gentleness about the place. Not just the Spinis. It's not just nostalgia talking to say this. It was nearly everyone. People cared more about each other now we were all in trouble. They'd go out of their way, do anything for you. Even Mom managed to think about Vera and what she must be feeling.

'What the hell are they playing at? That Micky Spini may be an Eyetie but what harm's he ever done to anyone?'

On 22 June the French signed the German Armistice. Mr Churchill expressed grief and amazement. The impossible was happening. The hot spring days passed agonizingly slowly.

Sometimes of an evening when I'd done all the chores I couldn't stand to be near Mom, her sitting there lifeless, half in a stupor, as if the world had already ended. I'd go up and lie on my bed, on the rough blanket, and look out at the light evening, the barrage balloon's silver tail. I often thought back to a year ago when everyone was home, squabbling, it's true, and looking daggers. But remembering it from where we were now, even with Lola there it had been normal. Blessedly normal.

I had to hold onto my dreams like Mom used to cling to the stories of the picture shows she saw. Mr Churchill said that if we could stand up to Hitler and beat him our lives would move forwards into 'broad sunlit uplands'. I liked the sound of them, those broad, sunlit uplands. They stretched out in my mind covered in golden corn and poppies and yellow and white flowers, with a warm breeze blowing and bare legs and the sweet, sweet smell of the fields.

July 1940

I heard the news over the factory wireless.

'Oh my God!' I was stuck to the floor like a statue.

'What's eating you?' Nancy snapped. Her voice was always tart as vinegar when she spoke to me and I could never make out why. What'd I done? 'Bunch of Nazis and wops,' she went on. 'Good riddance to them, I say.'

I was too upset to pay too much attention to Nancy. The appalling news was sinking in. The Germans had torpedoed a ship called the *Arandora Star* and sunk it off the coast of Ireland. The vessel had been carrying 1,500 German and Italian internees bound for Canada, and it looked as if an awful lot of them had drowned. Vera and her family still had no news, not of Micky, nor Stevie, nor Uncle Matt. For all we knew they could have been on that ship.

'What's up, Genie?' Doris leaned round me. 'There's surely no one of yours on there?'

'I don't know.' I was numb just then. 'That's the trouble. Could be.' I struggled to keep my eyes on the screw pitches of the brass caps in front of me.

Doris and the others were making sympathetic noises.

'Poor kid,' I heard someone say. 'Another thing to cope with.'

'While you don't know there's still hope,' Doris's deep voice came to me.

'Didn't know you was one for mixing with Nazis

and wops,' Nancy said. Now she'd picked on that phrase she was obviously keen to work it to death. 'Did you, girls?'

'Shut your trap, Nance,' someone said.

Nancy gave them her coyest smile, which was designed to melt hearts, and I felt like slapping her one. I turned on her. 'What do you know about it, you ignorant little bitch? Just you watch what you're saying.' I marched round to her side of the table. 'You're talking about my best pal. One more word out of you and my nails'll be making a pretty pattern on your face. Got it?'

'Did you 'ear that?' Nancy turned in exaggerated outrage to the others.

'You asked for every word of it, Nance,' Doris said. 'So just shut it, eh?' The others agreed with her. None of them liked Nancy, despite her pretty looks and winning ways. Didn't take anyone long to work out she was as two-sided as a half-crown.

'You'd better pack it in the lot of you,' another voice said from down the far end. 'Mr Broadbent's about today and you don't want him 'earing this carry on, do you?'

We certainly didn't. I went back to work, picking up each bit of moulded brass, trying to check it as thoroughly as I could. Mr Broadbent was a kind, straight man and I'd do the very best for him I could. When I glanced up I could see Nancy looking hate at me along the table, her auburn curls pushing out from under the snood we had to wear. Even in the dull light from the grimy factory windows I could see she had rouge on her white cheeks, and her thin, heavily plucked eyebrows made her face look wrong somehow – cheap, like one of Morgan's trollops. I saved that insult up for the next

232

time I might need it and gave her my best 'and bugger you too' look down the long table.

If I could have kept my attention on all the most horrible insults I could think of to hurl at Nancy it would have been much the better for me. But I spent the day in the most agonizing state of mind, imagining terrible things. I kept seeing Micky and Stevie and Theresa's jolly Uncle Matt struggling in the waves, sinking down and down until they were lying on the bottom of the seabed but somehow never dead, always alive, peering helplessly up into the murky water.

After work it was still warm and sunny. I found Teresa packing up the shop for the day. She was wearing the orange dress with the splashes of yellow on it. Without saying anything I picked up one of the boxes from outside and carried it inside for her and together we gathered up the empty crates on which they arranged the pyramids of fruit.

When we'd finished both of us straightened up and I looked into her stricken face. She was holding on tight, I could tell. She couldn't seem to speak. After a moment she shrugged despairingly.

'Oh Teresa – come 'ere.'

We stood in each other's arms and Teresa held me very tight as I did her, our cheeks pressed together.

'We don't know they were on that boat,' she said fiercely. She squeezed me to make the point more strongly. 'We've got to believe they're not – till we know for sure. But we haven't heard from them . . .'

I saw her pull her mind away from that thought.

'You're brave, Teresa. Much braver than me.'

She shook her head. 'Not brave. It's just, if we think of the other, of what might've happened, we can't go on. Mom says the same.'

Teresa bent to bolt the doors of the shop, the orange dress tight over her hips. I thought how grown up she was, now she was allowed to be.

'Genie—' She stood up, hesitating. 'It's just – we're all going to Mass now. Would you come?'

In all the time I'd known Teresa I'd never once been to Mass with her. In fact I'd not often been to church at all. Mom and Dad certainly weren't regular attenders, just went sometimes at Christmas. I had been on occasion with Nanny Rawson who barely ever missed a Sunday. Mom said she used to go to get an hour's peace from my grandad and his keeping on, but I reckon it was more than that. I don't know how you'd carry on the way Nanny Rawson did, keep steady, without faith in something or other flickering inside, and the religion she'd been given was Church of England. Sound and solid and no lurching from one extreme to the other. No fripperies, preferably no smells and bells, and what little I'd seen of church was along those sober lines.

The Catholic religion was seen by people like us as something very different from ours. Foreign, baffling, full of dread. The Pope and lots of what Nan called 'paraphernalia' like statues and incense and rosary beads. She'd been up in arms when Lil announced she was marrying Patsy, until she saw that even though he was a Catholic he was no more religious than she was and probably less so.

So it felt peculiar to be walking across towards Digbeth to Mass with the Spinis.

'Are you sure they won't mind?' I whispered to Teresa. Vera was beside us carrying Luke, and Teresa was leading Giovanna by the hand.

'Course not. People'll be pleased.'

Vera's face was drawn and stony and none of us had said much on the way across town except Luke who kept chattering, and we took it in turns to answer. All Teresa said to me on the way was, 'Now I know what it must be like for you.'

St Michael's was in Bartholomew Street, near the railway. Inside it seemed very dark after the bright afternoon and I liked the strange smell in there, the whiffs of wax and incense and floor polish. It was stuffy and cosy and the candles made me think of Christmas.

A row in front of us sat the little stooping figure of Nonna Amelia, Vera's mom, and beside her Vera's other two brothers, Marco, with his pretty wife and two children, and Paolo who wasn't married. Their hair was black as crows' feathers and clipped very neatly round their ears. Nonna Amelia had a black lace mantilla over her white hair and when I looked round I saw Vera, Teresa and Francesca were wearing them too and they looked pretty. Nonna Amelia turned and nodded at me, a warm expression in her eyes. A moment later she swung round, passing me a dark green handkerchief embroidered with white at the edges. As I took it from her gnarled hand, Teresa whispered, 'Put it on your head.' Nonna Amelia nodded as I laid it softly over my hair.

Most of the women I could see were kneeling down holding rosary beads and the Hail Marys were rattling out at top speed. I was surprised how quiet and well-behaved the kids were. Luke sat wide-eyed next to Vera, sucking his thumb.

A bell rang and the priest suddenly started speaking from absolutely miles away down the front somewhere and I wondered why they didn't get him to shift forwards a bit so we could all see him. '*In nomine Patris* . . .' Everyone was crossing themselves and I was completely lost after that. Couldn't understand one word of it. And it looked to me as if he'd lost quite a few of them there because they just carried on all the way through with those rosary beads as if nothing was happening at all, not seeming to take the blindest bit of notice. I mean in my nan's church people tried at least to look as if they were listening.

But I started to feel really grateful for being there. Normally at this time of night I'd be pelting about at home cooking tea with people on at me. My heart was so heavy and at least here I had some time to think. All these people came to my mind, Micky and Stevie and Uncle Matteo, and my own dad, and my mom too, until I thought I'd burst with sadness there in that church. Vera's face looked so grieved, and I thought about Mom struggling on at work and all that had happened to us. I'd wanted to believe that if I tried really hard I could somehow make things right. Make my family all right. Now though, I saw there wasn't much I could do about anything except to hope and pray.

After lighting candles at the end of Mass the family gathered outside the square-fronted church. Nonna Amelia shuffled out on her little bowed legs, supported by the arms of her two sons, the mantilla pulled softly back to lie on her shoulders. She wore little black mules on her feet and a black shawl, and rosary beads the colour of gunmetal hung from her waist. She had not put on mourning clothes for her son or her son-in-law. Mourning colours were her permanent state, her everyday clothes since the death of her husband, Papà Scattoli, eight years earlier. With her hunched shoulders it was hard for her to raise her head completely straight and she looked more at home in a chair than standing.

I'd always liked Nonna Amelia, even though I could barely understand a word she said. This was partly with it being in Italian, but also because she had no teeth. Her lips had shrunk into a web of deep wrinkles all pointing inwards round the little dot which was all you could see of her mouth, like water being sucked down a plughole. She was all there, Nonna Amelia, even though she didn't sound it, because the words came out all soggy, as if she had a mouthful of sawdust. Her eyes were sunken and brown like a little monkey's but glowing with life. There was a slight tremor to her neck which made it look as if she was nodding wisely at whatever was being said.

All of us went ceremonially to kiss her velvety cheeks and she nodded at me kindly and mumbled a greeting as I handed back her hanky, just as if I was one of the family. Her son Marco stayed with her while his wife and Paolo distracted the kids, Paolo throwing Luke high in the air so he gurgled, and tickling Giovanna and teasing her by untying the bow in her hair.

The rest of them gathered round Vera. Marco put his spare arm tightly round her and for a moment she said something to him in a low voice and leaned gratefully against him, closing her eyes. Her two sisters embraced her as well, their eyes full of concern, of fear.

There were similar groups along the pavement. The attendance at Mass was far higher than usual that evening. The priest came out and mingled among the crowd. He was Irish, not Italian. A priest would visit once a year or so from Italy and preach a sermon in Italian and this was always an occasion. But this priest was able to give them his sympathy none the less. A lot of the people there were still in their work clothes, the men in boots and caps, women in old everyday frocks, not like their Sunday best. I stood by Teresa as people milled back and forth, all talking in Italian. I didn't need to ask Teresa what they were talking about.

You could see the shock and worry that the sinking of the *Arandora Star* was causing in the Quarter. Some of the internees, especially the younger ones, had been released and sent home not long after they were arrested. Some families had heard from their relatives that they were safe in transit camps, but there were a few others in the same position as the Spinis, who had seen and heard nothing of their men since their last hurried visits in Steelhouse Lane police station, and they all knew that the very worst outcome, the news they most dreaded, was far from out of the question.

People kept coming to talk to Vera and Teresa, nodding to Nonna Amelia who had earned a lot of respect and liking in the district. She barely spoke, her eyes moving from face to face from the support of her son's arm, but her silence seemed to speak of their pain more than the words of those around her.

A young man came up to Teresa and put his arms round her shoulders for a minute. He looked older than us, had a head of black, curling hair. Immediately the two of them were off, gassing away, and I watched, puzzled. Teresa seemed to know him well, was at ease with him. There was none of the dizziness I'd seen in her over Jack and Clem. She talked to him as she would have done Stevie or Tony. He did a lot of the talking, seemed worried.

Teresa interrupted him. 'Carlo – this is my friend Genie. I s'pect she's had enough of hearing all this Italian.'

'Sorry.' He smiled, held out his hand. Two blazing blue eyes looked into mine. He was so handsome, even dressed in his old work clothes. 'Nice to meet you, Genie.' He frowned at Teresa. 'I've heard of Genie, haven't I? How come we never met before?'

Teresa shrugged. 'She doesn't come to Mass. We've been pals for years. Her nan lives up the road from us. Hey, look—' She nudged Carlo and pointed.

Three men were standing together, one of them, the oldest of the three, talking loudly at the others, arms moving back and forth, touching the fingers of one hand against his forehead then beating the air.

'Fausto Pirelli's uncle,' Teresa explained. 'Sparks flying there all right. They think Fausto's being moved to Brixton. They send the real naughties there.'

'All this fuss about Fausto,' Carlo said scornfully, 'He knows nothing about politics. He's all hot air. Come to think of it.' He nodded his head towards the uncle. 'How did he slip through the net himself? If they took your dad?'

Teresa shrugged, eyes still on Fausto's aerated uncle. 'What's the matter with the stupid bugger?' she snapped suddenly. 'I'd rather know Dad and Stevie were in Brixton than—' She stopped, struggling to control herself. I squeezed her hand.

Carlo looked round at her and said softly, 'You all right, Teresa?'

She nodded hard. 'Have to be.'

Carlo suddenly pulled her close to him, his arm round her shoulder.

The air was cooling, the street full of shadow now. People were starting to drift hungrily home. There were cooking smells in the air from houses near by.

'*Ciao*, Carlo,' Teresa said, pulling away rather carelessly from him.

'*Ciao*.' He raised his hand, watching her. Suddenly it was as clear as day to me. Any idiot could have seen from the smile he gave her what he felt for her except, quite obviously, Teresa herself.

I don't remember you talking about him before,' I said as we began the walk back with the family.

'Carlo? I've known him years. I must've mentioned him, haven't I? The family are always there at Mass. He works in the terrazzo trade with his dad – laying floors and that. We used to do Italian classes at the church as well. I s'pose he was just part of the furniture.'

'He looks absolutely gorgeous,' I said, trying to raise a laugh in her.

'I s'pose he is.' Teresa sounded offhand, her mind elsewhere. 'Says he wants to join up but he's not sure how they'll treat him in the British army.'

Giovanna was chatting away on the other side of her, getting no reply. 'Uncle Marco says I can go to the park on Sunday with Adelina and Maria.' She gave a little skip. 'Just girls. Just me. Not Tony or Luke!'

I tried to answer Giovanna's babble since Teresa so obviously wasn't paying any attention. When we got to Gooch Street the shops had long closed, the blinds wound in, and the air was full of the smell from the brewery.

'I've been so stupid,' Teresa suddenly burst out, making me jump. Her face was fierce. 'All that matters is my family. I'm going to do everything, *everything* I can for them.'

'D'you know I've always envied you your family?'

'Have you?'

She'd never seen it up till now. They'd always just been there too, like air.

The days passed still bringing no news for any of us, not of my father, nor Micky Spini. Since there was no choice in the matter we kept on doing what we had to do, day in, day out.

Very early one morning when I was barely out of bed and Mom certainly wasn't, there was a great banging on the front door. Still in my nightdress I snatched up the crocheted blanket from a chair and flung it round me as I sped into the hall. Dad! was my first illogical thought.

Gladys was talking before I'd got the door properly open.

'You'd better get yourselves ready for a shock!' she informed the street at the top of her voice.

I was confronted by her and Molly, both already dressed in enormous frocks, baggy as potato sacks and covered with splodges of coloured flowers. Gladys was holding Molly tightly by the arm as if she might be of a mind to take off.

'Come in,' I said as they steamed past me though the hall, Gladys flicking the blackout curtain by the door out of the way as if it'd personally insulted her. She was off again before I'd got the door shut.

'Right goings on.' She dragged poor Molly along with her. 'And then what do I find?'

'Sit down,' I said. 'I'll get Mom.'

'You'd better do that,' Gladys called after me sanctimoniously.

Mom was no longer sick nowadays, but she still found it devilishly hard to shift herself out of bed of a morning and I had trouble rousing her. She rolled over and looked blearily at me. 'Gladys Bender? What the heck does she want this time of day?'

'She says we're in for a shock.'

Her face tightened immediately. Victor. News about Victor, and already she was half out of bed, twisted round too quickly and winced. Then she tutted, relaxed. What did Gladys Bender know about anything?

When we got down Gladys didn't even give her a chance to open her mouth. She propelled herself out of her chair and pointed at Molly, who was sitting hanging her head.

'It's not you should be coming down, it's that brother of yours!'

'Sssh,' Mom said tiredly, flapping a hand as if to shoo away the noise.

'This one 'ere's in the family way and your Len's the Jack Rabbit that got 'er that way. So what've you got to say about that then?' She just managed to fold her arms over her mountainous bosoms. In the light from the window I could see her specs were all smears.

We hadn't got anything at all to say. Not a thing for quite a few seconds.

'No,' Mom got out eventually, any wind she'd had in her own sails expelled completely. 'That can't be right. Molly, that's not true, is it?'

'Days it's been going on now. She's off her food, sick every morning. She's 'ad a go already today, isn't that right, Moll?' Gladys leaned over her, shouting.

Molly lifted her head and you could see from her face

242

she wasn't feeling any too well. Her normally pink cheeks were white and her hair was hanging lank and straight.

'But it can't be Lenny,' Mom stuttered, blushing heavily. 'Surely he hasn't been . . .?' She was looking at me and the blood rose in my cheeks. 'Genie?'

I didn't say anything.

'Genie – you knew all about this, didn't you?'

'I never! I never knew Molly was expecting!'

'What's been going on?' Mom was shrieking at me.

'What d'you think's been going on?' Gladys retorted. 'My Molly's got a bun in the oven that's what—' She tapped Molly heavily on the shoulder. 'And it didn't get there by itself.'

'Well it's not my fault, I wasn't even here,' Mom said. 'How was I supposed to know what they've been up to? You should keep your daughter under control. I can't be watching Len every moment of the day. There's a war on – I've got a job to do!'

'Oh, and you don't think I 'ave?' Gladys was hands on hips, cheeks plum red.

It was turning into quite a shouting match and no one was taking any notice of poor old Molly, as if she was a sack of turnips they were haggling over, so I went and sat down by her. 'You all right, Molly? Feeling bad, are you?'

'I want Lenny,' she said tearfully. Poor old Molly, I'd never seen her miserable like that before, with everyone shouting about her head and not really knowing what was happening to her.

Just then, woken by the racket, Len appeared, shirt hanging out, hair standing on end, only half awake.

'Ah,' Gladys said accusingly. ''Ere 'e is.'

It all went quiet suddenly. Len stared round at us,

rubbed his eyes like a little kid, then looked at me as if I should explain everything. Then Mom was looking at me too. So it was up to me again was it, to take responsibility? I was damned if it was.

''E's got to know,' Gladys said, back in the arms-folded-over bosoms position. 'So you'd better get on with it.'

I stared hard at Mom. This isn't my job. Not this.

'Len . . .' Horribly embarrassed, she took Len's arm and he turned his great head and frowned at her, struggling to get every word. 'You know you and Molly—'

'Molly!' Len pointed suddenly as if he'd only just seen she was there. ''Ullo Molly!'

'Len, listen. You and Molly like each other a lot, don't you?'

Len nodded very hard.

'Well, Molly's having your babby, Lenny. It is his, isn't it?' she hissed at Molly who stared back, then nodded.

Len still looked as if he'd got caught fast in a monkey puzzle tree and couldn't get out.

'Molly's got a babby in her tummy,' Mom spelt out slowly. 'And it was you that put it there, see?'

'And don't try saying it weren't,' Gladys threatened.

Len moved a few steps closer to Molly. 'You got a babby, Molly?'

Molly nodded again looking scared, poor child that she was. The two of them seemed stuck, Len standing there, Molly in the chair, not knowing what to do.

'Well, there's nothing for it,' Mom said. 'We're going to have to get this sorted out one way or another. I s'pose the next thing is to fix a wedding day.'

Molly gazed across at us as if she just couldn't believe what she'd heard.

'Wedding day, Molly? How would you and Len like to get married?'

The light dawned. Slowly, bit by tiny bit, Molly's mouth turned up into a whopping great banana of a smile.

The factory was abuzz with excitement. Doris was full of organizing a lunchtime show and trying to bludgeon as many as possible into a performance of a sort. It was amazing how much work they could get done while their minds were on other things.

'Come on, Agatha,' Doris wheedled. 'You've got a few rhymes up your sleeve. And Joan – you can do your trick with the bottle and string.'

'Oh not again!' Joan groaned. 'Everyone'll be sick to the back teeth of that.'

'No – you can't see that one too many times.' Doris was writing her down in a little notebook regardless.

'Don't know why you're bothering,' one woman said. 'More trouble than it's worth.'

'You old misery.' Doris's cackling laugh rang round the warehouse. 'Got to 'ave some fun from somewhere. What with tea going on the ration as well, there won't be any pleasures left at all soon!'

Her laughter moved closer to my ear. 'Right, Genie – put you down for a song, shall I?'

'I've got no voice!'

'Oh you 'ave, bab, I've 'eard you singing round the place – when you 'ad more to be cheerful about any rate. Sweet little voice you've got. From your nan I

245

expect. It is 'er I've heard up the Eagle, isn't it? And your auntie – oi–' She held on to my arm and called out to the others for agreement. ''Ow about Genie gets 'er nan and 'er auntie and your mom is it? – over 'ere? The Andrews Sisters of Balsall 'Eath!' She laughed again. 'That'd liven us all up.'

'They couldn't – they're all at work,' I said, not sure they'd agree even if they hadn't been.

'I could sing with 'er,' Nancy butted in, jealous of the attention I was getting.

'Sorry, Nance,' Joan said. 'Not meaning to be rude or nothing but you've got a voice on you like a pair of clapped out bellows. I should stick to the day job if I was you.'

Nancy scowled viciously.

'Eh – I tell you what, girls,' Doris said, clasping my arm even harder. 'Let's make a real go of it and 'ave it of an evening. Get Genie's nan along with 'er squeeze box, 'ave a bit of a drink and that – what d'you reckon?'

There were cheers and a few scattered handclaps.

'Go on – we could do with a bit of a laugh.'

'It'd get me away from the old man for a night any rate!'

'You could bring 'im along.'

'Not on your life I won't!'

'But there's no room for a proper concert here,' someone pointed out.

Someone suggested the yard at the back and they were chewing over how it could be cleaned up when Doris cut in with, 'I know – the roof!'

Broadbent's had a flat roof with a parapet running round it.

'But we'll never get a piano up there – it's four floors!'

'Oh yes we will,' Doris said comfortably. 'Course we will.'

There was a hubbub as everyone started making plans and picking the day, which was quickly chosen as the Friday, giving us two days. Doris with her little note-book, was jotting down names before they could even volunteer.

While this was all going on, out of the corner of my eye I saw someone come in through the door from the factory at the front and stand quietly waiting, watching what was going on with a smile on his lips. I half guessed immediately who he was, and it was only seconds before his presence was noticed by the others, and Nancy in particular, who let out a shrill, excited screech, 'Look,' She pointed. ''E's back!'

Instant excitement to top up what was already there. Joe Broadbent was surrounded by a bunch of chattering women, the older, more motherly ones kiss-ing him, and more forward ones making smart-alec comments and others just standing round chatting and giggling, demanding why he wasn't in his uniform. A few of us carried on with our work, listening to the others.

Nancy, of all of them, was by far the most forward. God Almighty, I'd never seen anyone behave like quite such a tit. Blushing, leering, simpering, she hung round him as he tried to make his way into the factory. It was sick-making. She was throwing questions at him like confetti and tagging his name on to each of them in such a syrupy way that I saw some of the other women grimacing.

'How've you been, Joe? How's it feel to be a pilot, Joe? Have you flown lots of planes? Have you got your wings yet, Joe?'

On and on until someone else said, 'Oh leave off, Nancy – you're enough to give anyone a headache.'

I'd heard more than a bit about the famous Joe while I was at Broadbent's and I was curious too, thinking he probably wasn't all he was cracked up to be, because they hardly ever are, are they? Tucked away in the background I had a chance of a good look at him.

He was tall, a head at least above most of the women, and the first thing I noticed was the way he had of tilting his head forward when he spoke to them, fixing everyone's face with his eyes, their questions holding his attention. Even Nancy's, for a while anyway. He didn't talk down to them as if they weren't worth the trouble, just like his dad didn't, and his manner was easy, standing with his hands in the pockets of his brown, worn-looking jacket. He had fair hair, half way between blond and brown, cut very short of course, forces standard, which looked a bit strange on anyone in civvies. His long, thin face was pale, tired I thought. But smiling out of it were dark brown eyes, the liveliest and kindest I'd ever seen.

I was affected by Joe immediately. He was a clever person, I knew. He'd been to grammar school and before the war had been due to go on to technical college, even university. This was an awesome thought for all of us because opportunities like that were way off the edge of our horizon. He seemed so grown up at nineteen, so admirable, yet for all that, so far as I could see, so very approachable. I'd never come across anyone like him before.

Nancy was proving difficult for him to shake off as he did his round of the warehouse, stopping to have a word with everyone on the way. He seemed to remember everyone's name, their family, their circumstances.

It really was a family firm and some of those women had been there years. Broadbent's was known as a good employer – fair, kind and reasonable.

'Nancy – get back and get on with your work,' Doris ordered her eventually. They were all browned off with her by now. Nancy pulled herself away with enormous effort as if she was strung to Joe by a piece of elastic and went pouting back to her place. With great ostentation she took the snood from her hair, which she proceeded to shake out, a long auburn mass of it, wavy down her back. She pulled her fingers through it, looking to see if Joe was watching her, and once she'd seen his glance turn her way she began coiling it briskly round her hand and put the covering back on it, patting it to make sure little wisps of her fringe were peeping out at the front.

'Quite finished, 'ave you?' Agatha said, sarky.

'Now here's someone I don't know,' I heard Joe say. 'Who's this then, Doris?'

My heart was beating so fast when he came up to me.

'This is Genie, the new checker,' Doris told him. 'Been here a few weeks. She's a good'un she is – Genie, Joe Broadbent. He's home on a week's leave, from the RAF,' she explained carefully, as if I was deaf and hadn't heard anything that had gone before.

'Nice to meet you, Genie.' I realized suddenly that he was holding out his hand to me. I wiped my left hand on my overall and held it out and then of course remembered it was the wrong one and had to start all over again. I felt such a scruffy little mouse in my overall and snood with draggly bits of hair falling out of it and my dirty hands, but I managed to look up at him. The smile that met me in his eyes gave me a feeling I'd never forget. Something that dug so deep in me I didn't understand what had happened except I felt dizzy

249

suddenly and new. Those dark eyes, striking against the light hair, held an expression that was so open, so sympathetic. After a few seconds I was able to smile back with all the warmth I felt.

'How d'you do, Joe,' I said, taking his hand. My heart was going so, I thought it must be showing, rattling my body.

'You getting on all right here, are you?'

'Very nice, thanks. It's by far the best place I've ever worked.'

My hand was still in his and slowly he released me. I noticed the rubbed look of his jacket. It was old, a favourite probably.

'Course, a lot of things have changed here since the war. They'll have told you that?' He glanced round at the others. Nancy was watching us, hard.

'Oh yes,' I said eagerly. 'You used to take maps.' Flustered, I lowered my eyes. 'I mean make taps.'

When I looked up he let out a loud laugh which after a moment I joined in.

'You're not scared of me, are you? Good heavens, there's no need to be.' With the laugh still in his eyes he leaned forward, resting his hands on the table. 'If it's so good here, tell me where else you've worked then.'

'You got half the afternoon to spare, have you? The worst place I ever worked was a meat factory ...' I found myself babbling on, telling him about the pork pies and the bloke's nose and the woman whose finger got grated in with it too. And I told him about the taxi firm and the pawn shop and a couple of the others, although I kept some of the list back so's he didn't think I was a complete waster.

He laughed a lot at what I was saying which gave me

courage and I relaxed and was able to talk more like my normal self.

'Why so many?' he asked.

'I get bored easily. Not here though,' I added quickly. 'I like it here.'

Still chuckling, he said, 'Seems I've led a very sheltered existence! You've managed to put me off pork pies for the rest of my life any rate.'

'I never said what they did to the sausage—'

'No, please!' He held up one hand to stop me. 'I'm surprised you lasted as long as a week there. Half an hour and I'd've been hanging up my overall I should think.'

After a bit more chatter Joe said, 'Well I'd better let you get on, or Doris'll never let me hear the end of it.'

He hesitated. 'See you around, Genie.'

When I looked across at the clock I saw with disbelief that we'd been talking for twenty minutes. It felt more like two.

He stayed a bit longer, exchanging pleasantries with a few people. I could tell he was pleased to be back. Two or three times I felt his gaze on me, and I couldn't stop myself watching him, following him with my eyes. I knew exactly where he was all the time he was in there. I watched the way he walked, his long straight back, his gestures, the way he moved his head.

As he left, going out again through the factory, letting in the clunking noises of the machines, his eyes found me again. Feeling the blush rise in my cheeks, I thought, it had to be a coincidence: he couldn't really have been seeking me out.

But as soon as the door shut, Agatha said, 'Ooh Genie!' Whatever else she might've said was interrupted by Nancy who was round to my position in seconds and grabbing me by the throat.

'Just you keep off 'im!' Her face was all screwed up. ''E's mine,' she hissed, silly little cow that she was. 'Mine, OK?'

I seized her hand and jerked it away from my throat which was sore where she'd clawed at me. 'What'd you do then, eh? Buy 'im at the Co-op?'

'Get back to your place, Nance,' Agatha ordered her. 'And keep your catty mitts off Genie. What the 'ell d'you think you're playing at?'

For the rest of the afternoon Nancy gave me looks of such poisonous hatred along the table that I began to wonder if she was a bit barmy. But it didn't touch me. Nancy Hogan could go take a running jump.

'Will he be coming to the show on Friday?' I asked Doris.

She grinned at me. 'Who would that be, Genie?' She relented quickly. 'As he's home I'd be very surprised if he doesn't.'

'I'm working Friday,' Mom said when she got home that night, unsteady with exhaustion.

'Can't you swap?' I called through from the kitchen. 'Everyone else's going.'

Nanny Rawson never took much persuasion to play and sing. It was her one escape from the house, the endless work. And Lil said she'd come and bring the kids.

Mom sat in an armchair, leaning down, rubbing her ankles. 'No, don't think so,' she said listlessly.

I heard her get up and pour herself a drink. Suddenly I was full of angry determination. I wanted this so badly, wanted us all singing there together on Friday, and I wanted Joe Broadbent to see us. Without Mom's high-reaching voice which complemented Lil's deeper one, it wouldn't be the same.

Standing by the kitchen door I watched her sit down with a glass half full of gin.

'You managed to sort your shifts out all right when it suited you to see Bob.'

She hesitated, looking round at me, the glass to her lips.

I held her gaze, stared back. 'Do this for me, Mom. Just for once, do something for me.'

She took two gulps, shuddering slightly at the strength of it. At last she said, 'Oh well – all right then.'

I'd never been on the roof at Broadbent's before, but anyone could see it'd been transformed. A group of volunteers had stayed on after work the night before to make the place ready, and considering the drabness of a smoke-stained factory roof, they'd performed a miracle. It was surrounded on three sides by a brick parapet, and the fourth abutted a tall, thin building, higher than Broadbent's, occupied by Cobham's, a firm of tool-makers. So there was a blank wall facing us, only broken by a couple of filthy air vents. Across that they'd fixed old sheets made into a banner, painted in red and blue letters on the white, which read 'Showtime at Broad-bent's – 1940'.

There were already a good number gathering up there. I looked round with our nan, Lil and Mom (no Len – the pull of Molly was even stronger than that of a sing-song) and the kids, who thought being right up there was the best thing ever. I lifted Cathleen up and we looked across at the roofs of factories and houses, some below so we could see all their loose tiles, others on the same sort of level. You could see the spire at St Martin's in the Bull Ring, and Cathleen pointed at the shining barrage balloons which seemed so much nearer from up here.

'Don't think I've ever been this high up before,' Nan said, still breathless from all the stairs.

Mom looked over the edge, dreamily. She was wearing a loose dress, sensitive about being seen to be pregnant, and she'd evidently decided to join in tonight, to play along.

They'd swept the tarred roof, which still felt spongy underfoot from the warm day, carried up trestle tables and what chairs and stools could be begged or borrowed, and arranged them in rows facing the wall and banner. Wonder of wonders, to one side, stood a piano.

'We borrowed some muscles,' Doris said, coming up to us. She said how excited she was to meet the family, Nan especially. 'This is my 'usband, Ray.' She indicated a massive bloke next to her, built like an all-in wrestler with the broken nose to match. In fact he was a boxer in his spare time. I had a strong feeling I'd seen him somewhere before. 'Knew 'e'd come in 'andy some time,' Doris laughed, and I could see our nan warming to her.

Doris admired Lil's kids, picked up Cathleen and cuddled her as everyone did, with her pretty looks.

'She'll be another like Genie,' she said. 'Bet she gets away with murder with them big eyes.' Cathleen stole the show at this point by putting her arms round Doris's neck and squeezing her face against hers.

'When're we on then?' Nan asked. She'd put her squeeze box down at the side of the piano.

'You'll be called,' Doris said. 'Ray 'ere's our master of ceremonies for the evening. 'Ere Ray – get Mrs Rawson and 'er family a drink, will you?'

There were a couple of barrels of beer, courtesy of Mr Broadbent, and a whole assortment of cups and glasses on the table. We'd brought a few ourselves, as well as sandwiches to add to the collection.

'Tizer for you kids?' Ray said. As he was opening the bottle with a 'swoosh' noise, I couldn't help myself keep looking round at the stairs, every time there was the movement of someone arriving. I knew that until the Broadbents were here the place wouldn't feel complete.

Nancy came up with another girl who I thought looked like her sister. She was wearing a black dress with huge pink roses on and dashes of white in it, with a nipped waist. I saw Nan stare at her. 'Is that that Nancy you were on about? Looks a bit of a hussy to me. And that's a lower neckline than's good for 'er – she could catch a cold down there.'

Some people had already sat down on the chairs and boxes and a few other kids had arrived, so Tom and Patsy were chasing round with them and Lil just let them get on with it. She'd gone over to the piano where Tony, one of the lads from the main factory, was tuning up on it, improvising, feeling his way into songs. He was good, had the touch, and Lil leaned with one arm against the top of the upright humming bits she recognized, winking down at him. He was such a young feller I could see he was dazzled by her, this gorgeous woman with red lips, raven hair and sequins on her dress. He stopped for a minute and they talked, then tried out the openings of some songs together. Not to be outdone, Mom went over with her tumbler of ale and joined in. I was proud of them both.

Please Mom, I thought, don't drink too much tonight. Just don't let me down.

I stood beside Nan, who'd taken a seat to rest her knee. A cheer went up as a trail of coloured bulbs which'd been strung across the top of the banner lit up, bright as boiled sweets although it was still golden daylight.

'This is one show'll have to be over by blackout time!' Ray announced.

'Let's get on with it then!' another voice shouted. 'What's all the hanging about for?'

More claps and cheers. The place was filling up and they were getting impatient. We all wanted to break the hard lines of ordinary days. We wanted to laugh, to sing and forget.

Mom and Lil came over, gathering up the kids, and stood by me and Nan, leaving the seats for other people. As the piano struck up again Nan turned to me. 'You look very nice tonight, Genie.'

I had to bend my head to hear her and smile. 'Ta Nan.' I had on the polka dot dress Mom'd put together, with its little scarf and I'd curled the ends of my hair and pinned it so it hung nicely round my ears.

Ray, Doris's husband, looked more the type to be handy with his fists than his wit but he stepped forward to do his bit as Master of Ceremonies and erupted into a patter that took us all by surprise and soon had everyone laughing and cheering.

Nan leaned over to me. 'I knew I knew that feller's face. Used to work the Bull Ring, selling crocks or summat. Haven't seen him in a while.'

When she said that, I remembered him too. 'He's on munitions now.'

'And our first number tonight,' he was shouting in

his gravelly voice, trying to beat the catcalls and whistles. 'I tell yer, if yer don't settle down you lot, there won't be time for any bleeding show!'

More cheers and raucous laughter but the message seemed to have sunk in. Gradually they got settled down. But when I looked round I saw Mr Broadbent arrive at the top of the stairs, a woman behind him I'd never seen before, blonde, with sharp, rather haughty features.

'That them?' Mom whispered to me.

I nodded. 'She must be one of the daughters.'

Behind me I heard a voice say, 'I s'pect Mrs B's got the other sister at her beck and call at home.'

In the front row people were standing and shuffling along as Ray commanded, 'Make room now, ladies and gents, make room there.'

As they moved to the front I saw the one thing that I needed to see before whipping my head round to the front so it wouldn't be obvious I was staring. Joe was following behind them. He was here. My heart answered, speeding up.

Mr Broadbent senior and the daughter accepted seats in the front row, she looking like a chilly-eyed cat and Mr B with smiles to each side.

'Another space here!' someone called in a voice that sounded decidedly like Nancy's.

'That's all right,' Joe's voice came from close behind me. 'I'm happy to stand, thanks.'

My skin was up in goosepimples, knowing how close he was to me. As Tony struck up on the piano again I found courage and turned round.

'Hello again, Genie. OK if I stand here?'

'Course. Can you see over my head?'

He gave a laugh. 'With plenty to spare.'

The first person on stage was one of the main factory workers called Dick. 'This is Dick Busby,' he kicked off, 'talking to you from a munitions factory somewhere in the Midlands,' which earned him a clap before he'd even got started on his string of corny jokes, trying to sound like Arthur Askey. He told them pretty well in fact and bowed himself off.

Then it was Joan's turn. She was plump, middle aged, apple cheeked, and waddled forward with a length of white string, an empty milk bottle and a deadpan face, and proceeded to perform a series of antics. After a few minutes of this there wasn't a person in the audience who wasn't laughing until they ached and not one of us could have explained why. I could hear Joe behind me and after a few more manoeuvres from Joan we were all helpless with it. Eventually she gave a sniff as if we were all completely beyond her in our stupidity, wound up the string, picked up the bottle and marched off to the loudest possible applause.

'By special request from our pianist here, we're now going to 'ave a song. I'd like to call upon Mrs Lilian Heaney!'

Lil went up to the front wearing a blush that only made her look more ravishing than ever. The silky green dress she wore hugged her lithe figure, its sequins winking in the sunlight. She'd pinned a dark crimson rose behind her left ear and stood swaying to the rhythm of the piano. She sang a couple of Cole Porter numbers. After the first one, into which she poured all the longing of her own sad heart, because that was the gift she had, I felt Joe's breath on my ear.

'She's a real find, isn't she? Who is it?'

As I was turning to answer he moved forwards into Lil's place.

'That's my auntie Lil.'

'Your aunt?' He looked at me, then back at her. 'She's got real talent.'

I smiled, pleased for Lil as her rich voice poured out over the Birmingham rooftops and her fairytale face to go with it cast spells in people's mind. The clapping was at least as loud as for Joan with her bottle and string. Joe moved respectfully out of the way when she came back to us. I saw Mom whisper something to Lil.

There were more jokes, some told to laughs, others to groans, while helpings of ale were passed round and we polished off the last of the sandwiches. Poems, some politer than others. The pianist played dance music on his own. Nancy got up, eyes fixed on Joe, to do a gypsy dance which went off a bit half cock but could've been worse. Just about. She gave me a filthy scowl as she flounced back to her seat to not exactly rapturous applause.

'We 'ave some guest performers here tonight. We can't give you the Andrews Sisters from Hollywood but we do 'ave our very own Andrews Sisters of Balsall Heath! Let's hear it for Doreen, Lil and Genie and their accompanist, the much esteemed Edith Rawson!' He put his hands together and led the applause and we went to the front, Nan carrying her stool. She settled herself on it with the accordion, arms through the straps.

Lil, Mom and I arranged ourselves round behind her and Lil did the introductions.

'We've got a number of songs for you tonight—' This was interrupted by clapping. They were all getting pretty merry out there, and this was a special night. They were going to milk every second of enjoyment out of it before the dreary return to the factory.

We started off with sing-along numbers like 'Knees

up Mother Brown' and 'The Lambeth Walk' and everyone joined in at the top of their voices, stamping and clapping. We spun 'The Lambeth Walk' on faster and faster until we were all falling over ourselves with the words and laughing and Nanny Rawson's fingers were a blur on the keys of the squeeze box, her right foot madly tapping the rhythm. It was going fine. The whole evening had gone well and I knew I had wings, lifting me specially, because Joe Broadbent had stood behind me all the way through. He'd sought me out. I saw him watching the four of us, all so colourful – Mom in red, Lil sea green, me blue and Nan also in a royal blue dress, all so different but with our voices blending. I saw Joe was smiling, singing along with everyone else. Please God, I thought, don't let anything go wrong tonight . . . just this once.

After the rapturous end of the song Lil held up her hand to quieten them. 'Right, you've had your fun. Now it's time to settle down for summat more serious.' There was a good-natured groan from out front. 'We're going to turn the tempo down now and turn our thoughts to –' she drew the word out to raise a laugh, 'lu-u-urve.'

'Oooh!' everyone responded.

Nan struck up and Lil sang the verse of 'The Very Thought of You', her voice rising to bring the rest of us in for the chorus, and then our voices chimed in, harmonizing, Mom quite in control tonight, her voice high and lovely.

I'd barely ever sung with them in public before, although at home we sang together in the normal course of things. We hadn't practised, there was no time for any of that, but I found I could move easily in time to the music and the songs were so familiar it came as naturally as singing in a bath tub.

When that was finished Lil stepped forward again. 'And now, since she's our excuse for being here at all, we're going to hear from the little 'un.'

With a huge jolt I realized it was me she was on about.

'She don't usually sing with us, this one. Says she hasn't got a voice.' There was a pleased laugh from in front of us, although the only face I fixed on at that point was Nancy's and hers was full of spite.

'We think it's about time she joined the troupe. So, judge for yourselves, ladies and gentlemen. We'll help her along from the back of course, but now I give you my lovely niece – we're all very proud of her – Eugenie Watkins. Step forward, Genie!'

Heck, I hadn't been expecting this! But I couldn't exactly let them down now, could I? Even Mom was smiling. I moved nearer the front of the stage, my suddenly damp hands smoothing the front of my dress, but I hoped, looking more composed than I felt.

'Let's hear yer, Genie!' someone shouted.

I gave a little bow and turned to Lil with a grin. 'I'll get you for this afterwards.' Everyone laughed. More quietly I gave her a choice of song.

It went almost silent then, and into the quiet Nan struck up on the accordion. The sun was setting, had sunk behind the factory walls and the air was smoky. The faces in front of me had fallen into shadow.

I sang an old song, a beautiful song, 'I'll Be with You in Apple Blossom Time', and when I'd gone through a few of the lines I heard Nan, Mom and Lil join in with me and felt them hold me up, give strength to my voice, which was tuneful enough, but weaker and smaller than theirs. I've no idea how I sang, how it sounded, but I know I tried to do it the way Lil did, pouring everything

261

I could into it. That song promised things would turn out happily in a time of flowers and it was something all of us ached for. Things had to get better. And while I stood out there I thought my family should spend all their time singing because the songs went through and out the far side of everything else and let everyone be happy together.

I sang the final notes of the song and bent over in a bow. When I stood up I caught Joe's gaze fixed on me. His eyes were full of a quiet seriousness, but when he saw me looking he smiled back at me and raised his hands to show how hard he was clapping.

'Wasn't she lovely?' Lil quizzed the audience, and they roared back. 'Shouldn't she sing with us all the time, eh?' Another outburst of agreement. My cheeks were on fire. So was my heart, to tell the truth. 'For anyone who doesn't already know it, Genie's a great kid. And I'm going to give her the choice of our last song tonight.'

'Make it something jolly!' someone shouted. They wanted something to jump around to. OK, we'd let them have it. 'What about "Run Rabbit"?'

And so it was, and we went back to our places still singing. I felt proud to bursting. Joe's obviously admiring expression had given me a rare pride in who I was and my family. We may have been a complete mess in every other way but this was something we could do. It was us at our finest and I'd been included too. As I moved to my place I saw Joe's sister, Marjorie, lean towards her father and make some comment. Joe was still clapping.

'That was so good,' he said as I reached my place. This time it was he who seemed more shy of me.

Mom touched my shoulder as she passed me and found me a smile. 'That was lovely, Genie.'

'Have you really never sung like that before?' Joe asked, lips close to my ear.

'Only at home. I leave the performing to the others usually.'

'It was tremendous – listen, you can hear everyone loved it!' Only now were they winding down the clapping.

Joe made sure he stayed next to me this time and Mom and Lil squeezed in closer to the wall. The sun was going down fast now and very soon the coloured bulbs glowing there against the brickwork would have to be switched off.

After a couple more numbers, both saying we were a hard act to follow, Tony played 'God Save the King' and everyone stood and blasted it out, loud as they could.

'Come on you lot,' Ray shouted. 'Once more – and make it so that bleeder Adolf can 'ear it this time!'

When it was over everyone was suddenly milling about picking up chairs and clearing the trestle tables or trying to get to the stairs. A few were detailed to stay on and finish off after the rest had gone. The light was dying and there was a rush to get it finished, make the place dark.

Mr Broadbent and his daughter came up to us as we were shuffling towards the stairs.

'That was a real treat,' Mr B said kindly. He was a smaller man than his son, with his hair now steely grey but the same very dark brown eyes. His face always looked lined and tired. 'I'm glad you could all come. I didn't know we had such a budding little talent in the warehouse.'

'It were a pleasure,' Nanny Rawson said.

Even the sister smiled. She didn't seem all that bad up close. Probably just shy. 'It was really nice,' she managed to say.

And then they were gone, carried along in the tide moving into the stairwell, and Joe turned to say a quick goodbye which felt snatched and unfinished. Fittingly, as they vanished, the necklace of coloured lights went off, leaving us with only a shred of moon to see by.

At the top of the stairs I felt someone push up next to me and grab my arm, pinching it. 'Proper little bitch of a show off, aren't you, Genie Watkins?' Nancy dug her nails into my wrist. 'You've spoilt everything, you 'ave. I 'ate you.'

'Get off!' I yanked my arm away. 'You're hurting me, you barmy cow you. Why don't you just get home and hang up that chest of yours, Nance, before it falls out the front of your dress?'

'What was all that about?' Lil asked when I'd shaken Nancy off.

'Nothing,' I said. 'Nothing that matters anyhow.'

People didn't hang about outside. We all had homes to get to and work to do and the street was dark and deserted now except for us.

'We'll come down your way,' Mom was saying to Nan. 'It's not the quickest, but we might as well all stick together.'

'Coming for a cuppa?'

'Nah – best get back to Len,' Mom said. I guessed it wasn't tea she was interested in either.

We'd only got to the end of the road when we heard footsteps running up behind us.

'Someone's in a rush,' Nan said. We all pressed into the side.

The running slowed.

'Hello? Is that the Watkins family?' His voice. 'I wanted a quick word with Genie.'

We wouldn't be a minute, I told the others. I persuaded them I'd catch them up, and we were left alone. I could barely see his face in the moon's tiny threads of light.

'I couldn't go just like that. I told them I'd left something—' I could hear his quick breathing. He was nervous. 'Would you think of coming out with me, Genie? Say tomorrow night?'

Mom was sitting there staring at nothing, miles away.

'How do I look? Mom?'

'Very nice.' Sounded as if it was all too much effort for her to speak.

'The dress is smashing. Thanks again for making it.' It was the blue and white one again. I had nothing newer.

No answer.

'Look, Mom—' I went and squatted by her chair. 'I'm sorry to go out and leave you tonight, but Lenny'll be home soon. And you have said you could do with a quiet rest.' Umpteen times in fact.

She nodded but I could tell there were tears not far away. We'd already been through how it wasn't all bad, what good form she'd been in at the show.

'But I'm cut off from everyone – everything,' she moaned. 'I feel as if I'm locked in a cage . . .'

Now she was getting worked up. 'It's all right for you,' she said, jerking her head from side to side against the back of the chair in frustration. 'It's all bloody right for you, isn't it? Even that fathead Len has someone . . .'

I stood up, backing away from her. 'I've got to go. I'll be late. I promised . . .'

'He won't want you!' she shrieked after me. 'What would he want you for? He'll think he's too good for you, you wait and see!'

I started off along the Moseley Road before realizing I'd forgotten the little scarf that went with my dress, and by the time I'd torn back to get it I was in a proper lather. Joe and I had arranged to meet in Moseley Village, about midway between where we each lived, and I ended up running half the distance as I was so afraid of being late.

That mile and a half or so was torture for me. I was already in a state of nerves and Mom's kind sentiments ringing after me pulled me right down. At the concert everything had felt right and full of promise. Joe's smile, his eyes so obviously finding me, those short hours of forgetting all the grief happening to us. A dream world. Now all I could think of were bad things. Mistakes and hurts like Walt and Jimmy. The way they'd taken my hope and need and crushed them without a thought. Maybe I was all wrong again, clutching the end of a rainbow which would melt in my hand? There were all these differences between us: Joe was a grammar-school boy, older, his mom and dad had a nice house in Hall Green, and I was just a very junior pair of hands in his dad's factory.

But I had enough hope left to keep my feet, in their white buttoned shoes, trotting up the hill into Moseley, panting.

I'll know this time, I thought. When I see him again I'll be able to tell whether I've got this all wrong.

After all my running and fussing I got there early. It wasn't yet six. But when I turned up towards the gates of the church I saw Joe was already waiting for me. He'd come. That at least. He had his hands in his jacket pocket and was leaning against the wall, but when he saw me coming he straightened up and freed his hands quickly in a way that made me see he was just as nervous as I was and it gave me courage.

He smiled. 'Began to think you weren't coming.'

'But I'm early,' I protested, pointing up at the hands of the clock. 'Look, it's only five to!'

'I suppose I just hoped you wouldn't stand me up.'

'Not if I said I'd come.'

'You sound out of breath.'

I joked. 'Didn't dare be late, did I?'

We were at a loss then and stood looking at each other, and it seemed Joe's eyes penetrated deeper than the surface of my face. It was like someone stroking me, trying to know me. The feel of someone looking at me like that suddenly made me want to cry.

So's not to, I grinned at him and said, 'So – we going to stand 'ere all night then or what?'

Joe looked at me steadily. 'We could go to the pictures if you like. Or as it's a nice night, how about a walk?'

'Oh yes, a walk.' After all, what was the point in sitting staring at a silver screen? That was for escape from life, and now we had life spread in front of us to move about in.

'There's a private park.' Joe pointed across the Moseley Road. 'My mom knows someone down there'd lend us a key.'

'Is there? I never knew.'

We borrowed a key from a thin, weary-looking

woman called Mrs Munro who lived at one of the grand houses in Chantry Road, promising to drop it in on the way back, and she let us walk through a well-organized looking garden. At the bottom was a little wooden gate, and then the sloping edge of the park.

'Isn't it lovely?' I said as we walked down together under the trees. 'Fancy this being here all the time and me not knowing.'

'It's certainly tucked away,' Joe agreed. 'Seems a shame it's private really, but then that's why it's so quiet. It's not all that big though. We could go on somewhere else if you like.'

In the dip at the bottom was a little lake. There were trails of white, cottony seeds on the grass and birds chattered loudly in the trees around us.

'Loud, aren't they?' I laughed. 'Sound like my nan's neighbours gossiping.'

'Jackdaws I expect.'

'They the ones that pinch things?'

Joe laughed. 'They're the ones.'

At the bottom a path ran round the water and in the middle of it was a tree, its roots forming a tiny island. Water birds bobbed and skimmed around it.

'Those are ducks,' I pointed. That was about the limit of my knowledge. 'What about them then?'

'Moorhens.' Joe squatted down near the edge, watching another group of nervous brown birds. 'Nice little things them. Always look a bit worried. Specially when they're out of the water walking about.' He watched them for a few moments, smiling, then straightened up. 'Shall we go round?'

The path followed the curves of the lake, shady with trees on one side, more open the other. At the top of the hill you could see the enormous, elegant houses, with their balconies and fancy woodwork and ornate trees growing around them. I wondered what they did with all the space they had in there.

Joe started asking me about myself, my family.

'I still can't believe that was the first time you'd sung with them. You looked such a natural. And what a family!'

Yes, what a family, I thought.

'First time properly in front of an audience, but I've sung with them all my life. Lil dropped me in it as a matter of fact. But we sing at home all the time, or at least we did before . . .'

'Before what? The war?'

'Mainly.' I didn't want to tell him too much. The less the better for now.

Joe was silent for a moment. 'Doris told me – I hope you don't mind, Genie – that your father's missing.'

'Yep. Missing. Maybe. Or dead.'

'Sorry. I shouldn't have asked.'

'No, it's OK. Not a secret, is it? We don't know, that's all, one way or another. Be easier if we did 'cause then at least we could adjust to it. We're not the only ones though.' I told him about the *Arandora Star* and the Spinis.

'God, how appalling! Yes, I remember hearing about that. But they still don't know where they are?'

'No. It's killing Mrs Spini, Teresa's mom. Very family minded they are. She can't sleep. Teresa's the one holding them all together.'

'What about you?'

I wasn't sure what he meant by this, what he'd seen in Mom. He was sharp, Joe was, even though Mom'd put on a pretty good act that night.

'Someone's got to be in the house,' I said stiffly.

'Mom's got her problems.' I told him about Lenny, risked telling about Molly, and his reaction wasn't shocked like I feared. 'And I've got a brother, Eric – he went with the evacuation. But he's eight years younger anyway so he's a bit young to take on much even if he was here.'

'That's not so young. That'd make him what? Ten?'

'No, he's only eight.'

'But that means – you can't be only sixteen! I thought you were nearly my age, specially with all those jobs you reeled off to me.'

'That was only some of 'em too!' But I was anxious now. 'Does it matter?'

'No, of course not. I'm just – crikey, that means you're younger than that dreadful Nancy!'

We both laughed then, easier together. 'In years anyway,' Joe added.

We talked a lot about our families that night, and never did move on anywhere else. We walked carefully, side by side, round and round that lake I don't know how many times and for all we noticed we could've been in the Bull Ring.

It seemed the factory's version of Joe's family was exaggerated to say the least. Joe sounded surprised when I asked about his mother's illness.

'She's not an invalid or anything. What gave you that idea? She just suffers from terrible headaches rather often. So the house has to be quiet and she just lies in the dark until it's over.'

He told me the younger of his two sisters, Louise, was still at school, and the older one, Marjorie, worked for a machine tools firm over in Witton, secretarial, and they thought, was on the verge of getting engaged.

'She's such a dark horse it's impossible to know what's going on with her.' Didn't sound as if they were close, but there was nothing in his voice to say she or her sister were the whinging vixens that Nancy and the others had made out.

'And you're set to take over the family firm?'

'Eventually. Dad's got a lot of go in him yet. But yes, I like it. Good enough way of earning a living. That's if things turn out.'

We both knew what things turning out meant. Joe went quiet and the silence stood out after we'd been talk, talk, talk all this time. I'd told him far more than I'd expected, stopping short only at Mom's pregnancy because it seemed too much to load on him, for him to have to accept. I was afraid of what he'd think. And, while it would seem disloyal to Mom as well, I also couldn't help thinking how like her it would be to come between us and spoil things. We talked so long it was almost dark, and the birds on the water were faint shadows, making plopping or quacking sounds somewhere to the side of us.

Joe put his hand on my arm for a second to stop me after these moments of quiet. 'Genie – look, I've only got a week at home. Less now in fact. I'll have to go on Wednesday night to be there for reveille Thursday morning.'

'What's revalley?'

'Oh – when they get us all up, reporting for duty. It's just I'd like so much – would you feel able to spend some more time with me? I don't want to seem pushy, but after this week I don't know when I'll be home again, or where I'm going next now I'm a flyer—'

I almost needed to laugh again, cover how much I

was feeling for him, because I wanted to say, 'I'd go anywhere with you, do anything,' and I was afraid. But I managed not to fall into joking.

'Course I'd like to.'

Joe nodded and I saw he was relieved. 'Would tomorrow be too soon?'

'It's my day off.'

'So have you got time, or . . .?'

'I can't think of a single other thing I'd rather do instead.' I still wasn't joking.

In what was left of the light I saw a smile spread across Joe's face. He had such a giving smile, with no falseness in it, and I knew I wanted to see it directed at me for the rest of my life.

'Good,' Joe said. 'Excellent. Neither can I.'

For once I put aside all that was happening at home. I was going out and that was that. This was more or less what I told Mom. They wouldn't starve, that was for sure, one way or another.

Joe suggested we hire bicycles. He'd given his away earlier in the war and I'd never had one, so we went to the Ladypool Road, and set off on two enormous pushbikes with saddles it would've been difficult to match for hardness and lack of comfort.

'I thought we could go along the canals,' Joe suggested as we set off. The canal system criss-crosses Birmingham and you could get on the paths and go for miles. Personally I didn't care whether we cycled round the Midland Red bus depot all day so long as it was with Joe.

The pushbikes turned out to be a disaster.

'Blimey,' Joe said after only about twenty yards, 'this

one's a boneshaker all right. Shan't have any teeth left by the time we get back.'

The chain soon came loose on mine and did it so regularly after that that I was soon spending more time off the bike than on it, and both our hands were black with grease.

'It would've been better just to walk, wouldn't it?' Joe said, exasperated as we had to stop and fix the chain on my tricky mount for the umpteenth time. He seemed flustered. 'I'm sorry, Genie – this isn't turning out to be much fun, is it?' He ran his hand through his hair in annoyance and left grease on its pale strands. 'It was a daft idea.'

I looked up at him from where I was bent over the bike, as I seemed to be able to fix the thing more easily than he could. 'What you on about? It doesn't matter, we'll get there. Bikes are always like this, aren't they?'

'Well, mine wasn't. Look, let's not let them ruin the day. Shall we take them back and walk instead? I wanted to see you, not deal with these blasted things all day long.'

So we walked the bikes back the scant mile we'd gone out of town to the bike shop, got cleaned up and went to join the canal in town. Joe gave a sigh of relief as we went and I realized he'd got himself more het up than I realized about the bikes, it not working. I suppose he wanted me to think well of him, and couldn't get it into his head that these sort of hitches were just normal life to me. The few days out I'd ever had with Mom, Dad and Eric had always been full of disasters great and small. These ranged from falling in rivers or cowpats to losing Eric or forgetting the food, and everyone moaning and being evilly bad-tempered because we all wanted to do different things and couldn't agree or afford to do any of them. This was nothing in comparison. And the company was the best.

Despite all the factories along the canal, stretches of it were very pretty, with grass and buttercups along the path, and bindweed, keck, mauve fireweed edging the railway tracks. Joe was much better on the names than me, liked to name flowers, birds, animals and seemed to know them all.

'I haven't done this for years and years,' I said, dimly remembering it from a time when the grass came almost up to my waist. 'There's never enough time for anything like this, that's our trouble.'

We walked along all morning, talking easily, pointing out the barges in all their bright colours, painted with roses and castles, jugs of flowers and birdcages, and the canal women in their bonnets.

'I wonder what it'd be like living on here,' Joe said. 'Seems very romantic but I'm not sure I'd like it for long.'

'Oh, I would. Nice little space, no one bothering you. I've always fancied living by a river, seeing trees every day and fields.'

'None too many fields round here!' Joe laughed.

We settled to eat our lunch in a pretty spot, smelling the canal water and hearing trains thundering past somewhere behind us, though not exactly sure any longer where we were.

We ate our sandwiches and some cake Joe's mom had sent along, swishing away the odd wasp, playing with strands of grass, shedding seeds.

'I'm ever so sorry about the bikes,' Joe said.

'You're not still on about those flaming bikes!' I gave him a playful nudge.

'You really didn't mind, did you?'

'No, I didn't. I couldn't care less as long as . . . Look, it's been smashing so far, OK?'

Joe reached out suddenly and stroked my cheek with the palm of his hand. 'I wish we had more time . . .' He looked away from me, at the rippling colours of the water. 'Then maybe I could be more sure of not making a fool of myself.'

'You won't do that.'

He heard the solemn tone of my voice and looked back at me. 'Won't I?'

As I shook my head he reached out and touched my face again. 'Don't look so sad.'

'I'm not sad, Joe. I'm anything but sad.'

His arms came round me and gently pulled me against him. 'After I met you, that first day, remember? I couldn't stop thinking about you. That was why I asked Doris about you. Genie—' He moved his arm up, rested his hand on my head so I could feel the warmth of it through my hair. 'You're lovely, d'you know that?'

I turned my head and looked at him deep into his eyes, making sure, quite sure, although really I already was, that he was speaking the truth, not giving me flannel, not teasing. And then I pulled him to me, this man, the one person in my life who really wanted me. I felt the beat of his heart against me and I knew I was safe with him.

When he said my name again, making me look up, we kissed, and my arms slid up round his neck. And for the first time I answered that kiss and loved it, and not once did I find myself thinking about groceries. At last I began to get an inkling of what it was Lil had been going on about all this time.

*

I stopped being the one who was responsible that week and spent every possible moment with Joe. He managed to get round his father, who had a soft spot for me already, and talked him into giving me a day off the day before Joe had to go back, though I didn't tell Mom about that. We took a tram out to the Lickeys. It was a beautiful day and we had the place more or less to ourselves. And blimey, wasn't it different from the last time!

This time I had a day of wonder, seeing all the lovely parts I'd missed when dragged along by Jimmy. We walked arm in arm round the green water of the lake.

'That's my dream,' Joe said. 'To have my own lake so I could keep birds. Imagine having something like this in your back garden!'

We wandered through the woods, smelling the pines, and found a warm patch of grass between sun and shade where we had our picnic and stayed on and on afterwards in each other's arms.

Joe lay back against a tree trunk and I lay on my front, half across him, looking and looking at him. He closed his eyes for a few minutes, face turned up into a little pool of sun. I watched him, holding on tight to every moment, trying to remember every line of his face, his slim, pointed nose, the dark eyebrows, his lips . . .

I moved up and kissed him. 'You comfy?'

'Not very.' He straightened his head, opening his eyes.

'Well, move then!'

'I might if it wasn't for this sack of potatoes slumped across me!'

'Charming!' I shifted myself over to lie on the grass

and Joe lay down and settled next to me, pulling my head onto his chest.

'I was trying to memorize everything about you,' he said. 'For when I go back. Big blue eyes—'

'They're grey!'

'Are they?' He leaned round and looked. 'No – blue! Well, somewhere in between. Long brown hair, high cheekbones, sweet face . . . But none of that's you, is it? I could describe you, but it wouldn't be you.'

'I was doing the same. I don't want you to go.'

'Why don't you want me to come to your house?' Joe asked suddenly. He'd offered to pick me up from home that morning and Mom would've been in.

'No,' I'd said, quick as a flash. 'I'll meet you in Navigation Street and then we can just get straight on the tram.'

I didn't want her anywhere near him this week, spoiling things. I wanted to keep this just for me. Ever since she'd known I was going out with Joe, that I'd found something of my own, she'd been poisonous with self-pity.

'Don't know how you can go gadding about like you do with your dad missing. You ought to be ashamed of yourself.' She was worried and frightened about everything I knew, but she wasn't taking this away from me.

'My mom's not always the easiest. Specially not that time of a morning. I just thought it'd be better if I came out on my own.'

Joe leaned up on one elbow. 'But I must meet her properly some time. It doesn't seem right.'

'There's plenty of time for that. Can't we just enjoy today without bringing her into it?'

'It's just, the way I feel about you I want everything to be right – with everyone. My mom and dad are happy we're walking out together and I'd like yours – your mom that is – to be as well. See?'

'I don't think my mom's got much idea how to be happy about anything.'

I must've said this in a bleaker voice than I intended because Joe rolled over and took me in his arms. He kissed my face then drew back, eyes searching me. 'I wish I didn't keep seeing you look so sad.'

'But I've told you, I'm not sad. I'm happier than I've ever been in my whole life before and that's thanks to you, Joe.'

He carried on looking at me for a time and then spoke the words his eyes were already telling me. 'I really love you, Genie.'

'And I love you more than anyone ever.'

We held each other so close. All the love I had ready to pour out on someone had found a place to settle.

'I never knew it could be anything like as nice as this,' I said. Joe's face looked happy. We kissed again, feeling the sun through closed eyelids.

That day drifted past in a haze. I had no idea at any point what time it was and I couldn't have cared less anyway.

But we couldn't shut everything out. Late in the afternoon we sat high on the hills looking back towards Birmingham. We had heard planes on and off that afternoon and there were ragged vapour trails across the blue. We had no idea then, but that very day as we sat there, Hitler was giving orders for the invasion of Britain. The first knocks of the Battle of Britain had already begun but it felt far away and unreal then. Gloria had given us news of dogfights over the Channel, the reporter making it all sound like an afternoon's football match.

'So don't you know where you're going next?' I asked Joe. I sat with my hand on the hard muscle of his thigh. I wanted never not to be touching him.

'I'm not certain. Down south I'd imagine – things are looking bad.' He never talked very much about the RAF or what it was like. 'I'd rather forget it all when I'm home with you,' he said. 'It's all too uncertain. Your mind can't quite take it in.'

'This is the best day of my life.'

Joe turned to me. 'So far. Think of it that way.'

'No. The very best ever.'

'Teresa was here,' Mom said when I got back late. She was drunk as a lord, only less gracious, her voice slurred.

'When – this morning? What'd she want?'

'I don't know. Didn't let her in.'

'You *what*? Why not?'

'Couldn't face it.'

I stared at her in disgust, hands on my hips. I could see she was barely awake now.

'Didn't feel like entertaining your friends at ten o'clock in the morning, if that's all right with you.'

Ten o'clock? It must've been something urgent for Teresa to have left the shop. I had to go to her, late as it was.

'Where's Len?'

Mom gave a nasty laugh, slumped back in the chair, her hair hanging loose. 'Where d'you think? Over at Molly's getting his leg over with never a thought.'

'You make me sick,' I said, heading for the door. 'Don't you ever think about anyone except yourself?'

'You're a fine one to talk,' she shrieked after me childishly. 'Takes one to know one!'

Despite the dark I ran most of the way to the Spinis. I felt I'd been woken up roughly from a dream, real life battering its way in at the door again. It was nearly eleven, but I had to see them and there'd be no time the next morning. I ran down the entry and saw there was still light showing downstairs in their house.

Teresa opened the door cautiously. When she saw it was me she stepped straight out and flung her arms round me.

'They're safe!' She was all aquiver with joy even now. Loosing me, she pulled me into the house and it was then I saw she wasn't alone. Carlo was sitting there with her.

'Mom's asleep,' Teresa explained. 'It was all too much for 'er – she's hardly had a wink since the ship went down. It all caught up with 'er tonight. Carlo's stayed on to give me a bit of company.'

Teresa laid a letter in front of me. 'Look – from Dad. They've been in Sutton Coldfield all this time if you please!' She laughed and I could hear a touch of hysteria in her voice, the days of pent-up tension only releasing themselves now.

Micky's letter was short. It said he and Stevie were in a transit camp which was 'not very comfortable' and that he'd been 'a bit unwell', whatever that meant. Uncle Matt had been moved on somewhere else a couple of days ago but Micky and Stevie were still waiting. Micky made a joke about holiday camps and sent his love. I felt my eyes prickle with tears when at the end of this short letter, after messages of love to his family, he'd written, 'and to little Genie'.

I looked up at Teresa. 'Oh, thank God.'

*

I went to the station with Joe on the Wednesday night, holding tight to every last second with him. Walking tall in his uniform, kitbags on his shoulders, he looked older, and I suddenly felt shy. In such a public spot for farewells as New Street Station it was still possible to find privacy because the place was so crowded, so full of traffic and clamour that it made you feel alone. Service people and their loved ones, people just travelling in civvy street, all of them were wrapped up in their own rush for a train or struggle with an awkward piece of luggage, with their goodbyes.

Holding Joe's arm, I passed through the crowds with him, banging against bags and haversacks, arms and shoulders clad in blues and khaki, through the cigarette smoke and shouting, the Tannoyed announcements and the hissing and chunking of other trains moving out, until we found Joe's. We'd cut it rather fine and Joe looked relieved he hadn't missed it.

Saying goodbye was awful. I couldn't stand it, felt I had to pull back, close in everything I was feeling, not let it wash over me so that it didn't hurt so much. I found suddenly I had nothing to say, and stood there next to Joe as minutes tore past, desperate for him to stay but incapable of even speaking to him.

Joe put his bags down and took me by the shoulders. At first I couldn't look at him.

'Genie – tell me you'll wait for me? You'll be here?'

I shrugged. 'Course I will. Don't be so daft.' I was awkward, angry almost, fighting back tears. All I really cared about would get on that train any minute and disappear to God knows where.

Poor Joe tried again. 'I love you, Genie. You do know that, don't you?'

I glanced into his eyes, then down at his boots, nodding. The whistle shrieked along the platform.

'This is it then.' He couldn't seem to let go of me. 'I'll have to get on . . .'

He bent to pick up his bags and move off. Turning, he said, 'See you then.'

The hurt in his eyes sliced through me but I couldn't seem to move. People were pushing past, scrambling for the carriages, shouting, snatching hurried kisses.

Joe was throwing his bags through the door, leaving them to the risk of being trampled on by all the boots clattering up and down.

Straightening up, he turned and his eyes found me again, me standing there all knotted up inside with my arms crossed tightly over my chest.

'Genie!'

He was going, really going. Another whistle cut the air like a scream.

'Joe. *Joe!*'

I tore to him, shoving and fighting past people, not caring, and pulled him into my arms, covering his face with kisses, frantic to tell him, to show him. 'I love you, I love you – I don't want you to go . . .'

Joe gave a shuddering laugh of relief, holding me so tight, kissing me back. 'Thank goodness. My love,' he called me. His love.

As the train moved off, I, like lots of other people, ran a few yards with it, kissing his hand through the window, hearing his laughter. My last sights of him were his dark eyes meeting mine, lips blowing a kiss, then his arm with all the other arms like bristles waving out along the train, until I wasn't sure any more which one was his.

August 1940

Joe, my Joe as I thought of him now, was posted up north, while every day the news from Gloria was full of the Battle of Britain. But at the moment, Joe was safe. And as the days went by I discovered he was a letter writer, and he wrote to me as often as he could, every two or three days.

'My dear sweet Genie . . .' He'd tell me a bit about the routine of the squadron – what he was allowed to tell without too much of the censor's blue pencil butting in. All day-to-day things. But by the end he always found something else to say – something specially for me. Things he might have been too shy to say to my face. And those bits I'd read again and again until I could remember every word. I'd recite them to myself in my head in the factory or in bed at night, trying to remember his face properly, the feel of him close.

'I never knew what it was to be truly happy until I met you . . . Every day I think of that night I heard you sing . . . I'll be home to you on the first train when they'll let me . . . You have taken a piece of my heart from me . . .'

And I wrote back and found it easier to say on paper what you really think because you don't feel such a tit doing it. It was just hard to find words for it all, when I wanted to fill the letters with 'I love you. I love you. Thank you for loving me . . .'

'When I used to work at the pawn shop,' I wrote to him once, 'this lady came in one day and passed away in the shop, right in front of me. And there've been all the other bad things that've happened, like Big Patsy taking his own life, my Dad going missing and my Mom never being happy. And now I've got you. I can't explain this properly – it'll come out all wrong. But things feel different. It's not that everything's all right suddenly of course. But it's as if before, there were all these bits hanging off. Like a tatty old mop. But now I've found the bit that holds them all together, the handle, sort of thing. Are you laughing reading this? I'm just trying to tell you that knowing you're there makes everything feel hundreds, thousands of times better than all my favourite dreams.'

Most of the news I told him would be about the factory because they were the people he knew. 'Nancy knows about us,' I wrote soon after he'd gone. 'She's really got it in for me, but I don't care.'

That's how it was then. Nothing seemed to get through to me, yet at the same time I could afford to be kinder somehow. Which was a good job, because if I hadn't had the protection of Joe's love my poor mom would've driven me completely round the bend.

Her emotions were like a big dipper ride, only the dips were a hell of a lot longer and wider than the heights. She was drinking of course. The first drink mellowed her and she could be almost pleasant. Then the slide began. Mainly she was sorry for herself. And angry – with anyone and everyone. Everyone's life looked rosier than hers.

One day the post brought a letter from Joe for me that set me singing inside (I didn't dare sing out loud in front of Mom) and one of the much rarer ones we had from Eric.

Dear Mom,

I hope this letter finds you well? I am in good health thank you. I am doing well at school and making progress on the piano. Mrs Spenser says I may be able to start on the violin. Her cat Lucy has had kittens and one is going to be mine.

Are you and Dad and Genie and Len all keeping well?

With regards from Eric.

This made her cry like anything. 'He didn't write that himself. She's just told him what to say – to his own mom! "Regards" – to us! He's not my little Eric any more. He doesn't even know about his own dad, but what use is it me telling him anyway?'

Eric did seem such a long way off, and not just in miles. Mrs Spenser had no kids of her own and was lavishing what she had in the way of middle-class comfort and opportunity on this kid she'd had foisted on her. I suppose we should've felt grateful really. But it was nearly a year now, a long time in a lad's life, and he seemed like a stranger to us.

But it was Joe's letters, the smiles they brought to my face, that Mom could stand least of all. She was used to me courting her, needing her to love me and hungering after it, and now I'd turned to someone else.

That night her despair was terrible. Len sat watching her, his big eyes frightened as Mom got more and more drunk and her tears drew lines of black mascara down her face, which she smudged with her fists. She sat on the edge of her chair, hands clenching and unclenching, crying, sometimes flinging herself back in the chair, jerking about like a child in a tantrum, only much more pitiful for the age of her. I just didn't know what to do.

'It's all right for you!' she yelled at me. She kept saying that, accusing me.

'Why is it all right for me?' I didn't dare touch her and I didn't get any answer. She just mewled and sobbed.

'Wasser matter with 'er, Genie?' Len said.

'Lenny—' I spoke as calmly as I could manage. 'Go and get our Lil, will you?'

It was late, and I knew as Len plodded off that Lil was going to be anything but pleased, but I was scared of Mom. I couldn't cope with all this on my own.

'Mom—' I sat down by her when he'd gone. 'Look, why don't you ask to give up work? You're getting too tired all the time.'

'Oh yes,' she snapped at me, voice thick with drink. 'Then what'll I do? Sit here all day?'

'There's loads to do here. If there was someone at home it'd make things a lot easier. There's the house, and I've no time to shop. The off-ration stuff is all queues and Saturdays're terrible for that now. It'd be a help to all of us – we mightn't all be so tired all the time.'

'Huh,' was all she said, but I did at least feel she was listening. There was a lull, before she started getting all in a state again.

'Where's your dad? I want him. When're we ever going to know if he's coming home or not? You tell me that. I can't go on like this . . .'

Wearily I went and set a kettle to boil in the kitchen,

partly to get out of her way. When Lil arrived she wasn't nearly as mardy about it as I'd expected, and she was all dolled up.

'S'all right,' she said cheerfully. 'I'd only just got in anyhow.'

'Where've you been then?'

Lil took me by surprise by giving me a wink and putting a finger to her lips. 'That'd be telling. Anyhow, sssh for now.' She went to Mom. 'Oh Dor – you can't go on getting yourself all in a state like this. It's no good for you or for the babby.'

Mom cried exhaustedly. 'I can't go on,' she murmured into Lil's shoulder. 'I just can't.'

Lil looked at me over her head, her eyes troubled. Len stood by the door.

'Ta, Lenny,' I said. 'Tell you what, you could take Gloria into the front for a bit, how about that?'

Relieved, and hugging his beloved wireless to his chest, he escaped, and we heard music drifting through from the other room.

Lil prised Mom off her and tried to look into her face, though her head was lolling.

'Look, Dor.' Her voice was sharp now. 'You've got to pull yourself together. You can't go on like this. You're making yourself ill.'

'I can't,' Mom groaned. 'Just can't.'

'You've got to. You don't have a choice. What about the babby? And Genie here?'

'But what about me?' Mom was wailing.

'You're supposed to be their mom. And there's Len's wedding. You can't just cave in now!'

The kettle was gushing steam. By the time I'd made tea things'd gone quiet and I went back in to find my mom falling asleep across Lil's lap, her breath jerky as a sobbing child's.

Molly and Len's wedding arrangements were causing quite a kerfuffle. This was partly because Gladys Bender was making sure they did, quite apart from everything having to be done at such short notice because of it being a wedding with a shotgun pointing at its head.

Gladys pestered us from morning till night, whenever anyone was in. She'd never in her dreams expected her enormous, not quite all there daughter to find a mate, and now she'd got the chance, Molly was going to be MARRIED, and married with bells on.

'Oh-oh, here she comes again,' we'd say, seeing Gladys steaming across in her slippers. A door slamming somewhere across the street was enough to send us scuttling to the window to see if we were about to have another lethal dose of her.

Then she'd be hammering at the door as if we were all deaf, and when we let her in, would often be as red in the face and beady with perspiration as if she'd run a couple of miles to get there. In she'd come, us grimacing at the smells of sweat and disinfectant. We put up with her self-righteous tyranny day after day because we had to: we were Len's family and he'd got Molly into trouble.

'I thought it'd be right for you to see to all the food afterwards,' she announced. This was half past seven one morning. 'Since I've got my hands full and there are more of you with a wage coming in like. And I've got all the trouble of the dress and Molly to look after in her condition . . .'

'Well, she is your daughter,' Mom snapped. 'And it takes two, doesn't it?'

There's the pot calling the kettle black, I thought. Felt like saying to Gladys, I've got one to look after an' all.

Gladys folded her arms, pulling herself upright so that a good inch of greyish petticoat showed from under her stained red dress and pinner.

'It's snowing in France,' Mom murmured, but this was completely lost on Gladys.

'You saying you're not happy with all I'm doing?' she bawled at us. 'D'you want to give Molly and your Len a good send off, eh? Or don't you think they're worth it?'

'We can do some food, can't we, Mom?' I looked nervously at her. Even as I said it I already had a feeling 'we' was going to mean 'me'.

Mom nodded, yawning at the same time. This was a bit early for her to start a slanging match. 'Lil'll give us a hand. Not as if there'll be crowds, is it?'

'There might be quite a number actually,' Gladys announced, now we'd safely volunteered. 'After all, I'm one of fifteen and there's no one'll want to miss seeing our Molly tie the knot.'

On the Saturday I went to Nan's for a conflab. The kids were at the table filling their faces with liver and onions and spuds and Lil was cooking more for her and Nan. The kids were staring at her and I stared too. What'd come over her? She was by the range, stirring gravy with a metal spoon and humming, actually humming.

'You swallowed a budgie or summat?' I asked her.

Lil turned, laughing, and gave me another wink.

'No, that'd be the sensible thing to do,' Nan remarked, limping in with a bucket of slack. The coal hole was in action again since there'd been so many months of not having to shelter in it after all.

I looked from one to the other of them. Only one thing would put that glowing pink in Lil's cheeks which had been pale and tired for so long.

'Who is he then?'

Lil laughed like I hadn't heard her laugh in years. 'Can tell you're in love all right. Takes one to know one, doesn't it? How is Joe, Genie?'

'All right.' I blushed as Lil came closer to look in my eyes, teasing. 'He's doing fine.'

Suddenly she stooped towards me and kissed my cheek, her dark hair brushing my face. 'I'm glad for you. Really glad. He's very nice. I'd soon tell you if I didn't think so.'

'You've hardly met him!'

'I met him at the show that night. His eyes hardly left your face.'

'Who's this feller of yours then?'

Lil went back to the gravy. 'His name's Frank. Met him when we were playing at the pub down Bissell Street.'

'Proper charmer 'e is,' Nan said drily, stoking the range. She didn't like men to be charming. Charm to her meant snakes in the grass, blarney and insincerity.

'He's not!' Lil said. 'Well I mean, yes, he is – but not how she means.'

I was sitting by Cathleen who was idly letting me feed her little squares of liver. 'What's he do?'

'He's a mechanic. Got a garage out in Kings Heath.

290

And he's part-time ARP. But there're a couple of little things he does on the side.'

'Yes, I bet there are.' Nanny Rawson straightened up, holding her back. 'No one's shoes should be as shiny as them 'e turns up in.'

Lil laughed in exasperation. 'Oh Mom! Frank's all right. He's not selling anything – not as such. He's interested in fortune telling, tarot, that sort of thing.'

I frowned. 'I thought it's only women do things like that?'

'Oh, he doesn't actually do it himself. He's got a room – lets it to this woman. He knows all about it himself though, how it's done—'

'I wonder what else she's selling while she's at it,' Nan retorted.

Lil started to get a bit shirty. 'I've had enough of this. You've condemned the man when you don't even know him. And he's very good to me.'

'Well, that's all very nice,' Nanny said. 'But you find out what 'e's after before you get in any deeper, because you can be sure there'll be summat. Now that's quite enough of this in front of the kiddies. Want some jam on that, Genie?' she said, seeing me eating bread and scrape.

'No ta. Let Tom have it.'

Tom gave me his handsome smile, gappy with missing teeth. There came a banging on the door of the shop. Nan's face turned thunderous. 'It'd better not be,' she growled.

'I'll go.'

Morgan. As I slipped into the shop I could see him through the glass, and the outline of the girl with him. When I opened up the door I saw she was a lot older

291

than she appeared from inside, in her little girly clothes, and she looked browned off with the whole set up before she'd even started.

'Forgot my key,' Morgan said in his castor-oil voice. 'Sorry to disturb you.'

'Not half as much as you'll disturb us in a few minutes no doubt,' I said, standing well back as they went in as if they were a passing stink bomb. They disappeared quickly up the stairs.

'Was that that bastard Morgan?' Cathleen lisped in an interested sort of way when I went back to them.

'Cathleen!' Lil exploded, although neither of us could help a smile.

Nan leaned over to her. 'It'll be mustard on your tongue next time if I 'ear any more language like that. Now off to bed with you all if you're finished.'

Nan had made sure, since Lil came back, that the kids slept in the back bedroom away from the dividing wall with Morgan's part of the house at the front. They were such tiny houses and the noises travelled with barely an obstacle through the walls and floors.

Cathleen was still up in the attic in a cot with Lil.

I changed her – the kids had nightclothes now Lil was earning better – and took her down for a drop of milk which she sat on my lap to drink, next to the range, quiet now with heavy eyes and suddenly sweeter. I kissed her soft cheek and stroked the fine blond curls. 'You sleep now, Cathleen. You're a tired little girl, aren't you?'

Once I'd carried her up to bed I went to see the boys, and read from an old book of ghost stories, Tom's hand resting on my arm.

'Now I've scared you witless you can get some sleep,'

I said when I'd finished. The springs creaked loudly as they climbed into bed. 'Night night.'

Downstairs, before the kids had even settled, we were soon aware of another set of bedsprings under strain on the floor above.

'How many's up there?' Lil hissed to me while Nan was upstairs. She didn't like any mention of them up there, any admission they existed.

'Only one.'

'Makes a change. Usually takes two to get him going nowadays.'

We heard Nan's slow tread at the top of the stairs and Lil made a face. 'You coming singing with us now you've got the courage? You enjoyed it, didn't you?'

'I can't leave Mom.'

'You've left her tonight. Anyroad, you don't need to leave her, she can come.'

'She won't though. And I haven't left her at home. She's at work.'

'Genie – look, Dor's in trouble, there's no doubt, and we're all sorry for her, the babby and that. But if your dad's not coming back she's just going to have to knuckle down and get on with it. It's terrible – I know 'cause I've done it. But she can't expect you to take over the running of her life for her. Because if you'll do it, she'll let you. That's what she's like, always has been. One for sitting back and letting everyone else do it all. But you've got your life to lead as well, so don't let her take it away from you. She's already wrecked Len's—' She stopped abruptly as Nanny Rawson walked in.

'But I still don't think I should leave her. Not when she keeps getting in such a state.'

'She may be in a state,' Lil said drily, 'but she's just going to have to get out of it.'

Nan was dishing up liver and spuds for us. 'Let's get going on Len's wedding,' she said. 'After all it's not just Molly's wedding, it's his too, and he deserves the very best we can give him.' I saw her eyes meet Lil's, and there was a hard look in them I didn't understand. 'He's owed that much.'

So, with years of practice, we ignored the thumps and squeaks from upstairs. The wedding was booked for a Monday, ten days away, and everyone was arranging the day off. Gladys had said, 'Molly can't possibly be showing if we do it that soon.'

Lil had snorted at this. 'She's such a size she could get to nine months without anyone being the wiser.'

Although Lil had pledged to do anything she could to help, she was full of doubts about this marriage. First of all was the fact that Len and Molly were, for the time being, going to carry on living where they were, in their separate homes.

'Don't seem right,' she said.

'Lenny seemed well put out at the idea of moving in with Molly somewhere,' I told her. 'Don't think it'd crossed his mind that anything might actually change. He wants to stop at home with us.'

'There's no houses to be had,' Nan said.

'What's Dor got to say about it?' Lil asked, grimacing at the colour of the tea. 'Proper maid's water this is.'

'Not much.'

Lil was still looking disbelieving. 'What about – where're they going to sleep and that?'

Nan gave her one of her looks.

'Search me,' I said. 'All they talk about at the moment is clothes – Molly's dress.'

'Who's this woman who's making it then?'

'A Mrs Van der Meyer.'

Lil frowned. 'That a Kraut name?'

'No, Dutch, and anyhow he's dead. She's a widow. Anyroad, Molly's not going to let any of us within a mile of that dress before the day.'

'Course not. Bad luck else, isn't it?'

'If you ask me,' Lil said, 'the whole thing's bad luck.'

For the time being Vera Spini was like a person reborn. When I came to the shop that Saturday after the good news I heard her singing. She looked younger suddenly. There was colour in her cheeks, she'd touched up her hair again and it was twisted into a straw-coloured knot behind her head.

'That's a happy sound,' I said. 'Nice to hear you. More like before the war.'

She was bustling around the shop with a broom and turned to smile at me.

'I can't say I'm not worried. It's all wrong what they've done – he shouldn't be there. There's no trial or nothing, so what are we supposed to do? I get so angry thinking about it. But for now—' She stopped and leaned on the broom. 'They're all alive. That's all I can think about.' Her expression turned bleak for a second. 'I don't know what I'd have done ... This is daft thinking about something that hasn't even happened.' She carried on sweeping. 'D'you want Teresa? She's round the back.'

'Is Carlo there?'

Vera looked round at me with a mischievous smile. 'You've noticed then?'

'He seems to be round a lot.'

'Well, he's not here now. Lovely boy he is. I just wish Teresa would open her eyes and see the lad's crazy about her. But that's Teresa for you, always facing the wrong way when it matters. He'll be gone and she still won't get the message.'

'Gone?'

'He's joining up.'

Teresa was washing the floor in the house so I climbed on a chair to talk to her, watching her egg-timer shape from behind as she knelt, circling the scrubbing brush on the tiles.

She looked up and grinned through black curtains of hair. 'Thought you were up to your eyes in wedding dresses.'

'Oh no – Gladys is in charge of all that. We know every stitch and tuck of it, except for the fact we've never seen it!'

'She wearing white?'

'Oh, I don't know about that!' Both of us laughed. 'Can't really, can she, in her position. You are coming, aren't you?'

'I wouldn't miss it for anything.'

'We're decorating the church tomorrow night – me and Lil. I've been down the Bull Ring buying up the flowers.'

Teresa asked cautiously, 'How's your mom?'

It was such a relief to have someone I could tell the whole truth to. 'She's bad. In a right state most of the time, Teresa. I can't get through to her at all since Joe and me . . .'

Teresa stopped scrubbing and sat back on her heels, pushing her hair out of the way with her arm. 'You really serious about him?'

I nodded.

'I can see you are. You're different. How does it feel, Genie?'

'What?'

'Loving someone – really.'

How to tell her? The very best best. 'What about Carlo?'

'I've always liked Carlo – a real lot actually. It's just I've known him so long. He's always just been there, like Stevie—'

'Up till now,' I interrupted.

She looked into my face. 'I'm very fond of him. He loves me, has for a long time, so he says. I suppose I thought it'd be more dramatic. Like in the pictures. He's always so polite. He hardly touches me—'

'A gent?'

'I s'pose. Shy of changing things, I think. I know I don't want him to go. I do know that much. By the way—' She stood up and lifted the bucket. 'Have you heard about Walt?'

'No,' I said stiffly. 'What?'

'He's got a girl into trouble. Run off to join up and left her instead of facing the music.'

'But he's too young to join up! He's only seventeen.'

Teresa put her head on one side. 'D'you know, since they took Stevie, and all the trouble we've been through with it, he never once came in to see us. No "How are you, Mrs Spini, any news about Stevie?" Nothing. Some friend he turned out to be. That girl's better off without him. So I don't s'pose lying about his age'll come too hard to him, do you?'

Lil and I did our best with the church. The flowers I bought were a whole mix of colours, and as well as those, Mr Tailor from down the road let us have some out of his garden which was decked out like a flower show every summer. It was from him we had a bundle of wheat which he grew because he liked the look of it and tight yellow rosebuds which made Lil say wistfully, 'Aren't they lovely? They're my favourites, they are.'

Mom half-heartedly offered to help, but she still had sewing jobs to do on Len's suit for the next day so we left her to it. Lil and I carried our buckets and ribbon and scissors down the road and let ourselves into the church in the evening light. Peach-coloured rays were shafting in through the west window. The atmosphere was stuffy and filled with the smell of floor polish.

Lil eyed up the wrought-iron flower stand. 'I'm not sure I'm very good at this. We'll have to hope for the best.' She turned to me. 'I want Len to have the best. Have we got hymns and that?'

'Mom's sorted it with the vicar. She wanted "Lead Us, Heavenly Father, Lead Us". She said that's a good one for a wedding.'

We managed, after a few false starts, to cut and arrange the flowers in a magnificent spray on the stand, and put vases of flowers round to decorate the altar and sidetables. We tied sprays of wheat ears with yellow ribbon and attached them to the ends of the pews.

'Looks like a harvest festival,' I said, tying bows and flattening them the best I could.

'No it doesn't.' Lil backed down the church, survey-ing what we'd done. 'It looks beautiful. Molly'll love it, bless her. Time something nice happened to her.' Lil was coming round much more to the idea of the wedding now she'd got caught up in the spirit of it.

'You've changed your tune.'

'It's just – seeing it all, like this . . . D'you remember my wedding – Patsy's and mine?'

'Course I do.' I was seven when they married. 'Wouldn't forget being a bridesmaid, would I?'

Lil shook her head. 'I was so happy that day. It really was the best day of my life – well, maybe except the ones the babbies were born. Not even a wedding beats that. My poor Patsy. I hope he don't mind me going about with Frank.'

'D'you really like Frank, Lil?' I asked shyly. Now I was with Joe it seemed we could talk woman to woman.

Lil picked up a long curl of leftover ribbon and started winding it round her fingers. 'I do, yes. At first – well, still really, because it's only been a few weeks – I couldn't stop thinking about Patsy. Comparing them, and feeling bad at being with someone else. As if Patsy was watching, talking to me in my head. I've felt that on and off since he died. At first he was always saying, "Why didn't you stop me? Why did you let me do it?" My own guilt talking, I s'pose. But I know really it wasn't my fault, wasn't anyone's. It was all an accident. Anyhow, after a bit I'd hear him saying more ordinary things, just like chat. That was nice, for a bit.' She gave a little laugh. 'Now though, it's more as if – how can I say it? – he's still there and I love him, but he's not part of now. I can see Frank without being ashamed. I can love both of them.'

'Our nan doesn't take to him, does she? I'd've thought she was a pretty good judge.'

Lil gave a snort. 'Mom? Are you kidding? She may be a good judge of some things, like how much stew a bag of scrag end'll run to. But when it comes to men . . . I mean look who she married! And she was wrong about Patsy, wasn't she? Had him down as a navvy and a waster. No, if you want advice about men, Genie, come to me, not my mom – and not your mom neither, come to that!'

We both laughed, but Lil with an edge of tears. 'Sometimes I just want to feel someone's arms around me so bad I ache with it.' She caught hold of the broom. 'Best get on. Be dark soon.' I followed her round with a dustpan and brush, and we went to search for a dustbin out the back of the church.

'Your Joe now,' Lil said, shooting flower stalks into the bin. I felt myself blush. My Joe! 'He's a good'un I reckon. You could do a lot worse than him, and you deserve to be happy, Genie. God knows, you do.'

The wedding morning dawned bright and we were all up and running like headless chickens before we were half awake. Our nan was down by half six carrying plates of stuff already cut with muttoncloth over them, I was brewing up tea for everyone and there were eggs on the go in a pan. Mom and Nan started laying up the table at the front, talking about beef and chicken sandwiches. We'd saved everything we could for that wedding, and lots of people had chipped in. We'd already done a trifle of sorts and there was tinned fruit, and Gladys was being very mysterious about the wedding cake, which was another aspect of things she'd taken on herself.

She soon made an appearance of course.

Mom rolled her eyes to the ceiling. 'Go and answer the door before she knocks it down, Genie.'

Gladys sailed in with a tray of little cakes. 'Straight out of the oven,' she boomed. 'I've been up since four.'

The smell of them drifted in after her, sweet and delicious, and they looked soft and golden. Good job our mom didn't volunteer for that bit.

'How's Molly?' Nan asked.

'Got her 'ead over a pail at the moment,' Gladys reported to anyone in the whole neighbourhood who might happen to be listening. 'She'll be awright with summat on her stomach though.' She wiped her hands on her pinner and lowered her voice, which was a relief. Looking round at us in grand triumph she said, 'We've got the dress. You're in for a surprise.'

We all stared at her. Were we supposed to ask questions?

'Can't wait,' I said since no one else opened their mouth.

'Anyroad, this won't get the babby a new coat,' Gladys said as if we were all in a plot to waylay her. 'We'll see you later.'

'Gladys,' Mom called across after her. 'Any idea how many you've got coming?'

Disappearing into her house, she called, 'Oh, quite a few . . .'

We had to get Lenny out of bed and get some breakfast down him. Nan had starched him a collar and she fixed it all for him, pushing in the studs. 'Chin up, Len. It's a bit tight,' she said, struggling. Len's huge face loomed over the tight collar which was biting into the side of his neck. 'How d's it feel?'

'Awright.' He was grinning, which was more or less what he'd been doing non-stop ever since we first got him up. She helped him into his trousers and jacket, fastened his tie for him, soaped his hair flat and combed it. 'Now – let's have a look at you.'

My nan stood there in front of her enormous,

damaged son, looking him over from his plastered down hair to his newly blacked shoes. I saw a nerve in her face twitch. I bet she never thought she'd see this day. Her Len getting married. She licked her lips to bring the tremble in them under control and, pulling out a hanky from the front of her dress, she looked down so her eyes were hidden.

Finally she said, 'You'll do.'

The wedding was at eleven. At the last minute I was still putting whitener on my shoes and searching for gloves. But we walked down to St Paul's in good time, Mom with her arm through Len's, explaining to him for the umpteenth time that when the service started he was to wait at the front for Molly to walk up to him, and then the vicar would do all the other things they'd practised.

'Remember what you have to say when he asks you the questions, Len?'

'I—'

'Do. I *do*, Len. That's all you have to remember.' She made him repeat it over. 'Anyway, Mom and I'll be sitting right at the front so if you need any help you just look at us, right?'

'Church looks very nice,' Nan said approvingly as we walked in, and it was true. The blaze of colour from the spray at the front, edged with the half-open yellow roses, looked beautiful, though Mom didn't bother to say so to us. Everything had to be perfect for her precious Lenny's wedding day but she wasn't going to hand out any credit for it. The only thing she said to me on the way in, in a melancholy voice, was, 'I wish Victor was here.'

Our side of the church was empty until we arrived. Nanny Rawson's sister over in Aldridge said she might get there but we never saw any sign of her and no one else knew it was happening. But over on Molly's side there were quite a few there already, all dolled up.

After a few minutes the lady organist started up and we saw more and more trickle in on the Benders' side. Nan, next to me, was watching them from under the same hat she'd worn to Lola's funeral, only this time she had on a flowery frock instead of the mourning-coloured coat. I knew she was sizing up the numbers, wondering if they were all coming back to the house and if we'd got enough food.

There was a tap on my shoulder. 'Genie!' It was Tom, all scrubbed and in his school shorts and jumper. 'Can I sit with you?' He didn't need to ask. As he squeezed into the pew he opened one hand and showed me a shiny shilling.

'Look what Frank gave us. Patsy's got one too, and he gave a tanner to our Cathleen.'

'Blimey, lucky you!'

I turned round full of curiosity. Lil was coming down the aisle towards us with Patsy and Cathleen. She looked marvellous, in a sunny yellow dress which matched the roses, her lips glossy red and her hair swept up with a few curling tendrils hanging down, and I was struck again by just how beautiful she was. It was so hard to believe Nanny Rawson had looked similar in her youth. Cathleen was holding Lil's hand, wearing a little pale blue pinafore dress with white rabbits appliqued on, which I knew Lil had stitched herself. But my glance soon shifted from her to the man whose face I could see over Lil's left shoulder. I saw immaculate, shiny black hair, a thin black moustache, and as they came nearer, a sharply pressed suit. He was following Lil closely, looking coolly down at the rest of us.

'Crikey!' I whipped round to my nan. 'Is that Frank? 'E looks just like Clark Gable!'

'That,' Nan said, thumbing determinedly through *Hymns Ancient and Modern*, 'is what I'm worried about.'

Lil, Frank and the other two children settled in the pew behind us and after a moment I turned timidly to have a peep. Lil gave me a gorgeous smile and a surreptitious wink. Frank was looking at me and Lil leaned over and touched his hand. 'This is my little sister, Eugenie.'

He held out his hand to shake mine. 'Very pleased to meet you.' And he smiled.

I felt rather wobbly. The resemblance was so striking I thought any moment he'd say, 'Frankly my dear, I don't give a damn.' But instead he said, 'I'm Frank.' I stared back at him hard and couldn't see anything in his eyes to make me suspicious so I smiled back and said hello.

Just then, behind them, Teresa came in and, to my surprise, I saw Carlo was with her. She gave me a little wave and they sat in the third row. I couldn't help wondering how things were going with Carlo.

The organ struck up louder and everyone stood. Mom pushed Len out to the front where he waited, lost looking for a moment and then, as he caught sight of Molly, beaming like a sunflower opening out. Everyone on both sides swivelled to see the bride.

There was a gasp from all round. We couldn't help it. All of us watched, riveted, as she swayed along the aisle on the arm of one of her uncles, since her dad had been dead years.

As they came closer I heard Nan mutter, 'God Almighty.' Afterwards Lil said Molly was the nearest thing to a jam roly-poly on legs she'd ever set eyes on. The dress was simply enormous. It had every possible combination of frills and leg-of-mutton sleeves and bows and flounces that you could ever imagine all crammed into the same space together. The sleeves made Molly look as if she'd been blown up with a bicycle pump, the layered skirts flounced hugely over her backside and the neck, cleavage, sleeves and skirt were all trimmed with huge floppy bows. Not only that, although the dress was white – a bit cheeky of Gladys, considering – the edges were piped with a bright rasp-berry-coloured material and half the bows were made of the same colour. On her head she wore a little white cloche hat with a long gauze veil trailing from it which was, at the moment, down over her face. Actually she looked more like an enormous summer pudding with only some of the juice soaked through the bread.

But she was Len's Molly, and his face was brimful of delight. The fact she looked good enough to eat would be a bonus in Len's list of priorities.

The uncle was quite a size as well, and the two of them had rather a squeeze to fit along. It was only once they'd passed we saw the bridesmaid behind, a girl of about nine, in a dress of a terrible bright acid blue. Nan looked at me and I could hear her thoughts: What could have possessed them? But the child, unlike every other member of Molly's family, was extraordinarily pretty, with long, wavy chestnut hair, striking light blue eyes and the longest eyelashes I'd ever seen. A real beauty. It was like seeing Snow White with all the dwarfs around her.

The service sped past. I could tell Mom was on edge, sober as a judge today, afraid of Len putting a foot wrong. But he said his 'I do's' with such feeling that there was a ripple of laughter from behind him. He fed the ring on to Molly's pudgy finger and was allowed to lift the veil and kiss her. Molly turned, smiling coyly. They were married. I wanted to clap.

Outside we deluged them with rice and confetti and they looked like the happiest pair of people I'd ever seen.

'Heaven help us if all that lot come back,' Mom panted as she and I sped down the road ahead of everyone else. The few photographs had already been done. 'We'd better keep some of the sandwiches back so they don't all go at once.'

The minute we were back in the house she was swigging at the gin bottle.

'Mom!'

'What? God, I needed that. What're you staring at?'

'Don't get drunk, Mom. Not today – please.'

'Don't be silly – course I shan't.' She let out a titter, putting the top back on the bottle. 'I just wanted a little pick-me-up. I don't get drunk, do I?'

'Not half,' I muttered, checking the things laid out on the lacy cloth.

'Think of our Len, married!' Mom's voice was high with nerves and excitement. Suddenly she burst into hysterical-sounding giggles, hand over her mouth. 'Oh, that dress – have you ever seen anything like it?'

I had to laugh with her then. 'It was a bit loud, wasn't it?'

Tears of laughter trickled down our faces. 'How're we going to cope with her here?' Mom spluttered. 'It'll be like having a minesweeper in the house—'

'And that bridesmaid – talk about Reckitt's blue!'

Mom wiped her eyes, trying to calm down. 'Pretty little thing though, wasn't she? Oh dear, it's good to have a laugh. Come on though, Genie.' She started flapping again. 'They'll all be here in a minute. How on earth're we going to manage for glasses?'

'Someone'll have to go round the pubs, see if they can spare us any.'

Soon we heard the first knock on the door, but it was only Nanny Rawson and Lil with the kids. Lil went off round to the neighbours and pubs begging use of more glasses, plates and cups. Mom was spreading more bread and Nanny Rawson took over the sandwich factory so by the time Molly got there we were as ready as we'd ever be.

Molly filled up most of the hall and with Gladys and Len trying to squeeze in too there wasn't a hope, so Mom shifted them all through into the garden. Then there followed a thick stream of Gladys and Molly's relatives and it looked as if every last one of her fourteen brothers and sisters had turned up, along with bits and bobs of family and children, so the place was soon heaving with them all. When Frank arrived I was impressed to find he'd stayed back to show people the way. He looked even more like a film star when set against Gladys's clan.

Looking at Frank carefully, I could see he was quite a bit older than Lil – forty-something probably. The suit was smart and you could have looked in the black toe-caps of his two-tone shoes to put your lipstick on. How Nanny Rawson was going to loathe those shiny shoes!

'How's it going, Genie?' He pushed in through the throng of the front room where they were already lighting fags and drinking beer. I had a good look at his face again. I felt protective of Lil. She'd had enough on her plate. He was gorgeous, but was he a chancer? The smile in those steely grey eyes was warm enough, so I gave him the benefit of the doubt.

'All right.' I smiled. 'Lil's still rounding up glasses somewhere.'

'Anything I can do?'

'Beers?' We'd got a couple of barrels in.

'Right you are, Genie. And anything else you want – just give me the word.' And he really did knuckle down and help, seemed like a worker all right.

Nanny Rawson came in holding two plates of sandwiches high so they didn't get knocked. 'Right!' she boomed, and everyone went quiet. 'There's more of you than we bargained for today which is awright. It's very nice. But you'll have to go easy on the grub and make sure everyone gets a share, awright?'

After that the party got into full swing and I went round offering food to a large number of people who looked very like Gladys and others of her relatives who looked totally different. Molly and Len stayed in the garden with a crowd, including the blue bridesmaid who was dashing about playing tig with Patsy, Tom and some other kids. Molly looked very hot in all her finery. Seeing me, she swooped down and clasped me in her arms so I was buried in bows, frills, bosoms and cheap scent. Up close I felt the dress was made of cotton.

'So you're my little niece now, Genie!'

I smiled. 'S'pose I am. You look lovely, Molly.'

Lenny and I had a big hug too. 'You did well, Len. We could all hear you.'

'I'm married now,' he announced.

'You are. And soon to be a dad,' I added more quietly.

'Never thought I'd be the one getting married.'

I squeezed his hand. 'I'll get you some grub.'

Inside, the house was full of chatter and smoke. Teresa and Carlo were there and I realized I hadn't had time to see them, but I caught Teresa's eye and grinned and waved as I went through the back room. In the front, Frank was still in charge of the beer and I heard him say to Nan, 'I hope you're going to give us a tune later, Mrs Rawson.'

'We'll 'ave to see.' Nan gave him a look as if to say when she did it wouldn't be as any kind of favour to him.

And then a noise broke through all the celebrating, a high, rising and falling whine.

'God Almighty!' Lil cried, 'It's an air raid!'

No one knew what to do. We weren't in practice for this. A bomb had come down last week across town but we had no routine.

'Well we won't all fit in the Anderson,' I said. Found I was giggling and didn't know why.

'Get Len and Molly in there, and the kids,' Nan said. 'The rest of us'll just 'ave to make do.'

For the next few minutes there was a low-level panic. Some of the guests went off saying they'd find a public shelter and Gladys pointed out that she had a cellar, so a few of her kin went across with her. Mom made sure she got into the shelter outside saying she was going to keep an eye on Molly and Len.

'Now isn't that just typical,' Lil hissed down my ear. 'I mean it's not as if she's got to worry about Molly getting pregnant now, is it?'

But in the end they found room for Nan as well. The rest of us sheltered in the little cupboard under the stairs – where I found myself with Lil and Frank – and under the tables front and back.

The raid went on for three and a half hours, and if it hadn't been for the absurdity of the situation and us all being together it would've been absolutely terrifying. The planes sounded so loud and close and when they were really overhead we all stopped talking and held our breath. We heard the crash of explosions in the distance.

'So it's really happening, isn't it?' Lil said as we crouched, ears straining, in the tiny space where there was barely room for the three of us.

'If I'd stayed out you could've had a lot more fun, couldn't you?' I said to them and Lil gave me a pretend slap on the cheek. 'Hey girl – what d'you take us for?'

When there was more of a lull we'd poke our heads out and call to the others under the tables. At the front were some of Gladys's family, who kept climbing in and out, polishing off the remains of the food, and Lil said it was a good job we'd still got the cake, 'if we ever get out of here.'

In the back room, under the smaller table, were Teresa and Carlo, and after the first time I popped in and found them wrapped tight in each other's arms, I thought I'd better just leave them to it. We heard their voices now and then, talking Italian mostly, and Lil winked at me. 'Lovely language, isn't it? Makes everything they say sound romantic.'

'Don't think they need the Italian for that by the look of things,' I said.

'Really?' Lil stretched out, put her head round the door, then drew back grinning. 'Ooh, I see what you mean!'

Frank told us jokes and stories to take our minds off it all, making us laugh. I was still trying to work him out, wasn't sure. He looked such a spiv, but at the same time in his face there was something worn and vulnerable that you didn't expect. And he did seem genuinely to care for Lil. By the end of the raids, what with all the laughs he gave us, I was more or less convinced.

The sun was low in the sky by the time the All Clear went, and we all crawled out to find the table empty.

'Greedy sods,' Lil said. 'Honestly.'

Gladys came back with her little band, although the lot who'd gone to find another shelter never reappeared and must've gone to the pub. Everyone was in a mad mood after the hours cooped up and we had a lot of laughs, ate trifle and evap and little cakes, then Gladys trotted back over to get The Cake.

When she stood it on the table everyone clapped and laughed. There were two tiers and on the top, moulded out of icing, was a little figure obviously meant to be Molly, with pink colouring piped round it something like her dress, and silver horseshoes at her feet.

'Where's the one of Len?' someone asked.

'You didn't want to crush the cake, did you?' another voice shouted. And amid the laughter and the cheers that everyone truly meant for them, Len and Molly cut the cake, each of them holding the knife with one of their enormous hands, both smiling madly and Molly's glasses misting up.

We hadn't got to the stage in the war when people were reduced to icing cardboard cakes. This was a real one with fruit and candied peel and it tasted delicious.

As the evening wore on, those who were left sang, led by Nan and Lil who dragged me in with them as well. Mom managed to get through the evening with barely a sniff at a bottle. Len and Molly were the picture of young love on chairs in front of me, Molly still in her amazing frock. And I don't know exactly what changes took place under the table in our back room that afternoon, but as we were singing, Teresa and Carlo sat smiling and holding hands, their shoulders touching like a couple of budgies. Life would have been perfect, really perfect, if my dad and Joe could have been there too.

Later that week my mental peace was blasted right apart by a letter from Joe telling me he was being re-posted down south, which could mean only one thing. He was going to join the fighters over the south coast and I could not rest easy again. The day I got his letter Gloria reported the RAF as having lost thirty-four planes that day. There was more bombing to the east of Birming-ham. The war was real now, and drawing closer. We were on the alert for raids. When the sirens went the tradesmen harnessed their horses to the back of the carts to stop them bolting. Nanny Rawson had cleared the coal hole and started to get back into the shelter mentality. But I wasn't really worried about the raids. My own safety didn't feel all that important. It was Joe I worried about, day and night. Gloria was on overtime and one night when the accumulator went in the middle of the news I found myself screaming at her.

And there was Nancy carrying on. She was as nasty to me as she knew how, and had been ever since she found out for sure I'd 'stolen' Joe from her. She tried to turn the other women in the place against me by telling malicious tales.

The others knew where Joe was and gave me a lot of sympathy, which drove Nancy into even sorer vexation.

'What're you asking 'er for?' she snapped one day when someone enquired about him.

'Because she's the one Joe's writing letters to,' Doris said, 'whether you like it or not, Nance.'

''E's not!'

'Course he is,' Agnes said. 'Ain't 'e, Genie?'

I nodded. 'A couple of times a week.'

Nancy suddenly came at me round the table, hands like claws. 'It was all right before you came along. 'E liked me best!'

She was held back by two other women, both telling her to pack it in.

'I'm going to give 'er one, the sly bitch!' she shouted, struggling.

I was wound up tight with worry as it was, and sick to death of her stupidity and all the spite I'd had off her.

'Joe doesn't even like you, Nance,' I shouted at her. 'And I'll tell you another thing. You don't care about Joe. You don't care about anyone except your pathetic little self, and while you're here having a go at me he could be out there getting killed. That's what I'm carrying with me day after day, because I love Joe and he loves me and there's nothing you can do about it.'

313

I'd hoped my voice would come out strong, but instead it sounded as desperate as I felt.

'Shame,' someone said. 'Poor kid.'

Doris took a firm hold on Nancy. 'One more spat like that my girl, and you'll be looking for a new place to work, make no mistake. I'll not 'ave it in 'ere.'

Nancy walked out of that factory at the end of the day and Doris never had to send her packing. We never saw her again.

The Blitz began for us at the end of August. The Luftwaffe shifted from the daylight raids to night bombing. They bombed the Market Hall in town, leaving desolate, smoking rafters and a terrible mess in the place where we loved to go shopping. I felt as if this must be a film or a dream and I would soon step out of it. But there wasn't a way out.

The next night we spent mostly in the Anderson: Mom, Len and me. As they came over they felt very close, and I can't say the shelter made you feel all that much safer. Less, if anything. What if there was a direct hit? For hours we listened to the drone of the planes, the whistles and bangs of the bombs and our ack-ack guns firing now and then.

I'd thought Lenny might go to pieces. We all jumped at every explosion at first. But Len just perched there with us as if this was normal. He'd always loved fireworks. It was Mom's nerves that took it badly. As we sat there in the light of the hissing Tilley lamp she kept digging her nails into my arm and sometimes, when something landed close, she let out a squeak or a cry. 'Oh, I can't stand it in here,' she cried. 'Can't stand it another minute. I'll go mad.'

I didn't choose to remind her of a time when she'd stood it in the shelter very well of her own accord.

In the middle of it all she said suddenly, 'I can feel it – the babby! I just felt it move.' She put her hand to her stomach and stared at the little dancing flame. 'What on earth sort of life am I bringing this child into?'

September 1940

'It's a year today since war broke out,' Mom said gloomily into her morning cuppa.

I was at the table with Len, both getting breakfast down us quick so's to get off to work, though I hardly felt like eating. Mom didn't seem too bad this morning though. I thought maybe she was trying to take Lil's advice and pull herself together.

There was a rattle at the front door which set my heart pounding. Post. Joe. Would there be a letter for me today? My first and last thoughts of the day were of him, and so many in between. Every day Gloria gave us a reckoning of the number of planes lost and pilots missing. I was constantly worried.

Mom was already out of her chair. 'I'll go. You get on with it.'

She padded off into the hall in her slippers and I heard her give a little grunt as she bent down. She moaned as if in pain. When I got there she was sliding down the wall on to the green lino in a faint, the letters slipping from her hand. In those seconds relief spread through me like warmth: Joe's writing on one of the envelopes.

'Mom?' I sat her up with Len's help and we propped her with her knees apart, head between them. She groaned again, her face white.

I picked up the other letter. A card in fact. *Recovering*

from wounds. Prisoner of War. France. Alive! My father was alive!

'Len, it's from Dad!' I shrieked.

'Victor?' A slow grin spread across Len's face.

'Yes, of course Victor. Mom – he's alive!'

She was going into shock. 'Oh God,' she kept saying in a distraught voice. 'Oh my God.'

We got her into a chair and I squeezed more tea out of the pot but her hands were trembling too much to take the cup. I told Len to get off to work and cooled a helping of the tea for her on a saucer and she finally got some down her.

'Go back to bed for a bit,' I told her. 'Give it a chance to sink in.'

Her mind was jittering, racing. She grabbed my hand. 'I'd just got used to the idea of having my babby. Of keeping it . . . I'll have to have it adopted now.' She stared hard into my face, wanting an answer from me. 'Won't I?'

'My sweet Genie,' Joe's letter said. It was written, I could see, in a very great hurry. 'The pace of life is very different here at ——. This'll have to be quick I'm afraid. Scarcely time to eat or sleep. Can't go into detail. Enough to say I'm on a crash course – but not literally so far!

'Just to let you know all's well. Longing to see you – you've no idea how much. Keep safe and well my sweetheart, until I see you.

'All my love, as ever, Joe.'

This short letter, tucked in the pocket of my dress, seemed to glow against my thigh all day and sometimes I took it out to read if I had a spare moment. I was loved, really loved by someone, and it was the best feeling in the world.

I was so excited that day I could barely keep still. 'My dad's alive!' I told everyone. At the factory they shared it all with me as if they were part of my own family. In fact with a lot more enthusiasm come to think of it.

Nanny Rawson scarcely said a word to start with, just carried on serving out the kids' tea.

'Uncle Victor?' Patsy said. 'He's been taken prisoner? By the Germans? Blimey!'

'Sit down,' Nan said sternly. 'Just get to the table.' She lifted Cathleen on to a chair, handed her bread and a bowl of soup and started absent-mindedly spooning it into the child's mouth.

'It's hot, Nan.' Cathleen spat it out. 'And I can feed myself.'

I could tell Nanny Rawson was turning things over in her mind but there was no use hurrying her. She poured me a cup of tea, then sat on the sofa in her pinner, thoughtfully rubbing her bandaged leg.

'I had a letter from Joe today too.'

'Oh ah.' She got up and beckoned me into the scullery. 'Eat up, you three.'

'Your mother all right?' We were squeezed in between the stone sink and the wall.

'She passed out. The shock. Said she'd have to get the babby adopted. She won't, will she Nan?'

Nan rolled her eyes to the ceiling. 'Daft mare she is.'

'D'you think it'd be for the best?'

'No. I don't. That's my grandchild she's casting off. Parting with your own flesh and blood – most un-natural. I'll 'ave to talk to 'er. Victor's a reasonable man, not like some.'

Lil burst in through the back door, face alight with smiles.

'All right, Genie!' she half sang. The kids looked round, mouths hanging open in amazement. ''Allo kids, what's up?'

'Victor's alive,' Nan said.

Lil flung her bag down, the smile wiped off. 'Oh dear.' Then she saw my face. 'Sorry, Genie. Good news really, in't it?'

'Yes, it is,' I said crossly. Teresa had flung her arms round me with joy as soon as I'd told her. There was a chance for us all now, that's how I saw it.

'How's Doreen taken it?'

We went through it all again in the scullery, the ifs and buts. Lil thought like Nan. Adoption was right out.

'How can she even think of it? Giving away a babby you've carried in you? Two wrongs like that aren't going to make a right whichever way you look at it.'

When this had been chewed over Lil whispered to me, 'Can you stay and give your nan a hand with the kids? I'm off out.'

I grinned. 'Course. Len'll slope over to Molly's if he gets hungry.'

After a quick bite Lil prettified herself, not that she needed to, being gorgeous already. She changed into the shimmery green dress, put her hair up and her lipstick on and she looked like a Persian queen. Although her life was as exhausting as ever, the colour had come back to her cheeks and her hair was glossy.

'You look really pretty, Mom,' Tom said, watching her with admiring eyes. 'You going out with Frank?'

'How did you guess?' Lil smiled into the glass by the door. 'That OK with you?'

'Yeah – 'e's awright Frank is.' He'd long bought the kids' affection with pieces of silver.

''E gave me a spinning top,' Cathleen piped up, enthroned on her potty in the corner by the stairs.

''E said 'e'd play football with me!' Patsy cried.

Lil laughed happily, kissing each of them, which was an unusual occurrence at the best of times. Indignantly Patsy wiped lipstick off his cheek. 'I'm glad you all like him 'cause I think we'll all be seeing a lot more of him.'

'What I want to know,' Nanny Rawson said, 'is where 'e gets 'is money from. I mean mending cars and the ARP – not places where you find a crock of gold, are they?'

Lil turned. 'What money?'

'Well it's obvious 'e's got money – the way 'e's dressed and that—'

'Mom,' Lil said patiently. 'Frank hasn't got that much money. What've you got that into your head for?'

'It's 'cause he looks like Clark Gable,' I teased. 'Nan thinks he's a film star.'

'Oh Mom.' Lil gathered up her coat. 'I thought you was the one who didn't hold with judging a book by its cover?'

I was alone in the house when Mom came in that night. Len had decided to stop over at Molly's. Her eyes were circled like a panda's from exhaustion.

Instead of heading straight for something alcoholic as she did every other night, she sat down on the edge of a chair in the back room, stone cold sober.

'What's up, Mom?'

'I've got to think,' she said in a far-away voice. 'Think things out.'

I wished I could tell her it'd be all right. That Dad wouldn't mind. But he would. Course he would.

'I went to the Welfare this morning. The woman said I couldn't give up a babby for adoption without my husband's consent. I didn't know what to do. I couldn't say, "He's in France", because I knew how she'd look at me and I couldn't tell her about its real father.'

There was a long silence before she said, 'It felt such a little thing I did, going with Bob. And it's turned into all this.' Bitterly, she added, 'Hasn't given him much trouble though, has it?'

On 7 September London had its first big air raid. Four hundred and thirty people died in London that night, so many we could barely take it in.

But the Battle of Britain wasn't over yet and Joe was still flying while those Germans were making up their mind exactly what it was they were playing at. Were they going to invade or not?

I had a letter from Joe sounding tired out, but full of affection. This affection that felt like a miracle, still unbelievable. Then nothing. Every day I rushed to the front door, waited, heart going like mad. Got to the point of crying with fear and worry when there was nothing. He'd been writing every other day when he could. Something had to be wrong. Of course it had to be. Things didn't go right for me.

'Joe – oh Joe, where are you? Write to me and make it all right again!'

I was choked with emotion but like everyone else, tried to keep it down. Always waiting, things out of our control.

''Eard from Joe?' the women asked.

'No,' I snapped, not meaning to turn on them. But they understood, kept quiet then, with knowing looks at each other.

On the Tuesday Mr Broadbent came in, so everyone suddenly put on that extra-busy look like they did whenever he put in an appearance. He took no notice, headed straight for me.

'Could I have a word a minute, out there?' He jerked his head at the back door, face terribly solemn.

The other women's eyes followed me out and they all had disaster written in them. He'd heard something, I knew it. The kind of telegram only moms and dads or wives are sent. I didn't want to follow him, didn't want to hear it.

We went out into the yard at the back and closed the door on the warehouse. I couldn't control myself any longer.

'Joe's dead, isn't he? You've had a telegram?' I couldn't help it. My heart felt swollen fit to burst.

'No, Genie love!' Mr B was overcome. 'It's all right – we haven't.' He put an arm round my shoulders as if he was my own dad. He wasn't that much bigger than me, smaller than Joe by nearly a head.

'I was only going to ask you if you'd heard from 'im, that's all. He's a good lad for letter writing but I'm sure 'e'd write to his young lass more than to us.' He was trying to sound light-hearted, make a bit of a joke of it, but I could hear the worry in his voice and this didn't help me, though I was grateful for his kindness.

I shook my head, tears pouring down my face. 'I haven't had a letter since Friday.'

'Oh,' Mr Broadbent said soberly. 'I see.'

Words were swirling round in my head. Where are you Joe? I can't bear it, I just can't bear it.

'Look.' Mr B rallied himself. 'They're very busy, under a lot of pressure. He'll get in touch when he can, love. I'm sure there's an explanation.'

The explanation, the only one possible it seemed, hung in the air between us like a cloud of flies and Mr Broadbent looked sorry he'd spoken.

'Just hold on, Genie. The moment I hear anything I'll let you know, all right? And you do the same, eh?' He patted my back. 'You take your time now, as much as you need, before you go back in there.'

The endless, gnawing worry took away most of my happiness in knowing Dad was alive. Nothing compared with the way I felt about Joe, how we'd had this bit of time together that was almost too good to be true. I couldn't talk to Mom about it, she was too wrapped up in herself. Only Teresa knew how sick with worry I was. Carlo had left for his army training and she came round to see me of an evening sometimes, knowing I'd just sit and fret.

'I know now,' Teresa said to me as we sat together that evening. 'Seeing the way you're feeling. If I thought something'd happened to Carlo I'd be exactly the same. Funny how I never saw him before, right there under my nose. Always trying to get away from the Italians and be different. This lot has made me see us all properly, the good that's there. I was such a stupid little cow, wasn't I?'

I managed a grin. 'I wouldn't put it quite that strong.'

'Hear that?' Teresa said. 'Wasn't that your door?'

There was another, louder knock.

Mr Broadbent was outside in the dusk, face all smiles, handing me a folded piece of paper.

'You'd never believe it – blooming postman delivered this wrong. It came two days ago and they put it through at 87.'

I must've just gawped at him.

'We're number 37,' Mr Broadbent explained. 'Joe didn't write it any too clear. He must've been in a rush. We've not been living there long, so they didn't know to pass it on to us. It's OK, Genie. Joe's all right.'

When he'd gone I opened it.

I'll write properly when I can. I love you. I love you. I love you.
    Joe.

I sat down opposite Teresa and burst into tears.

The daylight air battles petered out in the middle of the month. The Germans had worked their way through attacking the coastal convoys, the airfields, the control centres, and now they turned their attention on the cities. London was getting it every night. Churchill made his famous speech about 'Never in the field of human conflict was so much owed by so many to so few.' They were heroes of the age, those flyers.

I was so proud of Joe, but I never had a minute's peace. His letter was like having him back from the dead, but I was sure that would never happen again. I knew he was alive and safe each time he wrote, but by the time it reached me? And the next day, and the next? I felt so unworthy of him I just could not believe he'd survive and come back to me.

This was different from anything I'd felt before. Frightening, because I couldn't just brush it off like I could with Walt or Jimmy. Joe had marked my heart and I couldn't get away from it.

That week Mom handed in her notice at work and a day or two later she was summoned to the Labour Exchange. She came back fuming with humiliation.

'D'you know what that hoity-toity little bit said to me? Cut-glass accent she had, can't have been much older than you. "Well, Mrs Watkins."' Mom was pretty good at taking off other people's voices. '"Are you quait sure you heven't got yourself in the femily way in order to get orf war work? Surely at your age you wouldn't normally be plenning to enlorge your femily?" Stuck up little bitch. What's she doing in a soft job like that anyhow? She could be in the army or summat.

'Anyhow, I told her she could keep her airs and graces and not talk to her elders and betters like that. She didn't like that, I can tell you.' Mom was roving round the room tidying, slamming things down on the table.

'Did they say you could give up war work though?'

'Yes, in the end,' she admitted grudgingly. 'Bugger this cowing war. Your life's not your own any more, is it?'

Music while you Work was blaring out as usual. 'We'll Meet Again . . .' and 'Bless 'em All' – thank goodness for the jolly ones because they didn't touch me. Horrible, being wrung out by music all day long. I wished they'd switch the flaming thing off half the time. My eyes and hands worked automatically, head down, not joining in with the jokes. They kept trying to cheer me up, bless them, but even though I tried to put on a brave face, nothing worked. I'd had one more very short note from Joe, but I'd got myself in such a state I was always consumed by worry.

'Genie!' A call passed along the warehouse. I hadn't seen the yard door open wide enough for his head to poke round. 'Mr B wants you out the back.'

All those eyes watching and my legs watery, nearly letting me down. If it was good news about Joe he'd have come right in. Run and told everyone, because after all everyone loved him, not just me.

By the time I reached that door I was trembling so much I could barely get it open. Someone helped, twisted the handle, shut it behind me.

My first breath on the other side of that door I gasped in so hard you could hear it. He was standing waiting for me across the yard, half smiling, uncertain. The time he'd been away felt so long.

'Oh—' I gasped again, grinding my fist into the middle of my chest. For a moment I couldn't speak. Breath came in jerks and pants.

'Genie . . .?'

I didn't remember crossing the yard. I might've flown for all I know. I was holding him, squeezing his arms, pressing his cheeks between my hands, pulling him to me tight, kissing and kissing his lovely face.

He didn't speak at first, calmed me with his hands, taking me by the shoulders to hold me at arm's length, and we looked at each other. His face was thinner, cheeks covered with a day's growth of stubble, dark eyes full of emotion. He pulled me to him and held me so tight.

'Joe, Joe—' My tears flowed, like fear dissolving down my face. 'Oh my God, are you all right?'

He nodded. 'I'm fine. On top.'

'You're here.' I couldn't let go of him, couldn't stop saying it again and again. 'You're here – really here . . .'

'Yes—' He sounded as if he couldn't believe it himself. 'Finally made it.'

'Don't ever, ever go away again,' I demanded.

Joe was holding me, laughing as Mr Broadbent came back out smiling, the worry lifted from him. He even looked taller. I mopped my eyes.

'Thought I'd leave you both for a bit,' he said. 'Betty, my wife, telephoned to say Joe'd got home and I said she'd better send him up here quick because there was someone losing a lot of sleep over 'im.'

Joe smiled properly for the first time. 'Thanks, Dad. But I was coming anyway.'

He only had four days and we spent every possible moment we could together. At the end of the week, while I was at work he stayed at home with his mom and sisters, catching up on sleep after the punishing weeks he'd been through. But he was young and very fit and he bounced back.

His first evening home Mr Broadbent asked me to come over and spend some time with them.

'Are you sure you don't just want him to yourselves?' I asked, uncertain about being included in the family like this. I knew Mr B was OK with me but I wasn't sure about the rest of them.

'Course not. And anyhow, if we don't get you along we shan't be able to tie Joe into his seat long enough to get anything out of 'im!'

I was nervous about meeting Joe's mom and his sisters. What on earth were they going to think of me?

Marjorie, the sister who'd been at Broadbent's show, opened the door of their recently built house in Hall Green with its fresh-looking white window-frames.

'We were just finishing off tea,' she said. I saw she had Joe's dark eyes and the same pale hair and skin. She did have an aloof manner but I think it was shyness, and she was trying to be nice to me.

'Sorry. Am I too early? I could go and walk round for a bit . . .'

'No!' She thawed further and laughed. 'We're expecting you. I'll never hear the end of it from Joe if I send you off again. Come and join us.'

Joe was coming out to meet me and introduced me to everyone – his mom and Marjorie and Louise. And he made it very clear I was someone special, brought me in as if I were royalty.

Marjorie was soon to be twenty-one, according to Joe, though as we sat round that evening I kept looking at her, trying to take this in. I couldn't help feeling I was older than her. There was something cardboard about her. Amiable enough, but with a bit missing somehow. She seemed like someone who was afraid of life, even her own shadow.

Joe sat beside me on their sofa and I basked in being close to him. Mr and Mrs Broadbent were in chairs on either side of the little tiled fireplace. Mrs Broadbent was, over all, a very pale woman. Looked as if she'd had a bad shock, the colour of her. Her hair was white-blond and her skin ashen and thin-looking so that you could see the veins in her neck. I was trying to puzzle out how she'd managed to build up the vile reputation she had round the factory. I came to the conclusion that because she was beautiful and fragile-looking she was like a red rag to a bull for some of those women. They were expected to be tough, coping, hard-working, whatever time of the month, stage of pregnancy or chronic illness they were suffering. Mrs B looked like one of those Victorian women who might get the 'vapours'. Actually her health seemed quite all right. Her manipulative illnesses must have been a factory legend that started small and swelled into something much bigger.

The fact was she was quiet and shy and pleasant and I was grateful to her that she didn't seem to mind me. After all, if she'd been half the snob she was painted as being she'd've objected to her son courting a factory lass. Maybe she thought it'd all blow over and he'd grow out of me, but either way, she was kind to me.

'I hear your father's been in contact,' she said, passing me an oatmeal biscuit. 'What a relief that must be.'

'Oh it is. Couldn't believe it when we heard. It's been so long, and no one telling us either way.'

'Like someone else we could mention.' Louise, Joe's younger sister, nudged him with her foot. She wasn't much older than me, with jet-black hair, Joe's cocoa-brown eyes and a lot of spark to her. She was in her last year at the grammar school. Her hair was cut in a pageboy with her fringe long and dead straight, level with her eyebrows. 'Next time just send us a piece of paper every day with a cross on or something, and then at least we'll know the Jerries haven't had you for breakfast.'

'Sorry,' Joe said, for what was obviously far from the first time. 'I did my best. It's not my fault if the postman can't read . . .'

'You've always had illegible handwriting,' Louise retorted, slouching back in her chair. 'Why *do* boys always write so much worse than girls?'

I wanted to tell her to shut up and leave Joe alone but

fortunately his dad did it for me. 'Leave 'im, Louise,' he said. 'Anyway, I thought you were off out?'

'I am.' She pushed the last piece of biscuit into her mouth and got up. 'The pictures with Laurie. Won't be late.' She nodded at me. 'Cheerio, Genie, nice to meet you.'

Marjorie drifted off as well, leaving the four of us sat round on their coffee-coloured furniture. They didn't make me feel awkward and I liked the way Joe and his dad talked to each other, man to man. Joe often turned to smile at me as we talked. I was still reeling from him coming home, didn't care where I was or what we did as long as I could be with him. Mrs Broadbent asked me about my family and later she made drinks of Bournvita.

As it grew late Mr B said, 'Are you going to run Genie home?'

'Can you drive?' I was impressed with that. No one else we knew had a car except the doctor.

'I'll give you a demonstration, shall I?' Joe took my hand to pull me up.

When we'd climbed into his father's Austin, me looking round the inside in amazement, he said, 'It's good to be home, but I've been dying to have you to myself.'

We waited while his dad gave us a wave and closed the front door, then Joe took me in his arms and I rested against him, smelling his familiar smell mixed with the leather of the seats. Our lips found each other's.

'I thought so much about what it would have been like if you hadn't come back,' I said, looking up at him. 'It felt as if anything good in my life had ended.'

Joe stroked my head against his chest. 'I thought about it too – about losing you. You've had raids here already, haven't you? And there'll be more if London's anything to go by.'

'Didn't you think about yourself – what danger you were in?'

'Only when I let myself. You can't too much. Hardly ever at Tangmere – otherwise I wouldn't be able to do the job. You don't think about dying. You get through every day, somehow. You have to be nearly as much of a machine as the planes.'

I didn't want to press Joe too much on the subject. Wasn't even sure how much I wanted to know anyhow. He'd said he was in an air crew at Tangmere and that towards the end of it all, Tangmere and Kenley had been the only sector airfields left to handle the defence.

'It's over anyway, that part,' Joe said. 'Let's think about the future.'

He started the car and drove across to the Stratford Road.

'How d'you fancy a day out tomorrow?'

'With you? Nah, don't think so.' I grinned at him as we pulled up outside our house.

'Cheeky hoyden!' He leaned over and tickled me until I was begging him to stop. 'Dad might lend us the car.'

'The car!' I sat up straight. A car to drive anywhere we wanted! 'Pick me up as early as you can,' I ordered him. 'I don't want to miss a single moment.'

Apart from the Lickey Hills, which just about counted, I'd never been out of Birmingham before. Joe drove us out to Kenilworth, me in a state of high excitement.

'There's a castle,' Joe told me as I was bouncing up

and down on the seat next to him. 'And lots of country round to walk in. That's if the car's still in one piece to get us there by the time you've finished.'

'I can't believe this, Joe,' I kept saying as we drove out along the Coventry Road, and Joe laughed again at my fidgety happiness as the edges of Brum faded behind us.

'It's not a very marvellous day,' he said, leaning forward to look up through the windscreen. 'Doesn't look as if it'll rain though.'

'I don't care if it does.' We laughed. Laughed a lot that day.

Now we were out of town I was full of exclamations about the fields, the fresh smell of the air, old cottages in the villages, cows and sheep, and the fresh hay bales spilling out of barns. All of it was exciting to me, like travelling into a story book.

'Oh Joe, I want to live in the country,' I said, overcome by all I could see and how lovely it all looked, even under a cloudy sky. 'I know it seems strange, no pavements and chimneys and shops and that, but I wouldn't miss them. Not if I could have all this.'

Warwickshire seemed at least as good as heaven that day.

Joe parked up the car in a narrow side street in Kenilworth and we walked through the little town with its pretty houses and generous green space in the middle. In the gardens there were still roses, beds of marigolds, golden rod.

'It all looks so small, doesn't it?' Joe said.

'It's beautiful,' I sighed, and Joe laughed.

'You're nice and easy to please.' He put his hand in the pocket of his jacket, and with his spare one, drew my hand through the crook of his arm. He leaned round and kissed me. I didn't care that it was in the street where people could see. I was proud to be there on his arm and I didn't give a monkey's who was watching.

We walked around, close together and very leisurely all morning, talking and laughing. We had a fish dinner in the Queen and Castle (a big treat), before going to see the real castle, not far away, at the edge of the town.

As we walked round inside the shell of the castle walls, where it felt very quiet suddenly, or set out along a path into the fields, I held my hand in Joe's, or sometimes slipped it into the pocket of his coat where his change rattled against the silky lining.

'I don't even know why you're wearing a coat this time of year – must be a born pessimist!'

We walked across the fields, climbing stiles, as the sky turned to lead, and watched the cows grazing, wondering when the rain was going to come. It wasn't long before enormous drops started to fall. Right away everything smelt lovely in the wet.

'Oh no!' Joe groaned, getting all bothered like he had over the bikes. 'Here, Genie. You have my coat.'

'No, I'm all right. I don't mind!' The rain made me feel wildly happy and reckless. It was heavy but warm, and the sound of it was all around us like a loud rustling. I turned my face up and held my arms to the sky, half dancing along the path.

'It's raining, it's pouring, the old man is snoring—'

I didn't care if I got drenched to the skin. I tore along, feeling it dash on my face and sink into my scalp through my hair.

Seeing me, Joe must have decided there was no point being worried, and he ran behind me and took my hand.

'Look!' he called out. 'Over the other side – we can shelter.'

The field we were running across was pasture for cows. It had clumps of enormous thistles with purple tops and there were cowpats all over the place. I was glad to see the black and white cows were all huddling right at the other end. Joe and I ran together, careful where we put our feet, laughing and whooping as the rain streamed down our faces.

'Crikey, what a downpour!' Joe shouted.

He felt very strong and fast but I kept up easily, even though it was all uphill, feeling as if I had an iron body and could have just gone on and on running.

The barn at the border of the fields was almost full. Joe picked me up and lifted me on to the ledge of straw bales which was about up to my chest, then climbed up himself and at last we were under cover. The rain was still coming down like mad, sweeping sideways across the slope of the field. We looked round, then at each other, and laughed again.

It was perfect. The stack was packed like a staircase, the bales at the back and sides piled right to the roof of the barn, but with a wide-stepped gap up the middle presumably designed so you could climb up to reach the ones at the back. It might have been made for us. The light was dim as we climbed further towards the top of the stack and the rain thundered on the roof. We settled down together surrounded by the fresh, prickly bales of straw, water seeping from the ends of our hair.

Still getting my breath back, I lay and looked up at the darkness. 'This is the most wonderful, exciting thing I've ever done.'

Joe turned and smiled at me, shouldering his coat off.

'I suppose you think that doesn't say much for the rest of my life? And that'd be about right. But it's doing this with you. That's the thing.'

He leaned over and wiped my face with his handkerchief, his own still shiny with water, eyes on mine. 'Some people would have let it spoil the whole day. Not you though.' Teasing, he pressed his little finger into my cheek as I smiled. 'Dimples.'

He mopped his own face, then absent-mindedly opened up the white square and laid it out flat on the other side of him, although there wasn't much hope of it drying. I think he was looking for something to do. Neither of us spoke for a time.

Things changed in those moments. I went from wild, crazy happiness to feeling solemn suddenly, affected by Joe's closeness to me. I watched him, wondering what he was thinking.

Joe had never said or done anything to offend me in any way. We'd kissed of course, touched outside our clothes, but he was always considerate and tactful. He'd never pushed me to do anything more than I wanted. I suppose he thought I was more innocent than I actually was, coming from households like ours and Nan's. I knew promiscuity led to punishment, like it had for my mom. That it was cheap and wrong to think of going with a man before you were married and that he'd probably think so badly of me if he knew what I was thinking . . .

Yet as I lay looking at him my whole body was full of longing. I found I was trembling with love for him and with need. I knew that at my age I shouldn't be wanting what I did then, from Joe. And as he turned and lay beside me all this desire and confusion must have shown in my eyes because I couldn't hide it. He leaned over me and in his eyes I saw the same struggle between thought and emotion, the same overwhelming longing.

I reached up and put my arms round his neck, shaking.

'Are you cold?'

I shook my head. 'No. Not cold.'

He understood me and half sat up again. 'Genie, the way I feel about you, I'd give anything, anything – But you're so young. I keep forgetting that. I don't want us – you especially – to do anything we'll regret.'

I sat up and put my arms round him again. Here he was. Now, in my arms. 'We could be dead soon. Either of us.'

Joe looked down at me, eyes full of emotion. 'I didn't know this feeling could be so strong. Wanting you all the time. I know I couldn't write, but you were in my mind so much. I kept thinking of you – your body.'

'And I did. I remember thinking I don't know you – all of you – what your shoulders are like. Your legs. And you might never come back and I'd never know. It's like a dream all this, Joe, to me. You've got to believe me – nothing anything like as good as this has ever happened to me before.'

Joe held me close. 'I love you, Genie. More than I can – anything I say never feels enough.'

'Joe—' My cheeks were burning suddenly. 'I'm only afraid of having a babby.'

He blushed then, fiddled with a wisp of straw. 'I can prevent it. Forces issue.'

'I want to tell you something.' Heart beating hard, I spoke all in a rush. 'Now, so I'm never hiding anything from you. It's my mom. She's having a babby and it's not my dad's. I need you to know, that's all. That's one of the reasons things are difficult at home. I never told you before because I was ashamed and scared of what you'd think.'

He let this sink in. 'Well, whose . . .? No, it doesn't matter whose, I suppose.' He kissed my hair. 'But it's not your fault. It's nothing for you to be ashamed of.'

'But when it's your own mom—'

'Look, you've nothing to worry about with me. It's not for me to judge her.'

'People will though. They do.'

We lay kissing and touching, both of us trembling, pressed tight together as if we could each slide under the other's skin. The hard, pummelling downpour had eased but it was still raining steadily and the light came to us as if through cobwebs. I could sense Joe's excitement and I sat up in our little half-lit funnel between the bales and undid the buttons of his shirt. His shoulders were slim, pale and strong as I'd known they would be. He sat up to pull off the shirt and I put my face to his chest, soft with hairs, and breathed in the smell of him, felt the pulse of his blood.

He undressed me with shaking fingers and his shaking made me love him more. I thought how I would never in a million years let Jimmy do this, see any of me, let alone down there, the private place between my legs, and I felt very shy even with Joe. But I trusted him as he peeled off my blouse, then my damp little camisole, hesitating before touching my tiny bosoms as if he hardly dared.

When we were both fully undressed we touched each other's bodies. I felt his warm breath on my skin. Our eyes kept finding each other's, talking with no words. When Joe's hands moved between my thighs I heard his breath catch and this desire, his need to keep control, made me lift myself to him, legs widening.

We lay there afterwards on the scratchy straw, warming each other. 'Joe, my Joe,' I said again and again, my arm tight over him. 'You're all I've ever wanted.' The small amount of light cast deep shadows on the dips and hollows of our bodies. Joe pulled the dry side of his coat over us.

'Has its uses, you see.' Then he said. 'My love. My love.'

There was silence, except for the rain.

'When I was a kid,' I said, 'and it was raining outside – at night like – I used to lie there and think of all the people out in it. Not just people. Cats and dogs, anything that had nowhere to go. And I used to wish I could bring them all in, know that everything was safe inside under shelter. I had this doll, Janet. I've still got her – she looks pretty rough now – and I'd cuddle Janet and talk to her and pretend we could rescue everyone. We had soup made, the lot, in our game!'

Joe squeezed me. 'Be nice if everything could always be safe.'

'I feel safe with you.'

Talking and staying silent in snatches we held each other until we heard the rain stop, then dressed, shivering, back in our wet clothes. When we climbed down from the barn on the sodden grass mingled with loose straw, a movement caught Joe's eye.

'Look, Genie!'

From across the field a long, ungainly bird pulled itself into flight, huge wings beating with what looked like an enormous effort, and long, thin legs trailing. It looked like an old man in a panic.

'Heron,' Joe said, eyes following the slow path of its flight until it disappeared over the bushes into another field. 'Wasn't it lovely? Marvellous they are, I think. What bit of luck spotting one today.'

I put my hand in his, sighing. 'I don't know about so many things. You'll have to teach me.'

Joe turned and took me in his arms again. 'With pleasure. Genie?' His face was serious. 'What we just did. I wouldn't want you to think it didn't mean anything more to me. One day I want to be able to wake up with you in a bed in our own home. Our marriage bed.'

On his last day, I asked Joe to come to my nan's. It was Sunday afternoon and everyone was there: Nan, Lil and the kids, Frank, Mom, Len and Molly. Mom was deadpan but in control, although I kept eyeing her to make sure. I wanted Joe to meet my family properly now because I trusted he'd accept us for what we were, even though going there meant taking him to a slum house, however clean.

'Hope you'll take us as you find us,' were Nan's first words to him when we arrived. She was smiling, had met him before of course, and was impressed. And he did just what she asked.

One thing was worrying me though. I didn't want Joe having too many shocks at once. In a moment's opportunity I took Lil aside. 'Any sign of him up there?' I rolled my eyes at Morgan's ceiling.

'No, and there shouldn't be with any luck. I hear he's got back trouble.'

'Ah, now I wonder why.'

'Cheeky girl,' Lil dimpled at me. 'But it's all right. I think you're safe.'

With everyone there it was a tight squeeze of course, but we all fitted in. Joe talked to Mom and managed to get some joy in reply and he seemed to cheer her up a bit.

It was a wonderful afternoon. Cups of tea and cake, sing-songs led by Nan which had Molly and Len rocking from side to side putting the chairs in danger, Len yelling out bits of song. Lil made me sing solo, and Joe, who was obviously thoroughly enjoying himself, egged me on too.

'You know you can do it – and I want to hear you.'

I liked the old songs – 'Apple Blossom Time' again and 'Maid of the Mountains', and Joe led everyone clapping me.

'Come on, let's hear you now!' I challenged him, and after protesting he couldn't sing, in the end he and Frank clowned about together singing 'Some Day I'll Find You' and 'The Little Dutch Mill'.

Seeing the two of them together, Frank with his dark Hollywood looks and Joe's fair, handsome face, Lil linked her arm through mine and squeezed it, giving me a wink as if to say, 'We've done all right there, kid.'

The two of them finished, bowing from side to side as if they were in the Albert Hall, then Frank snuck up behind Lil. 'Here, I want to show you summat.'

He stood at the back of her and laid his hands on her head, feeling around.

Lil squealed. 'What the hell are you playing at? That feels really funny. Eh, pack it in!'

'You can tell a lot from feeling the shape of someone's head,' Frank said, kneading Lil's skull. 'I've learned a bit about it from a pal. It's a branch of science, you know.'

'Oh ah,' Nan said, rubbing her bandage. 'So's flying to the moon on a magic carpet.'

'Gerroff will you!' Lil stood up, poking him in the tummy.

'Awright.' Frank gave in. 'C'mere Joe, boys. Who knows some tricks?'

Patsy and Tom crowded round, keen, and Joe sat watching Frank dealing cards with a flourish, a fag hanging jauntily from the side of his mouth. Even Mom laughed at his antics and Lil stood at his shoulder. Only Nanny Rawson was giving him sceptical looks and sniffing over her teacup as if to say 'Huh!'

Some time in the afternoon we heard planes, and we all stiffened and went quiet except for Joe and Frank, who rushed out to see, looking for the formation, but they'd already passed.

'No siren anyhow,' Lil said. 'Must've been ours.'

But it seemed to remind Frank of something. He looked at his watch. 'Got to go.'

Lil frowned. 'Where're you off to?'

'Couple of things to see to, that's all.' He gathered up his cards, then leaned forward and kissed her. Our nan scowled so you could almost hear it. 'See you tomorrow.'

Lil looked disappointed, but there wasn't a lot she could do about it. I suppose she wanted things settled, wanted married life again.

Later in the afternoon we had a visitor. A little black and white terrier with tan eyebrows and bright liquid eyes was peeping in at us. Joe, sat by the open door, was the first to notice.

'Who's this then?' he said. 'Hello Mister!'

'Never seen him before.' Lil snapped her fingers at him. 'C'm'ere!'

The small, wiry body came in, wagging a stump of black tail so hard its whole body snaked from side to side, face turning fast from one to the other of us. Then it launched itself into Len's lap.

341

'Oi!' Len laughed as the terrier pushed its wet nose against his ear and Molly leaned over and rubbed at him roughly with her big meaty hands.

'Well where did he come from?' Lil said, bending over to stroke the rough, fidgeting back. 'Not from round here, is he, Mom?'

'Not as I know of,' Nan said. ''Ere – get 'im off the table!'

There were shrieks of laughter as the dog leapt skidding off the table and went round the room sniffing at everyone's legs.

'Ooh, he's tickling me!' Mom giggled. 'He's a proper livewire, ain't he?'

Then he was in my lap, scratchy tongue on my face, and I cuddled him. He felt warm and comforting. Joe reached round and stroked him and looked into the dog's face and I saw a kind of communication there that he seemed to have with all creatures. Patsy, Tom and Cathleen gathered round, squabbling about who could stroke him next.

'Wish we could keep him,' I said.

'I s'pect he belongs to someone,' Lil said. 'But he's nice, isn't he?'

'Could be a stray.' Joe was still making a fuss of him. 'If you haven't seen him before.'

Our nan got up to put another kettle on. 'Looks well enough fed, doesn't 'e? We'll just 'ave to see. Really and truly we need 'im round here like an 'ole in the 'ead.'

I didn't want that afternoon to finish. I kept shutting my mind to the terrible thought that not only would it have to end but that Joe was leaving today. We'd come so close and now we'd have to be torn apart again. All afternoon we were close to each other, nearly always touching, legs, shoulders, hands, or Joe's arm round me.

As we all left Nan's, the dog followed.

'He likes you, Genie!' Lil called from the door.

'He's got good taste,' Joe whispered.

'You're not going to get rid of him in a hurry.'

'Go on – go home!' Mom turned and swished at him with her hand. He stopped for a moment, puzzled, then followed again as soon as we started walking. 'Shoo!' she tried again, but it was pretty half-hearted. I could see she'd taken a shine to him. And there was no stopping Molly turning round, chuckling and calling to him, giving him every encouragement.

When we got to Brunswick Road he was still there like our shadow.

'Oh, can we keep him, Mom? Please? He'd be company.'

'Well . . . I s'pose if he belongs to someone he'll take off home later.'

But he ran into our garden at the back, sniffed around and cocked his leg as if he owned the place.

'He staying then?' Len asked.

'Dunno.' Mom's eyes followed him as he did a tour of the Anderson's roof. 'But he looks as if he might have it in mind.'

I couldn't face the railway station with Joe this time, so we said our goodbyes more privately, on the way to his house, where he had to go and change and get his kit. But it was even more terrible than before. Hard as I tried not to I cried this time, just wanted to hold on to him and drink him in, make up for all the time I wouldn't be able to touch him or have him close. The nearer the moment came for us to part the less we spoke, but this time it was not fraught and unsure, just full of longing for things to be different. And I still had my feeling of not deserving him, a sense of doom, that this was too good to last.

When we said goodbye Joe held me close, chin resting on my head, and my arms were tight round his waist. He kissed the top of my head, and I could tell from his silence he was as emotional as I was.

'Ssh,' he said after a while. 'Don't cry, Genie. I'll be back soon, you'll see. We'll be together. And one day we'll be able just to stay together without all this.'

I reached up and put my arms round his neck so our cheeks were pressed together. Then we kissed as if it was the last kiss in the world.

'You're everything to me, Joe.'

He smiled down at me and I loved that smile so much my tears started falling again. 'You're part of me, Genie, you always will be. I love you.'

When at last I had to watch him walk off it was with a terrible tearing feeling, as if a piece of me was being snatched away and taken into the hands of an evil force that might not let me have him back.

October 1940

The leaves started to crisp and fall and Mister was still with us. From the day he followed us home he was a fixture. Now and then he used to wander off and we thought we'd lost him, but sooner or later we'd hear him bark out the front and Mom'd say, 'Oh-oh, here comes trouble,' and she was nearly as glad as I was to see him back.

I called him Mister because that was the way Joe greeted him that day and when I thought of Joe holding and stroking him it was like some contact with him apart from his letters, which were what I lived for these days.

Whenever I got home from work, Mister was there, jumping to greet me like a mad thing, panting and licking, on the teeter for food. I'd try and find him some scraps, telling him about my day almost as if he was Joe.

The bombing started gradually at first. They were taking more of an interest in us up in the Midlands, but it was like the lull, that early part of October. Mom was calm for a bit then. It was as if she'd put herself through so much agonizing and worry that her mind had blanked out. She was quiet, moved round the house doing odd jobs, went shopping in a loose dress she'd knocked up, slept and wrote letters to Eric. She smoked and drank, but for the moment, not as much as she'd done before.

She knew there was talk about her, bitching on the street, and they didn't trouble themselves to keep their voices down either. Mrs Marshall, Mrs Terry, Mrs Smith. You'd've thought they had enough to do with themselves without poking their noses into other people's lives. They got a thrill out of calculating the length of a pregnancy and talking about it loudly as we went past. We just looked hard faced and ignored them. But it was horrible, and you got to dread going out.

Teresa's Carlo came home on leave and one Saturday night they came over to see us. I liked Carlo, warmed to him. He was a year younger than Joe. His wiry black hair was cut shorter now, he had those striking blue eyes and a loud infectious laugh. He told us about some of the ragging he'd had as an Eyetie in the British army, though he seemed to be able to throw it off. Teresa, who was looking as beautiful as I'd ever seen her, sat close to him, and it was obvious she was just plain crazy about him. She kept turning, smiling into his eyes, and there were moments when the rest of us might as well not have been there. I was so happy for her, for them both.

Len and Molly were with us, Molly looking even more enormous already, although she still had four months or so to go with the pregnancy. Len sat between her chair and Gloria on the table, alternating between fondling each of them.

'Ssh!' Mom said, holding a hand up. 'Listen!'

A tiny, nervous voice was coming out of Gloria.

'It's Princess Elizabeth!' Teresa said. 'Ah – listen to that.'

We listened in wonder. We'd never heard her voice before. She was broadcasting a message to the evacuees.

'My sister Margaret Rose and I feel so much for you,' the high, cut-glass little voice was saying.

Mom scowled heavily as the Princess talked about the 'kind people who have welcomed you to their homes in the country'. By the end, as the little girls said their goodnights, she was dabbing her eyes with a hanky. 'Oh my poor Eric!'

'Oh, don't upset yourself, Mrs Watkins.' Teresa leaned forward and took her hand. 'Eric's safe as houses, ain't he? And it looks as if they were right about the bombing now, don't it? So he's probably well out of it.'

Mom tried to smile back. It was hard to resist Teresa. She could deal with my mom far better than I ever could.

'I know,' she sniffed. 'It's just hard to feel someone else's bringing up your son.' She rallied herself. 'Any more news of your dad, Teresa? And Stevie?'

Teresa's face fell. 'They've been moved, we think. There was a lad came home not long back – lived up by my nan. He's only fifteen, should never've been taken in the first place. Says they're moving them but he doesn't know where. Mom's ever so worried about him again now, because of his chest. I mean we don't know what conditions they'll be in – sleeping out and that.'

Carlo stroked his hand down Teresa's back, trying to reassure her.

'If only we knew more. We've had no letters for ages and we don't know what's going on or where they are. Sorry.' She tried to smile. 'I don't want to put a damper on the evening. We've all got our worries, haven't we?'

I put my hand down and stroked Mister's black and white back, remembering Joe's hand doing the same. We certainly did all have our worries. But for those brief hours, things were as OK as they could be.

Our days had already been broken into by the chilling rise and fall moan of the air raid siren. But none of those interruptions – the scramble we made to the cellar at Broadbent's, smoke canisters going off outside to screen the factories, the singing to pass the time – compared with the night raids.

Birmingham's Blitz began at full strength in mid-October. There was a raid every night after that for the next two weeks.

We weren't ready for the first raid. At the sound of the siren, Mister put his head back and set up a shrill howling. Maybe it hurt his ears – it certainly jarred ours – but his high yowl made it all even more nerve-racking.

'Can't you shut 'im up?' Mom snapped. She couldn't seem to think what to do, just kept picking things up and putting them down again. 'Give him summat to eat – anything so's he'll pack that racket in.'

Not having a routine for this yet, we grabbed hold of things we thought might be useful – a lamp, Thermos, rugs, coats – and struggled down the garden into the shelter, seeing the searchlights criss-crossing in the sky. We had no idea how long it might go on for.

Len sat perched for a while on one of the shelves that made thin bunks on each side as the planes droned closer and closer overhead, then lay down and went to sleep, his bent knees hanging over the edge because the bunk wasn't long enough for him.

Mom and I sat side by side on the other bunk facing him across the narrow gap. The planes came over in waves, the noise growing louder, our hearts beating faster. It was like standing on a railway track, knowing there's a train coming. With every explosion outside, our heads ducked. If it was close enough you felt the impact under your feet. And all you could do was sit there, waiting.

It took me a little while to notice what a state Mom was in. That first night as they came over she was feverishly smoking and biting her nails but she was quiet. She'd lit the lamp and her eyes, stretched with fright, reflected back the flame. When it'd gone on for a time she said, 'Jesus – I wish I had something to drink.'

I reached down for the flask. 'There's some tea—'

'A proper drink!' she half yelled at me. 'It's bloody horrible in here. They're going to hit us, I know they are.'

'It'll be all right,' I said, though my legs were rubbery with fright. I cuddled Mister, who was more scared than I was, to steady myself. 'We're supposed to be safe in here.'

Mom gave a harsh laugh. ''Bout as safe as an empty peach tin.'

'Why don't you try and get some sleep?'

'Sleep? You barmy? How the hell's anyone s'posed to sleep through this lot? Well, 'cept him of course.' She jabbed a finger resentfully at Len.

It was terribly frightening. More than I could've imagined. My hands were sweaty, stomach all churned up. It was like being alone in all the world with the bombs. The rest of the city might as well not have existed.

I was exhausted too. To the extent that it was beginning to fight with the fear and to win. Mom could sleep this off tomorrow but I had to be at work. Tiredness could make you fatalistic. Whatever would happen would happen. You had to sleep, just had to. That was my first taste of the half-awake, half-asleep state you found yourself in during the raids. Asleep and yet not. Still half aware of the planes, the screams and thuds of the bombs in the soapy haze that your over-stretched mind had become. And whenever Mom thought I was nodding off she poked me awake. 'Don't leave me alone in this, Genie. I can't stand it.'

When it stopped and the sky went quiet, the All Clear finally sounded its two minute relief and we crawled up out of that damp hell-hole feeling as if we'd come out again into a different, miraculous world where there were stars in the sky, the shapes of houses round us, still standing, and fresh air. We were not just alive, but reborn.

'Oh, I can't go back in there again,' Mom said, stretching her arms to the sky. 'Never again.'

But we were back in there that night and for many nights after. This was the striped existence of the bombing raids. The days full of brightness, sunshine and fading leaves on the trees casting yellow light. After sitting there in the dark of the night, terrified and weary, the possibility of death coming at you all the time, the light of day was like an enormous cheer breaking out. We're alive. ALIVE. Everything felt bigger and more vivid than usual, the sky close and blue, our house bolder and more solid, the colours of flowers a cause of wonder and every building in the city, however functional, a great work of art. Every day we came out into the rank smell of smoke across Birmingham, looking round to see what had been destroyed in a city that until then we hadn't realized we loved with a passion.

From the second night Mom made sure she had a bottle of the kind she preferred with her. Len tried bringing Gloria in but she crackled and beeped and didn't seem at all happy in the shelter, and what with all the racket outside we couldn't have heard her anyway. So he stowed her under the stairs in the house after that.

The strain began to tell on us. Even in the daytime there were enough hazards. Dread of daytime raids, though they'd mostly stopped them now, unexploded bombs left over from the nights and glass blown out by the blast, the checking and rechecking that everyone was all right, had survived the night.

But it was the nights, those hellish nights. Mister, made distraught by all the noise, would burrow as deep as he could into my lap. Len sucked barley sugars, or hummed to himself, which drove Mom round the bend. She spent the time swigging gin, trying to drink herself into oblivion. And I sat in there with them all, so glad of Mister to cuddle, thinking of how it must have been for Joe up in those planes, holding on to the thought of him and trying to swallow the panic which rose in me like bile.

'Can I have some?' I asked Mom one night as she held tight to the neck of the bottle. No messing with glasses for her now.

'Go on then, have a sip. It'll make you feel better.'

I took a mouthful, felt it burn down inside me and gagged. 'Ugh – it's horrible.' My stomach was already to pot from fear and lack of sleep.

More than once Mom drank until she passed out and I was left alone, as Len could sleep through anything. I sat holding my dog, counting the seconds between each whistle of a bomb and the crunch of the impact, trying to keep a hold on my mind out there in the dark garden, with only this tiny metal hub between me and death.

When it was time to crawl out, blinking and squinting

351

as the door opened, I had to shake and shake Mom, and more than once just had to leave her there to sleep it off.

Another time she woke wild and hysterical, as if her dreams were a worse hell than the raids themselves.

'No,' she screamed at me, 'I can't go on – can't stand it—' clawing at me in a crazy way, and I was frightened. Her hair was loose and her face crumpled with drink and tiredness. I wasn't sure she was even really awake.

'Look,' I said desperately. 'Why don't you just go back to sleep for a bit?'

To my surprise she did lie down again and close her eyes. I think she spent most of the day asleep now, because there wasn't much sign of anything getting done except her managing to get to the Outdoor for more drink. We were lucky if we got a meal down us before the sirens went off again. Sometimes we ran down with steaming plates and ate in there off our laps.

One night, when we got to the shelter, she found that the gin supplies were disastrously low. There were only a couple of fingers left in the bottle.

'Christ – I can't get through it with only that.' The skin of her face looked thicker nowadays. She was puffing out with the pregnancy, but the boozing can't have helped. 'I'm going to have to get some more.'

'You can't,' I begged her. 'You'll just have to make it last.'

She looked at me as if I was a prison guard. 'You're getting a bit of a bossy miss round here nowadays, ain't you? Don't leave much room for me, does it?'

'I'm not!' I said, hurt. 'And anyhow, there'll be plenty to do when that one arrives.' I nodded towards her bump.

'Oh yes, that one.' She drank from the bottle, then gave a crooked smile. 'D'you think it'll be a boy or a girl? I bet it's a boy, don't you? And what do I call him then? Bob? Or Victor? Bictor, or Vob?' She laughed her stupid drinking laugh.

I thought, Lil wouldn't have been like this. Lil would've coped. But then Lil wouldn't have got herself in this mess in the first place.

'Do us a favour, Genie?' She had to speak loudly now, over the noise outside.

'What?'

'Go down the Outdoor for me and get some more?'

There were planes overhead. I stared at her in disbelief.

'I'll go for you,' Len said.

'No you won't, Len,' I snapped at him. 'They'll be in the cellar anyhow. They don't just stand there selling gin day and night in this lot. None of us is going anywhere.'

Mom pouted like a child. There was a long silence then, except for Mister's frightened whimpering and a tired moth battering against the lamp. Mom was sulking and I was too furious with her to speak.

With every wave of planes passing over I felt my heart bang harder until it was almost a pain. You couldn't move, you couldn't do anything about it – you just had to wait it out. Sometimes I wished I was old enough to be a warden, so's to get out there and do something.

It was a heavy raid that night. The first wave brought incendiary bombs, 'breadbaskets' of them rattling down to set the city alight, turn it into a beacon for the heavy high explosive bombs following close behind. The smell of smoke found its way to us. What was burning tonight? What would be left when – *if* – we got out of here in the morning?

Mom didn't have enough drink to knock herself out. She sat slumped on the bunk, leaning against the crimpy wall near the front of the shelter, staring at Len who was now sleeping like a princess in a fairy story.

I was so stung, so angry at what she'd asked me to do, I couldn't let it go. In the end I burst out, 'So you think more of a bottle of booze than you do me?'

She frowned, focusing on me slowly. 'What?'

'You'd send me out in this – just to get booze for you?'

She nodded in a befuddled sort of way and for a moment I thought she was too far gone to answer me. But eventually she said, 'Well that's me for you all over, ain't it?'

There was a sudden escalation of noise outside and both of us ducked, cringing, protecting our heads with our arms. The impact was loud and horribly near, shaking the ground, and the crashing and whooshing outside seemed to go on for ever.

'God, that was close,' I said as it started to die away. It was hard to straighten up. You got stiff and crumpled with fear.

In the lull that followed Mom nodded across at Len. 'I suppose you know why he's like he is?'

'Like what?'

'Like he is.' Her voice was harsh. 'Soft in the bleeding head, what d'you think? Thought your nan might've let on to you.'

'No. I always thought he was just born that way—'

'Nah, he wasn't born like it.' She shook her head as

354

hard as a Punch and Judy puppet. 'It was me did that. Ain't it always?'

She talked with her eyes fixed on Lenny's face.

'When he was born I was two – two and a half more like. He was a big babby, always was huge right from the start. And he was like six Christmases rolled into one for me. He was my dolly, my babby, he was going to be my best friend. And he was. I was all over him, all the time. Mom didn't mind. I took him off her hands and that suited her. She needed a hand, she was that pushed, what with the house and all the extra work she took in and our dad being the way he was. So Len was as much mine as he was hers really.

'Anyroad, he grew. I'd cart him about – course, he was heavy and I was a skinny little thing. Then one day when I was turned four Mom said she was going out to take some things up for a Mrs Brigham who lived in another yard up the road. The lady'd just had a babby and she wasn't any too good, so Mom was helping her out, the way she always has. She said to me – I can still hear her – "I'll only be a few minutes. Don't come up. You stay with Len."

'"But Mom—" I started arguing with her. "I want to see the new babby. Can't I come with you?"

'"No," she said. "You stay put. You'll only be in the way. Mrs B's not herself and she won't want me carting you two up there as well."

'And off she went. I was furious. I remember punching the couch downstairs with my fists, shouting, I was that cross. Don't know why I wanted to go so much really – there were always babbies about. But I s'pose I saw myself as a kid who was good with them and I wanted to be counted in.

'So in the end I wrapped my arms round Lenny, sort of in a hug, and picked him up. And I ran up the road after Mom. With his big head in the way I couldn't see where I was going and he was such a weight. I tripped and fell down right on top of him. His head went down with a bang on the pavement. Knocked him out. He wasn't quite two then, and he'd been starting to chatter on, but he never said another word after that – not for about five years, and he was never the same again. The doctors said he had brain damage . . .'

I could see it all, the little girl hoiking her baby brother along the road. Nan's face, the anger that even now she couldn't help spilling out on occasion when she spoke of her eldest daughter.

'You didn't mean it though, did you Mom?'

She shook her head, crying now, like the frightened child who'd done the deed. 'Course not. I wouldn't have hurt him for the world.'

I crept closer and sat by her, not quite daring to take her hand.

'Look at him.' Her cheeks were wet. I wondered if her tears tasted of gin. 'He's going to be a father and he's still only a kid himself. Thanks to me.' She looked at me. 'I deserve them hitting me after all the things I've done. One of these nights they'll get me.'

'Mom, no,' I said, frightened. 'Of course not. You didn't do anything on purpose. You're just . . .' I trailed off. Just what? Unlucky? Careless? Foolish? 'You've just had some accidents, that's all. You've had enough punishment.'

Later in the night, when she'd quietened, we felt sleep coming over us even though the raid wasn't finished. It was more distant and I found I'd blanked out for a time, I didn't know how long. It could have been seconds or hours. But then they were hard over us again and I was suddenly awake. The battering of noise was back, the planes, ack-ack guns with their tennis-like rhythm, the whining and crashing. I sat up, wide awake. The lamp had gone out.

Mister was still lying beside me, but I stretched out on the bunk. Mom wasn't there.

'Lenny?' I shouted across to him. 'Where's Mom? Where's Doreen?'

'She's your side.' He must have been awake already because he sounded alert.

'She's not.' I wondered if she'd tumbled on the floor. 'Mom? Where are you?' I felt around in the dark. Nothing.

'Len, take Mister. I'm going to see out there.'

I wrenched the door open and stepped up into the crazed, coloured world outside. The sky was copper streaked with yellow and red, and puffs of white from the ack-ack fire. Fires across the city – beacons to guide the bombers – were filling the air with acrid smoke and the searchlights scratched at the sky with their cold beams. The explosions of light now were from the foul-smelling high explosive bombs.

But my eyes were fixed on Mom. She was standing with her back to me half way down the garden in her nightclothes, staring up at the glowing sky, her arms stretched out in front of her, open, as if she was in the act of embracing someone. Just standing there, quite still.

'Mom – for God's sake!' I ran to her, wondering if she was asleep or awake. Her pale nightdress stuck out at the front over her belly and I realized she'd taken off her coat. She must have been frozen. Her eyes were open.

'What're you doing?' I bawled at her. 'Come back in for Christ's sake.'

'I thought I'd just get it over with,' she murmured, so I could only just hear.

There came the most massive bang from very close by that snatched the ground from under us and we curled on the ground like babbies, our hands over our heads. I squeezed my eyes tight shut. The noise seemed to go on for ages and ages, the crashing and splintering and explosions of glass. When we stood up, instinct guiding our hands to our bodies to check everything was there, tongues of fire were shooting up from the street behind our house. There was already the sound of fire-engine bells somewhere near.

Mom and I dashed into our dark house. There was glass everywhere, front and back, strewn like a hard, crunchy icing on every surface we touched as we groped our way through to the front. I heard Mom gasp, cutting herself. The blackout blinds at the front were in tatters and through them we could see that a great swathe of the opposite side of the road was gone. Just matchwood and rubble, burning, and more to see than usual of the sky.

Mom's hands went to her cheeks, breath sucking in. 'Oh, look!' She was gulping breath in and out and couldn't speak for a moment. 'They got it – not me . . . Someone else got it!'

When the light came we could see it all. The three of us walked out dumbly into the dawn, only half dressed, to see our familiar street changed utterly. We stepped over fat hoses squiggling along the road, leaking feeble arcs of water and lying in a mouse-brown mess of wet plaster and brick dust, and more glass crunched under our feet.

'Lord above, look at it.' Mom stood with her arms folded, a rough dressing on her cut finger. 'God in Heaven.'

Gladys and Molly's house was still standing, as were those on each side of it, but not much further along a great block had been blasted out of the terrace, the inside walls of some still left standing pointing jaggedly up, with their pathetic strips of wallpaper, their picture hooks and damp stains, and the rest of the houses smashed to charred rubble, bits poking out at all angles like spillikins.

There were people out all along the street. Len rushed across and banged on Molly's door and after a time Gladys opened it and the two of them came out, already dressed as they'd most likely been all night. The pair of them looked as tired and dishevelled as we must have done. In the quietest ever voice Gladys said, 'Wasn't it awful? Just a few more yards this way . . .' and she looked along at the shattered houses, her eyes filling.

Len put his arm round Molly, who huddled close to him. Along the street a vicar, shabby old mac flung over his cassock, stood comforting a man who was watching the rescue squad, his face full of fear and desolation. They'd already been working out there for several hours, and the flames had all been put out. We could hear sawing and drilling and the men calling to each other. A team was waiting with stretchers. Other neighbours were gathering round. Mr Tailor from our side of the road stood out in his braces, and everyone was squinting in the shocking sunlight, no one saying, but all of us thinking, as we stared glumly at the houses opposite, 'Who's in there still? Who's dead?' A horrible, dank smell hung over everything, of wet, charred wood and plaster, wisps of grey smoke still floating in the air like the ghosts of those already dead. And mixed with this, the sickening smell of gas seeping from broken pipes in the houses.

One of the gossips I recognized from down the road was standing in front of what had been her house, two toddlers clinging dumbly to her coat and a baby yawling in her arms.

'Look,' Mom said. 'Mrs Terry.'

We went to her, seeing her shivering, the shock on her face.

'We was in the Anderson,' she said. 'In the Anderson. The Anderson at the back.' Their faces were brown with grime like panto gypsies but they all seemed unhurt. There was a mobile canteen at the end of the road handing out tea and we led her down, handing her carefully over the rubble because she didn't seem able to look out for herself. As we waited for our turn they carried a stretcher past to a grey ambulance, the face covered by a sheet. We all watched, no one speaking, but somehow we couldn't take our eyes off it.

Those who could go had already been taken to first aid posts, but the workers were still having to follow the trail of the buried or dead, listening for moans, tiny gasps, any flicker of life entombed under the houses. I heard a voice somewhere saying loudly over and over that we had to boil all our water. The bombing cracked and destroyed water pipes and the water wasn't safe.

As Mrs Terry sipped her tea, handed out by the cheerful woman in the mobile canteen, we stood trying to offer her comfort by our presence, not knowing what else to say. Mom held the babby for her, trying to quiet it.

'You can come back to ours and rest for a bit,' she said. 'They'll find you a place to go after, won't they?' None of us was sure. We couldn't think straight and it was all too new. Later we'd be able to gather our wits and ask one of the wardens where she could go.

Mrs Terry shook her head. She didn't know anything. She was in a state of paralysis. But she did hold out her arms to have her babby back. The two kids were chewing on the canteen's stale buns, both of them unnaturally silent.

A shout went up from amongst the wreckage. 'Here! There's someone under this lot!' There was urgent activity, equipment carried over at a jerking run, men sawing, lifting chunks of masonry, throwing out objects here and there when they got further down, a clock, a clothes-horse, a skein of baby-pink wool. It seemed to take so long. After a time they called a nurse through to give an injection.

'Morphine I s'pect.' Mom shuddered violently, arms folded tight. 'Christ, imagine being under there.'

As we watched, a man appeared in the street in trousers but bare at the top, blood dark on his head and stains of it on the shoulder underneath. His feet were bare as well and he was turning his head frantically from side to side as if looking for someone. One of the ambulance crew led him gently away.

'I've got to get over to your nan,' Mom said. 'See if they're OK.' She was agitated suddenly, pulled her fags out and was about to light up, hands shaking.

'No!' The warden almost flung himself at her, knocking it from her hand. 'Can't you smell the gas? You'll have the whole bloody street going up!'

'Sorry,' Mom said. 'Oh I'm sorry, I never . . .'

But he was too busy to listen to apologies and had already gone.

We were leading Mrs Terry and her children down towards our house when a murmur rippled through the straggling group of neighbours, a low moaning sound of everyone breathing out together. The rescuers were now pulling a body from the house where they'd heard the tiny sounds. It was a woman, and at the sight of her I saw Molly turn and bury her face in Len's chest with a whimper of distress. So slowly and tenderly they lifted her out, as if they were handling some treasure precious to their own lives. She was unconscious now, drugged out of her agony by the morphine, but how and what she had suffered these hours was more than any of us could bear to imagine. Her face was almost untouched except for a few small cuts, and the upper part of her body appeared unscathed, though it was hard to tell as she'd been trapped down there and could be crushed. But when the bomb came down she'd fallen, and been trapped by the weight of her house, next to where the fire burned in her little grate. For these past hours the heat of it had smouldered along the lower portion of her body so that all that remained of her feet were gnarled things like charred twigs which crumbled, dropping in small bits as they moved her, despite all their carefulness. The clothes on the lower part of her seemed melted round her like black tissue paper. Her head lolled to one side.

She can't live. Everyone must've thought the same. Not after that. I knew her face. Mrs Deakin, a widow in her late sixties who'd always been kind. I saw the nurse who'd given her the injection turn from the sight of that grilled body on the stretcher and take deep controlling breaths. She was young, with light freckles on her nose.

Silently we led Mrs Terry to our house, where yellowed leaves piled gently against the door as they would on any October morning, except that today they were mixed with ash and glass.

After work that day I hurried across to Belgrave Road. There was a lot of damage in the area, gaps and mess where before it'd been whole. Life itself was wobbling. I had to rush because sometimes they came over as early as six and the sirens'd be off, barely giving you time even to get home.

Teresa and Vera had volunteered their house to the WVS as a respite point where people could be taken temporarily for rest and help.

'Otherwise we're no use to anyone, are we?' Vera said. 'It's the least we can do.' It gave them a sense of purpose, and they both seemed lifted by it.

At Nan's they were already preparing for the raid. Lil had made a makeshift bed for herself and Cathleen under the table. The others would go down the coal cellar and they had coats and shoes rowed up and blankets ready.

Lil, cooking chops, was in a state about Frank. 'He was on yesterday and he's on tonight. Thinks he's got a charmed life. God, I do hope he's careful with himself after that lot last night.'

Mom'd told them about our street, but the other news on everyone's lips that day was the Carlton Cinema. A bomb had come down in front of the screen when the place was packed. Killed nineteen.

'They say they were just sat there as if they were still watching the film,' Lil said.

'That'll be the blast.' Nan was filling a flask with cocoa. 'Does odd things. D'you know, Genie – when we came up this morning every window in the house was open?'

I looked round. 'All the glass is in.'

'No breakages. But they were all open. Wouldn't credit it, would you?'

I only stopped there a few minutes, but in that time it would've taken an idiot not to notice there was something wrong with Tom. He wasn't himself at all. I tried talking to him, making jokes, but he was pale and very jumpy, poor kid, very sunk into himself.

'This is all making him bad,' Lil whispered to me. 'I don't know what I can do for him.'

I could do no more either, except give him a cuddle and say goodnight to go and face the next round. The days which had seemed such hard work before now seemed like a rest cure compared with the nights.

And then it stopped. After two weeks of raids every night, suddenly there were days of no siren, no Mister howling, no shelter. It felt really peculiar. The bombing had so quickly become a way of life. But all the same you couldn't relax because there was no guarantee it was over. They might go and bomb somewhere else but they'd be back, and we never knew when. The siren could go off any time. So throughout those days there was still the same fluttering heart and acid stomach. A couple of times during the raids I'd been woken suddenly from a quick snatch of sleep and been sick, such was the shock to my system. Even on those nights of quiet I kept waking, blood rushing, ears straining, not being used to a full sleep.

One morning Mom came down, grey faced with tiredness and nerves. 'I've decided. I'm never going out in that shelter again.'

I gave a sarky laugh, readying myself for work. 'Not till the next time.'

'No. Never.'

'Mom?' I walked round and peered into her face but she was looking out somewhere way beyond me, one hand absent-mindedly stroking her big belly as if it was too tight and she needed to ease it. 'You all right?'

There was a long silence and I nearly asked again. But then, more firmly than I'd expected, she said, 'I'll be all right.'

Something about her bothered me, though I couldn't say what. It wasn't as if I wasn't used to her being lost to me, depressed or drunk, but she was stone cold sober this morning and she frightened me, nearly as much as she did when I'd found her standing out in the garden holding out her arms to embrace the bombs.

I put tea in her hands. 'Why don't you go over to Nan's today? Have a bit of company.'

'Don't fuss, Genie.' She spoke dreamily. 'Just get off to work.'

To start with she was on my mind that day. I couldn't get Mrs Deakin out of my head either, the horrible thing that had happened to her. I tried to think, Mom'll be better once the babby's over with and born. Give her something else to fix her mind on. I was beginning to look forward to that, a babby in the house, whoever its father was.

It was a busy day at the factory with all the work and talk and the women asking me if I'd heard from Joe.

Yesterday's letter from him, safe for the moment with his squadron, was folded close to me in my pocket. I thought of us making love and blushed, blushed even more when they noticed and teased me. It had brought us even closer. I had no shame, no sense of wrong. Not with Joe. And not now during this war when you couldn't take anything for granted. You took what you could and were grateful.

I wanted to go round to Nan's at the end of the day and look in on Tom, talk more to Lil about him. But by the time work finished I felt I ought to get home to Mom. Some instinct I had, that made me run half the way there in a cold sweat, not stopping to queue for any food. I don't know what I was afraid of. I suppose I expected her to get drunk and have an accident one day. Fall when there was no one in.

When I clattered in through the front door, Mister came at me like a cannon ball, yapping and jumping round my legs in ecstasy, licking whatever bits of me he could reach.

'Mom, where are you?' I needed to hear her voice.

There was no answer, but then she hardly ever did bother to answer when I called.

To my surprise she was in the kitchen standing by the stove. Cooking of all things. And the place looked as if she'd had a tidy up too.

'Thought it was high time I did a meal,' she said.

I was all smiles of relief. 'You feeling better?'

'I'll be OK.'

I picked up Mister who was still frantic for attention beside me. 'D'you go to Nan's today?'

'I popped over. Picked up a few things on the way

back.' She was stirring the pot, looking so frail standing there in the gaslight, pregnant, her hair loose, seeming younger than her years.

'We'll wait for Len,' she said. 'He can eat with us tonight, not at Molly's.'

She'd done stew and spuds, even a kind of egg custard for pudding, and the three of us sat together round the table, Gloria playing to us. Mom didn't drink. Not a drop all evening.

'Quiet without Jerry, isn't it?' I said. We were still waiting, could hardly believe it was another night free.

'When all this is over,' Mom said to Len all of a sudden, 'you and Molly'll have to get yourselves a little house somewhere.'

'If there's any left standing,' I joked.

She looked solemnly at me. 'And you and Joe. He's a very nice boy, Genie. The sort who'll really look after you.'

'And we'll look after you too, Mom. Don't you worry. And little'un in there.'

She just gave a bit of a smile at that, as if to say it wasn't her that mattered. She was so calm. Perhaps I should have seen that as odd but I was just glad. Things felt normal, whatever that was nowadays.

We sat listening to Gloria and then Mom took herself off to bed. As she passed by my chair she rested her hand on top of my head. 'Goodnight, Genie.'

I was the last up. I switched the lights off and left Mister snoozing by the remains of the fire.

The high wailing sound woke me and I was out of bed, completely awake, pulling on the coat I'd left at the foot of my bed. It stopped. Started again. It was only then I

367

realized it wasn't the siren but the other noise we normally heard along with it. Mister was howling, somewhere outside. I went and opened my window over the garden.

It was very dark and I could only hear, not see him, howling and whimpering under my window.

'Mister? How d'you get out there, boy?'

There were more yowls as he heard my voice and the rasp of his claws scratching against the back door.

'OK. I'm coming.'

Going to the door, I wondered whether I'd dreamed him being by the fire when I came up, or whether Mom'd been down, put him out and forgotten him. But as soon as I was on the landing I smelt it, that stink of the mornings after the raids, the mean, seeping smell of gas. I tore down the dark stairs.

When I opened the kitchen door the rush of it set me coughing and gasping. I could hear it hissing in the dark and the thoughts going round in my head were, who the hell, who'd been so stupid as to come down and leave the gas on in the middle of the night? I groped towards the back door and heard my feet knock into glass, bottles crashing together. Then I tripped over her legs and fell across the floor, banging my head and side. I got up and struggled with the back door key knowing now, knowing what was happening, taking gasps of air as I got the door open, sick with the gas. Mister tore inside and disappeared somewhere into the front of the house yelping and howling.

Everything was automatic now, with a kind of perfection born of instinct. My steps across the kitchen, one hand over my nose and mouth, the other going to exactly the right dial on the cooker to shut it off.

The hissing stopped. With more strength than I

knew I had, I bent and pulled out the dead weight of my mother's body from where she was lying, head resting on her crossed arms in the greasy base of the oven.

November 1940

Mr Tailor was the one I went to for help, after I'd knelt in the black kitchen, feeling along her wrist. My finger-tips found the veins slanting across her bones and a tiny pulse like a bird's.

I was retching from the gas and sobbing out all sorts of stuff to her. 'Don't die. Don't do this . . . Don't you bloody well go and die on me . . .'

The smell was still awful in there – there wasn't much of a breeze coming in – so I lifted her under her flopping arms, her feet bumping down the step into the garden and the cold air. I found the crocheted blanket and laid it over her. Mister was running in circles in the garden, barking.

I went and picked him up, so glad he was there. 'We've got to get help, boy.' I ran down the road with his soft head pressed to my face.

Mr Tailor was marvellous. Didn't make a fuss. He found a working phone box and dealt with the ambulance, while Mrs Tailor was kindness itself in the face of my shaking. She made me sweet tea. I clung to my little dog and couldn't stop my teeth chattering. They asked no questions. Most likely guessed most of it in any case. They took me to my nan's, said they'd go round to Len first thing. It was three in the morning and I had to tell Nan what had happened. Nan sat down and stared ahead of her. It was Lil who did the crying for all of us.

She was a long time in hospital. At first I was just scared she'd die, and she came very close. Death's door, that's what they say, and she was on the step, hand raised, knocking. She lost the babby. The labour came on with the shock and was born dead, much too small for this world. They said it was another little girl, although she'd thought it was a boy. She haemorrhaged badly and had to have a blood transfusion. For days she lay barely conscious and we'd sit with her in that ward at the Queen Elizabeth. Dots of light flashed round my eyes from exhaustion and I couldn't keep my food down. They were bombing every night again now and we crouched in Nan's house thinking 'What if they hit the hospital?'

But Mom didn't know about these worries. I'd sit watching her white, sunken face, wondering what I was going to say to her when we could talk again. Nan kept bringing in things for her to eat, bits of fruit, little custards or junket she'd made. But she never even had a response from Mom, let alone got her to eat anything. I'd grip her hand but got no squeeze from her in return. Only later we found out why. As she regained consciousness the doctors said she'd lost the use of the right side of her body – the right arm completely, the leg showing little flickers of life.

The first time she came round while I was there, her eyelids seemed so heavy she could barely prise them open as she bubbled slowly back up to us. Her right eye wouldn't open.

'Mom.' She croaked the word, coughed, tried again. Only half her mouth was working. 'Oh, God, Mom – Genie—' She couldn't say any more. Tears seeped down her face.

'Mom, oh Mom ...' I could only bow my head,

resting it on her, and cry too, overcome by her misery and my own shame.

There was Mom and there were the raids. That was what made up our lives. Nan and I went to the hospital every day, Lil when she could. I told Mr Broadbent my mother was ill. He told me to have days off, take my time. 'The others'll rally round,' he said.

I was staying at Nan's and Len was at Molly's. All other aspects of life faded into the background. Something happened to me during those days. Everything had changed from my life before, like a coin flipping over. The thought of seeing Joe appalled me, revolted me even. No, never again. Such things were not meant for me. This was family, and only family. And not even my family knew the depth of pain I was carrying in me over what had happened.

I couldn't look my nan in the eye. I'd let her down. Let us all down. I hadn't looked after Mom properly. That had always been my job. I was the one who saw her out there, arms out, calling to the bombs, and I should have known how near the edge she was. I should have been able to save her.

Nan did what had to be done, though she'd aged in a week. I thought she was angry with me. I couldn't stomach food, kept being sick at odd times. I wished I could be like Lil and let it all out. Lil could say all the things she needed to say, 'Poor, poor Doreen – fancy us not knowing she was that bad. Was she bad, Genie? And the poor little babby . . .'

But it was my nan I couldn't stand to be near. I couldn't bear the grief pushed down in her as she ran the shop still, day after day, in her pinner, her jawline held proud, listening to the grievances of her customers. She didn't let on about her own.

By the early evening the sirens were screaming and it was a terrible rush to get some food, get organized. The minute it started Mister was howling and Tom would be curled up under the table quivering and refusing to move.

'I ain't going in that coal 'ole – I'm never going down there again!'

The poor kid. When he was awake he was terrified and when he was asleep he was thrashing about screaming with nightmares and wetting the bed. He nearly jumped out of his skin at the slightest sound.

So we arranged it that I'd stay up with Mister and Tom under the table. I was happier up there in any case, what with my sudden bouts of sickness, and because I was happier away from Nan, couldn't face her. I also wanted to do the best I could for Tom. I told him stories and we both looked after Mister, who was just as scared as he was, or we lay curled up together, the darkness in the house made even thicker by the heavy table above our heads, while the sky was set on fire outside.

This particular night as we lay there I said to him, 'D'you know what day it is today, Tom? It's fireworks night!'

We both managed a bit of a laugh at that. 'Don't exactly need to bother with it this year, do we?'

Tom clung to me, shaking, as the noise escalated outside.

'I wish it'd stop,' he said. 'Stop and never come back.'

'So do I.' All the time I was thinking about the hospital, what a big target it was. At least Nan's house was small.

When the All Clear went, some time late in the night,

my muddled brain didn't know how much time had passed. Tom had finally fallen asleep, his arm across me, and I lay there listening to his breathing, his restless muttering. Poor kid.

There was light moving in the room and I heard Lil taking Patsy and Cathleen up to bed. It went dark again. After a time Nan's slow tread came up the steps and through from the scullery. She went to the range and struck a match to light a candle. Her shadow moved nearer the table and I shut my eyes, sensing her bending to look under at us, taking it that we were both asleep. After a moment I heard a spoon chink against a cup and knew she was taking Turley's Saline to settle her stomach. I waited for her to move the candle and find her own way to bed, but instead of that she went and opened the door. Picking up a chair she carried it outside, came back in to put her coat on and blow out the candle, then disappeared again, quietly latching the door.

When she didn't come back in I moved Tom's arm off me and crawled out from under the table. My insides churned and I stopped, wondering if I was going to retch, but it passed. I felt my way to the window and moved the blackout curtain. There was a tiny piece of moon in the sky and I could see stars. And right the other side of the glass criss-crossed with tape I could see the back of Nan's head. She was sitting out there, quite still.

It took me quite some minutes to pluck up the courage to go out to her. But I couldn't go on living with her the way I was. Not with the shame I felt. She didn't turn her head when she heard the door open, was looking up at the moon, her hands folded in her lap, and I stood there by her shoulder.

'Can't you sleep, Genie?' She spoke very quietly.

'No. Tom's gone off, though.'

She nodded slowly.

'Nan—' My heart was like a throbbing pain. I needed her forgiveness, for her to say it was all right, although it wasn't, none of it.

She waited.

'Nan, I'm sorry. I'm so sorry – I know it was my fault.'

She seemed really startled and looked right round at me. 'Genie love? What've you got to be sorry for?'

I wished so much that I could cry. I tried to make the tears come, to ease it, but they wouldn't. 'I let you down. I was supposed to be looking after her. It was my job. I should've been able to save her.'

'But bab, you were the one that *did* save 'er.'

'But before – I should've known ... I should've woken up. But the day before she seemed better than she'd been—'

Nan gave a sigh then, the great breath of someone pressed by a heavy burden.

'There's no blame on you, Genie love. She's been a poor mother to you in many ways and you've been better to 'er than she ever deserved. It's a hard thing to 'ave to say about your own daughter but it's the truth. When I think back, 'ow things might've been different, what I could've done...' She shook her head and brought up one hand, clenched in a fist, to her lips, the elbow resting on her other arm.

I thought of Lil's saying, 'Kids – when they're young they break your arms, and when they're grown up they break your heart.'

I saw that all this time she'd been blaming herself as well. I don't know if Nan's heart was broken. She'd had enough in life to chip it all right, from her dead babies and my rotten grandad right the way through to this, and it all sank somewhere deep in her like a stone so the world never saw what she was feeling. I'd have done anything, anything to make her feel better.

After a week at Nan's I went back to work. There was nothing much I could do at home and I felt I owed Mr Broadbent, but I was nervous about facing them all, or disgracing myself if I was sick without expecting it. It didn't happen all that often, maybe once every day or two, but it was always very sudden. Just happened, not much warning. Put me right off eating.

'How's your mom?' they all asked, and I made up something about how she was poorly and getting better.

'You awright, Genie?' Agnes asked me. 'You're looking terrible. You're all skin and bone.'

The others agreed. 'You want to get some flesh on them bones, girl. Joe'll think we're overworking you when 'e comes back!'

Course, everyone was tired and jumpy, not just me. The sound of a car engine in the road'd make you start violently. Every noise felt like a bomb coming to get you, even in the daytime. I just tried to smile at them through it all, praying my innards would behave themselves, at least while I was here.

I went back to our road, dreading the house. I called in on Len, told him Mom was OK. At home there was a letter from Joe. I picked it up and stared at it. His writing seemed like something so foreign to who I was now. I couldn't open it, couldn't stand to read his words of love when I felt so hateful. I knew how terrible it was not hearing, that I owed it to him to write back straight away, but I couldn't. There was nothing in my head except the bombing and what had happened to Mom. I had nothing to give Joe in a letter. Nothing to give him full stop. And I'd been a silly little fool, living in a dream world to think I could be with someone like him. I may have had Nan's forgiveness, even if she thought none was needed, but I couldn't forgive myself.

I put the letter in a drawer up in my room, still unopened.

It came on when I got to the front door, a sudden rush so I only just made it back into the kitchen, retching over the bucket, nose and eyes running, until I was empty and wrung out. I sat on my heels on the floor after, too weak for a while to get up. If only I could cry instead of this. Stop feeling so numb. This was my punishment. I didn't deserve Joe and now I'd lose him. If he wanted to know how I was he'd have to ask his dad. He wouldn't get an answer from me. Not from someone who'd died inside.

On 13 November there was a daylight raid on the Austin Aero factory, but thank God, Lenny was safe. On the night of the 14th the Luftwaffe flattened Coventry, bombed and burned it to the ground. Nowhere else disappeared as thoroughly as Coventry. As Teresa said to me after one of the endless, terrifying nights when they'd been over us, 'What the hell will there be left when they've finished?'

The night they bombed Coventry was a rest for us, but they were soon back. I was at Nan's all the time. That day it was her and me went up the hospital. Mom just lay there, face white as the sheets, her one open eye blank and empty. She had no energy to give it any expression. But the blankness looked like an everlasting sadness that no one would be able to take away.

We always tried not to look at the women in the other beds round us, with their rasping lungs or odd swellings. Sometimes you just couldn't stop yourself looking round, your eyes pulled by a noise or a smell, but we'd try to fix everything on Mom. We never knew what to say to her though. Nan put her coat on to go up there like a suit of armour, always as smart as she could manage, hat on too.

That day, nestling in the bag she always carried, was a carefully wrapped little cup of egg custard, carried delicately as if it were the actual shell of the egg. She fed it to Mom with a teaspoon, Mom half sitting up, bending her head forward, bits of custard slipping back out of the right side of her mouth.

'This'll 'elp get your strength back, Dor,' Nan kept saying. 'We'll soon 'ave you out of 'ere and back 'ome where you belong.'

Mom's good eye looked at her. 'I want to go home,' she whispered, mouth twisting against her will.

'Soon, Mom.' I took her hand, my heart thumping. I was almost afraid of her. 'They say a bit longer – maybe next week.'

'When you're a bit more yourself,' Nan said, stowing the little cup from the custard back in her bag.

What was 'a bit more herself' going to mean now?

'I've brought you a drop of beef tea. Will you have some?'

Mom closed her eyes as if in revulsion. Nan's face twitched. She put the bottle back in her bag and sat turning her wedding ring round and round on her finger,

cuddling the bag on her knees as if she thought someone'd nick it if she put it down for a second.

I picked up Mom's brush and stroked it over the hair
round her face. She hated to be a mess. Her eye flickered
open and closed. She was falling asleep.

On the bus home, full of smoke and the smell of stale
old coats, Nan and I sat without talking. Nan's hands
were clasped tight round the handles of the bag. The
lights were very dim in the bus, and when tears started
rolling down my face I didn't think anyone would see.
Just a few tears I was going to allow myself, but
something caved in in me on that bus ride when I
thought of my mom so far away from us and so sunk in
despair she might as well have been dead. I even
wondered whether stopping her when I did had been
the right thing. I'd kept her alive into something worse.
I started sobbing and couldn't stop. I was too far gone
to control myself, just pushed my face into my hands,
trying not to make too much noise. All the fear and
guilt and worry of the past fortnight came over me and
I couldn't help myself. I was only sorry for embarrassing
Nan.

''Ere, bab.' She didn't tick me off like she might have
had things been different, just leaned over and gave me
her hanky and that made me cry even more. She took
one of my hands and hers kept clenching and unclenching on mine. When we were nearly back into town she
led me off the bus and crossed over to the bottom of
our road where she stopped me, took the hanky and
mopped my face.

With no warning I was heaving, sick in the street. I
rushed to the gutter, so glad it was dark, and stood there
gulping in misery when it was over.

Nan led me by the arm. 'There now. You shouldn't

be in a state like this, that you shouldn't. Let's get you 'ome—'

Next thing, the air raid warning was cutting her sentence in half and everything was forgotten in the fear that noise brought up in you. I took Nan's bag off her to carry – it was hard for her to hurry with her bad legs – and as fast as we could we raced up the hill, terrified of being caught out in the road. The last tears dried on my face.

'Thank God,' Lil said as we came in. The room smelt of stew. Tom was curled up under the table and Lil, in a tizzy, was trying to persuade Patsy to take Cathleen down the coal hole, and dishing up plates of food.

Coat off, Nan started sorting out saucers and stubs of candles for the cellar.

'Fetch me a couple from out the front, will you Genie? We shan't get far with these bits.'

The sirens had stopped by now and although we were all doing things we were straining our ears to hear the planes coming, those minutes between the two usually one mad rush of getting ready.

I ducked under the counter into the shop, holding up one lighted candle stub, fumbling for new ones on the crowded shelves. It didn't take me long to realize there was an argument going on outside. Morgan's voice and no mistake, right outside the shop door, and a girl, pleading with him, it sounded like.

Pulling back the bolts I opened up to the moonlit night.

'Ah,' Morgan said, seeing me. 'Course, you've closed early tonight. I couldn't get in.' We weren't supposed to bolt him out but Lil had shut the shop right up without giving it a thought.

'Course we're closed – there's a flaming raid on in case you hadn't noticed.'

As I appeared, the girl made to take to her heels but Morgan grabbed her by the arm, and although she couldn't get away she wrenched round away from us, hiding her face. Seemed a bit timid this one, not like some of the brazen hussies he brought along.

'Don't be silly now,' Morgan said to her. 'You can't go rushing 'ome – as Miss, er ... Miss Genie 'ere says, they'll be over any moment.'

The planes moved into the range of our hearing as he spoke.

'Get in then.' I stood back to let them past, making sure he didn't so much as brush against me. He kept hold of the girl, who from what I could see was plump and quite young, and she kept her face pushed down in her coat collar.

'What the hell're you doing here tonight?'

'Thought there wouldn't be a raid.' Morgan let go of the girl now I'd shut the door and rubbed his hands together.

'Course there wouldn't be a raid. Why should there be a raid? I mean they only smashed the living daylights out of Coventry yesterday.' Must admit, I was rather enjoying myself. 'I don't know how we're going to fit you in. You can't go up there, can you? Mrs Rawson's really going to love you turning up.'

As I turned to lock the door, the girl gave out a noise like a whimper and moved over to me, speaking with her head still right down. I thought she seemed a bit odd. 'Let me go,' she whispered. I could hardly hear her. 'I'll just go 'ome.'

'You mad? Hark at them out there! It's the daft

381

bugger you came with wants his head looking at. See –
he don't care about you. He's in there saving his own
skin already. You come on in. I dunno what you've
heard about my nan but I s'pect even she'll call a truce
in this.'

'I can't.' This time it was almost a sob. I picked up
the stub of candle on the saucer and held it by her face.

She cringed away from me. 'Don't.'

'Shirl?'

Turning away, she put her hands over her face. 'I'd
no idea in the world 'e was going to bring me 'ere,
Genie, honest I didn't. He just said it was somewhere in
Highgate. I couldn't believe my eyes when it was your
nan's . . .'

The first bombs were falling and I rushed her through
the back and under the table with Tom. Shirl sat crying
and I put my arm round her. Nan must've told Morgan
he could shelter under the stairs if he was prepared to
clear himself a space, because we could hear him banging
about, moving out Nan's enamel wash pot, the bucket
of sand and stirrup pump, some old crocks and something that fell over with a crash which might've been a
clothes-horse.

From feeling so down before, my emotions swung
right the other way and I suddenly got the giggles,
hearing Morgan's muffled cursing from under our stairs.

'Hark at him,' I spluttered to Shirl, who actually
managed to look me in the face for the first time and
mopped her eyes, seeing I wasn't about to have a go at
her. Some other hard object came flying out with a
clatter, we heard Morgan say, 'Bugger it,' and I was in
stitches as the planes came over, Tom clinging to my
legs, still holding on to Shirl, the old wood smell coming
from the worm-eaten table.

There was a bang from upstairs, no explosion, just a real big thump from the roof and the planes passed over, followed by more.

'Mrs Rawson—'

I half crawled out from under the table and saw Morgan's scrawny figure standing over the entrance to the coal hole, his shadow enormous on the wall behind him.

'I think you've 'ad one of them incendiaries come through your attic . . .'

'What do you mean *my* attic?' Nan's voice came back loud and clear. 'This is your 'ouse, Morgan, not mine – you'd better get up there with that bucket of sand mighty bloody quick.'

So there was Morgan forced into being the big man, creeping off up with the bucket. We didn't know where it'd come down but he went to look up on his side. I imagined his gloomy attic with the white light of an incendiary up there sputtering like a firework.

'Just hope he knows what he's doing,' I said to Shirl. I kept trying to be light and cheerful because I was embarrassed for her, but I didn't want her to think I was going to hold anything against her, even though it wasn't exactly normal behaviour to turn up at my nan's as one of Morgan's trollops. But now wasn't the moment for explanations. We were all too busy listening to the movement of the planes. Keep going, you found yourself thinking. Just keep on going. Go somewhere else . . .

Next thing was, Morgan came crashing down the attic stairs, first the bucket, him following, effing and blinding his way down making a hell of a racket until he landed with a groan in the shop.

Shirl looked at me. 'D'you think we'd better look?'

383

'Not cowing likely. Not with this lot.' Bombs were falling, proper explosives. 'He'll be all right.'

He came through a minute later, groaning and cradling his right arm with his left. I peered out from under the oilcloth.

'I think I've bust my arm,' he moaned.

'For God's sake get under the stairs!' I yelled to him and retreated back in to save my own head. Shirl had her arm round Tom.

'D'you put it out?' Nan's voice boomed up from the coal hole. 'Or couldn't you even manage that?'

'Heartless bitch,' Morgan mumbled, backing into the stair cupboard. 'Oh Christ, my arm!'

The house shook, the windows rattled and a lump of something fell from the ceiling.

I saw the gaslight flicker. 'Blimey, this is a bad one.'

Even with all the noise, we could hear Morgan groaning and carrying on. 'Serves him right,' I said. 'Oversexed little bugger.'

Shirl turned away, embarrassed again. I thought how different she looked tonight – hair all fluffed up, heavy eye make up and lipstick.

It didn't suit her. She had a sweet face normally.

'What the hell're you playing at, going with him of all people?' I suddenly found myself shouting at her.

Shirl shrugged sulkily, still holding on to Tom who trusted her instinctively, despite the tart disguise she was wearing. 'He was nice to me.'

'*Nice* to you!'

When there was a lull, she said, 'There's only me and Dad at home, see, and he's never had any time for me, even before Mom died. My life with him's like a servant's – nothing else. He isn't even there at nights most of the time because he works a night shift now. But even when 'e is ... 'E hardly treats me as if I'm human, Genie. Never a word except "Get this – fetch me that. Sit down and fucking shut up." He kicks me out of the way as if I'm a dog. On my life, Genie. I wouldn't lie to you. I've been so lonely, specially since you went. It was so nice with you at the factory, and I used to love coming 'ere.'

I swallowed. All along I'd thought she was doing me a favour.

'I met Eric down the pub—'

That knocked me back a bit. All this time I'd never known Morgan had the same name as my brother.

'I know he's not God's gift, 'ow 'e looks and that. But 'e'll spend time with you. Say nice things—'

'To get what he wants.'

'He comments on how I'm looking and that. No one's ever done that before. Dad never even looks at me. I'm sort of invisible so far as 'e's concerned. Anyhow, after a bit Morgan started asking me to dress up for him a certain way – like this – because you know I don't as a rule. Next thing was coming out 'ere. I knew what 'e was after and I'd have given it 'im. I was that lonely and that grateful.' She looked at me with her huge eyes. I remembered they were china blue in proper light.

'I've never done it before, I swear to you. I s'pose you haven't the faintest what I'm on about, 'ave you Genie? What with all your family round you.'

'I had no idea things were so bad for you. I do know what you're on about, sort of. But Shirl, *Morgan*. I mean, he's vile.'

'Beggars can't be choosers.'

'But why should you be a beggar? You're so pretty and kind – I bet loads of blokes'd give their right arm to go out with you—'

Another moan came from the stairs cupboard. Shirl rolled her eyes. 'Sounds as if someone already 'as.'

That really set us off then, even Tom too, watching us, and Shirl and I were helpless with laughter and for a time the stupidest little thing set us off.

'Oh, I'm glad you're here,' I said to her, wiping my eyes.

It was a long, long raid that night, nearly ten hours of it until we heard the All Clear. There were some lulls when we crawled out and had a drink. Nan managed to fix up a makeshift sling for Morgan using an old strip of sheet, with a look on her face when she had to touch him like someone clearing a dead frog out of a drain. Morgan had to put up with whatever treatment he got and sat quietly sipping Bournvita. Seeing her with him then it dawned on me why she'd put up with him all these years. Amid all the hurts and setbacks of her hard life, which had, I think, cast her lower than any of us had guessed, Morgan was the one person she could always guarantee feeling superior to.

'Much damage up there?' Nan asked him.

Nose pointing into his cup, he nodded, swallowing.

'Your side?'

'Yep. Great 'ole in the roof. Room's in a hell of a state.'

'Shame,' Nan said. 'Well, that'll cramp your style for a bit, won't it?' And sparks of triumph glinted in her eyes.

*

We were all exhausted next morning as much from tension as lack of sleep. Morgan drifted off saying he was going to get himself seen to, which Nan shouted after him was not before time. We sat round trying to rouse ourselves with weak cups of tea, because sleep or no sleep, there was work waiting.

Of course Nan would normally have blown a gasket at the first sight of Shirl in Morgan's thrall, but what with all the goings on in the night she'd had time to calm down. We'd spent most of the hours talking, Shirl and me, and it'd been a huge relief for me so that once again I felt it was her doing me a favour. I told her about Mom, about how I felt. Swapped my shame for hers. I didn't talk about Joe though, couldn't even speak his name.

Between us we'd come up with a kind of plan.

'Nan – Shirl's not happy at home with her dad hardly being there nights and that and I've said she can come and live with us, back home, when Mom comes out of hospital. I could do with the extra help.'

Nan considered this, looking sternly at Shirl. 'You know what I think of the company you're keeping. You'd better mend your ways. For your own sake as much as anything.'

Shirl blushed a heavy pink and looked down at the floor. 'It was the first time, Mrs Rawson. And the last. You can be sure of that.'

Nan kept the kids home from school and they were already back in their beds sleeping the morning away. We heard Tom crying out in his sleep.

Lil tutted, leaning towards the mirror to put her

lipstick on. 'I ought to get him away from here. It's making him really ill.'

The three of us, Lil, Shirl and I, set out for our different factories in the morning's custard-coloured light. It was raining, but even in a downpour you'd have that new-born feel of it being a miracle after the long, threatening night. Even in all my sadness and worry I felt my spirits lift. This was now, today, and I was alive.

But there was so much devastation outside. Houses down along the road and all the morning shock and horror of it, the way everything looked squalid, and stank even worse. The wardens were on the street with the rescue squads, helping and reassuring. Someone said they'd hit the BSA over at Small Heath and a lot had been killed.

'I hope Frank's all right,' Lil said.

Vera and Teresa were out too, Vera helping a woman along the road with cuts on her face, taking her to their house. Teresa came over to me, hair scraped up in a hurried ponytail.

'How's your mom?'

'Same really. They're talking about her coming out next week.'

'How're you going to manage? You handing in your notice?'

'I might,' I said.

I hadn't decided until then, but even as she asked I knew that's what I was going to do. Mom needed me and I found seeing Mr Broadbent very awkward now. Sooner or later he was going to ask why I wasn't writing to Joe and I couldn't answer. If I was going to be unhappy it was no more than I deserved, but I didn't want to have to explain to him. Or to the other women who kept asking about Mom.

'You all right, Genie?' She touched my shoulder.

I turned away. 'Yeah. Better get on.'

'Genie?'

I looked round at her again, noticing properly the strain in her face. 'Nonna Amelia's very bad. They don't think she's got long. I thought you'd want to know.'

'Oh Teresa,' I said helplessly. Because that was the only way we seemed to be able to feel now about anything. Helpless.

The next heavy raid on Birmingham wrecked a lot of the water mains. Instead of us boiling water after the raids there was now none at all for a period and they were having to send water wagons round. Without a hot cuppa first thing in the morning after a raid you felt hopeless. Couldn't cope with the exhaustion, the jangled nerves and all the awful and weird goings on in the Blitz. The way everything was turned inside out, terraces ripped open like dolls' houses, showing everyone's private rooms. You heard stories about people caught on the toilet by a bomb, tales of relatives who'd died years ago appearing out of the dark, rumours of Fifth Columnists. All this was a bit much without Brooke Bond in the morning.

In the middle of all this chaos, Lil dropped her own bombshell. She was leaving her well-paid job at Parkinson Cowan, and Frank, who so far had survived the raids like a cat with nine lives, was going to 'set her up.'

'He's got me a little place in Hurst Street,' she told

us, aglow with excitement. 'The rent's a pound a week and he's going to pay it for me to start with. Till I get going.'

'Setting you up as what, in 'igh 'eaven?' Nan hadn't really got started on her yet but you could see it was coming. The world had truly gone mad.

'A phrenologist and clairvoyant.'

Nan opened and shut her mouth quite a few times before she could get going, like an old pair of bellows. 'You *what*?'

'He's been teaching me.'

'But he's a mechanic!'

Patiently, and with what seemed an astonishing steady sureness given the barminess of it, Lil explained. All this feeling of our heads that had gone on lately was practice for the real thing. Add to that knowledge of tarot cards and palm lines, throw in a crystal ball, and Lil was in business.

But this was only part one of the grand explosion. Parts two and three were to follow swiftly on. Two: there was another wave of evacuation from Birmingham and she'd decided to send Patsy and Tom.

'Look at the state of Tom,' she said. 'He can't sleep without screaming, can hardly talk to you without twitching. He's as thin as a rake and it can't be doing him any good at school. Patsy can go and keep him company. And I'm not just sending him anywhere. Frank's got an auntie lives over in Stoke and she says she'll have 'em while things are bad.'

Before Nan had had a chance to field that one, we were on to part three. 'And I'm moving in with Frank over the garage. Me and Cathleen. It's not far, and Kings Heath's not getting bombed anything like as much as over 'ere. Don't worry, Mom. I'm not going to be leaving you on your own all the time. Frank'll be out so much with the ARP anyway we'll probably be here as much as we ever are now!'

I went back to our house to pick up letters. I never opened the ones from Joe. I gave Mr Broadbent my notice, speaking to him formally, not meeting his eyes. He was my employer, nothing more.

'But why, Genie?' He ran his hand through the white-streaked hair, absent-mindedly smoothing it down.

'It's Mom. I've got to look after her. There's no one else.'

'I'm sorry, love – serious as that, is it?'

I nodded, looking down at the floorboards.

'That'd explain it. Joe said in his last letter he hadn't heard from you. If you'd said, we could've arranged more leave for you.'

'It's all right, thanks. I'll need to be at home for good now.'

Mr Broadbent came round from behind his desk towards me and I felt myself cringing. I set my face, chin out. Don't be nice to me, I shrieked inside. Don't give me sympathy or try to soften my feelings, because if I let myself go under any of this I shan't be able to bear it.

'Genie? You don't look at all well yourself, love. You've got so thin.'

It was true. There were pits under my eyes you could crawl into. 'Everyone's tired, aren't they?' I still couldn't look at him. 'You can't be anything else with the nights the way they are.'

I think he was probably a bit hurt, certainly puzzled, by the way I was behaving. But he was too nice a man,

Mr B, to try and force his way past my wooden determination.

'You're sure this is the right decision? Everyone'll miss you.'

'I'm quite sure.'

They had to carry Mom into the house that Friday when they brought her back. Two plump women were in charge of the ambulance and they laced their frozen hands together, gripping each other's wrists, and made a kind of chair to lift her between them. I had a fire going inside and offered them tea but they said no, they had to go. Seemed to be relieved to be out of there. I didn't blame them.

Lil, who'd already given up work too, was with me, though Shirl hadn't moved in yet. I couldn't have stood it on my own. Lil was in enough of a state about the boys going off the next Monday, and seeing Mom there with her arm hanging all floppy by her side, and that dead half of her face, she started crying all over again.

'Oh Dor – Dor.' She knelt down and put her arms round Mom's waist, resting her face in her lap, shoulders shaking.

Mom looked down at Lil's sleek head, and after a moment she brought up her good hand and started stroking Lil's hair.

She looked across at me as I stood watching, torn up inside, wishing I could cry as easily as Lil.

Mom's lips were moving. 'I'm sorry,' she whispered, then managed it louder, her own tears falling now. 'I'm so useless to everyone. I'm sorry . . . sorry . . .'

*

Shirl moved in over the weekend. Just packed her bags and never told the old man where she was going.

'Teach 'im a lesson,' she said. ''E'll be round to fetch me back else. 'E can learn to fend for 'isself for a bit.'

I was so glad she'd come I hugged her. Even though I'd given up my job and could manage the house I was scared to be alone with Mom. Even Nan visiting when she could and Len popping in to escape from Gladys carrying on at him were not enough. Mom was like someone who'd been trapped in a dark well full of icy water and the coldness of it still billowed out from her. I was scared of catching her chill.

Shirl was one of those people who's happiest looking after others. Even with her doom-laden voice she could give off cheer like catkins shedding pollen. She was still working of course, but come the evening she'd be rattling the front door to be let in and I'd feel relief rush through me.

''Ere y'are.' Most days she'd thrust something into my hands, flowers or cheap meat. 'Been over the Bull Ring. Thought these'd 'elp.' It was her way of showing gratitude even though there was no need. My thankfulness was a giant compared with hers. I'd just about stopped being sick now Mom was home.

Shirl and I'd cook together, chat. She'd tell me about her day. She brought news to us, what buildings were down across town. And she stopped me brooding as much as I'd have done left to myself. I never mentioned Joe to her. I thought I could cope, just about, with these other things. With Mom. But I couldn't talk about Joe. Couldn't allow myself to think about him. I thought of Mister as my dog now, shut the memory of Joe's hands stroking him out of my mind. His letters were in a drawer, unopened. Soon he must stop writing and then that would be that. I could forget those kind of hopes, thinking I could have love like that. I didn't know the state I was in, couldn't see it for myself.

I had a job to do here, that's what I thought. And it was going to take everything I'd got. The doctor said that in time, Mom could recover. Perhaps not completely, maybe not the arm which was too dead. But she could learn to walk and probably to talk properly again. Only time would tell. She could get about on one leg holding the furniture with her good arm, steadying herself with the other foot. It wouldn't take the full weight, but she had some feeling in it. She had to arrange the position of her right arm with the left one, bending it to rest in her lap when she sat down. And she sat for hours, not even trying to talk, listening to Gloria.

If it was the last thing I did, I was going to make sure she got better. Looking after her was my job, and up to now what a miserable mess I'd made of it. But this time I was going to give it everything. I had to save her.

Saying goodbye to the boys, Tom especially, was terrible. I couldn't bear the thought of losing him as we seemed to have lost Eric.

'Soon as it stops we'll come and get you,' I told him, hugging him tight. Tom nuzzled his face against me, seeming younger than eight.

'Promise, Genie?' He looked up at me, those melting brown eyes full of tears. He was trying so hard not to let them fall.

'I promise.' I was struggling too, holding back my own tears. I may have longed for the release of it on lots of occasions but this was no time to start blarting. 'It'll be an adventure. You know, when I went out of Birmingham—' I came out with that without thinking and stopped short. My day out with Joe in Kenilworth. How long ago that seemed! It had happened to someone else. I couldn't think about that now. 'It was beautiful. You'll see. And you'll be able to write and tell me all about it and I'll write back.'

Lil and I went to put them on the train and waved them off, their little faces at the window, Tom's glum, Patsy full of bravado.

'So like his dad, our Patsy,' Lil said.

I comforted Lil. Nanny Rawson was livid with her and had been since she'd announced her intention, as Nan put it, 'to pack your kids off so you can play about with That Chancer of yours.'

'But Mom,' Lil had said to her, 'things are so different now. If you find a bit of happiness why not hold on to it and bugger the rules?'

'That's all very well,' Nan retorted. 'But whose rules are you living by now, eh?'

'It's not like that, Genie,' Lil sniffed as we walked through town on the way back. 'I'd have sent Tom anyhow, the way he was. And Frank says he wouldn't have minded them living with us. He likes kids. Wants some of his own.' Lil blushed, looking away.

'Nan knows really that they're better off out of it,' I told her. 'It's you living in sin she can't stand. You'll never see eye to eye on that in a million years. She's waiting for lightning to strike you.'

Lil looked sober. 'Like Doreen.'

When I got home I found Mom had got up and moved. In the still, silent way she had about her now, she was standing with her back to me, leaning on the doorframe which led out of the back room, staring across the kitchen.

'Mom?' I hurried to her.

Her eyes were fixed on the cooker and I felt terror rise in me. She was thinking about it. She's going to do it again! Jesus Christ, no.

'I can't remember.' She brought out the words, turning to look at me. Her face was so thin now, her open eye looked enormous. It was terrible seeing her face in that state. The worst part. 'Don't remember doing it.'

'Mom, come and sit down.' I helped her to the chair, her leaning on my shoulder, hopping and shuffling. 'I'll make a cup of tea.' She seemed glad to sit down and as I filled the kettle I told her the boys had gone.

'Poor Lil,' she said.

When I brought her the tea she whispered, 'This is no life, Genie.' I thought she meant her own reduced, miscarried, crawling-about existence, and I opened my mouth to tell her again how much better she was going to get, when she added, 'Not for you.'

I knelt down and took her hand. 'I don't mind, Mom. I just want to help you get better. You're my mom, and that's all that matters, honest it is.'

She shook her head, wouldn't believe it. 'How's your Joe?'

I managed to bring a smile to my face. 'He's all right, Mom. Things are fine. Really they are.'

December 1940

Shirl and I stood outside Lil's shop in Hurst Street. It was a narrow, scruffy frontage, squeezed between other shops, with filthy maroon paint flaking off the woodwork and its old sign, saying 'Stubb's Pawnbrokers', roughly whitewashed over. The golden balls had gone from outside though. Lil had evidently given the windows a going over but it still looked seedy and depressing.

'Bit of a dump, innit?' Shirl pulled the ends of her mouth down comically. 'I thought this was supposed to be 'er big break?'

'Well, give her a chance. She's only been here a week.' I was trying to be brave on Lil's behalf. She deserved some sort of new start, even if it did feel she was leaving the rest of us in the lurch.

On the pavement in front of the shop an old piece of blackboard had been leant up under the window. Chalked on it in swirly writing were the words: 'Liliana – Professional Phrenologist – 2/6d, 5/-, 7/6d.'

'Flipping 'eck, not cheap, is it?' Shirl exclaimed.

Underneath in smaller letters it read, 'Tarot, Fortunes, Palm Readings.'

''Allo girls, come on in!' Frank stood in the doorway in his shirtsleeves, although it was freezing, looking miraculously handsome. 'Lil!' he shouted into the shop. 'Your Genie's 'ere!'

'Cor, look at 'im!' Shirl hissed at me. ''E's a bit good to be true, ain't 'e? Can see why she'd risk 'er everything for that.'

I nudged Shirl hard with my elbow to shut her up and Frank stood back to let us in. It was dark inside and made even more gloomy by the winter day outside.

Lil, though, was looking anything but gloomy.

'Blimey, Lil. What do you look like?' I stood back staring at her, laughing. My auntie had been transformed into a gypsy. She had on a very full skirt in blues, reds, orange and green and a blouse which was just as bright with pink, orange and black flowers. She had her hair pinned up and a red silk rose, which matched her red lips, fastened over her left ear, and there were big gold earrings clipped to her earlobes. She pulled the skirt out at each side, curtsied, then twirled round on the wooden floor so it billowed out like a parachute.

'What d'you think of 'er?' Frank said, sounding like someone who'd just bought a new motorcycle. 'Looks right for the part, don't she?'

She did look gorgeous of course, but so strange and different I wasn't sure what to make of it. Was this Frank's influence, changing her, making her into some-one else? And was what they were doing all a con anyway?

'This is it,' Lil said, turning round to look at the room. 'What d'you think?'

Course the place was very like Mr Palmer's shop in a way, only a bit bigger. The room was painted the colour of milky tea and there were long, filthy marks along the walls where shelves must've been taken down, and damp stains on the ceiling, which was flaking. There was still a counter at the back with oddments of clothes and crocks left by the previous owner, and Lil and Frank had put a table and two chairs in the middle of the room. On the table was a tiny vase with another silk flower stuck in it, and a crystal ball.

'Ooh,' Shirl said. 'Can I 'ave a look in?'

'You can look, but you won't see much,' Lil said.

Shirl bent over the table squinting into it. 'Well what d'you see then?'

'Oh, you'd be surprised.' Lil laughed mischievously. 'I had this woman in yesterday, said she could see mountains in the crystal ball. Convinced, she was. Said she'd always had this dream of going to Switzerland. "I'm going to go!" she said. "After the war's over." So there's one very happy lady thinking she's going to see the Alps. D'you know what it was?' She pointed over the counter. 'See them egg-holders?' Upside down on the counter was a white china holder for a half dozen eggs. 'It was them she could see reflected in the glass!'

We all laughed, Frank loudest of all. I mean it was funny after all, but I couldn't help wondering about it. 'Well, is any of it true then, what you tell 'em?'

'Course,' Frank said, through a fag he was lighting. The cigarette hissed and crackled between his lips and he pulled it out and glared at it. 'Christ! What are these things they're passing off for fags nowadays? It's a proper profession. And it'll be a good little earner. She's got quite a talent for it your auntie 'as.' He winked at Lil. Shirl was poking around in the leftovers from the pawn shop.

'Has Nan been to see you?' I talked to Lil. Wasn't any too sure about Frank these days. He was taking over a bit much for my liking.

'Nah, not on your life.'

'Well she wants to see you.'

Frank tutted. 'Never lets up, does she?'

I turned on him. 'She's Lil's mom. And she was looking after her long before you came on the scene.'

'Oi, Genie, no need for that,' Lil said. I saw Shirl look round at me. 'Frank didn't mean anything, did you?'

Frank gave me his most charming grin. 'Course not, no offence, Genie. She's a great old stager your nan.'

I stared hard at him. Cracks were showing here. No one, as Nan kept pointing out, should have a smile so bewitching or shoes you could see to powder your nose in.

Some woman came in then with an anxious face wanting her palm read, and Shirl and I took off to do our shopping.

'Go and see Nan,' I said to Lil before I went.

She touched my arm. 'Don't fret. It's all right, Genie – things are OK. I'll go tonight.'

'I just hope she knows what she's doing,' I said to Shirl. 'Our Lil thinks she's the world expert on men, but I can't say I'm any too sure about that one she's got there!'

The other person in our family who was happy as Larry was Len. Molly was coming up to seven months pregnant and was like the side of a house. Her big belly fascinated Len. Actually it fascinated Shirl too and she was forever leaning over Molly, asking questions about how it felt, was it kicking and all that. Len was a funny mixture of behaviour with Molly. He could ignore her for ages at a time while he fiddled about with Gloria, chuckled away at wireless programmes and forgot even to answer her as if she plain didn't exist. Other times he was all over her, feeling the babby moving whoever else was about, and stroking and kissing her as if she was a dolly or a pet dog until sometimes she got a bit sharp with him.

'Aw leave off, Lenny, will yer?'

Mister loved Molly and had been in the habit of curling up on her enormous cushions of thighs when she was around.

'Ooh!' Molly cried, shaking with laughter one evening when Mister leapt up in a great hurry and shot off her lap. 'The babby's kicked 'im off of me! 'E's going to be a footballer 'e is!'

The two of them often came over and sat with us, eating anything in sight, Gloria on, completely comfortable with everything in a way I never saw in anyone else. No restlessness, no question about Mom or worry about the way she was. No discontent. Nothing. That was Len and Molly – happy in chairs, for ever.

They were there when the siren went early on that month and Mister leapt up – this time off me – and howled, head back, the black and white fur across his throat stretched tight.

'Oh Lor,' Molly grunted, struggling to get out of her chair and not managing. 'Pull me up, Lenny. I'll 'ave to get over to Mom's.'

As she went, Lenny taking her along, Shirl and I started organizing. Tea in a flask. No booze. Light, coats, rugs.

'Len,' I called, hearing him come back in. 'Come and help with Mom.' But he lumbered in, picked up Gloria before anything else and stowed her under the stairs.

'My God,' I said to Shirl. 'What happened to women and children first?'

'No—' Mom was struggling to speak. 'I'm not going. Not out there.'

401

'Please, Mom, come on. We've got to.'

'NO.' She pulled her bad arm in close with the other one and leaned forward, curling in on herself.

What with the siren going and Mister howling and my nerves already in shreds before all that, I felt as if I was going to explode.

'What the hell am I s'posed to do?' I raged at Shirl. 'I can't force her, can I? What does it matter if we go out there anyway? We could all get killed whatever we do.'

Shirl took over, squeezed my arm. 'You're awright, Genie,' she said, sounding like Mr Tailor. She bent over Mom. 'Mrs Watkins, we're going to take you to the shelter. You can't stay 'ere.'

Mom hadn't the strength to resist us for long but I could feel the distress coming from her and I felt terrible. But I couldn't help thinking about Mrs Deakin and we struggled down the garden and got her inside. I put the Tilley lamp down on the floor and we laid Mom on one of the bunks, covering her up well. She turned her face away towards the corrugated wall.

Len brought Mister and closed us in. As the door shut I thought about tombs. Mister whimpered and came over to me.

'I'm so glad you're here,' I said to Shirl for the umpteenth time.

Her big eyes shone in the lamplight. 'Not 'alf as glad as I am, I can tell you.'

'What does your dad do – in the raids I mean?'

'Oh, 'e'll be all right. The factory's over Duddesdon – they've got a shelter there.'

'What, so you was on your own of a night?'

'Went round the neighbours – they've got a cellar. But I'd much rather be 'ere with you, Genie.' She turned her head. 'We're OK, aren't we Len?' she said, squeezing his arm. She nodded across at Mom and mouthed at me. 'She awright?'

I reached round, took Mom's good hand and held it. 'You asleep, Mom?'

She made a little noise so I knew she wasn't.

'You warm enough?'

'I'm OK.' It was a hoarse whisper.

When I turned back to Shirl I could see the pity in her eyes and I didn't know if it was for Mom or me. But seeing someone else looking in on my life made me feel so terrible about everything, the way it'd been broken and changed. First Big Patsy, Dad and Eric – even Lola, I felt sad about her – Mom and Bob and the dead babby, and Joe. But no, not Joe. I wasn't even going to let myself think about him . . .

Shirl made jokes to try and keep us going and I tried to laugh, thankful to her because it wasn't as if she had a lot to laugh about either. We talked in short bursts, going quiet when the planes came over, shrinking our heads down into our necks and cringing until they passed. A couple of times as it was going quiet Len put his arm round Shirl, and she said, 'Oh, you're a devil, you are.'

And I held Mom's hand and felt her silence like a leaden weight behind me.

I found Nan alone in her house the next day, down on her hands and her one good knee, the other bent up in front, blackleading the range.

'Here, let me do that.' I took the cloth and polish off her and tried to rub off some of my outrage at Lil on to its black surface.

'She said she was going to come back. Sod her! I

mean it's not as if Frank would even have been in with a raid on!'

'It would've been too late for 'er to come with the raid already started.' Nan had managed to pull herself stiffly to her feet. 'And anyroad, I'm awright. Take more than a load of Jerries to frighten me, I can tell you.'

She looked tired though. 'It's just not right you being on your own. Lil should know better.' I found I was shaking with anger, wanting to scream with it. There was never anything you could do about anything. I wanted to come and keep my nan company of a night, but how could I with Mom the way she was? And going into her house felt awful – no Lil, no kids running round.

Nan waved a hand at me to shut me up. 'How's your mother?'

'Same.' I was scrubbing like mad at the range.

'You're all skin and bone. You still being sick?'

'No.'

She absorbed this, then said. 'Morgan was bombed out last night – 'is place over in Aston.'

I stopped and looked round. 'D'he get out?'

'Oh, that sort always do. Rat out of a sewer. 'E was in the cellar, not a scratch on 'im. 'E was over earlier to see what state the room up 'ere's in again.'

'He's never thinking of moving in here?'

'Not unless he wants rain on his face every night. D'you know what 'e 'ad the nerve to ask me?' She didn't sound all that outraged, just exhausted. ' "You being on your own now, Mrs Rawson, I was wondering if you could spare me one of your rooms for a bit?" Rubbing 'is hands together how 'e does.'

'Nan, you never . . .?'

A wicked twinkle came into her eyes. 'I told him I only ever live with men if I'm married to 'em, ta very much. That drained the colour out of 'im I can tell you.' She let out a big laugh and it was good to hear her. ''E says 'e's lost his business and 'e can't do any repairs till 'e gets the insurance and there's no telling 'ow long that'll take. So that'll keep 'im out of action for a bit!'

'Nan!' I laughed with her.

Wiping her eyes, she said, ''E's 'aving to find somewhere else to move in with his Mom!'

'God, you can't imagine him being anyone's son, can you?' Remembering, I pulled a letter from my pocket. 'This came today. I haven't shown it her.'

Eric's letter contained the usual wooden scraps of news that we'd had to get used to, but in the middle he wrote, 'Mummy says I can stay here for good if I want to.' Mrs Spenser had let him leave it in. She'd obviously wanted us to see it.

'Mummy?' Nan flared. She stared in disbelief. It wasn't just Eric thinking of Mrs S as his mom, it was him sounding like a toffy-nosed twit into the bargain.

'She can't do that, can she? She can't just keep him?' I was tearful all of a sudden. 'Soon there'll be nothing left.'

Nan gave my shoulder a pat. 'She can't just keep 'im, not unless—' She broke off and I knew she was thinking of Mom, of what sort of life Eric was going to come back to here. He wouldn't be getting piano lessons, that was for certain. I could see the grief in Nan's face, just for a quick flash. 'No. She can't just do as she likes.'

Teresa and her mom were spending as much time as they could over in the Quarter because it was obvious

Nonna Amelia was dying. But Teresa found time to call in and visit us and ask if I wanted to go and see the old lady for what would surely be the last time.

Teresa hadn't seen Mom since she'd come home. Mom hated anyone in the house, couldn't stand to be seen in her state. And Teresa couldn't keep the shock out of her face.

'It's terrible, Genie,' she said as we set off towards town. 'Is she going to get any better?'

I told her the little bit of hope we had. Even talking to Teresa I felt at a distance from her, and fiercely protective of Mom. I was almost sorry I'd let Teresa see her. Mom wouldn't go out at all, didn't want the neighbours' tongues wagging any more than they had already. Teresa was an outsider in this. It was Shirl who'd come in and got involved and I felt closer to her nowadays, and somehow that was another sad thing. I could tell Teresa didn't know what to say to me and I couldn't speak to her. If I asked about Carlo she'd be bound to bring up the subject of Joe, so I said nothing and walked along with my old friend feeling distant and tense.

Vera was already at Nonna Amelia's house with her sister and the youngest of the children. They greeted me warmly, but whether in Italian or English, everyone was speaking in hushed voices, as if Death was already in a conversation with the old lady that they were afraid to interrupt.

'You want to see her?' Vera led me upstairs, treading very quietly on the staircase. Teresa stayed down. Vera showed me into the room and then, to my surprise, left me and went down again. Soon I knew why. Communing with the dying's best done on your own.

There was no light in the room. It was a grey, overcast

406

day, and the curtains had been half drawn, leaving a gap of only about eighteen inches between them. Nonna Amelia was lying in her enormous bed with its high wooden bedstead in such deep brown wood it looked black. The only part of her to be seen was her face because the rest of her was well covered up with sheets and blankets, an eiderdown and a brocade coverlet. They seemed to have piled everything possible on top of her to try and keep the warmth in her tiny, shrunken body.

I could barely even see her face in the dim light and I moved closer to the bed. Her white hair was swept back behind her head which was resting on a white pillow slip embroidered with green leaves at one edge. I licked my dry lips and went to stand right by her. I didn't feel frightened or sad, just awed. Like a tiny, new-born babby, she was already half somewhere else that the rest of us have forgotten, with this life we know still just clinging to her. Now those wise, dancing eyes were closed there was only a shrunken, bony face, the skin yellow, the Nonna Amelia we knew blown out like a match. But she was still there. I could hear her breathing.

'Nonna Amelia?' I whispered, putting my face close to hers. 'It's Genie – Watkins. Teresa's friend. I don't know if you can hear me. I just wanted to say—' What the hell did I want to say? What do you say to someone when you know it's the last thing you'll ever say to them? And if she could hear me she most likely wouldn't understand a word.

I pulled up a chair and sat leaning forward towards her. For quite a time I didn't say anything and that was OK. But then in a funny sort of way I felt as if she was listening to me, not like her, the old her, but just a sort of presence there to listen, like a priest or a statue.

407

'I wanted to say—' I hesitated, then looked away from her face and kept talking. 'I've always looked up to you, Nonna Amelia, because you're the sort of person who everyone loves. D'you know that? You might not have noticed, like Teresa hadn't until the war came – I expect you have though, because so many things have happened to you, haven't they, to make you wise?' I talked in fits and starts, not sure half the time whether I'd said something or just thought it. 'All I can say is I envy you your life because you've made a lovely family who all respect and love you. That's all I've ever wanted really, to have a family who are happy and who love me. But I can't seem to make it happen however hard I try. I thought, just for a little time – the best time of my life—' As I said this my throat started aching and I had to stop and swallow hard. 'I thought I might be able to have it with Joe. I tasted what it might be like ... But now I know that was only a dream ... I've wrecked everything and I know things don't happen for me like that, and it's all falling apart round me and I can't keep it together ...'

Words kept coming out of my mouth, about Mom and Joe and how bad I was feeling. Words I couldn't have said to anyone else. I felt she was listening, but maybe that was because I wanted someone to. After, I leaned down and kissed those cheeks, soft as flower petals, staring into the shadowy face of this old lady whose life was laid out in front of me.

A light sigh came from the bed, a lift in the breathing, little shudders in the rhythm as she breathed out. I stood up and managed to smile at her. 'Thanks, Nonna Amelia.'

It was a moment before I saw that had been her final breath. No, it couldn't be! I lifted the covers and felt around in a panic for a pulse in her frail wrist. Nothing. I hardly remembered getting downstairs.

'She's gone, Mrs Spini,' I said. 'I was just standing there, and—'

It was expected, but still a shock. Vera's face tightened and she gave out a long breath almost as her mother had done. I was upset and embarrassed. I wasn't family. I was the wrong person to have been there. Why did old women have to keep choosing to die suddenly when I was around?

But Vera stepped forward and embraced me, kissing my face on each cheek before she went upstairs. 'I think it was a compliment to you.'

Thick clouds and foul weather saved us from bombing that week but also meant that the day of Nonna Amelia's funeral was cold and wet. Whatever the weather the Italians were going to send Nonna Amelia off with all the pomp and splendour they could gather together.

I paid my respects to her again once the women had laid out and clothed her in a stiff black dress. Now she was dead her face looked like someone else.

They carried her to the Requiem Mass at St Michael's in a horse-drawn hearse. The six black horses, blinkered and adorned with noble black plumes, gleamed in the rain, their breath snorting out jets of steam around them, and walked with high steps as if they sensed the honour of the occasion.

Vera's brothers and other friends of the family carried wreaths to the church, the biggest taller than they were themselves, and there was an enormous crowd inside. She had been very much loved, that old lady, for her kindness, and very much respected.

Teresa walked in with Vera and the other girls, all in their black lace, and Nanny Rawson limped beside me. Nan could swallow her misgivings about Catholics generally for the sake of this family in particular.

The strain was showing on Vera's face. As we settled in our pews, Nan steadfastly refusing to bob up and down to the High Altar or any of that, I whispered, 'If only Mr Spini was here. It's so hard on her, in't it?'

After the solemn Mass Nonna Amelia was taken off to Witton Cemetery with the closest of the family. But we called round later to join in the wake, the men and bottles ensconced in the front room, the women in the back, some of them crying as if they were there with the job of letting out grief on everyone's behalf.

We sat with the women for a time, everyone in black, accepting food and drink. Teresa came and sat by us in her black crêpe dress, looking worn out.

'You all right, love?' Nan said to her.

'I'm OK, ta. Thanks for coming both of you.' She seemed a bit distracted I thought, in a bit of an odd mood, because through all the tiredness and formalities she looked somehow excited. While the other women were talking loudly she moved closer to me. 'I've got summat to tell you.'

I looked round at her.

'Carlo's asked me to marry him.' I hadn't imagined it then, that light in her eyes. He'd written to her, couldn't even wait to come home and ask.

'He's such a hothead,' Teresa said affectionately. 'Not quite the same as going down on one knee, is it!'

I didn't have to ask what the reply was going to be.

'But at your age – what does your mom say?'

'I'll be seventeen soon and she adores Carlo. Always has. I s'pose if it wasn't for the war she'd tell us to wait, but she was so scared I'd go off and marry a Prot and leave her, she's quite happy. A good Italian Catholic boy with his family in the Quarter, she's not going to let that one slip past!'

I flung my arms round her. 'I'm really happy for you, Teresa. Nice to have some good news for once.'

'Well, good luck to you both,' Nan said when we told her, though we had to keep our congratulations low as no one else was to know yet. Even despite the sadness of that day Teresa did look happy and settled in herself.

As we left she kissed me extravagantly and hung on to my arm, hugging it. 'Maybe you and I should make a double wedding?'

Gently I pulled away. No one was going to see the ache in my heart, not now. I covered it with a laugh. 'Bit tricky that one, ain't it, since neither of us are Catholics!'

That Sunday afternoon I answered a knock on our door to find Mr Broadbent standing there. His car was parked across the road. My knees went weak.

'Genie?' He looked ever so uncomfortable having turned up like that. I couldn't ask him in. There was Mom asleep in a chair and out of pride I didn't want him seeing her. And I guessed why he was here. I just couldn't let him near me because if he said too much I knew I'd cave in completely. I stood stiffly in the doorway, my expression closed tight as an iron door.

'Sorry to bother you, love,' he said. 'I know it's a bit funny me calling. But Joe's very anxious about you. Said he hasn't heard a thing from you for ages and he asked me to check and see if you were all right.'

I swallowed, looked past him seeing the ground was

wet outside and it was filthy still, mess from the street's wreckage continually trodden back and forth. 'I'm awright.'

Mr Broadbent seemed so embarrassed I felt guilty, but I couldn't help him.

'He keeps hearing about the raids of course. It's not as bad where they are, nothing like.' He paused. 'Are you sure everything's all right, Genie? Only Joe's wondering why he hasn't heard. He's upset and worried. You mean a lot to 'im.'

I shifted my weight from one foot to the other, arms folded tight, stared over Mr Broadbent's head across our smashed-up street.

'I can't write,' I said, holding on tight to myself inside and out. 'Just can't. You'd better tell Joe he's made a mistake. Tell him to forget me.'

'Oh.' He stroked his hand back over his hair. 'I didn't know it was like that.'

I was moving back into the house.

'But Genie – wait, love . . .'

'Love' undid me. 'Got to go. Mom's calling.' And I shut the door. Leaned on it, gulping, and closed my eyes.

Tuesday. And there was Lil at Nan's, sobbing her heart out, and Nan's face clenched like a rat trap with 'What did I tell you?' written all over it. It took me quite a time to get the whole sorry story. Nanny Rawson, it seemed, had been right about Frank with a vengeance.

'That didn't take long, did it?' Nan said. 'Talk about living in Cloud Cuckoo Land – people like that believe their own lies.'

Lil sobbed even harder.

'So you mean he's got another woman?' I said, trying to put together the bits of information dribbling out between Lil's snuffles and sobs.

'I – I was so sure about him,' she wailed. 'How could I have got it all so wrong? How could he tell me so many lies?' She had no make up on and her lids looked naked, pink and puffy. She put her head in her hands, so betrayed and dejected. I looked at Nan, framed in the window's dying light. She folded her arms, glanced at Cathleen who was on the floor with a rag doll.

'Not only is lover boy already married with a kid, 'e's got this other trollop set up across town – where is it? Hockley or somewhere – doing all this fortune telling and that . . . Only she's a bit more to 'im than 'e was letting on before!'

'And there's a flat over the top of that one,' Lil wailed. 'I reckon she sees more of him than I do!'

'Christ,' I said, 'how does he manage it?'

Nan frowned at my blaspheming.

I didn't know whether I was surprised or not. I mean I was, by the facts, by Frank's cunning, his sheer energy. But somehow not by the actual truth of it. He was much too good to be real, too charming, too slippery.

'So how did you find out, Lil?'

'Oh—' She waved a hand tiredly, as if that hardly mattered any more. 'He didn't come home.' She gave a harsh laugh. 'Not that that should surprise me, by all accounts. Anyway, he'd been on duty, or so he said. So I went up to the ARP post. I mean it's not as if we've had any raids, is it? They were ever so funny with me at first, wouldn't say a thing. Didn't know where he was. So I was going, then one of them came after me and said Frank'd been in an accident. They'd gone into a bombed out warehouse and Frank'd had a load of stuff come down on him and done his neck in bad. So I go carting up the General to find 'im . . .' She sat twisting her hanky round and round. 'I'm sat there by the bed when this bird walks in, looks at me as if I stink and says, "Who the hell are you?" So I say, "Well, who are you?" And she says—' Lil's voice broke again. ' "I'm his wife." They've got a little lad an' all, six years old, called Bertie.'

'Well, what about the other woman?' I could feel rage rise in me for my poor auntie Lil. What I wouldn't do to that smarmy . . .

'She, his wife, knew about her. Suspected anyway. Didn't know about me.'

Did now though.

'The raids gave him the perfect excuse,' Lil sobbed. 'He was always telling us he had to be somewhere else. And the flat over the garage was a bit bare, but I thought it was just his bachelor way of life.'

Nan's fury twitched in her cheeks. She sliced bread for Cathleen, loaf under one arm, with a look of it being Frank's neck.

'Oh Lil,' I said. We put our arms round each other and I stroked her back. Sweet, loving Lil. It knifed me through to see her so hurt and destroyed, so alone all over again.

'How could he do it?' she sobbed, shaking. 'How could he? What have I done to deserve this? How could he lie to me and me not know – and to her? Poor cow's got a kid and she's saddled with him. The worst of it is . . .' She pulled away from me and sat up wiping her eyes with the wet hanky. 'I really loved him. I still do. I mean if he walked in here and spun me some tale about it was all a mistake and none of it was true I'd have him back, I would.'

414

Nan yanked the blackout viciously across the window. 'Then you're a bigger fool than you look.'

'Can't all be like you, can we, Mom?' Lil said, without aggression. 'Some of us have to believe you can have something better.'

Nan didn't rise to that, just slopped tinned pears in Cathleen's bowl.

'What're you going to do, Lil?' I said softly.

She sat very still, staring into the fire. 'I dunno. Oh God. I suppose I'll have to come back here – if Mom'll have me.' She didn't look at Nan. 'Go back to Parkinson Cowan or somewhere. The factory. Right back to square one.'

When I left them, feeling guilty that I'd be so late home, I was bursting inside. I had a tight feeling in me from pent up emotion about everything that had happened, and seeing Lil in that state of betrayal and lost hope had brought it all to the surface. We were all so stuck, waiting, and not knowing whether what we were waiting for was going to bring more pain and more disaster into our lives. We could lose the war, my mom was stuck in a mockery of what was once her body, I'd rejected a good man who loved me because of my anger with myself – and now this. Now I'd seen Lil fall victim to Frank's self-obsessed greed and lust.

It was already dark as I stormed along the Moseley Road, trying to release some of the feelings. If it was light I'd have run. This time of the evening there was too much danger of colliding with someone or knocking myself out on a lamp-post. But the sky was clear and there was a moon. Bomber's moon, I thought. *God.*

It was as if my thoughts set it off. The sirens wailed

round me so loud and horrible I wanted to scream myself. People out on the street started rushing and I could see threads of light from torches moving fast, combing the pavement.

I needed to get home quick. At least Shirl was there. Wonderful Shirl. She'd get Mom and Len organized. But the thought of the shelter, of sitting still in there when I was so frantic with anger and frustration was hateful.

Turning the corner of St Paul's Road I could just make out that someone was standing there, and as I passed, in the quick yellow flare as a match was struck, lighting the end of a fag into a glowing orange bead, I knew those features. Dark brows, heavy-set face. Bob. My rage boiled over.

'You bastard! You shit-faced bastard!'

With all the fury of my compressed emotion I flung myself at him, taking him completely by surprise, yelling and screaming against the noise of the siren. I tore my nails down his face with every bit of my strength, kicked at him, grabbed something, his hand, took the fleshy bit above the thumb knuckle in my mouth and bit right into it until I felt it crunch.

'Aaagh – what the *fuck* . . .?'

He caught hold of me, easily stronger now he'd got his act together and was furious and in pain, pinned my two hands together, pulled out a torch and shone it in my face.

'You! You little bitch!'

With pleasure I saw blood on his cheeks. I drew up a big gob of spit and let him have it in one eye.

'Christ.' He had to wipe it with his shoulder, moving his grip to the tops of my arms, pinning them to me hard.

416

'Get off me.' I struggled, fighting him. 'Don't you touch me.'

'You evil little bitch, you—'

'My mom nearly died because of you. She was having your babby, the one you ran off and left her with, you lump of dog muck. She put her head in the gas oven and now she's a cripple thanks to you. I hate you! I hate you ... Get your fucking hands off of me. I've got to get her into the shelter – she can't walk properly. Let me go ...' I was sobbing and cursing, beside myself, and Bob relaxed his grip on me. I twisted free and started running.

'I hope they get you—' Through my tears I screamed at the sky. 'Come on you stupid Jerry bastards – come and get this one!'

They were overhead, the planes, but I just kept running. This area was a favourite of theirs of course. They thought a lot of the factories were here instead of on 'shadow' sites like Castle Bromwich. They were after the BSA – Birmingham Small Arms – the big munitions factory which made motorbikes in peacetime. They'd already hit it but they were back for more. Looking up through my tears, I saw planes pass black in front of the moon. That wave of bombs fell over to my left, further north. It sounded as if there were a lot of them out tonight.

I tore along Brunswick Road. Thank God for Shirl, I thought again. If she'd not been there I'd have been too late. I dragged my hands impatiently across my wet eyes. There was no more time for emotion.

The house was dark of course, like all the others. There was no point in banging on the door so I ran to the side gate, struggling with the latch, caught my sleeve on the fence and then stumbled down the garden. There

417

were more planes and the whistle and crunching boom of the explosions. Even before I got to the shelter one came down very near and I threw myself down, curled up. The ground snatched under me and the sky lit up. I heard glass breaking.

'Shirl. Shirl!' I yelled. 'Get the door open for me!'

She couldn't hear me over the racket. They'd be worried about me. Head down I covered the last few yards, pulled the front off the Anderson and flung myself in. To find it empty and dark.

There should have been matches but nothing was there. I felt around every inch of the floor but couldn't find them. It was pitch black.

'Damn! Damn you, Shirl. Where are you? Why aren't you all out here?'

I felt my way up on to one of the seats and perched on the edge, once more boiling over with anger and frustration. Did I have to do everything? And I wanted Mister, the distraction of comforting him in my lap and being able to think about him and Mom instead of my own skin.

The shelter seemed to close in round me. I had a picture of it in my mind as a flimsy bubble, thin enough to give off rainbows in the sun, out here under all the bombs. I didn't like being alone in the dark. I pulled my legs up, resting my heels on the edge of the berth and curled tight, hugging my knees.

When it lets up a bit I'm going in, I thought. Couldn't do it now, it'd take too long to move Mom. She couldn't just run down the garden like the rest of us. I wondered where Len was. Maybe he was at Molly's and Shirl hadn't been able to manage on her own?

I lost track of time. I wasn't sure exactly when I'd left Nan's – I guessed it had been about half six – or how long I'd been in the shelter. Seemed like hours. I couldn't keep my mind on anything but how scared I was, because it was all too much, much worse on your own. My mind did something it'd done before during the worst raids, it sort of closed down until I was repeating just one word: Please, please, please . . .

One came down very near. The ground shook and I pulled my head tight on to my knees, hearing myself moan with fright. Clifton Road at the back, it sounded like, though the noise could mislead you. I was thinking who did we know, did we know anyone in Clifton . . .?

I didn't hear it coming, not that one. Just knew one minute I was sat there, the next I was choking, buried, my mouth and nose full of soil, earth over me, terrible the close fit of it, buried alive. Every muscle of my body was clenched in a mad, fighting panic, wrenching and twisting, spitting, coughing, savage with desperation for a clear unclogged breath. In a second I found I could move, so it wasn't a deep cover. Clawing with my hands, I felt air above and I fought my way out, hawking and spitting, feeling the soil crunch between my teeth, the horrible thick plugs of it in my nose and its tightness on my face, weighing down my lashes.

The door of the shelter had been blown right inside and was jammed in at a tilt, so I had to crawl past it to get out, forcing my shoulders out into the garden.

The next thing I remember was running up and down the street under an orange sky, not knowing what I was doing. A warden loomed from the shadows yelling at me, 'Get under cover! For God's sake get in!'

'Our house—' I stood pointing, lost. It only took one look from him. He steered me to a doorway. 'You can't hang about. Got anywhere to go?'

And then I was tearing along the Moseley Road

again, a road that had seen so many ordinary days, ducking in and out of doorways as the sky seemed to tear apart above me.

We were down there as soon as the All Clear sounded, even though it was still dark, holding on to each other, Nan, Lil and me, braced for the sight.

They were working on our house. The air was full of dust which coated the inside of your mouth and once more there was the queasy-making smell of gas, but today we noticed these things only in the very far back of our minds. Morning dawned slowly, the colour of an old net curtain, and with the light more and more people came out into the road, watching and murmuring to each other. An ambulance waited near by.

We stood in silence. There was nothing to say. We had long ago done the things we could do: called at the Benders' house; no, no Len. He'd stayed home. Lil, the only one of us who could function at all, ran, jumping the hoses, to one of the wardens and grabbed at his sleeve. He listened, shaking his head. Couldn't tell her anything. Not yet.

As we stood there with Gladys and Molly a nurse with red hair came to us from the ambulance, seeing who we must be, and spoke to us in a reverent sort of voice. 'Maybe it's better if you don't watch. It can be distressing. Would you like to come and wait over here?'

But we couldn't move, shook our heads dumbly. Cups of tea were given us by people whose faces we didn't even see. I didn't remember drinking except suddenly I was holding an empty cup, until someone took it away. I heard Molly sobbing.

It took a long, long time, eyes straining, listening to the grunts and shouts of the rescuers, feet crunching on glass and rubble, sometimes the noise of a saw or drill on the cold morning air. And we could do nothing except stand and wait.

'Quiet!' The man who seemed to be in charge of the team eventually waved his hands. 'I need quiet. I can hear something.' Silence came down like a chopper. We all strained our ears and heard tiny mewling noises from somewhere in the wreckage. The men looked at each other. I knew as soon as they did that that wasn't a human sound. It was a dog – Mister, alive somewhere in all that. My spirits lifted for a second. But what about the others? What about Mom, Len, Shirl? What we all wanted to hear, what we yearned for from the depths of our being, was to hear their voices crying for help so we knew they were alive. But apart from Mister's frantic scratching and whining, there was nothing to hear from inside, just quiet. Deathly quiet.

They brought Shirl out first, covering her bloodied face with a sheet. We couldn't see the rest of her. I gripped Lil's hand. There was no need to ask if she was dead. With each body they brought out, so carefully, so painstakingly, a ripple, that low murmuring sound passed through the scattering of people, a sound of horror and sympathy, a long, wordless, human breath.

Mom was next. It took them some time to bring her out. They did their best for us, closing ranks, their backs to us as they arranged on the stretcher the parts of her they had salvaged, shielding her, and us, before they could decently cover her. They didn't look at us as they carried her away. Nan's hand came up and clasped over her mouth and stayed there, her eyes fixed on the house as they carried her children out. She didn't move. She was waiting for Len.

They had to move more rubble from the brown, crumbling heap that was our house. Mister didn't let up whining. Some of our things were scattered in the road, looking small, dirty and humiliating. Scattered bits of furniture, shreds of a chair cover, the mantel clock with its glass shattered rolled out into the road, pink-backed playing cards turning over in the breeze. Shirl's black bag. *Oh Shirl.*

Len's fleshy, schoolboy body was soaked in blood. When she saw them bring him, Molly threw herself forward, taking the rescue team by surprise, falling on him, a great howl coming from her that seemed to crack the air apart. 'Len – Lenny – my Len – no-o-o-o-o.' She kissed him again and again and came up with blood on her face as they prised her away, belly shaking with sobs. Gladys drew her into her arms, her child with child.

When they brought Len to the ambulance Nan walked forwards, pulling her coat round her. Lil and I followed.

'It's better if you don't—' the nurse started to say.

Nan held up a hand to stop her. 'It's awright, love, I'm not going to make any fuss. Just give me a minute – there's no harm.'

She pulled the sheet back and looked at him. Len's eyes were half open, his face cut by glass but not disfigured.

'Good lad.' She ran her rough hand over his matted hair. 'You've been a good'un, Len. A good son.' She gave him a last, long look, then covered his face again and started walking away.

'Mom.' Lil took her arm. Nan's eyes were glassy. She was in shock, we all were. 'Where're you going?'

'Home. There's nowt to stay 'ere for, is there?'

'I've got to stay,' I said. 'For the dog.'

Mister was freed shortly after from the cupboard under the stairs and he tore out still yapping hysterically. When I called to him he rushed into my arms in convulsions of quivering, and licked my face. It was only then my own legs started trembling, and it was all I could do to stay standing.

Later that day there was a knock at Nan's door. It was Mr Tailor. His house was still up.

'I'm sorry, love,' he said to Lil. 'Sorry what's hap-pened, and for barging in on you like this. Only they found this – under the stairs, so it's kept safe. I thought you'd like to 'ave it before some bugger nicks it.'

In his arms was Gloria, plus accumulator, without a scratch on her.

'The King's 'ere,' Mr Tailor said as he went. 'Walking round town. Come to see the damage, I s'pose.'

We laid Gloria on the table. Nan sat by her, stroked her hand over the dusty veneer. Slowly, lovingly, she touched the knobs. Then she laid her head on her arms and wept.

I was ill after that and the days disappeared. My throat was so painful I could hardly even stand to swallow water. It must have been all the soil and muck I'd had in my mouth, and I had a very high temperature and delirium. A lot of the time I couldn't remember what had happened in a direct way, but all the sensations and dreams wrapped in that hot, twisting fever were threatening, sometimes shapeless, sometimes clear, always awful.

In one of my dreams Mom was back in our house as it had been. She was speaking to me and I knew what she was saying was the last thing I'd ever hear her say, but however much she strained and forced her slack mouth to shout, she couldn't make me hear her. I sweated with concentration trying to remember the last living thing my mother would say but I always failed.

There was another dream. Again I was in our house. Pieces of my mother were lying in a chaotic jigsaw puzzle round the rooms and I had to put them together before – before what I didn't know. Before it was too late – for something. I ran from room to room picking up an arm here, a hand or foot there. I had to save her. The horror of the dream was knowing all the time I wasn't going to make it. Once when I dreamed that dream it was Joe, not my mother, whose limbs were lying scattered.

Again and again I woke trying to scream, my throat a ring of fire, and Lil would come to me, trying to quiet me, her hand cool on my forehead. Day and night I couldn't stop my hands from shaking.

I don't know how my nan got through those days. I was so sick, and it was Lil who held on, who was strong for us all. She knew bereavement, perhaps knew how to survive.

'It's all right, Genie love.' She held me all the times as I mumbled out, feverish, all the things I blamed myself for. Kept going on about Shirl, Shirl's dad.

'None of this is your fault, love. None of it. The only person to blame for all this is Adolf bloody Hitler. That's who's the cause of all of it. You stop blaming yourself. You've been a really good kid and no one could've done more than you. You've just got to get yourself better now.'

The fever left me and I lay in bed weak and thin as tissue paper, looking round at the bare walls where Tom and Patsy slept when they were here. I barely had the strength to move and my throat still felt as if I'd been gargling with gravel.

'Look.' Lil came in one day carrying a card. 'From Victor – from your dad.'

She held it in front of my eyes. A card from a POW camp addressed to Mom. His health was good, it said. At the bottom he sent 'Best regards to yourself, Genie, Eric, Len, Edith, Lil and the rest. Happy Christmas. Yours ever, Victor.'

I looked up at Lil. 'Of course he doesn't know. We'll have to tell him.'

She looked away out of the window, her eyes very sad. 'Yes we will. Poor old Victor.'

Teresa came and her face in the doorway looked scooped out and deathly white.

'You better, Genie?'

'Think so, ta.' I hid my trembling hands under the covers. 'Bit wobbly still.'

'Your nan says d'you want a drink?'

'In a bit. What's up?' I pulled myself up on one elbow, disturbed by the way Teresa looked.

425

She sat on my bed. 'Stevie's home.' Her voice broke up and she spread her hands over her face, distraught. Only after a few moments she managed to say, 'Dad's dead.'

'Your dad – dead?'

She lowered her hands despairingly. 'They didn't even bother to let us know. Probably didn't think a wop traitor was worth it.' I'd never heard such hate in her voice before. 'They just sent Stevie out to do it for them.'

'When, Teresa? What happened?'

'Stevie says a fortnight ago. He caught pneumonia. No one'd do anything, although Stevie went on and on at them – said Dad's lungs were already bad and he needed attention. They didn't get him to hospital until it was already too late.' She thumped her fist on the bed, her face twisted with anger. 'No one was there when he died. None of us. Not even Stevie.'

'Oh God, Teresa. I'm so sorry.' I thought of Nonna Amelia's death, all the family waiting to hand her gently into it. And Micky so much younger, shouldn't have died at all. Micky who was told the Mother of God would catch him when he fell.

Teresa wiped her red eyes. 'I've been to see you before but you was too poorly. You looked really bad.'

'Felt it.'

'I'm sorry – your mom, Lenny ... It's terrible, Genie.'

I nodded. 'Your dad, Teresa – he was good to me.'

'I know. I knew when he'd gone – what I'd missed. And then when I got to know Carlo properly I started wanting to know all about his life over there, Dad's childhood, his mom and that. I used to get fed up with him trying to tell me – I was so arrogant. I thought,

426

when he gets back I'll be able to ask him . . .' She trailed off, wiping her eyes. 'Oh, what's the use?'

She shifted closer and we put our arms round each other.

'God, Genie, you're skinny!'

'I can feel your bones too.'

We rested our cheeks together.

'When Carlo and I get married, will you be my bridesmaid?'

I squeezed her. 'Course I will.'

I stayed in just about all the time, mostly up in my room, often lying on the lumpy bed but not asleep, not exactly awake, but in a weak, dreamlike state brought on by my illness. When I thought about moving I had to concentrate hard to make an arm move or a leg. Mister often came and lay on my bed to keep me company and I liked his warm weight by my feet.

Now and then I found the strength to go down, even outside. But people stared, and once I had Clarys bitching at me in the yard. 'I hope you 'aven't brought your bombs with you.' People believed that, that the bombs followed you. Not that we were having much in the way of bombing at the moment anyhow. But I stayed in. It was freezing out. Now and then I sat down by the fire, Mister at my feet. I switched Gloria on, stroked her sometimes. She was all that was left of home as it had been.

Lil and Nan were just getting on with it. Keeping going. The shop opened, the jobs got done, Nan's hair was suddenly almost white, the skin looser on her face. Lil too looked very haggard, but everyone was gentle. We knew we were all we had.

Now I'd surfaced I started to remember other things. That it was nearly Christmas for one. And that Lil had lost Frank. She never mentioned him, just came and went, looking after me and Cathleen like an angel. She even tried to decorate the house up a bit for the season.

'What're you going to do, Lil?' I asked her, watching her hang snippets of holly on the mantel. I was huddled in my nightdress and a coat by the fire. 'You going back to the factory?'

She stood back to eye up her decoration. 'No.' I saw her chin come out, determined. 'I've been doing a lot of thinking. I may not be able to have Frank, but one thing I've got out of all this is that shop. I was doing well at it – got a bit of a flair for it.'

'But Lil, is it real? It looked like a big con, that lady thinking the egg-holders were the Alps and that?'

'Depends on your attitude,' Lil said seriously. 'Course you can trick people. Tell 'em any old rot. But there's a skill to the cards and the palm reading and the rest. You can use your instinct. Really try and feel your way into a person, who they are. I can do it – I know I can. People trust me. Sort of open up to me. I'm going to keep the lease and make a go of it. Make it nice inside with a little grotto for the crystal ball and the palm readings. I've coped on my own before and I can do it again.' She grinned at me suddenly. 'Not as if Frank's the only bloke in the world, is it?'

She frowned then. 'Why aren't you opening your letters, Genie?'

Our post came redirected now, from the old house.

'Letter. There's only been one.'

'Well – one then?'

I shrugged, looking down, pulling the old brown coat close over my knees. 'Don't, Lil.'

'Don't what?'

'I don't want to talk about it.' I'd thought he'd stopped writing. I was glad. It was over. But then this other one had come.

Lil knelt down in front of me, staring up into my face. 'You loved him, Genie. Don't shake your head at me. It was clear as anything.'

I stood up, pushing her away, my throat aching with tears.

'I told you, I don't want to talk about it. You don't know what you're on about. Just leave it.'

I went up to bed again, swallowing hard, Mister following me, his claws loud on the wood stairs.

We got ready for Christmas out of habit, even though there was nothing to celebrate except the lack of bombing. The night air had been a lot quieter lately. You could sleep right through if habit allowed you. Preparing for Christmas was a way of remaining steady, keeping some of the normal things going when the rest had been smashed apart.

Nan ran the shop, accepted people's condolences and put up with blokes coming and going to mend Morgan's roof. Morgan was desperate to get back his access to a private place away from his elderly mom as soon as possible and he kept coming and eyeing up the work, demanding to know how many days it would take. It was a sign of how things were that Nan made not a murmur. Even the thought of Morgan creeping back and forth had suddenly become a sign of longed for normality.

We didn't speak about Mom or Len much. We all knew what had happened to Mom and no one wanted to bring it out in the open. It was too terrible. Nan hadn't even been able to see her at the end. In secret shame I wondered how Mom's life would've gone on if she'd lived. Would I have kept finding her eyeing up the gas oven until one day she finished it that way for good?

Instead of talking about Len, we talked of Molly. She was heartbroken, poor thing.

'We'll have to give her any help we can,' Nan said. 'After all, I'm the babby's grandmother, aren't I?' It was clear to see that if there was ever a little babby going to be swamped with doting nans, this would be the one.

On Christmas Eve we sat round the fire, Nan and Lil drinking hot toddies. Cathleen, full of excitement, was allowed up late and the rest of us were doing our best for her, although I could tell Lil was low. She and Cathleen were missing the boys and it'd really hit home tonight. She'd sent parcels for them out to Leek and was toying with the idea of bringing them home.

'It's not over yet,' Nan said, swirling her drink round to cool it. 'Now you've sent them you might as well wait till it's safe for 'em – even if it is *his* aunt. She's good to them by all accounts, and you don't want Tom all worked up again.'

'So you don't think I was all wrong sending them?'

'No. Even if your reasons were dodgy at the time.'

'I do hope they're all right,' Lil fretted.

'They sound it. Sure you don't want a drop of this, Genie?' Nan offered.

'No ta.' I stuck to tea. Mom'd given me a horror of drink. I'd have signed the pledge the way I felt about it. And I still wasn't well. I felt feverish again tonight, turning hot and cold, my hands shaking so I could only just control the cup.

'Look at the state of her,' Lil said. 'You poor kid.'

I tried to give her a smile.

We had carol singers round, kids mostly, and stood outside the front door listening, door closed because of the blackout. Their feet crunched on the frost and I was shivering.

'Once in Royal David's City,' they sang, not quite in tune but well enough to make you fill up. Made me think of those stories of the last war – the Christmas truces, carols floating across the trenches. How blooming peculiar the world was.

The singing brought our emotions to the surface and we couldn't stand much of it. We gave them a couple of coppers to get rid of them. We hadn't sung together at all. Not without Mom and Len. Back inside we were all quiet, full of that swell of emotion that Christmas brings, but for each of us this time, an unbearable amount worse. It brought us up against all we'd lost. I knew everyone was thinking of it.

In the end Lil said, 'You're going to have to take her place now, Genie. Should we sing, Mom?'

We both looked at Nan. Her jaw tensed. 'No,' she said quietly. 'I don't think so. Not yet.'

We got Cathleen ready for bed, eyes still bright with excitement, like a Christmas angel herself in her little nightdress. I thought of how she used to sleep in her raggedy vest and bloomers before the war when times had been so hard for Lil.

'You get off to sleep now,' Lil and I told her. 'Or Father Christmas won't come.' Lil had bought her a puzzle and a cheap little ornament, a mermaid with a shiny blue tail. She was going to love it.

On the way down from saying goodnight to her I came over dizzy and had to sit down quick to stop myself falling downstairs. Lil looked at me anxiously.

'You're not right yet, are you? Nowhere near.'

'No. I feel pretty bad. I'm going to turn in too.'

I lay in the dark feeling the fever come over me in hot waves, shivering one minute, pushing the covers off the next, sea-tides of hot and cold pushing me back and to. Thoughts seemed to clang into my mind harder than usual, chopped up, distorted by fever. Thoughts of how this house felt like a home to me, always had, downstairs, Nan's shop, how I'd once dropped a drawer full of reels of coloured cotton and they'd bounced and spun off all over the shop going 'plok-plok' on the floor and it seemed to take for ever to pick them up. The sound echoed loud now in my mind. Eric had been there, a babby then, crawling round the floor, and he stopped, mouth wide open, head turning this way and that and not knowing which one to watch. Everyone paraded through my mind – Dad, Len, Mom, Bob. That fantastic feel of Bob's thumb crunching between my teeth.

I was asleep yet not asleep. I knew Mister had jumped off my bed and pattered off downstairs. He was barking for a time. Gloria must've been on. Music, then voices talking on and on. I wasn't sure how much time had passed, and whether I'd slept in the middle of it.

There was a light in the room, the unsteady glow of a candle, very vivid. Not a dream. Lil come to look in on me. Very drowsy, my eyes kept opening and closing.

'Can I have some water?' I managed to say in a hoarse whisper.

I thought I heard her talking, low voices, and I said, 'What?' Then the cold cup came to my lips as I half sat up, cold suddenly, teeth knocking against it. I opened my eyes, sipped. 'Ta.'

Not Lil. Was this a dream? Joe sitting on my bed, face full of anxiety. I heard myself gasp.

'Genie?'

'Joe. Joe?' In my weakness I lay back in the bed and found I was already crying. The wave broke over me, a great wash of tears that I couldn't hurry or stop. I heard the forgiveness in his voice even when he'd said so little, I saw it in his face, and it began to release everything. The terrible loss, the pain and fear and guilt of these past weeks that had been locked down in me, keeping him out, punishing myself as unworthy of him.

He knelt by the bed and took me in his arms as I sobbed hoarsely. 'It's all right.' He held his cool cheek against my burning one. 'It's all right now, my love. Sssh, my sweet one.'

'I'm s-s-sorry, Joe. I'm sorry. I'm sorry.'

I felt him take in a deep, shuddering breath and I clung to him, this miracle of love and forgiveness who'd appeared out of my dreams.

'Mom's dead. And Len.'

'I know. Your auntie Lil told me.'

I frowned, all muddled up. 'When?'

'Just now. I've just got in. From the station. I wrote and said I was coming . . . I know, you've had a terrible time.'

'Did she tell you Mom tried to gas herself?'

His head jerked back, horrified. No, she wouldn't have done.

'I felt so bad. So ashamed. I let everyone down. I thought you were too good for me. That's why I didn't . . . couldn't . . .'

'Sssh, Genie. It's OK.' He soothed me like a little kid

and that was just how I felt. I wanted someone to be my mom, my dad, my love, all in one. He sat me up and held me on his lap, stroking my hair.

'I didn't write because I thought—' I was still sniffing and gulping. 'I don't know what I thought. I just hated myself and it made me think you couldn't want to see me again.'

'I was worried.' There was a flash of hurt, of anger. 'Your letters were what kept me going, see. But Dad said he'd been to see you and said something about your mom being bad so I thought maybe you were too busy to write.'

I looked up into Joe's face. Mr Broadbent hadn't passed on my message. Not what I'd really said. Maybe he hadn't wanted to hurt Joe. Or did he just plain not believe me?

'Soon as I got here I had to come and prove to myself things hadn't changed. And of course when I got to your house, I saw—' I could hear tears in his voice. 'Jesus, I thought you were dead, Genie. You were dead and that's why I hadn't heard anything. When I saw your house – smashed up, gone – I felt as if everything had been destroyed, everything I'd hoped for, all we talked about doing together. Torn apart. It was the worst moment I can remember, ever.'

Wretched, I stroked his face and he took my hand and kissed it hard, a lot of times.

'I'm sorry, Joe. I'm terribly sorry.'

'No – I just wish I'd known. All that's happened . . .'

'D'you really love me – still, after all this?'

'I could never not love you.'

I held on to him so tight. 'I thought I'd lost everything. Almost everything. And then suddenly, oh Joe, you're here.'

We kissed, his lips pouring new life into me. We sat there quietly in each other's arms. I didn't know it was possible to feel so happy while I was so sad.

'You're very hot,' Joe said, feeling my head and neck. 'Your nan said you've been really bad. She's been worried about you.'

'She must be,' I said, cuddling against him in a haze of joy. 'Otherwise she'd never've told a bloke to come up into my bedroom!'

After a time Joe tucked me back in bed and kissed me. I put my arms round his neck. 'Don't go,' I said sleepily. 'I might wake and find I dreamed you.'

'You didn't dream me. I'll be back, love, every minute I can be.' He watched my face. 'I can't believe my luck. Now we've just got to get you better.'

'Oh, I'll be better now. I'll be better tomorrow!'

My eyes followed him to the door, candle in his hand. He turned, his lovely smile across the room more powerful than any medicine. 'See you tomorrow. Good-night, sweetheart.'

On 1 January 1941 the BBC launched a new programme called *Any Questions* which became very popular and was later renamed *The Brains Trust*. That day, I spent in my nan's house, my home for now, with Nan, Lil and Cathleen, and Joe on the sofa by my side, my bony hand held in his. Gloria sat, newly polished and shiny on the table, the voices pouring out through her sunburst. Mister was on my lap, a fire in the grate, tea in our cups.

Joe's eyes met mine as we first heard the posh, chattering voices and we laughed. I leaned into his arms and felt his kiss on the top of my head.

'Hor hor hor' laughed the chappies on the wireless. Lil's eyes filled, although she was smiling. She looked round at us all. 'Wouldn't Len have loved this?'

The ecology of natural resources

I. G. SIMMONS

Edward Arnold

First published 1974
by Edward Arnold (Publishers) Ltd
25 Hill Street, London W1X 8LL

Boards ISBN: 0 7131 5733 X
Paper   ISBN: 0 7131 5734 8

Printed in Great Britain by
Butler & Tanner Ltd
Frome and London

Preface

There are now so many books dealing with man's relationships with his environment that yet another deserves some apologia for adding to them. My reasons for writing it spring from several years of teaching in this field, during which I found that many of the books I read and recommended to students were either too limited in scope or spatial coverage or too strident in their viewpoint for my taste. This book is the end-product of my reaction to that situation. I hope it will be primarily useful for students reading appropriate courses at second- and third-year levels in British universities, and for upper-division courses in North America; but I would stress that it is intended as an introduction and no more. Each component section has its own greater complexities, and I hope that some readers will use this book as a springboard for deeper studies. Beyond these people, other readers with an interest in the subjects discussed here may find in it some materials upon which to base their views as citizens.

To use the word 'ecology' in the title demands some further explanation, since it is a word whose meaning has latterly become not only elastic but stretched so far that it is unlikely to hold anything up. I take it to mean the study of the relationships of living organisms to each other and their inanimate environment, and I include man as one of those organisms. I have avoided the term 'human ecology' because I think that the local concept of ecology is a holistic viewpoint which is broken up a little more every time a qualifying adjective is attached, and I prefer to conceive of an 'ecology' in which, from time to time and place to place, one or other of the components may be dominant. In cities it is man, at the North Pole it is nature. But the admission of man means not only a particular species of tool- and material-using beast but a cultural animal also. If, as I believe and as will become apparent as the book progresses, ecology teaches us about the limits imposed by the dynamics and structure of natural systems, then we must also realize that all adjustments within this envelope must be made through the medium of culture. Thus economics, ethology and ethics all have a role to play in bringing about more harmonious interactions between man and nature. The special contribution, if any, of the geographer lies in his interest in (would that I could say understanding of) the points at which both natural and social systems meet.

Trying to cover such a wide field of knowledge and opinion brings two major problems. The first is that important material may be overlooked and, equally important, wrong interpretations may be made of published data and views. Oliver Goldsmith suggested that 'a book may be amusing with numerous errors, or it may be very dull without a single absurdity', and I would rather be classified in the first category: I shall be surprised if those thus offended do not make my mistakes clear to me. A second difficulty is the ageing of material between final draft and publication, especially in many of the areas covered in this book. As a partial attack on this problem, an Appendix written at the time of the submission of final proofs has been included: this sketches some of the more outstanding developments between the summer of 1973 and the early spring of 1974.

To acknowledge adequately all the help I have had would require a chapter in itself, but some debts are so great that they must be mentioned here. The basic idea of this type of book was conceived in that fertile womb, the Berkeley campus of the University of California. I am grateful to the American Council of Learned Societies for their award of an American Studies Program Fellowship, which made possible that year of study, fruitful also in fields other than resource studies, and to James Parsons, Chairman during 1964–5, who made me so welcome at Berkeley, then and since. During that year I first met Dan Luten, under whose genial but mind-stretching tutelage I have subsequently always regarded myself, even when the physical distance between us has been considerable. I have also benefited greatly from a Winston Churchill Memorial Trust Travelling Fellowship held in 1971 and 1972, which enabled me to visit North America and Japan to gather valuable information and meet interesting people. During the academic year 1972–3, I was Visiting Professor at York University, Toronto, and as well as paying a handsome salary, that lively institution provided time in which to prepare the final draft. Florence Davies, my secretary at York, typed furiously but accurately, checked references, packed parcels of manuscript and, most important of all, acted as intermediary between me and the Secretarial Services unit who actually produced the final typescript. The Chairman of the Department of Geography, Bill Found, who probably realized his Visiting Professor was more a visitor than a professor, bore this situation with a calm cheerfulness for which I am very grateful.

From my undergraduate days onwards, I have had the benefit of advice from and discussion with Palmer Newbould, currently of the New University of Ulster; much of this took place in contexts where that admirable material, ethyl alcohol, was consumed, and he can always claim that I thus misinterpreted totally what he told me. Since 1962 my membership of the Department of Geography at Durham has been a secure base from which to work and travel, and in particular its Head, Professor W. B. Fisher, has striven to provide conditions conducive to the production of academic work. Early drafts were typed by the grossly overladen secretarial staff of the Department, among whom Suzanne Eckford must be specially thanked. During 1969–70 a particularly lively group of students wrote essays along the themes of this book; none has been directly plagiarized, but some provided interest and stimulus, especially those by Cathy Goulder, Richard de Bastion, John Richardson, John Button, Alastair Steel, Jill Evered and Roger Weatherley.

My wife Carol deserves more than a paragraph to herself, for she has read, commented on, punctuated, corrected and re-read practically every word of this book, more than once while coping with domestic chores as well as this academic drudgery; only I know just how much she has helped.

Finally, this book is dedicated to my parents, Chris and Charles Simmons, as an inadequate, if sincere, expression of filial gratitude.

Contents

Names of organizations abbreviated in text and bibliography

AAAS	American Association for the Advancement of Science (Washington, DC)
AAG	Association of American Geographers (Washington, DC)
BTA	British Travel Association (London)
FAO	The Food and Agriculture Organization of the United Nations (Rome)
IBP	International Biological Programme (London)
IUCN	International Unions for the Conservation of Nature and Natural Resources (Morges, Switzerland)
NAS/NRC	National Academy of Sciences/National Research Council (Washington, DC)
OECD	Organization for Economic Co-operation and Development (Paris)
RFF	Resources for the Future Inc. (Washington, DC)
UNESCO	United Nations Educational, Social and Cultural Organization (Paris)

Part I
Introduction

1

Nature and resources

Man is a material-using animal. Everything he uses, from the food needed to keep him alive to the objects he fabricates, whether tools or sculptures, comes from the substances of the planet on which he lives. Wastes are then returned to the biological and abiotic systems of the earth. And because of his acquisition of culture, man desires to use these systems for non-utilitarian purposes of a recreational or spiritual kind.

If we look more closely at how man utilizes and processes materials from his surroundings, we see that a first group consists of resources which are used in the processes of the metabolism of his body, such as food and water (Table 1.1). These allow the growth and renewal of tissue and provide energy for chemical processes such as movement. The energy is consumed: it is transformed from chemical energy to heat and given off to the atmosphere, from whence it cannot be reclaimed. As a result of energy consumption and metabolic processes, excretory matter is produced. This often contains mineral substances which could be of value, for instance as plant food, and so use does not here necessarily mean consumption. The fact that in industrial societies these 'waste' materials are usually dumped in the nearest large body of water is not relevant to the basic chemistry of the processes. The substances which go to make up our bodies are theoretically available for re-use upon our death—as T. S. Eliot put it:

> . . . and ashes to the earth
> Which is already flesh, faeces
> Bone of man and beast, cornstalk and leaf.

The pattern of material use within the body is genetically and biologically determined, but the disposal of waste products and dead individuals is subject to considerable variation owing to different cultural practices among dissimilar groups of men.

The use of materials outside the human body, whether raw or chemically or biologically processed, is likewise subject to variations in practice. Many of these materials are non-renewable resources, like metals or stone; but some, such as wood and wood products, like paper, come from renewable resources. Re-use of the objects possessed is usually theoretically possible except where a transformation process is used to get rid of it, as in the disposal of waste paper by burning. That the opportunities to re-use materials may not be taken is again irrelevant to the basic characteristics of the resource.

A third group comprises resources used outside the body, the gathering of which leaves them unaltered. Such features of our surroundings as scenery, wildlife (if observed rather

TABLE 1.1　　Daily human metabolic turnover

Male of 154 lb (69·8 kg)		
Input		*Output*

Input				*Output*	
		Water	2,220 g	Water	2,542 g
Protein	80 g				
Fats	150 g	Food	523 g	Solids	61 g
Carbohydrates	270 g		BECOMES	Carbon dioxide	928 g
Solids and minerals	23 g	Oxygen	862 g		
				Other substances	54 g
				(CO, H_2, CH_4, H_2S, NH_3 plus organic compounds)	

Source: McHale 1972

than hunted) and water, for swimming or sailing, remain unchanged by our use of them for recreation and aesthetic satisfaction. Attrition of scenery may occur because there are too many users, or water may be fouled by the sailors and thus rendered unusable for the swimmers, but the potential exists for entirely non-consumptive and non-transformational use.

The total flow of a resource from its state in nature through its period of contact with man to its disposal (either consumptively or in a form available for re-use) can be termed a *resource process* (Firey 1960). Resource processes can be studied in a variety of ways. We can, for instance, see them as a set of interactions between living and non-living components of the biosphere in all their various solid, liquid and gaseous phases, and man may play a dominant role in these systems or may indeed have no part whatsoever. Such a viewpoint is generally termed ecological.

A second approach is to explore the manner in which the distribution of resources to people is achieved in various societies in attempts to match the demand and supply of a particular resource, i.e. the viewpoint of economics. Another method of study judges how man ought to use the biosphere and its resources, both for particular cultures and for the species as a whole: this is a particular branch of ethics. Yet again, the relationship between man's culture and his surroundings can be inspected in a behavioural context, thus studying the psychological activity leading up to the use of the earth's substances and habitats: this is clearly part of the field of ethology.

This book aims to emphasize the first of these four categories, the ecological point of view; but it recognizes that the objective, scientific study demanded by ecology does not portray the totality of man's interaction with the systems of this planet which comprises resource processes; it allows that many other factors, and in particular those usually designated as cultural, are of considerable importance. The next section of Part I expands upon the themes of nature and culture, especially the outgrowths of the latter such as economics and ethology.

Nature

The natural world may be studied in many ways, and the classification and cataloguing of phenomena have occupied many workers during human history. For our present purposes, studies which emphasize the connections between the various components, and especially the dependence of living organisms upon their abiotic environments, are most useful; hence the emphasis upon ecology, which can also encompass the impact of man upon natural systems. Since ecology is the study of living organisms and their relationship to each other and their surroundings, it is therefore mostly a study of the biosphere, which is influenced by the lithosphere, as in soil parent material, and the atmosphere, as in the incidence of climatic elements. The aggregate may appropriately be called the ecosphere. Since most of man's resources come from the ecosphere and since in gaining them he has greatly changed the ecology, the relevance of ecological study to our present theme cannot be gainsaid.

Within the subject of ecology various divisions have been made, generally focusing on one of the components of the biosphere and studying how all the other parts affect it. Thus plant ecology centres upon how plants and plant communities are affected by climate, soil, animals and other variables; animal ecology is concerned with their effect upon animals. Both may also study the reciprocal effects of the organisms upon their environment: how a growing forest affects microclimate, for example.

In every ecological system there are natural limits to the total amount of living matter that can be supported. These may be set by something as basic as the amount of solar radiation incident upon that part of the earth. Clearly, the polar regions receive insufficient of this to support the unaided growth of banana trees. On the other hand it may be spatial: a rocky islet may be filled to capacity at the nesting time of a particular bird and thus will determine the population level of those creatures, even if the sea around is teeming with fish waiting to give themselves up. Another important limitation is often the supply of a nutrient element: nitrogen and phosphorus frequently play this role. Ecology hence provides an envelope criterion for resource processes by telling us whether in the long run a particular process is possible or impossible. If it tells us that the maximum number of people that can be fed on the incident solar radiation trapped by photosynthesis is x billion, then this is an absolute limit. If it tells us that the continued practice of shifting agriculture or moor-burning will result in devastating soil erosion, then the presence of an absolute limit has been demonstrated and cultural adjustment must seek to work within it.

Ecosystems

A system is usually defined as a set of objects together with the relationships between the objects and their attributes: the ecology of an area can thus be categorized. The view of ecology encouraged by such a framework is obviously one which stresses interaction between parts and the mechanisms which control such connectivities. We can therefore designate a special class of systems dealing with ecological components, and call them *ecosystems*.

The term ecosystem was coined in 1935 by Tansley, but the concept has a much longer history, many attempts having been made to characterize the immense complexity and holistic character of the natural world. Thus the terms *microcosm, naturcomplex, holocoen* and *biosystem* have all been used from time to time for what is now generally called the ecosystem, with the major exception of the Soviet Union, where the term *biogeocoenose* is used with more or less the same meaning. As Tansley (1935) stressed, the term ecosystem includes not only the organisms, but

> also the whole complex of physical factors forming what we call the environment.

Terser and more rigorous definitions have been given by Lindemann (1942):

> a system composed of physical-chemical-biological processes active within a space-time unit of any magnitude

and E. P. Odum (1959):

> any area of nature that includes living organisms and non-living substances interacting to produce an exchange of materials between the living and non-living parts is an ecological system or ecosystem.

Scale

Two important characteristics stand out. Firstly the concept can be applied at any scale: a drop of water inhabited by protozoa is an ecosystem; so is the whole planet. This immediately introduces the problem of boundary definition: few ecosystems can satisfactorily be defined in space because one or more of their components overlaps with another system. A pond may appear to be a clearly bounded system, but the behaviour of wild ducks belies this simplicity.

A second feature is the reciprocity between living and non-living parts of the system. Not only does the 'environment' affect the organisms, but they in turn may change it. This has long been realized from studies of ecological succession, but in resource studies it becomes important to realize that use of the biotic member of an ecosystem as a resource may bring about changes in the non-living part too. The relationship between a forest and its soils is a very closely interconnected one, for example, and the replacement of deciduous trees by conifers in the temperate zone will often bring about a change in soil type from a Brown Earth to a Podzol.

The scientific study of ecosystems is clearly difficult: mere inventory of all the components will not tell us about the connectivity which has been so strongly stressed, and *Processes* research has indicated that two of the most important pegs upon which to hang functional studies of ecosystems are the flows of energy and matter within a given (and often imperfectly bounded) ecosystem.

Energy in ecosystems

In all ecosystems, as indeed in all studies of resource processes, the role of energy is crucial. Without the input of energy from the sun, life could not exist; the movements of air and water in the atmosphere are driven by this source, and even non-renewable resources of a geological nature have been formed as the result of solar energy. Coal and limestone are obvious instances; sandstones derive from weathering processes that are themselves impelled by inputs of solar energy. Nothing more fundamental to the nature of the planet can be imagined (Woodwell 1970a, Gates 1971).

The total amount of solar energy that reaches the earth's surface is probably in the order of 3,400 kcal/m²/day. This is an average figure since the amount (flux density) is different from place to place. The maximum conversion of this energy by photosynthesis absorbs c. 170 kcal/m²/day (5 per cent); the average is inevitably lower (H. T. Odum 1971). The whole of organic life depends upon this small fraction, for the only way of fixing solar energy for use by living creatures is by green plants; our stores of energy from coal and petroleum are merely fixed solar energy in a compressed and fossilized form.

Photosynthesis is the process by which green plants trap energy and incorporate it in complex organic molecules which then form food for themselves and other organisms. In a very complex series of reactions, water and carbon dioxide combine to synthesize sugars which may then be metabolized to starches, or which by the addition of mineral nutrients will form the very complex molecules (amino-acids and proteins, for example) which are the basis of living matter. But not all the energy gained by photosynthesis appears as plant tissue, for some is used in the metabolism of the plant, e.g. in the process of respiration. Thus in the Silver Springs ecosystem in Florida studied by H. T. Odum (1957):

Insolation	1,700,000 kcal/m²/yr	
Absorbed by plants	410,000 kcal/m²/yr	
Photosynthesized	20,810 kcal/m²/yr	Gross primary productivity
Photosynthesis minus respiration	8,833 kcal/m²/yr	Net primary productivity

Of the original incident energy, therefore, only c. 0·5 per cent appears as plant material. The production of living matter by plants is clearly a vital element where biotic resources are concerned. The rate of production of organic material after respiration has taken its toll is called *net primary productivity*, and the study of production ecology is ideally part of the necessary knowledge about any biological resource.

Biological productivity

In natural ecosystems many of the plants are eaten by herbivorous animals. These in turn may be consumed by carnivores and thus is built up the idea of a simple food chain. The important feature, so far as energy is concerned, is that at each stage of the food chain energy is lost to the system. This is a direct consequence of the operation of the second law of thermodynamics, which states that all energy which undergoes a change of form will tend to be transformed into heat energy. Thus the 'concentrated' potential energy present in living tissue is 'dispersed' as heat by the metabolic processes of the organisms. In a simple food chain of the type described above, therefore, even if the herbivores were to eat all the plant material, the use of energy and hence dispersal of heat would ensure that a much smaller amount of energy became visible animal tissue. This quantity of organic matter is called secondary production. It follows that carnivores have even less energy available for their consumption, and should there be yet another carnivore then the amounts of energy available to it will be very small indeed. In the Silver Springs example quoted above:

Net primary productivity	8,833 kcal/m²/yr	First trophic level
Net secondary productivity (herbivores)	383 kcal/m²/yr	Second trophic level
Net secondary productivity (carnivores)	21 kcal/m²/yr	Third trophic level

The efficiency, therefore, with which each stage (called a trophic level) converts energy is very low. The implications for resource use are clear: the further away from the primary production stage that man takes his crop, the less energy per unit area will be available, and so, to be efficient, he must act as a herbivore.

Rarely is all the tissue at one trophic level cropped by the next: a terrestrial herbivore usually eats only the aerial parts of a plant; similarly many herbivores die without being eaten by a carnivore. At death, therefore, another type of food chain forms in which non-living organic material is the energy source. This second chain is usually called the detritus or decomposer chain and the organisms in it are taxonomically very diverse, but an especially important group are the fauna and flora of soils which break down dead organic matter into its components: fungi and bacteria are notable components of this group (Fig. 1.1).

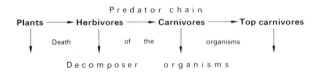

Fig. 1.1 A schematic diagram of trophic level structure of an ecosystem showing the basic energy paths through the organisms, beginning at the green plants. Not shown at each transfer stage is the loss of energy as heat

In addition, there are parasites on many organisms. These can be regarded either as a separate food chain or as components of the predator chain representing the next trophic level.

To summarize, energy enters the ecosystem as free, solar energy and leaves it as heat, having undergone changes from a 'concentrated' to a 'dispersed' state. Within the ecosystem is found energy-rich organic matter which upon the death of the organism, either plant, animal or fungus, undergoes decomposition. The complex organic materials are broken down to relatively simple inorganic compounds, with consequent dispersal of energy (Fig. 1.2).

Needless to say, the situation in nature and even in much modified ecosystems is more complicated. A herbivore may feed off many species of plants and in turn be eaten by several species of predators. A predator may have a preferred food source but shift to others in a time of scarcity. Omnivory is not uncommon, where an animal will eat plants, other animals and also be a scavenger on dead material: brown and black bears are examples of this and doubtless until affected by modern squeamishness our own species could rank thus. At any rate we are currently both herbivores and carnivores. Watt (1968) has diagrammed

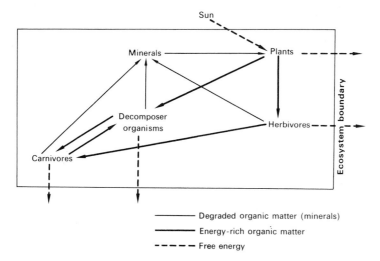

———————— Degraded organic matter (minerals)

———————— Energy-rich organic matter

– – – – – Free energy

Fig. 1.2 The form in which energy and matter move through an ecosystem: the 'free energy' traversing the ecosystem boundaries outwards is the heat loss. Within the system, matter travels either as energy-rich organic matter or as mineral matter low in energy content.
Source: O'Connor 1964

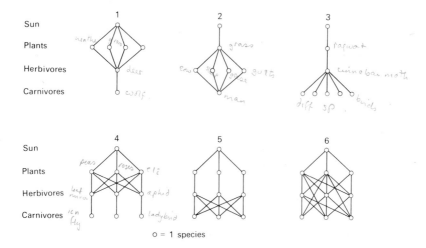

o = 1 species

Fig. 1.3 Representations of trophic level relationships. In (1) a herbivore grazes several species of plants but has only one predator; in (2) a single species of plant is eaten by four herbivores which form the prey of only one carnivore; in (3) the single herbivorous species is the food of five species of carnivores. In (4) three herbivores range across three species of plant but are eaten by a prey-specific predator; (5) and (6) depict various states of omnivory and show a relatively high number of energy pathways. They would suffer a lower loss of stability if one species were to disappear.
Source: Watt 1968

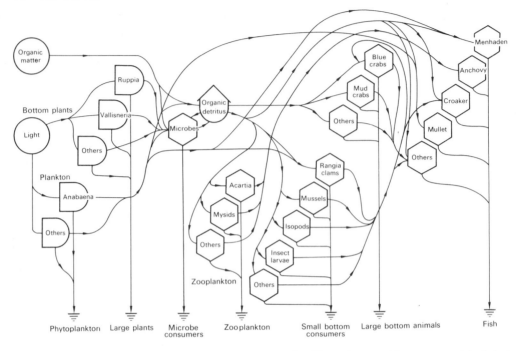

Fig. 1.4 An actual food web for an estuary in North America. The various trophic groups are labelled at the foot of the diagram. More detailed explanation of the compartment symbols is given by H. T. Odum (1971). The ☰ symbol represents heat loss.
Source: H. T. Odum 1971

some of the different types of relationship that can exist at different trophic levels in eco-systems (Fig. 1.3). At even more complicated levels, it is probably more realistic to talk about *food webs* rather than chains, since the points of contact (at which energy is trans-ferred) are so many (Fig. 1.4). Even this concept is perhaps insufficiently close to reality, and Elton (1966) has expanded it into the idea of a *species network*, where not only food but other relationships, such as competition for space and other forms of competitive interfer-ence, are considered. These latter factors, he notes, do not necessarily cause any immediate transfer of energy or materials from one species to another; relationships within such a network do not imply simultaneous activity or existence.

The implication of such models for resource processes are quite simple: the multiple interactions within the networks mean that when man crops a species as a resource, accommodating shifts within the system will probably be made. Because of the complexity of the system, these are unlikely to be predictable (although increased knowledge and use of computers is improving this situation), and inevitably some of the consequences have been deleterious to further human activity and the continued viability of the ecosystem.

The loss of energy as heat at each trophic level in the ecosystem ensures that the amount of potential energy decreases through the species network. Thus the numbers of organisms and the amount of living tissue per unit area (usually measured as dry weight) usually

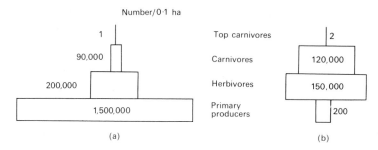

Fig. 1.5 Number pyramids of two ecosystems, exclusive of micro-organisms and soil animals. (a) is a grassland in summer, (b) a temperate forest in summer where the producers are trees which are large organisms and few in number.
Source: E. P. Odum 1971

diminish through the stages of secondary and tertiary productivity. A series of pyramids can be seen to exist which reflect this. The first is of numbers: in a measured area, the number of plants is many times the number of herbivores, which in turn greatly exceeds the quantity of carnivorous individuals. Carnivores and second carnivores are, therefore, relatively rare species (Fig. 1.5).

Such a relationship is made even clearer when biomass or standing crop is inspected (this is not the same as productivity, since biomass is a static measurement at one point in time whereas productivity is a rate). Again, the biomass of plants is much higher than any of the dependent organisms (Fig. 1.6). The calorific value of the tissues at various trophic levels

Fig. 1.6 A biomass pyramid (dry weight/unit area) for an 'old field', i.e. an abandoned agricultural field left to natural succession.
Source: E. P. Odum 1971

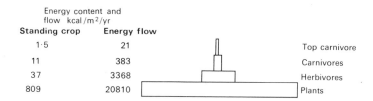

Fig. 1.7 An energy-content pyramid for Silver Springs, Florida. The pyramid represents the data for energy flow through the trophic levels in the course of a year. The standing crop biomass (left-hand column of figure; it is considerably less than the yearly flow in this instance, but in, for example, a grassland it might be almost equivalent to the annual productivity.
Source: E. P. Odum 1971

is perhaps the best guide to energy relations, and here the pyramidal form of the numbers is confirmed (Fig. 1.7). We may note that there is a tendency for the size of the animal components to get larger as the predator chain is followed: being bigger than your prey is an obvious advantage for a predacious species.

Inorganic substances

Living things require between 30–40 of the 90 chemical elements which occur in nature. Their supplies come from many elements and compounds which undergo constant cycling at a variety of scales: some have gaseous phases and hence involve the atmosphere in their ecosystems; others are either in a solid or dissolved state and remain in the terrestrial and aqueous parts of the biosphere. In the first category, CO_2 is an obvious fundamental substance since it is required by plants for photosynthesis. If this were not continually produced by respiration and by combustion of organic material, then the plant cover of the world would exhaust the atmospheric supplies in a year or so. Constant cycling of nitrogen, oxygen and water is also necessary for the support of life. Many mineral elements with sedimentary cycles, such as phosphorus, calcium and magnesium, are also essential for the growth of living tissue. These elements, along with many others, may impose checks upon the populations of a component of any ecosystem if they are in short supply.

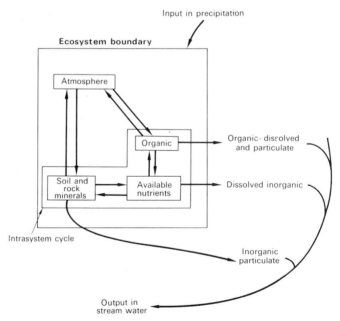

Fig. 1.8 A diagram of the flow and storage of essential elements through a terrestrial ecosystem. They cross the ecosystem boundary in an aqueous medium: in via precipitation and out via runoff. The atmosphere is regarded here as part of the system, i.e. that part of it performing gaseous exchange with the green plants. Within the system the lithosphere also acts as a *de novo* source of mineral elements in contrast to those which cycle between the organic matter and the pool of available nutrients.
Source: Bormann and Likens 1969

In nature, an ecosystem receives its inputs of inorganic materials from a number of sources. As with energy, the plant is the initial point of incorporation. The atmosphere contributes CO_2 to plants, also N_2 to species with nitrogen-fixing bacteria living symbiotically with them, and in turn the plants give off O_2 needed for the respiration of animals. The weathering of the rocks of the earth's crust further contributes basic minerals such as calcium, magnesium and phosphorus: they may also find their way into the atmosphere to be rained out (Fig. 1.8). Water makes its contribution both by assisting in weathering processes in the soil and sometimes, in the form of floods, by spreading nutrients around, as well as transporting them to the sea if they have been lost to the organic components of ecosystems. Its role in the transpiration stream is critical in the transfer of nutrients from the soil to the plant in terrestrial ecosystems.

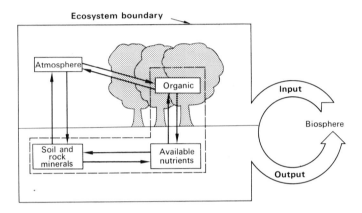

Fig. 1.9 A simplified and more graphic form of Fig. 1.8 showing the compartments for which nutrient levels can be measured.
Source: Bormann and Likens 1969

In the natural state, the flow of nutrients is conserved within an ecosystem. Input and loss are usually small (in terrestrial systems especially) compared with the volume which circulates within the system. In a forest, for example, minerals originating in the rocks enter the soil, become part of the tree, descend at leaf-fall, are mineralized by the soil fauna and flora and then are again available for uptake by the tree (Fig. 1.9). Litter fungi are especially important in forests, where they act as holding sinks for nutrients such as Ca, Fe, Cu, Na, P and Zn. Rhizomorphs may hold mineral concentrations of up to 85 times that of the leaves and have a 99·9 per cent efficiency in retaining them against leaching (Stark 1972). Animals have varying functions: in terrestrial decomposer chains they may perform a crucial role in physically commuting organic debris, and in the oceans the smallest zooplankton appear to be the key factor in the circulation of phosphorus and probably also of nitrogen; large terrestrial animals, however, appear to play a trivial role in nutrient circulation (Pomeroy 1970). Where climate seasonally inhibits many of the soil biota, as in boreal coniferous forests, unmineralized organic matter piles up on the forest floor and so fire may play a similar role. In natural terrestrial systems, the living organisms are very important in the retention of essential elements, and about 50 per cent of the total reserve appears to be incorporated in both living and dead organic matter. Succession appears to be a process by which enough nutrients are accumulated to make possible the rise of succeeding populations, and a climax community perpetuates its stability by conserving its essential elements (Pomeroy 1970). A stable system such as a forest retains most of its nutrients by circulating them within the soil-vegetation subsystem, and losses to runoff are balanced by inputs into the system, as shown by Bormann and Likens (1969) for calcium in a New Hampshire forest (Fig. 1.10). If the nutrient pathways are blocked by the destruction of one component of the organic material, such as the vegetation (for example, by clear-cutting or catastrophic fire), then there is a rapid loss of mineral elements and particulate material,

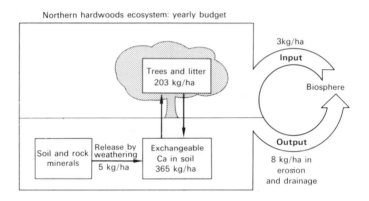

Fig. 1.10 The quantities of calcium present in a hardwood ecosystem in New Hampshire. The major feature of the diagram is the small quantities which cross the ecosystem boundary compared with the amounts cycling within the intrasystem cycle. The output equals the inputs from precipitation and the weathering of soil and rock.
Source: Bormann and Likens 1969

thus contributing to eutrophication and siltation downstream. After disturbances, successional species, such as shrubs and small trees, may play an important role in the rebuilding of the cycling and retention of nutrients. In New Hampshire studies, the pin cherry (*Prunus pennsylvanica*) had an annual uptake of nitrogen 50 per cent greater than that of undisturbed forest, and the rapid growth of such pioneer trees clearly acts to minimize nutrient losses from the ecosystem by the channelling of water from runoff to evapo-transpiration and so reducing losses by erosion and in solution; by producing shade and hence reducing rates of decomposition of organic matter so that the supply of soluble ions available for loss via runoff is lessened; and by incorporating into the vegetation any nutrients that happen to become available (Marks and Bormann 1972). Both successional and stable communities therefore appear to be geared to maximum retention and recycling of essential nutrients.

    On a larger scale, the major flows in the world's nitrogen cycle have been modelled by Delwiche (1970) and the critical points can be identified. For example, the loss of N_2 to sediments is apparently balanced by the gain from volcanic action, and indeed the N_2 content of the air may have increased during geological time. The fixation of atmospheric nitrogen is limited to a few, but abundant, organisms like the free living bacteria *Azotobacter* and *Clostridium*, symbiotic nodule bacteria on leguminous plants like *Rhizobium*, and some blue-green Algae; these are the keys to the movement of N_2 from the air reservoir into the productivity cycle since no higher plants are able to fix nitrogen alone: legumes only do so with the help of their symbiotic bacteria.

Another element essential for living tissue is phosphorus, whose reservoir is the crust of the earth. Thus the release of P into ecosystems is very slow, whereas its loss can be very rapid, especially where soil erosion occurs. Such phosphorus is washed into the deep sea sediments and is for all practical purposes lost to ecosystems. Some, from the shallow sediments, is returned to the land via the guano of sea birds and some as fish, but of the 1–2 million tons of phosphate that are mined every year, most is lost to the sea, and of that only 60,000 tons/yr (60,420 mt/yr) is recovered. Compared with nitrogen, phosphorus is relatively rare (in the ratio of about 23 : 1 in natural waters), and so although crustal reserves are very large, some concern has been expressed about its future availability if a recycling interval shorter than that of major geological upheavals is not accomplished by human intervention (E. P. Odum 1971).

Man requires all 40 essential elements for his metabolism and most of the rest for extra-somatic cultural activities. The overall tendency of his use of these materials has been to speed up the natural cycles so that pulses occur: as an ironic counterpart to the possible phosphorus shortages mentioned above there is the eutrophication of many water bodies because of the output of phosphorus-enriched water from agricultural and urban areas (Hutchinson 1970). One of the results of the acceleration of natural cycles has been to speed up the movements of crustal elements into the oceans, from which their recovery, even if technically possible, is likely to be very expensive and ecologically disruptive. Resource processes which 'short-circuit' these flows seem therefore to be highly desirable.

Productivity and cropping

It will be apparent that biological productivity (the rate of appearance of energy and matter as living tissue) is the basis of all our biological resources, and it is involved with abiotic parts of the planet too. The metabolism of plants and animals is instrumental in maintaining the gaseous balance of the atmosphere, and the world's hydrological cycle interacts at several points with biological production. Again, 'fossil' matter sources appear in productivity considerations because of the limiting effects upon plants of inadequate mineral supplies, and in man-dominated ecosystems because of fuel-energy inputs into resource processes such as agriculture.

Although biological productivity is of considerable importance in human affairs, the study of production ecology is a recent one and subject still to wide margins of error. The measurement of rates of production, for example, is a difficult task involving sophisticated instrumentation in a field setting. Often the only practical way of proceeding is to measure standing crop biomass; this, however, may be very different from annual productivity since there are likely to be seasonal differences or, in the case of short-lived organisms, a turnover rate several times higher than the biomass at any one point in time. In order to reduce some of the errors, and to standardize measurements internationally, the International

Plate 1 An estuary in west Wales. These habitats have a very high biological productivity and biotic diversity, and are often nurseries for offshore fisheries. In economic terms they are valued mostly as potentially reclaimable land for industry or for waste disposal. *(Aerofilms Ltd, London)*

Biological Programme for the study of Biological Productivity and its relation to Human Welfare was carried out during the mid-1960s–1970s. Research Programmes for each major biome have been aimed at providing comparable information on biological productivity.

Results of measurements of primary productivity from various ecosystems reveal, in general, the pattern expected from the visible biomass which is expressed in the physiognomy of the vegetation. Net primary productivities of major biomes (Table 1.2) clearly reflect the intuitive values suggested by the physiognomy of the vegetation type. The values for gross primary productivity given in Table 1.3 portray the same basic picture, using *per diem* data and including some man-manipulated ecosystems (Plates 1 and 2).

A very large proportion of the earth's surface therefore comes into the category of open oceans and arid/semi-arid lands, and thus has strongly constrained primary productivity (Fig. 1.11). In such comparisons we should be careful not to confuse productivity in its biological sense with yield to man or cropping, for even where productivity may be high, it may be of a biological product which for economic or cultural reasons does not form a vital resource.

Given the attention that cultivation brings, it is not surprising that during periods of maximum growth, such crops have very high productivities. On a year-round basis, however, the relatively simple nature of the ecosystem means that the amount of energy trapped is usually less than in a natural system; this is revealed by comparing the data in Tables 1.4 and 1.5. Such differences are emphasized by the data in Table 1.6, when all the measurements are made within the same region, and where the agricultural crops will

Plate 2 An arid steppe in California. Productivity and diversity are low, but owing to proximity to large urban centres, demands to convert such areas to recreational housing or to allow unrestricted access by cross-country vehicles are very high. The ecosystems easily break down under such pressures and regrowth is very slow. *(I. G. Simmons)*

Fig. 1.11 The worldwide production of organic matter during a single season, without complete adjustment for losses to consumers, decomposers and substrate. Thus net primary production may exceed the values shown here, but economically usable products may be much less. Values are g carbon/m²/yr.

Lands	g C/m²/yr
	Over 800
	600-800
	400-600
	200-400
	100-200
	0-100

Waters	
	0-50
	50-100
	100-200
	Over-200

TABLE 1.2   Estimated net primary productivity
(major biomes, c. 1950)

Vegetation unit	Mean NPP (g/m²/yr)	Total for area (10⁹ mt/yr)
Forests	1,290	64·5
Woodland	600	4·2
Tundra	140	1·1
Desert scrub	70	1·3
Grassland	600	15·0
Desert	3	n.a.
Cultivated land	650	9·1
Fresh water	1,250	5·0
Reefs and estuaries	2,000	4·0
Continental shelf	350	9·3
Open ocean	125	41·5
Upwelling zones	500	0·2
Total continental	669	100·2
Total oceanic	155	55·0
World	303	155·2

Source: Leith 1972

TABLE 1.3   Average gross primary productivity of world
biomes and land uses (g/m²/day)

Deserts and semi-arid grassland	0·5
Open oceans	1·0
Continental shelf waters, shallow lakes, forests, moist grasslands, agriculture	0·5–5·0
Coral reefs, estuaries, mineral springs, evergreen forests, intensive agriculture	5·0–20·0
Maximum rates for short periods in very productive ecosystems	60·0

Source: E. P. Odum 1959

have received an energy 'subsidy' from fossil fuels and added fertilizer. The reason for the greater dry-matter production by the trees is linked to the maintenance of a higher leaf-area index for the whole year by the pines compared with the low leaf area and short duration of the crops. The accuracy of measurement and the difficulties of comparing managed and unmanaged ecosystems are discussed by Newbould (1971a), who points out that the differences in seasonality of production and in the biochemical quality of the organic matter may render purely quantitative comparisons meaningless.

TABLE 1.4   Natural and semi-natural ecosystems

	Year-long net primary productivity (g/m²/day)
Giant ragweed, Oklahoma	3·95
Spartina saltmarsh, Georgia	9·0
Pine plantation 20–35 yrs old, England	6·0
Deciduous plantation 20–35 yrs old, England	3·0
Desert, Nevada	0·11
Seaweeds, Nova Scotia	1·98

Source: E. P. Odum 1959

TABLE 1.5   Cultivated ecosystems

	Year-long net primary productivity (g/m²/day)	Growing season only
Wheat, world average	0·94	2·3
Rice, world average	1·36	2·7
Potatoes, world average	1·10	2·6
Sugar cane, world average	4·73	4·7
Mass algal, culture outdoors	12·4	12·4

Source: E. P. Odum 1959

TABLE 1.6   Forestry and agriculture in the English Breckland

	Net above-ground primary production (mt/ha/yr)
Scots pine, maximum production	
23–31 yr age-class	22
mean production 0–55 yr span	13
Wheat	5·2
Barley	3·5
Sugar beet	9·0
Carrots	6·5
Mangolds	6·0
Grassland (hay)	7·5

Source: Ovington 1957

If there are difficulties in measuring primary productivity, then they are greatly compounded when secondary productivity is considered. At the simplest level of perplexity, animals move; and harvesting of them for biomass or calorific value measurements may produce problems, especially if the species is uncommon. Studies indicate that even in intensively managed ecosystems, only about 10 per cent of *gross* primary productivity appears as animal tissue. A measure often adopted is the ratio

$$\frac{\text{(calories of growth)}}{\text{(calories consumed)}} = \text{net growth efficiency}$$

which for beef cattle on grassland is about 4 per cent. The equivalent measurement for pigs, young beef animals and young chickens is of the order of 20 per cent, which is clearly used to advantage in modern intensive farming methods for 'baby beef' and broiler chickens.

The summarizing theme of all discussions of biological productivity is that of limits. These include the overall limit dictated by the quantity of solar radiation incident upon the earth, the efficiency of photosynthesis in fixing the energy, and the limits imposed by the ratio of gross to net primary productivity. Inorganic nutrients may also prescribe constraints by virtue of their short supply and the length of time they take to go through cycling processes. And since there is a loss of energy at each step through a food web, there are limitations imposed upon the productivity of the second and subsequent trophic levels.

Populations

In an ecosystem the flows of energy and matter in the form of organisms, and the adjustment of the individuals to the space dimension of their habitat, are expressed in terms of the dynamics of population of a given species. To understand the dynamics of the numbers of plants, animals and men is to be a good way down the road to the rational cropping of an ecosystem.

In the animal world as in man, the numbers of individuals of a species are determined by the relationship between natality and mortality. Usually these quantities are expressed in terms of time: thus a population increases when birth rate exceeds death rate. Conversely, if the death rate exceeds the birth rate then a population will dwindle and die out.

Three is an incremental rate of recruitment to a breeding population and the general form of the equation for such an expansion is (Boughey 1968):

$$N_t = N_0 e^{rt} \tag{1}$$

where N_t = numbers at time t
N_0 = number at time zero
e = base of natural logarithms
r = rate of population increase
t = time elapsed

which can be expressed logarithmically as

$$\log_e N_t = \log_e N_0 + rt \tag{2}$$

A growth curve derived from these equations is shown in Fig. 1.13. Such a rate of growth is called exponential, and its capacity for effecting rapid increases in numbers is very high. For example, the time taken to double a population can be tabulated thus:

Rate of increase % p.a.	Number of years to double population
0·5	139
1	70
2	35
3	23
4	18

From this we see that quite low percentage rates will produce high absolute numbers quite quickly, a fact not unfamiliar to people repaying mortgage loans at 11 per cent, for instance. As an extreme instance of the potential of the exponential curve we may quote the example of a bacterium which divides into two every 20 minutes. This could produce a colony 1 ft deep over the surface of the earth in 15 days; 1 hour later the layer would be 6 ft deep. That this does not happen is due to a number of factors which are generally termed *environmental resistance,* a term which subsumes a great many influences which affect animal populations (Figs. 1.12 and 1.13).

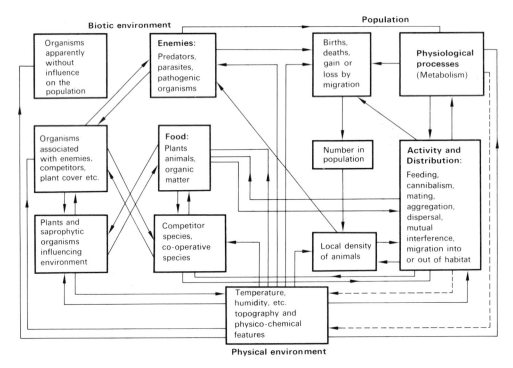

Fig. 1.12 A diagram of the major influences affecting animal populations. Apart from the virtual absence of predation and cannibalism, most of them apply to man too.
Source: Solomon 1969

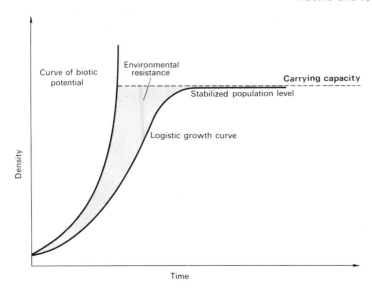

Fig. 1.13 The logistic growth curve flattens out at the carrying capacity, owing to increasing environmental resistance such as the factors in Fig. 1.12. If it were not for that factor, the curve of biotic potential would produce immense absolute numbers of any organism.
Source: Boughey 1968

Without such resistance, a population could fulfil its biotic potential to expand indefinitely. In reality, the exponential curve always levels off, at a value which is termed the carrying capacity of the habitat; it may approach this value gradually from below or it may overshoot and, by virtue of high mortality or low fertility, fall back (with the possibility of oscillations) to the carrying capacity level (Fig. 1.14). The concept of carrying capacity has been elaborated by Dasmann (1964b), who suggests that there is firstly a survival capacity where there is enough food for survival but not for vigour nor optimum growth, and where slight changes in ambient conditions can be disastrous. An optimum capacity appears superior since there is adequate nutrition and individual growth except perhaps for

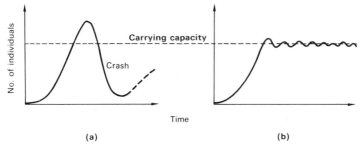

Fig. 1.14 Some populations rise rapidly, exceed the carrying capacity of their ecosystem and 'crash'; others level off near the carrying capacity, although oscillating around that level rather than maintaining it unvaryingly.

a few individuals. A third type is based largely on density, and is the tolerance capacity or the level at which territorial considerations at an intraspecific level force surplus individuals to migrate, or to be denied basic necessities like food, or the opportunity to reproduce. Populations at the survival level may also exhibit such characteristics. Some parallel with the human population may be seen if we equate the survival and tolerance capacity groups with the poorest nations and the optimum capacity with areas like North America and Western Europe; however, the density tolerance considerations might extend to the cities of the richer people too.

If we compare the dynamics of the human population with that of animals, some similarities emerge. The curve for the numbers of the species, upon which there seems a wide measure of agreement between authorities, resembles a J-curve, but so far without any tendencies to reach an upper level. This has given rise to fears that the human population may breed itself beyond the carrying capacity of the earth and has renewed interest in the mechanisms by which animal populations regulate their numbers, especially since many of them stabilize below the numbers which would be expected if all the energy and space resources of their ecosystems were used.

There is some disagreement among zoologists as to the causes of the phenomenon, some of which may be explained by their investigations in particular kinds of environments, and it is not clear which if any of the mechanisms apply to man. Andrewartha and Birch (1954) stress the importance of factors external to the study population, such as food supply at critical periods and sudden shifts in weather, and note the lack of stability of the numbers of any one species even when the whole ecosystem is apparently not prone to large-scale fluctuations. Much of this kind of pattern operates in unfavourable environments or concerns organisms with a short life-span, and by contrast workers in more benign areas such as Lack (1966) stress the importance of density-dependent factors such as intraspecific competition and territoriality, and the role of biological controls such as predation. The homeostatic mechanism, according to Wynne-Edwards (1962), operates via the social behaviour of many animals. Features such as territoriality (in birds especially), the emergence of a hierarchy of dominance (usually called a peck-order and often a male phenomenon), and male sexual displays which are usually designed to secure status among other males, not to woo the female, are all ways in which breeding can be confined to a selected group in the population; in times of low rates of natality there are presumably eugenic consequences with survival value also. The need for the inception of the limitation mechanisms seems to be established at mass displays of either the whole population (the aerobatics of starling flocks are a possible example) or of the males, as in displays at the beginning of the breeding season which involve a number of individuals, like the virtual tournaments of sage grouse or ruffs.

It is tempting to seek analogies of these instances in human populations. Recent trends in male fashion could perhaps be linked less with the desire to attract an already economically independent female and more with the need to establish status in a society which overtly prizes equality; mass synchronous social displays take place every morning and evening in large cities (often more or less coincidentally with the starlings) and are called 'rush hours': it is noteworthy that the display of social characteristics needed to gain admission to an American university fraternity or sorority is called 'rushing'. Further human displays occur on Saturday afternoons except in high summer: these are largely composed of males and bright plumage is not uncommon. It would be worth seeing if any foundation would finance a project to see if commuters and football fans tend to have fewer children than the rest of the population.

With more scientific logic, however, Wynne-Edwards (1962) concludes that *Homo sapiens* has lost its population regulation mechanisms. At the hunter-gatherer stage of culture this capacity was almost certainly present and contemporary 'primitive' groups provide evidence of population control, especially by infanticide. With the coming of the production of food surpluses by agriculture and the ability to store them against hard times, together possibly with growth in absolute numbers, the control of reproduction passed from society to individuals. It has remained there from the agricultural revolution to the present day; current controversy over 'the right to produce' centres fundamentally on whether society should reclaim that control and enforce it through cultural measures such as contraception and induced abortion. Writers such as Stott (1962) produce evidence that stress in animals is often induced by overcrowding in advance of food shortages, and it triggers off mechanisms which reduce fertility or the survival rate of the young; he adduces similar evidence for the human species, based on gynaecological studies, and concludes that a world population 'crash' by starvation will be forestalled by increased rates of the incidence of sterility, perinatal death and unhealthy children, together with malformed and mentally impaired people. Avoidance of such unpleasant conditions must come via the cultural alternatives which are open to us.

Culture

Man sees the world around him through the spectacles of culture, and nature is thus transformed into resources. The elements of behaviour and technology which are fused together to make up culture are very varied, and the mix is different for diverse times and places: for some the spectacles are rose-tinted whereas others seem to see their world through a very dark glass indeed. The sensory perception of the environment and the psychological translation and information of that knowledge into a decision to act, or not to act, upon the environment is a complex study, since between the perceptive input and the executive output lies a shadowy set of values conditioned by experience, imagination, fantasy, and other assorted intangibles derived from both rational and irrational sources. The ability to act is dependent largely upon the effective technology that a group or individual possesses, but behind the motivation lie the more elusive factors outlined above. There are, of course, cases where technology is used for its own sake: the alleged propensity of engineers to build dams whenever and wherever possible, irrespective of the need, is perhaps an example.

In general terms, the world exists not in absolute dimensions but in people's heads. The study of this state essentially consists of trying to understand the workings of the 'black box' of the human brain or group of brains, between the perceptive input and the output of action. The ways in which investigation may proceed vary according to the period of historical time involved. For the preliterate past, there is only inference from the data furnished by archaeology. From such sources it is difficult to make firm statements about the relationships between man and nature in the distant past; it is not, however, impossible to speculate usefully, particularly if ethnological parallels may be accepted. In the later chapter on the relations between unmanipulated ecosystems and hunting-gathering-fishing societies, some observations about this type of relationship will be found. In the case of the literate past, we have writings as a source of evidence for man's attitudes to nature. Some of these will deal explicitly with such a theme, others only implicitly, and there is in published work a great concentration upon the intellectual history of the West in this particular instance; other cultures have in general been little explored from this point of view. The use of written sources as a guide to themes in the relationship of man and nature carries over into the present, where many sources yield both clear-cut and covert clues about the ways in which men view their environment. But those who write about such phenomena may not be typical of those who act, and here the study of the environmental cognition or perception of resource managers of all kinds by means of the methods of psychological research has become of some interest and importance.

By such means the mental attitudes of man towards nature, and hence towards resources, can be studied in the same manner as his attitudes to other phenomena. At the present moment we shall concentrate heavily on the second and third of these sources of information, since both the numbers of men and the level of technology in the preliterate past have generally been such as to exert relatively little influence upon the development of the world's ecosystems.

Man and nature in the past

As hinted above, the evidence derived from written sources can sometimes be criticized as unrepresentative of the reality of its age: a partial sample of a social stratum far removed, perhaps, in values and motivations from those actually engaged in dirtying their hands with real resources. Yet such writers are the formers of images of the world, no less than the recorders of other people's images. They deserve consideration, for many people act according to the image of the world that they have in their heads rather than in the light of objective 'scientific' information, and in any case the whole intellectual climate of opinion of a given time may determine whether or not 'scientific' knowledge is used, or indeed, misused. Keynes said, 'a study of the history of opinion is a necessary preliminary to the emancipation of the mind', and to discern trends in man's view of nature, where externalized in communicable forms such as writing and art, is a necessary preliminary to any study of man–nature relationships, and the ecology of resources is no exception.

From the times of classical antiquity to the eighteenth century, as Glacken (1967) points out, certain themes have dominated man's view of nature in the West. The rest of the world has had its traits also, but they are more diverse and less practical than those of the West, and less widely exported. The idea of a designed earth, for example, is strong in the Judaic-Christian tradition. This essentially theological idea envisages the earth created for man or else for all life with man at the apex of a chain of being. Before the coming of evolutionary theory and ecology this was the West's great attempt to formulate a holistic concept of nature. In this way as many phenomena as possible were brought within the scope of the central theme, demonstrating a unity which was the achievement of a Creator. Although the seventeenth and eighteenth centuries saw criticism of this idea (not of the concept of design but of the relation of this order to the creative activity of the Deity), it could be extended to accommodate the theory of evolution when this began to emerge. At present indeed, the preoccupation with ecology, whose message is essentially that of seeing systems as wholes and of perceiving the order within them, is a logical heir to this tradition of thought. Part of it also is the concept of 'man's place in nature': the postulation of a division of man from the rest of nature was recognized very early and written about by Sophocles, for instance, and it appears most powerfully in Genesis (I, 28–9) where God says to men 'be fruitful and increase, fill the earth and subdue it, rule over the fish in the sea, the birds of heaven and every living thing that moves on the earth'. The persistence of this theme is symbolized by the papal encyclical of 1967, 'The development of peoples', which reasserts the idea of the creation of the earth by God for man. This book, while not aspiring to the authority of those two documents, also accepts that man and nature are different and must be reconciled.

A counter-argument to this theme finds it impossible to admit of a world being created especially for men when they themselves are often so wicked, and when the physical constitution of the world is obviously so imperfect as a habitation for them. In this tradition are the ideas of St Francis of Assisi, who asserted that, although man might be at the apex of creation, this did not mean that all life was for him and at his disposal. The same thoughts are exemplified in present-day protagonists of wildlife, who assert that plants and animals must exist in their own right rather than just by leave of, or for the use of, man.

A second major strand has been the study of environmental influence upon culture. This was one way of interpreting the endless array of human differences, and a powerful aid to the stereotyping of nations since men could be expected to behave as they did on account of the place where they lived. It carried with it the corollary of environmental limitations, and so we find Malthus's concern over the adequacy of food supplies falling within this theme. As is well known, he claimed that the growth of population would always outstrip the means of subsistence, and hence the potential perfectability of man being promulgated by some of his contemporaries was, for environmental reasons, an impossibility.

The Reverend Thomas also dilated upon the modification of the earth to accommodate the growing populations of men, thus participating in the long-lived philosophical theme of man as a modifier of nature, a third major strand of thought. In some forms this was an optimistic tradition: man's skill was to put the final touches to God's unfinished work, or he was to be a bringer of order to, and custodian of, nature. If Ray and Buffon were optimists, then Malthus and, later, George Perkins Marsh were pessimists, for they saw chaos instead of order and profligacy instead of stewardship. Malthus in particular did not believe that nature would improve or that institutional reform could alter his basic principle of population. Nature was niggardly and man was slothful (except, presumably, where the passion between sexes was concerned): optimism about the future of man had to be guarded and the possibility envisaged of only limited progress.

Marsh (1864) was mainly concerned with places rather than people. His writing about the changes wrought by man pointed out that not all these had been injurious to the environment, for soils had been improved and marshes drained so that civilized life might be enjoyed. He also pointed out that environmental change was a geological fact in many cases, but he is best known for his strictures on the misuse of nature that resulted in soil erosion, silting, fires and other downgrade processes. In many ways he is the intellectual forefather of the present all-pervasive concern with the disruptive effects of the technology made possible by our command of energy sources. His words might well adorn the portals of every resource agency in the world:

> man has too long forgotten that the earth was given to him for usufruct alone, not for consumption, still less for profligate waste.

Man and nature today

The themes of man's place in nature, of his subjugation of other components of the planet and his modification of its systems, cannot be said to be dead, although their context has been completely altered by the events of the nineteenth century. In practical terms the industrialization of the West was single-minded and inexorable; it produced the greatest alteration of nature, the greatest inroads on the world's resources and the greatest contamination then experienced. One effect seems to have been the heightening of confusion about man's place in nature. Omnipotence seemed to be manifest, yet the lot of many was so obviously unimproved. One twentieth-century reaction to drifting man, cut off from the earth by the advent of urbanism, has been labelled alienation. It appears to be partly due to the low quality of contemporary man–nature relationships and partly a result of the sheer numbers in our society: the old and the new are vividly portrayed by J. B. Priestley and Jacquetta Hawkes (1955), in their contrast of the Indians of New Mexico and the 'anglos' of South Texas. One literary expression of alienation comes in, for example, the plays of Samuel Beckett, for whose characters the world is unreal and cannot be related to themselves. Man no longer belongs in any natural setting and his externalities (including the environment) are alien and almost certainly hostile. It can thus be treated aggressively or at the very least be regarded as a storehouse whose depletion is of concern only to the owners. The inventiveness and applicability of nineteenth-century technology meant also that the resources of the world appeared to be infinite, for new means of making them accessible and new markets for material products went together. The generally cornucopian view of nature (provided that the proper social structure is present) promulgated by Marx and his later followers is an example of the attitudes to the relationship of man and nature which the nineteenth century produced. In the view that no environmental limits were apparent, Marx was a child of his time (if the bearded Colossus of Highgate may be so personified), but the attitudes live on. Colin Clark (1967), for example, values population growth because it forces innovation and social progress, and large populations enable economies of scale to be practised. He considers that it is possible to feed many more people than are at present alive but does not consider the environmental implications of doing so, and has been strongly criticized by Davis (1968) for being selective of only those aspects of population and economic growth which bring benefits. Deriving from a similar intellectual ancestry is much democratic socialist thinking, as of Crosland (1971) in the Labour Party of Britain. He contends that only continuing growth creates enough wealth to clear up the mess left by nineteenth-century industrialization, and that any diminution in the rate of economic growth results from the snobbery of the middle class in trying to prevent the workers from attaining what the wealthy already have. A slightly ameliorated version of the same document is taken by the committee of authors who wrote a British document (Verney 1972) in connection with the UN Stockholm Conference of 1972. The traditions of the mastery of man has become a central idea in, for example, contemporary Russian versions of Marxism and has led to various environmental disruptions (Goldman 1971). Traditional Chinese ideas about the harmony of man and nature have since 1949 been overthrown by the instilling of the necessity for man to dominate; but as Yi Fu Tuan (1968) has shown, the dichotomy between the philosophy and the actuality in ancient China regarding the treatment of nature was very wide, owing no doubt to the divorce between philosophers and peasants. The current emphasis in China on thrift and the avoidance of environmental contamination may well produce the least ecologically disruptive period for many centuries.

Alienation of a more intuitive character is expressed in the West in the 'dropout' or 'alternative society' concepts practised by some people, and it is significant that a return to older, land-based ways is advocated by many of them. (Their agricultural productivity is generally low, if the evidence of the Taos commune shown in the film *Easy Rider* is typical, so that a wholesale adoption of this philosophy would be nutritionally disastrous.) More conventionally, a scientific alienation is taking place. As a result of scientists' abandonment of control of their discoveries, various catastrophes could threaten, such as biological warfare, geophysical warfare and pesticide poisoning. Foreseers of doom have thus begun to emerge from science to postulate anew the 'dismal theorem' which Malthus first stated. The numbers of man and his treatment of the planet will, they aver, condemn *Homo sapiens* to speedy extinction: from starvation, from nuclear war, from poisonous compounds in all parts of the environment or from sheer breakdown caused by the impossibility of controlling and keeping healthy so many millions of people. A few more decades of present trends in resource use and population growth may, according to Ehrlich (1968), produce an 'ecocatastrophe' whose basic cause is the outstripping of the world's carrying capacity for people. The examination of this position is one of the purposes of this work.

The foregoing discussion has emphasized a dichotomy between man and nature. Whereas 'primitive' people seem to have enjoyed a close association with nature (probably too close for our present ideas of comfort), literate man has erected a dualism, in which 'progress' is linked with control over nature. For many commentators it becomes an increasingly unsatisfactory idea and to them the future would scarcely seem to permit the indifference to the natural world, our environment and provider of our resources, which this attitude allows and may even encourage: it appears healthier for man to regard the planet less as a set of commodities for use and more as a community of which he forms a part. They concede that such an attitude will mean the abandonment of the central theme of our intellectual heritage and especially of its religious accompaniment, its anthropocentricity. To do that requires a revolution in thought, involving essentially the realization that our survival as a species is dependent upon non-human processes; an idea antithetical to most of the traditions of thought discussed above. Too often they advocate, or are interpreted to advocate, a return to some pastoral idyll. There are already too many people for such a relapse and we cannot reverse the time-trajectory of our man-directed systems. In managing the earth for our survival there is no way in which technology can be abandoned: what appears to be essential is a deeper knowledge of the relations between man-made machine-dominated systems and the bioenvironmental systems, and ways in which a stable co-existence can be procured.

Economics

The practice of economics is today the single most important feature governing the relations between man and nature. Based simply on the premise that no substance is in unlimited supply for all individuals, it aims at bringing together supply and demand by the mechanism of price. The concept appears to be identical whether the currency be conch shells, gold or Eurodollars. As far as resources are concerned, economists suggest that they are very largely created by price. If a material becomes scarce, then its raised price will make economic its extraction from poorer quality sources or will enforce a substitution, the invention and production of which is one of the proper roles of science and technology.

In some ways, economics is not always totally suitable for regulating human resource needs at present. At the most elementary level, price cannot always be equated with value, or to put it the other way round, some things of value have no price. They may be thought to be beyond such considerations or there may be no accurate method of fixing a price. Nobody knows the true value of a large area of unspoilt land of outstanding scenic beauty, for all the methods normally used to fix prices fail in some respect or other. In this case, large numbers of people attach value to such an area simply because it is there; they may have no intention at all of using it. When a controversy arose over the construction of a dam in Upper Teesdale in NE England, the 'conservationist' party could not assess the 'value' of the rare arctic-alpine plants, some of which would be destroyed, whereas the Water Board could easily quantify the 'value' of the extra water to be gained from the impoundment.

This relates to another generality, namely that some resources, such as food uncontaminated by residual pesticides, or clean air, or indeed the whole complex of values usually called 'environmental quality', are not in the market, and hence are not subject to the choices normally experienced there. Unless we are very rich we cannot go into the resource supermarket and buy an absence of air pollution, for example, as we could iron ore or wood pulp. In connection with the side-effects of particular processes, we should note that the market mechanism frequently overlooks what are called 'external diseconomies'; the full social costs are not taken into account because they are paid for, usually by society at large, elsewhere in the economy (Mishan 1967). The increasing use of 'disposable' articles, and the whole industry of packaging, is an example in point: the price of disposable, wear-once, clothes for ladies does not include the costs of removing them from the household, converting them to ash and carbon dioxide, and taking the ash where it will not be deposited on the non-disposable clothes of the lady which are hanging out to dry. The external diseconomies of widespread private ownership of motor cars in relation to air pollution, noise and premature death are not reflected in the bargain price which the dealers seize every opportunity to acquaint us with.

Economics has long been concerned with a rational man who optimizes his spending in accordance with carefully chosen criteria. But Galbraith (1967) has argued that the manipulation of the market by large industrial corporations backed particularly by demand manipulation through advertising has made nonsense of the myth of 'consumer sovereignty'. Economics therefore is less and less concerned with the individual's basic needs and spontaneous demands: rather is it more and more determined that he shall buy what industry thinks he ought to have.

The outgrowth of these and other trends in values to which economics appears to have given rise is a series of priorities which have been unquestioned at least since the industrial revolution but which now are beginning to be examined more critically. Initially, attention has focused upon the high place given to the production and consumption of commodities, where a rapid rate of throughput (achieved where necessary by 'built-in obsolescence') is sought. To sustain and enhance this rate, indices like the GNP are watched as barometers of the nation's health, and if the GNP should fail to rise at a pre-ordained rate then dire consequences are forecast and everybody is exhorted to work harder (Boulding 1970). The world view adopted appears to regard the population as being a system with an infinite pool of resources from which to draw and with a sink of infinite size down which to flush unwanted by-products and other discarded materials. The thrust of industrial states, both capitalist and socialist, is towards increased production and throughput of materials, without any valuation of what biologists would call a dynamic equilibrium.

Although the views of established economists are still accorded prophetic status in most of the counsels of the world, challenges have come from radical thinkers such as K. E. Boulding (1962), whose contribution to the infusion of ecology into economics is discussed in the last part of the book; at present, however, the price of a material is usually what governs its pathway through a resource process. The ecological consequences of this movement are studied in more detail in this work since it is suggested that they deserve greater consideration.

Environmental perception

The role of the study of environmental perception or cognition has been briefly mentioned. The articulate expressions of attitudes may be seminal in determining long-term trends, but the majority of people make decisions at a more intuitive and less verbalized and rationalized level. Just as we have examined man–nature relationships viewed in terms of scientific and intellectual history, now we may turn to their study from within: how more ordinary individuals view the world about them and their use of it (Sewell and Burton 1971). Many aspects of the man–nature interaction result in patterns of resource use which are not 'rational'—rational in the eyes of Western science, that is, for we have a tendency to regard Western science as the answer to all problems, just as Western missionaries thought that putting primitive people into trousers might make them less 'savage'. The irrationalities which we detect in both industrial and non-industrial societies are plainly the result of conflict within the various elements of the resource process. In particular, the role of culture is very strong, and while we may study objectively the results of a particular cultural trait in terms of resource use, it is valuable to be able to penetrate the mind of the individual and see the way in which decisions come to be made (Saarinen 1969). The study of the environmentally orientated mental process of the individual 'resource manager' faced with the problem of what to do with his effluent may act as a key to the understanding of many of the irrationalities in resource management and use.

A number of processes are involved. There is firstly the sensory perception of the environment. At the 'primitive' level this is confined to the organs of the human body. Sight is clearly the most important of these as far as resources are concerned, but touch and smell may also be involved. Extra-somatic aids are generally simple: the domestic animals may be used, as for example with dogs flushing out deer or pigs sniffing for truffles. Using a dowsing-rod for water divining is the forerunner of the immense battery of electronic machines which is now used for the detection of materials where the capabilities of technologically advanced societies are available. In this respect, remote-sensing technology is becoming very important. Starting with conventional aerial photography, this has developed into a tool of immense precision using satellite photography, multi-spectral sensing, radar, and computer rectification of received images. In this way, photographs of infra-red reflection for example can be used to study variations in primary productivity, disease infestations of plants, or sources of thermal contamination of water. The United States currently has in orbit a satellite specifically designed for resources work and which transmits imagery from a number of optical-mechanical scanners and microwave bands. Radar imagery is of course independent of weather and diurnal conditions. Inventory and mapping of ecosystems and resources, quantification of ecosystem flows of matter and energy, and the monitoring of change are all facilitated by the application of this kind of technology (Badgley and Vest 1966, Colwell 1968, Johnson 1971). It may be noted, however, that for some substances, especially those in the earth's crust, the age-old methods of trial borings or diggings have to be adopted in the end. But the perception of resources is becoming ever more keen and the inventory of potential supplies more complete, although clearly we are a long way from knowledge of the entire stock of the world's potential resources.

The next stage is also very important. It is here that culture, in its myriad facets, plays a leading part, for the transformation of the perception of the source of a material into the cognition of a resource occurs at this stage. Here resources 'become'; the 'cultural appraisal' takes place. The values informing the cultural appraisal are many and varied. Knowledge, especially of an objective scientific kind like knowing the uses of a particular forest tree or the edibility of a fungus, is central; but so are various types of prejudice, experience and imagination. An item of knowledge may become ritualized into a prejudice, as may have happened with pork in the Middle East; religion and magic are often powerful at this stage, hence the selection of a settlement site may in some cultures be determined less by the environmental suitability than by the interpretation of the numinous qualities of the place by the practitioner of spiritual affairs. Numerous examples of apparently irrational cognition of the qualities of the environment can be discerned, and incomplete appreciation of the properties of a resource is termed cognitive dissonance.

Even in the most sophisticated societies, the completeness of the resource manager's cognition is imperfect. The constraints are many: the costs of obtaining additional information, the lack of technological knowledge, human fallibility and chance are all possibilities. The complexity of the ecology of environment and its social veneer means that the capacity of the human mind for formulating and solving complex problems (even when aided by the computer) is very small compared with the size of the problems whose solution is required for objectively rational behaviour in the real world. Resource managers then become, according to Kates (1962),

> men bounded by inherent computational disabilities, products of their time and place (who) seek to wrest from their environment those elements that make a more satisfactory life for them and their fellows.

In deciding between alternative resource processes, managers may elect to choose consciously, or may adopt more reflex attitudes such as habitual choice with its recourse to traditional or repetitive behaviour, or may engage in unconscious or trivial choice. The choice must then be implemented. Apart from institutional considerations, the primary factor here is the technology available to the manager: the extension, as it were, of his arm. Although physically and temporally separate from the cognition process, it is in reality also

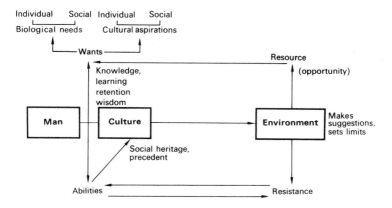

Fig. 1.15 A diagram of some of the factors involved in environmental perception. In reality there must be many more feedback loops than can be suggested in such a scheme, and culture appears to be very diverse.
Source: O'Riordan 1971b

part of the cognition process, for knowledge of technical capability is an important part of the decision-making process. The whole system can be approximately summed up in diagrammatic form (Fig. 1.15). The reality is much more complex, especially in the number and nature of feedback loops, but the diagram presents a useful summary model.

Whatever the complexity of the processes, the outcome in terms of cognition of, and adjustment to, the resources of the environment is of some importance. For sophisticated groups this result may mean the difference between comfort and discomfort, profit and loss; for subsistence cultures, life and death may be at stake. Nevertheless, before the advent of Western culture, some 'primitive' groups had been notably successful in adapting to extreme environments in which there appears to our eyes to be a paucity of resources. The Bushmen of the Kalahari Desert are an often-quoted example: to them the recognition of sources of moisture in their arid surroundings is the critical element. Thus all manner of plants and animals are used for food and some of these probably function largely as sources of moisture. The people become adept at spotting the traces of delicacies such as buried ostrich eggs, for example, which add a valuable element to their diet. The Eskimo groups of northern North America were also notably successful in adjusting to the food and material supplies of their unyielding environment. This success traditionally involved limitations of the population level of a group by means of infanticide and the exposure of non-productive old people. Contact with American culture has changed some of the Eskimo ways, and Sonnenfeld (1966) has suggested that landscape preferences among them may be related not only to their economy but to the degree of 'Westernization' which they have undergone.

Environmental cognition by more advanced people is often a very pragmatic consideration. It may often be important, for example, in the recognition of the probability of environmental hazards where these phenomena are not regular. This is particularly so in areas where such a hazard may make a great deal of economic difference to an individual or group. The role of drought in the farming of the Great Plains is an example, studied by Saarinen (1966). This unpredictable feature of the regional climate was perceived at varying levels. The nature of the hazard was best understood in the driest areas, not surprisingly, but the amount of experience of drought that a farmer had had was also significant in his recognition of the hazard, as was his particular personality. Although greatly variable, this latter generally resulted in an over-optimistic attitude; except in the driest areas almost all farmers underestimated the frequency of meteorological drought.

This somewhat unwarranted optimism is paralleled in work on the perception of storm-flood hazards on the urbanized eastern shoreline of the United States. Here, Burton, Kates and Snead (1969) found contrasts between the technical perception of the hazard by responsible public agencies, and that of the lay people who were the resource managers for much of the housing development along the coastline. They responded to the randomness of storms

> either by making the events knowable, finding order where none exists, identifying cycles on the basis of the sketchiest of knowledge of folk insight, and in general, striving to reduce the uncertainty of the hazard by making it certain. Or conversely, they deny all knowability, accept the uniqueness of natural phenomena, throw up their hands, and transfer their fates into the hands of a 'higher power'.

As one respondent remarked when asked to comment on the likelihood of future storms, 'God doesn't tell us things like that.'

The significance of environmental cognition and subsequent behaviour towards the local resources is not confined to instances of 'economic' activity such as agriculture, industry and settlement. Lucas (1965) has shown how the perception of the qualities of the Boundary Water Canoe Area (Minnesota-Ontario) varies with the type of user. Those who paddled their own canoe were willing to tolerate a lower level of obvious human use (i.e. logging) of the surrounding forest than those who used outboard motors. Clearly this has significance for the 'wilderness' type of recreationist for whom ecological virginity and the absence of fellow humans are paramount. Management of the resources of such an area can thus be directed at maintaining a certain mental condition through supplying the correct perceptive stimuli which assure the user that he is in a wilderness area. This may have considerable application in crowded countries where wild recreation areas are difficult to find.

The mind of the beholder is clearly of paramount importance. A landscape such as that of a British upland area like the Yorkshire Dales or Dartmoor may be perceived in different ways by different groups. One category of people may see the landscape as a set of concrete objects—farms, moorland, trees, roads—which can be preserved or altered. Landscape architects and planners perhaps fall into such a division. Another view is utilitarian: the land represents economic activity, the place where some people, such as farmers and quarrymen, make a living; all other features are subjugated to this central fact. Yet more people respond emotionally to the scenery, since for them it is a scene of beauty which stirs them and to which no change should come. For a last set of people the landscape is symbolic in that it represents freedom, a different place, 'the land beyond', or some other intangible. There is no need to have seen the landscape for it to have this significance. When all these groups are represented on a planning authority committee, the scope for disagreement over the future of the area is wide.

Different backgrounds can lead to differing opinions as to the significance of a given body of facts. This is very noticeable in the gap between some social scientists and most natural scientists over the 'population explosion' and its effects on resources and environment. The former tend (with notable exceptions) to be optimistic and to regard sustained population growth as an acceptable and even desirable phenomenon; the latter are often Malthusian in outlook and make gloomy prognoses. These divergent views of the relations of population and resources are clearly germane to the theme of this book and will be examined in more detail in Part III.

Ecology and economics

Of all the attitudes to the relationships of man and nature that have been discussed, ecology and economics have become most important, and of these two the latter is dominant. Its purpose, as Caldwell (1971) points out, is simple, direct and obvious: if material wealth is seen as the natural and proper goal of man's activities, then the mastery of man over nature (and the pre-eminence of economic thought over ecological thought) becomes a fulfilment of human destiny. The perspectives of ecology are different from those of economics, for they stress limits rather than continued growth, stability rather than continuous 'development', and they operate on a different time-scale, for the amortization period of capital is replaced by that of the evolution of ecosystems and of organisms. So some reconciliation of the two systems of thought might be held to be desirable, in which the findings of one science might be translated with some precision into its impact upon the other, and the values suggested by ecology might become the operational dicta of economics and *vice versa*.

Attempts to find isomorphic concepts and to transfer the language of economics into the realities of environment have been made for example by Boulding (1966b, 1971) when he compares vital flows in both systems, such as energy in one and money in the other. Economic accountings of 'production' of goods and services such as GNP are in fact mostly measurements of decay, since cars and clothes wear out and food and gasoline are oxidized. The bigger the economic system, therefore, the more materials that have to be destroyed to maintain it. Holling (1969) also draws parallels which rely on common features between ecological and economic systems, such as high diversity and complex interactive pathways, distinctive historical character and important spatial attributes, and important structural properties such as thresholds and limits. These led Holling to simulate the process of recreational land acquisition as a comparative process to that of predation in ecological systems. The possibility of energy as an intermediary between ecology and economics is fairly obvious, since it is important in ecosystems at all scales and can also be bought and sold; H. T. Odum (1971) attempts to provide energy flows for a set of marine bays in Texas which bring together all the flows of the ecosystem and man's industrial and recreational use of it, principally by allocating a dollar value to each kcal of energy expended in any activity, e.g. each visitor is assumed to expend 3,000 kcal/day in the area. Even more explicit is Deevey's (1971) statement that energy is the 'key to economic growth and the proximate cause of environmental pathologies', and he ranks the energy flows of the world in the following ratios:

Plant biosphere	Industry	Husbandry	Personal
300	25	2	1

noting that only the former is actually production, the others being consumption, and that the figure for industry represents a level of organization which he finds superior to pastoralism. He stresses, however, that if any of the 25 units is 'invested' in making the 300 non-renewable in a long-term perspective, then this is courting trouble; yet much of the use of energy by man in the cause of gaining economic wealth appears to be doing just that.

Energy appears to be a workable intermediary between ecology and economics in an empirical and descriptive context: we can say that so much energy has produced a particular degree of ecological change. But prediction is much more problematic, for some ecosystem energy-flows may be totally disrupted by the removal of one component, possibly by a very small input of man-manipulated energy, whereas others may require a gross perturbation before they are deflected from their stable state or their successional trajectory; without knowing most of the functional and structural characteristics of an ecosystem, the impact of economically directed energy flows is impossible to foretell except in the most general terms. The relations between order and diversity and the use of tools such as information theory may help to build a body of empirical and theoretical knowledge about this critical interaction, as may other scientific techniques; it is clearly a field in which the practical applications would be considerable.

Interactions

As has been stressed above, energy forms a medium of connection between man and his surroundings, no matter in what form it is used. The first and most obvious of the forms is manpower itself, which requires only social organization in addition to normal survival conditions for its effectiveness. Other forms of energy have to be harnessed and therefore at least to some extent understood before they can become useful ways of doing work.

Animal power was the first, made possible by the use of domesticated beasts in order to perform various tasks, particularly those associated with agriculture. Inanimate sources of power were for long dominated by wind and water, the latter being especially responsible for much industrial development before the nineteenth century; it persists in the importance to many societies of hydro-electric power. But the great surge of industrialization dating from the nineteenth century is linked to the elaboration of ways in which to exploit fossil fuels, dominated at first by coal and more recently by oil and natural gas. In the mid-twentieth century atomic power has been added, where the energy of the nucleus of the atom is released in a controlled fashion to provide immense quantities of energy, usually made available in the form of electricity.

It is possible therefore to divide the history of man–environment relationships into periods characterized by cultural stages in which man's access to sources of energy played a leading role.

The first level we can distinguish is that of the hunter-fisher-gatherer. Present in Europe during Palaeolithic and Mesolithic times, a few groups employing this mode of subsistence have persisted elsewhere to the present day. They have had access only to human energy for their environmental relations, which are dominated by the acquisition of food. The more advanced types have been able to channel this energy technologically: the blowpipe, bow and slingstick represent ways of concentrating the power conferred by human anatomy. Using these weapons, their access to environmental resources concentrated on the cropping of biotic organisms for food, with preferences for large mammals and fish being exhibited by many groups. Wood was used, and where a cutting edge or penetration power was required, then stone, especially in the form of flint and chert, was a common inorganic resource. Many other food sources such as small mammals, birds, berries and fruits were taken, but we may speculate that the expansion of human numbers took place up to the limits of a preferred food source rather than a total supply. Even so, such an economy required considerable space, and territoriality was probably well developed in the various biomes colonized by such people. Surprisingly, the extremes of both desert and tundra have been occupied at this level of technology, as well as the less hostile intermediate life zones. It seems likely that such groups altered their environment insubstantially, but access to a partly controllable energy use like fire was undoubtedly the most powerful way of altering the ecology of their territory. With it beasts might be run towards traps or over cliffs, and underbrush cleared for easier sighting of game. In forested terrain the regular use of fire would gradually produce a more open habitat, as is happening in regular burnt savannas today.

The emergence of *Homo sapiens* was an evolution; his learning of the techniques of domestication was a revolution. In particular, the early farms of the Neolithic of west Asia and Europe represent a tremendous change in the resource base of men. Now the food supply was under much more direct control and it was more concentrated; much less territory was required than for a purely hunting and gathering existence, although these activities persisted. Energy use at first was human-based only, via the hoe and digging stick, but the introduction of light ploughs made possible the use of draft animals. As metals like copper, bronze and iron came into use, so specialists in their fabrication emerged, and there is evidence from certain outcrops of rock in Britain that axe-factories with a far-flung trade network were established. The soil became a perceived resource, as did the forests, grass-lands and savannas which provided the background for much of the early agriculture of the shifting cultivation type. In Bronze Age Britain, for example, evidence of the differential clearance of lime (*Tilia* sp.) trees has been interpreted by Turner (1962) as indicating a knowledge that good agricultural soils would be found underneath such trees. Even relatively primitive forms of agriculture, such as that described by Rappaport (1971), show favourable energy relationships for the societies involved. Tono-yam gardens in New Guinea, for example, had a yield : input ratio (measured in kcal/ac) of 20 : 1 and sweet potatoes of 18 : 1, energy expenditures in weeding, harvesting and carrying the crop all being counted. As might be predicted from ecosystem energetics, the introduction of pigs reduces the ratio to 2 : 1 at best, and it is often < 1 : 1, the pigs being valued then for their protein rather than their calorific value, and for non-dietary purposes.

The success of agriculture, coupled with increased knowledge about the storage of sur-pluses, may well have led to the removal of the decisions about family size from the group, as in hunting societies, to the family, where it has subsequently remained; one result was usually a considerable increase in population levels whenever agriculture was introduced or evolved.

The uncertainties of crop failure from blight or drought are combated by more advanced agriculturalists of the types found in ancient Mesopotamia or medieval Europe. Their use of energy was greatly improved by the possession of the wheel, which made possible the more efficient use of the energy output of domestic beasts. Environmental resources already known assumed new degrees of importance: soil, for example, may be critical to success, and so the selection of the best soils for a particular crop, the draining of fields as by ridge and furrow ploughing, and the maintenance of soil fertility by replacing lost nutrients in the form of manure became subject to group decision and control, as in the manorial system of medieval Europe. Fossil sources of fertility like the calcareous Crag rock, which was used to add lime to the sandy fields of East Anglia, enter the resource nexus, and the uncultivated land or 'waste' beyond the fields was seen as a feeding ground for protein sources such as pigs as well as a source of raw materials and fuel. The overcoming of water shortages through irrigation is an aspect of environmental management and alteration. Its success in arid areas like the ancient Near East led to the accumulation of permanent surpluses which in turn permitted the development of urbanization. Large numbers of people were divorced from everyday contact with their natural environment, but at the same time they often became the rulers of societies characterized by a centralized authority. Ecological mistakes were sometimes made, as in Mesopotamia, where salinification of the irrigated fields and the choking of the irrigation canals with silt from overgrazed watersheds may have caused the downfall of great cities (Jacobsen and Adams 1958). By contrast, the agriculture of western Europe has been markedly stable in its environmental relations, although it is currently beginning to show some signs of breakdown in soil structure. Another effect of agricultural surpluses was the development of urban specialisms such as writing, which is crucial to centralized authority. In this manner, official attitudes to and uses of environment can be promulgated, and the archaeological evidence of the state religions of Egypt, for example, reveals a high degree of attunement to the hydrology and ecology of the Nile. In medieval Europe, authority might through the possession of literacy order an inventory of the resources of a kingdom: by no other means could Domesday Book have been compiled.

The age of the use of fossil fuels, which started in earnest in eighteenth- and nineteenth-century Europe and which flourishes unabated today, has marked a great difference of kind as well as degree in the environmental relations of man. Access to energy stored in coal and oil, with the later addition of hydro-electric power, has allowed the use of the earth's resources on a scale hitherto unimaginable. The steady improvement of technology has meant the recovery of progressively poorer deposits, so that scarcity, except on a regional basis, is practically unknown, thus encouraging moves towards energy-intensive economies (rather than labour-intensive ones) in industrial nations. A great environmental impact has been felt from the use of these energy sources in the mining, smelting and use of minerals and other materials of the earth's crust, so that every industrial region is marked with a million holes and heaps.

The environmental effects of this 'industrial revolution' have been massive and are well catalogued; in most Western countries they are still with us. Urbanization has been the most noticeable: in many ways quite unobjectionable but all the same providing concentrated sources of atmospheric pollutants, together with industrial and domestic effluents to affect the biota (and other men) far beyond the cities of their origin. There have been many other effects also, such as the devastation of forests to provide lumber for building and pulp for paper; more efficient hunting techniques have brought whales to the brink of extinction and some species of plants and animals have been exterminated due to habitat alteration or to increased accessibility allowing more thorough hunting: the passenger

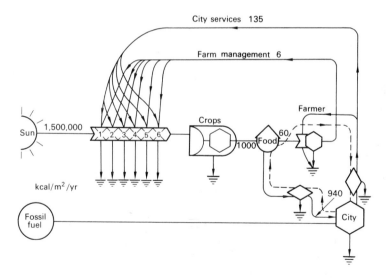

Fig. 1.16 An energy network diagram for modern agriculture. The chief feature is the application of fossil fuel (in this instance channelled via the city acting as an organizing centre rather than directly to the farmer) and the use of much of this energy in management and city-based services. The agricultural population can thus support 32 times its number in cities.
Source: H. T. Odum 1971

pigeon owes its demise to a combination of all these. Agriculture too has become industrialized, with energy from fossil fuels replacing the work formerly done by man. Planting and seeding have become mechanized and are preceded by commercial preparation of the materials; industrial fertilizers have replaced the virtually closed cycle of cropping and manuring; weeding is carried out by mechanical and chemical means, as is the preparation of the soil; and insecticide use further reflects the binding of agriculture to the industrial world. Thus, as H. T. Odum (1971) has calculated, an agricultural population living at 170 persons/km² can support 32 times that number in cities. A production yield of $60/ac ($24.30/ha) for grain in the USA, for example, is due to input worth $54/ac ($21.87/ha) for goods and services from the industrialized culture. The energy flows of an industrialized agriculture are summarized in Fig. 1.16.

Man has so far found he is able to remake the world according to his own plans, and his attitude to the natural world (at any rate the Western attitude, which at the height of European imperialism meant the attitude of much of the globe) has been by and large to maximize economic gain in the short run. The long-term consequences of actions have only rarely been considered and so there has been a build-up. In the past, further expansion of activity has often been seen as a cure for present problems, an attitude given much credibility by the explosive growth and impressive achievements of science and technology. Of late there has been a swing from the unbridled optimism of the nineteenth century, and concern over the protection of nature and scenery, moves towards pollution control and anxiety over the effects of population growth on the biosphere have all become fashionable in industrial nations; underdeveloped countries are as yet inclined to feel that these negative aspects of economic growth are bearable if they bring with them the enhanced prosperity enjoyed by industrialized countries.

The year 1945 was the beginning of the atomic age, with the release from the Los Alamos bottle of a genie of quite ferocious power, and one whose destructive powers have been subject to considerable augmentation since then. Energy from nuclear fission is used for power generation too but is also available for boats, mostly submarines. Nuclear fusion is currently difficult to control, but if it becomes more tractable, and available in small doses, we shall then have a virtually unlimited source of energy. We need to be reminded, of course, that whatever comes from planetary material is eventually finite, and that energy made to perform work is dissipated as heat. The rate of increase of the energy consumption of the USA, for instance, if projected for a few hundred years would make its land surface as hot as the sun.

The introduction of large-scale power is dominated by its cost in relation to the rising expense of the recovery of fossil fuels; and the true cost of nuclear power is not yet known, since at present its use is subsidized by fossil fuel utilization in the process of prospecting for nuclear fuel, for example, and in many other ways. The potential environmental effects of nuclear energy are immense. In an unlimited nuclear war, a great part of the surface phenomena of the earth would be devastated and the legacy of the explosions would live on physically during the lives of the radioactive fallout particles and genetically for innumerable generations of whatever organisms were left: imaginative playwrights and SF writers seem to favour either rats or insects as the ecological dominants. Extraordinary effects could be deliberately wrought. Edward Teller has suggested blowing huge holes deep in the earth's crust in which to store rubbish, and the possibilities of thus 'digging' a second and larger Panama Canal at sea level are under active exploration (Rubinoff 1968). Tables 1.7 and 1.8 help to summarize the role of energy as a crucial element in man's environmental relations. Table 1.7 shows in particular the relative productivities, in both dry matter and energy content, of different food-producing systems, in which the dramatic increase between non-fuel-subsidized systems and those with fossil fuel input can be seen and extrapolated to its extreme condition in algal culture.

TABLE 1.7   Food yield for man

	Edible portion of net primary production	
Level of agriculture	Dry matter (kg/ha/yr)	Energy (kcal/m²/yr)
Food-gathering culture	0·4–20	0·2–10
Agriculture without fuel subsidy	50–2,000	25–1,000
Energy-subsidized grain agriculture	2,000–20,000	1,000–10,000
Theoretical energy-subsidized algal culture	20,000–80,000	10,000–40,000

Source: E. P. Odum 1971

TABLE 1.8   Energy requirements for life support of one man

	Area/man (ac) (1 ac = 0·405 ha)	Organic matter (10⁶ kcal/ day/person)
Pygmies in deep forest	640	341
Monsoon agriculturalists	1	0·16
US man	12	
Fossil fuel base		0·6
Photosynthetic input		1·0
US city dweller	0·0064	0·1
Astronaut in capsule	0·001	2,740,000

Source: H. T. Odum 1971

Table 1.8 compares the living area needed to support one person at various economic levels with the quantity of energy needed to keep him alive. The non-agricultural pygmies must garner their supplies from a wide area of forest, whereas agriculturalists live off a smaller base both areally and energetically; industrial man in the USA receives energy from both photosynthetic and fossil sources in the order of 100–1,000 times the 3,000 kcal/day needed to maintain his metabolism. The quantity of energy support needed by lunar expeditions is astronomical.

Man and ecosystems

Abstraction about the crucial role of energy flows in man's relations with the natural world are not the only generalizations that can be made about his interactions with ecosystems. His effect upon other features of their metabolism, such as limiting levels and their self-regulating mechanisms, must also be briefly considered, as must the outcomes of the magnitudes of the manipulations which he exerts, i.e. the transformation of natural ecological systems into resource processes, whose landscape expression is often identified as land use.

Human effects upon ecosystem processes

There are a number of facets of the ecosystem concept which relate to resource processes, among which the notion of limiting factors occupies an important place. First enunciated by Liebig as a 'law of the minimum' with respect to the supply of chemical materials essential for plant growth, it has widened to include more factors. The idea of tolerance is now used, since it is realized that the continuing presence of an organism depends on the completeness of a set of complex conditions. The efficiency or indeed superabundance of any factor may mean that the limits of tolerance of the organism are exceeded. Tolerance, not only of 'environmental' factors but of intraspecific aggression and interspecific competition, varies with regard to each particular factor and may change synergistically in combination with other features of the organism's environment.

In any natural ecosystem the overall limiting factor must be the amount of solar energy incident upon it, but within this context many other boundaries may operate. The supply of a particular mineral nutrient may not only limit plant growth but because of its importance in animal metabolism may limit the number of animals too. Schultz (1964) has hypothesized that the short supply of phosphorus in the arctic tundra is basically responsible for the regular supply of lemmings: at the height of a lemming peak all the available supplies of that nutrient in the ecosystem are locked up in the small rodents, and only when they die and the element is mineralized, thus becoming available again in the lemmings' forage, can the population build up once more. The heavy grazing by large numbers of lemmings allows more solar radiation to reach the soil surface and speed the release of more phosphorus from the subsoil. The discovery of the importance of trace elements like boron in animal nutrition has highlighted the way in which a limiting factor may result from a quantitatively small component of an ecosystem. In his activities, man may alleviate a critical limit, as by using artificial fertilizers. Alternatively, he may introduce a new lower limit: the disposal of untreated sewage into coastal waters for instance, where its sheer physical presence may decrease the amount of light reaching the littoral and sub-littoral vegetation and hence limit productivity. Such an action also puts a limit on the recreational use of the system.

Another feature of ecosystems which can be relatively easily measured is its diversity, usually expressed as a species : number ratio or a species : area ratio. These ratios increase during the early and middle stages of succession but appear to decline slightly once a steady state or climax condition is reached. Diversity is taken to indicate a state of complexity where energy flux and transformational efficiency are at their highest. A species may have a wide variety of food sources and an equally diverse array of predators so that any accidental disturbance will be damped down. Thus has arisen the hypothesis that stability of ecosystems is a function of their diversity (MacArthur 1955). Such an idea is probably too simple to apply generally, and other research has indicated, for example, that stability at herbivore and carnivore trophic levels increases with the number of competitor species (Watt 1965); and in one study, greater diversity at one trophic level was accompanied by lower stability at the next higher level (Hurd *et al.* 1972). Again, in some systems a key component can determine the stability of the whole of the system, as suggested by Paine (1969) in the case of the Crown of Thorn starfish irruptions. In the case of ecosystems cropped to provide resources or into which wastes are disposed, the concept of overall stability is more important, i.e. the ability of the system to return to an original condition after a perturbation or even its ability to achieve a new level of stability under a permanent stress. Stability thresholds have been studied empirically, as in the case of trampling on alpine tundras (Willard and Marr 1970), and a good deal of research on computer modelling is designed to allow prediction of the changes that will follow a given natural or man-made input into the ecosystem (Woodwell and Smith 1969). The analysis of the resilience of ecosystems to human modification is nevertheless at an early stage and is a field in which considerable advances would be of great practical importance (Schultz 1967, Margalef 1968, Watt 1968, Hill 1972).

Ecosystems also have a multiplicity of homeostatic mechanisms, called feedback loops in cybernetic terms, which tend to maintain the system in a stable condition. By means of the growth, reproduction, mortality and immigration of the organisms, together with the process involving the abiotic components of the system, the quantities and rates of movement of matter and energy are controlled.

Instability in systems is a consequence of disorder and has been compared by Schultz (1967) to the thermodynamic concept of entropy: systems in which disorder is increasing are becoming highly entropic; those which are building up order are negentropic. Life itself would thus appear to be a massive and continuing accumulation of negative entropy. If it were possible to measure the rate of change of entropy or its real equivalent in ecosystems, then this parameter would possibly be a measure of the 'health' of systems from the human point of view. Its role in the manipulation of resource processes would be helpful, since man's main activities seem to be to remove the homeostatic mechanisms and promote instability, sometimes to the point of outright destruction: consider the example of an overgrazed range which first of all has rapidly declining plant productivity (and hence animal yields) and then undergoes soil erosion.

In ecological terms cropping means the removal of energy-rich matter from a particular ecosystem at a particular spatial scale. The products of the resource usage are then put back either into the same ecosystem or into another. Energy is irrecoverably being given off as heat, but the other products are not in fact lost to the world ecosystem, if we except astronauts' excreta. Man's cropping is at both herbivore and carnivore level but is less usual at top carnivore level because of the relative scarcity of the animals at this stage, unless they are gregarious organisms such as some species of fish. Solitary carnivores may often be utilized for culturally desirable products such as eagle's feathers and leopard skins. The detritus chain also supplies animal products: *moules marinières* are a crop from such a source.

The input of man consists of energy and matter in various forms. Much of the energy input into all resource processes is now from fossil fuels and some matter is also fossil, in the form of mined rock. The whole process of cropping is accomplished by the application of man-directed energy and matter. The mobility of man over the surface of the globe conferred by access to energy sources and the development of technology has also meant the transmission of species of plants and animals from their natural habitats to other places. Many of them are unable to survive in their new lands, but some have been spectacularly successful, as with the rapid spread of the starling into the urbanized eastern seaboard of the USA; the history of the rabbit in Australia is perhaps the best known. Success seems to occur either when there is a vacant niche that no native animal has succeeded in filling, or when the introduced species can outcompete the indigenous biota. Often too, the transplanted organism leaves behind its natural predators and may not have any in its new home. Highly manipulated ecosystems, such as cities, waste ground and agricultural land, frequently provide habitats for introduced species.

In the pursuit of crops, the removal of competitors becomes important because they represent energy and matter that man cannot or will not garner. Plants other than the chosen crop become weeds; animals that compete for forage at the herbivore level or predate upon the chosen crop species become pests. 'Weed' and 'pest', it must be emphasized, are cultural concepts since there are no such things in natural ecosystems. Such simplification reduces the energy flow through the system by reducing its diversity (Fig. 1.17). Inducing the food chains to converge upon man may well increase the net crop for man and make it more concentrated in protein, but the overall flux of energy in such systems is lower than in the natural state, since gathering and processing stages result in net losses of energy which are subsidized by fossil fuels in an industrial context (Fig. 1.18). Man very often thus puts the brake on succession (which represents the building up of diversity) and maintains systems at an early stage. Overcropping may well cause an ecosystem to revert to a very early stage of succession, one with much bare ground and hence susceptible to soil erosion for instance, and in some places this may mean a change to a more xeric kind of vegetation. Overgrazing on the semi-arid grasslands and the steppes of western North America or the Saharan fringes has enlarged the desert areas, and though this is not proven, the outbreaks of locusts could very well be a consequence of the years of overgrazing of the parts of the world in which they occur: removing any woodland or scrub that might harbour bird predators, for example, and providing suitable sites of oviposition in open sandy soils. The British grouse moor, reduced by management practices to a monoculture of heather (*Calluna vulgaris*) and grouse (*Lagopus scoticus*), with all other plant species burnt off and all other animal species shot off, is highly unstable. Heather bark beetle can spread very rapidly, as can grouse ringworm. They are in fact epidemics whose transmission is facilitated by the ready availability of more host organisms, and so they spread with the rapidity of hysteria in a women's college at examination time. Man's response to instability is usually to increase his inputs of matter and energy, thus producing an ever-increasing spiral of manipulation in which the inputs needed to promote temporary stability themselves require higher inputs to achieve equilibrium at a later stage.

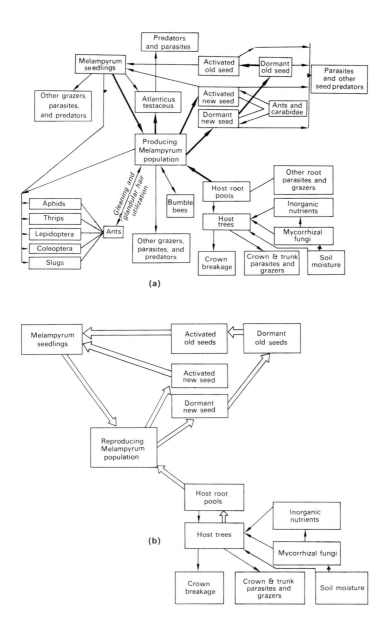

Fig. 1.17 An ecosystem centring around a plant parasitic on tree roots, *Melampyrum lineare*, in Michigan: (a) the natural system, showing biological relationships; (b) the system after the application of insecticides had eliminated certain components. The simplified nature of the ecosystem in (b) is apparent.
Source: Cantlon 1969

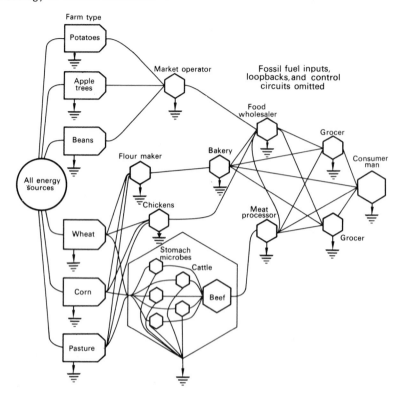

Fig. 1.18 An energy network diagram (unquantified) of the convergence of food chains necessary to develop high-quality (especially high in animal protein) nutrition in industrial countries. The network of 'middlemen' who perform the gathering-in are a source of numerous losses of energy from the system. 'All energy sources' refers to fossil fuels used in agriculture as well as solar energy; industrial power sources are also needed to enable the convergers to perform their functions.
Source: H. T. Odum 1971

One aspect of simplification is the extinction of biota. By various methods, from outright killing off for food or pleasure to the alteration of habitat, a wide variety of plant and animal species have been eliminated at local or regional and world scales. Where these groups were rare anyway and possibly towards the end of their evolutionary term, then man has perhaps merely accelerated a natural process. But it is difficult to imagine this to be true of the passenger pigeon, whose flocks were said to have darkened the sun at noon in the Mid-West of the nineteenth century but the last specimen of which died in a Cincinnati zoo in the 1920s. Neither is it likely to be so of the blue whale or the Javan rhinoceros or the oryx, to name but a few of the animals on IUCN's list of endangered species. Such devastation must be placed in perspective: the phenomenon of 'Pleistocene overkill' indicates a long history of man's effect upon animal population. Extinction of biota appears therefore to have been a long-term concomitant of man's status as an ecological dominant, although there are now powerful cultural currents, in the Western world at any rate, to try to halt this process. By definition, however, the loss of currently rare species is unlikely to produce unstable ecosystems: it is more probable that large uniform strands of very common species will produce that particular effect.

Man's manipulation of ecosystems

We turn now to providing an introduction to the major part of this book, the consideration of man's uses of the world's environments, considered in ecological perspective. Each of the themes briefly reviewed here is taken up at greater length in a section of its own.

At some stage in the last million or two years, all the ecosystems were unaffected by man: they were pristine or virgin. A few such places remain, but much of the rest of the terrestrial surface has been altered in some way. The nature, intensity and antiquity of his transformations enable us to compile a simple ranking of the land-use systems according to their degree of manipulation away from the pristine condition. At one end are ecosystems which are either left untouched or which it is desired to keep in as 'natural' a condition as possible; at the other man's structures obliterate entirely those of nature. Thus the lowest manipulation is typified by the sea or the high peaks of the Andes, the most alteration by Manhattan or Europoort.

At present, our knowledge does not enable us to compile all the data about these systems that we would like, such as their primary and secondary productivity, their response to increased demands for their components, and the history and type of man's alterations. Many of these features are known about at a quantitative level and the work being pursued under the aegis of the International Biological Programme (IBP) will doubtless yield a great deal of knowledge about the productivity of ecosystems. For the present we are mostly confined to more general accounts.

Apart from completely unused land, areas used for *outdoor recreation and nature conservation* represent the condition of least alteration. Where there is a single-use management aim for these, the object is generally to disturb the *status quo* as little as possible, and to maintain the ecosystems as they are at the time of designation or even to restore a former condition. This concern may even lead to the confusion of trying to stop natural processes such as fire or succession in order to preserve particular biota or landscapes even though under natural conditions they would be transient. Limiting factors in this system usually relate either to the numbers of a particularly favoured organism or to the populations of the observers, which if large enough diminish the quality of the crop. In this case it is mainly aesthetic satisfaction: the difficulties over the management of the National Parks of the USA illustrate this point. Most manipulation in these systems involves the control of animal populations which exceed the carrying capacity of the Reserve or Park because its legal limits are unrelated to the true boundaries of the ecosystem of which they are a component.

Requiring little more manipulation is *water catchment*, and indeed in many wildlife areas it is successfully combined with the preceding land use. Apart from the major landscape changes induced by dams and the subsequent replacement of terrestrial by aquatic systems with possible consequent modifications in local climate, the watershed area is often little altered, especially since there is not complete agreement about whether trees are beneficial to water yield (in terms of steady release) or harmful (by transpiring a goodly proportion of the system's water back into the atmosphere). Once caught, the water may be managed to effect far-reaching alterations such as irrigation or industrial growth, but the areally larger watersheds are not often subject to large-scale manipulations.

The *grazing* system represents the large-scale pastoralism of a selected domesticate. All other herbivores, together with the carnivorous predators of the chosen animal, are regarded as pests. Characteristically there is no return of minerals to the soil other than as the excretory products of the animals. (Intensive grazing with highly controlled conditions of herbage yield and fertilizer input is regarded as part of a sedentary agricultural system.) If it is not to degrade the plant cover, pastoralism must be wide-ranging and long recovery times are necessary, especially in arid and semi-arid environments. If flocks are too large and come back too soon to a patch of forage, then trampling may result in puddling of soils and thence their erosion; and selective grazing will certainly eradicate the palatable species in favour of tougher grasses or xerophytic plants such as thorny scrubs or succulents. Manipulation of apparently natural pasture lands has been proceeding for several millennia, in consort with the evolution of domestic herbivores and the use of fire as a management device. Recent research, especially in East Africa, has suggested that a higher amount of living tissue per unit area (biomass) is found under 'natural' conditions, and that as far as animal protein yield is concerned it is better to harvest the native fauna; also they do not degrade the habitat as do domestic beasts. This is one way of altering the whole dimension of a critical limit; more conventionally used are fertilizer input (e.g., by aerial dusting) and vegetation control using various methods of encouraging palatable and nutritious species which help to raise the carrying capacity for stock.

The longstanding but gradual system modifications represented by a pastoral economy are paralleled by one type of *forestry* which 'grazes' through virgin forest, allowing natural regeneration in its wake. On the other hand, modern forest plantation in Europe for instance is more like contemporary farming, exhibiting controlled inputs of nutrients, careful thinning out, lavish use of pesticides and orderly harvesting. So forestry is difficult to place on a gradient of manipulated systems since it can occupy most places from the barely altered to the totally artificial. A reasonable position seems to be to regard it as more manipulative than grazing and less so than agriculture. In biological terms forestry represents the removal of nutrients from the local ecosystem and the disappearance of the dominant of the community. Even if only temporary, the effects are therefore strong: careless forestry can lead to drastic soil erosion and consequent river silting, to quote two well-attested examples. As far as plant nutrients are concerned, the practice of removing and often burning leaf-bearing branches *in situ* means that many of the nutrients essential for tree growth find their way back into the local ecosystem and only the lignified wood is borne away, with its smaller complement of elements likely to be in short supply in the system, whereas soil erosion inevitably carries away mineral nutrients.

Towards the highly manipulated end of the scale must be placed *shifting agriculture*. Although after the plot has been abandoned the system may revert to its original condition, there are suggestions that this is never totally achieved and that small differences in the secondary system always exist. As Geertz (1963) points out, the most interesting feature of shifting agriculture in tropical forests is that the crops planted in the clearing imitated the former community. The miniature forest of crops gives complete cover of the site, so that it is not exposed to the leaching effects of the heavy rainfall. The rapidly fluxing mineral cycling of the forest is not initiated, since the plot is cultivated until the nutrients are more or less exhausted and it is then abandoned to regain higher levels under the secondary forest. In the normal working of the system the critical points are probably the initial nutrient supply which, in tropical forests especially, is mostly in the vegetation and not in the soil (hence the practice of slash-and-burn) and the maintenance of soil structure. Under present conditions very little is usually done about either of these. The overall critical point comes when population levels make it necessary to re-utilize a plot before its nutrient levels and soil structure have been built up again, and diminishing yields coupled with soil erosion are the frequent consequence.

The most highly manipulated of all the non-urban systems is *sedentary agriculture*. Here, the food chains are subordinated to the monocultural production of a crop which either comes to man as a herbivore or is fed to herbivores for subsequent animal protein yield. Thus all competitors are removed and this necessitates either high inputs of energy, as in weeding and bird-scaring, or of matter, as in the form of chemical pesticides. The mono-cultures are usually prone to epidemics, so that the high yields of the intensive agriculture areas of the sub-tropics (where usually water is a limiting factor and irrigation is the means of lifting its threshold) and temperate zones are achieved only at the price of high inputs by man. This is especially true of mineral nutrients, for the use of the crop may be thousands of miles from the area in which it is grown, and few of the metabolic products find their way back to the fields: most are dumped in the sea. Although much of the energy gained in this system can be cropped by man, there is nevertheless a great reduction of fixed energy compared with the system which preceded it: compare for example the amount of photosynthetic tissue per unit area of a forest with that of a typical row crop, growing for perhaps five to six months of the year.

In the process of manipulating ecosystems for his own ends and in recovering and processing his resources, man may well affect the systems by the material which he returns to them. Very often these are unwanted and even toxic products and they are generally referred to as pollution. This topic along with other negative features of resource use will also be dealt with in Part II.

Further reading*

BOUGHEY, A. S. 1968: *Ecology of populations.*
BOULDING, K. E. 1966: Ecology and economics.
CROCKER, T. D. and ROGERS, A. J. 1971: *Environmental economics.*
FIREY, W. J. 1960: *Man, mind and land.*
GLACKEN, C. J. 1967: *Traces on the Rhodian Shore.*
GREENWOOD, N. and EDWARDS, J. M. B. 1973: *Human environments and natural systems.*
ODUM, E. P. 1971: *Fundamentals of ecology.*
ODUM, H. T. 1971: *Environment, power and society.*
WATT, K. E. F. 1968: *Ecology and resource management.*
— 1973: *Principles of environmental science.*
WATTS, D. 1971: *Principles of biogeography.*

* Full publication details are given in the Bibliography.

Part II
Resource processes

2

Unused lands of the world

In this section we are concerned with those parts of the world where the terrestrial eco-systems appear to be virtually unaltered by man, either because he is present but does not exert any manipulative effect on the ecology, or because he is, in increasingly fewer places, absent. Men may be settled at a particular point and rely on outside sources for nearly all their materials and hence by their self-sufficiency not exert any resource-using pressures on the environment, as in the case of service camps like the US base at the South Pole which is supplied by air. In another category are the settlements which produce within their own area most of their needed resources and obtain the rest by trade along routes where self-sufficient transport is used. Desert oases with their accompanying trade (traditionally carried by the frugal camel) are examples of this category. At the point of settlement there is admittedly a more or less complete obliteration of the original ecology, but it is limited in area, and there is no tentacular reach into the environment for resources.

Man is also said to function only at an animal level in some ecosystems where he is subject to the same competitive and predatory pressures as other mammals. Only hunting, fishing and gathering cultures can be regarded as belonging to this group, and we shall look at examples of such people to try to assess the validity of the supposition that they do not in fact manipulate the ecosystems to which they belong. A schematic layout of these categories is given in Fig. 2.1.

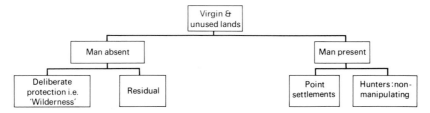

Fig. 2.1 A scheme of the various types of unused land and wilderness referred to in this chapter.

Hunting, gathering and fishing

Hunting and gathering was once the dominant mode of existence of our species, but by AD 1500 only 15 per cent of the world's land surface was inhabited by such peoples, at a time when the ecumene was more or less fully occupied. Today only a few pockets of hunters and gatherers survive, and their culture has almost always been altered by Western contact. Some Indian and Eskimo groups in North America exist largely on hunted products, although contacts with whites are at a high level; less influenced perhaps are people such as the 5,000 Bushmen of southern and south-west Africa who pursue a very largely aboriginal form of life. In such a category also may be placed some of the non-agricultural groups of the 170,000 Pygmies of central Africa such as the Aka, Efe and Mbuti, the Aborigines of Australia, and some Indians of the interior of Brazil and Venezuela. Together with a few other groups, they form possibly about 0·001 per cent of the present population of the world (Murdock 1968).

Such a sample is not therefore the best material for estimating whether or not they exert long-term effects on their ecosystems. To add to the difficulty, most of the studies done on them have been on their cropping as it relates to features of their culture rather than long-term investigations of subsistence patterns and the ways these might have been affected by the hunting and gathering patterns of the people themselves. Most of what follows is therefore inferred from anthropological studies designed for another purpose.

At a very simple level of subsistence are the !Kung Bushmen described by Lee (1968) who live in the Dobe area of Botswana. Here, 466 of them lived in 14 independent camps, each associated with a water-hole. Around this focus, a 9·6 km hinterland (i.e. within convenient walking distance of the water hole) was exploited for subsistence materials. The !Kung practise very little food storage, for rarely more than 2–3 days' supply is kept at hand, and the main foods are vegetable in origin, comprising 60–80 per cent by weight of the diet. The main item is the Mongongo nut, the product of a drought-resistant tree, which contributes about 50 per cent of the vegetable intake and which yields 600 kcal per 100 g edible material and 27 g protein per 100 g. Although many kilograms of these nuts are eaten, many more are left to rot on the ground, so apparently the resource is not fully used up. Of the other sources of vegetable foods, 84 species of edible plants are recognized (including 29 species of fruits, berries and melons, and 30 species of roots and bulbs), but of these 75 per cent provide only 10 per cent of the food value and thus the use of them must be light. There is a parallel situation with regard to meat-eating. The Bushmen name 223 species of which 43 are classed as edible, but only 17 are hunted regularly. It is not said whether this has always been the case or whether such a selectivity represents the end point of a long period of shifting numbers of animal populations. The adjustment of these Bushmen to the resources of their semi-desert environment is successful, for even though 40 per cent of the people do not contribute to the food supply, signs of malnutrition are absent and Lee (1969) estimates that they receive about 2,140 kcal and 93 g of protein per capita per day when an adequate diet would consist of 1,975 kcal and 60 g of protein. No starvation, even of the unproductive people, is necessary because of the basic dependence on reliable vegetable foods adapted to the local ecological conditions. It would seem therefore that no manipulation of the environment is necessary (nor indeed may it be possible) provided the population does not over-use the vegetable resources, and this appears not to happen, though Lee does not comment on any conscious attempts at population control.

In some ways the situation of the Bushmen is paralleled by a community like the Hadza of Tanzania (Woodburn 1968). They also subsist largely on vegetable matter, but meat and honey make up about 20 per cent of their diet. Even in times of drought, the 10 species of plants which contribute the main part of their nutrition do not fail and so there is never any general shortage of food. As with the Bushmen, the predominant activity of the men is hunting but although this brings in a prized food supply, it is scarcely an essential one. No attention is paid to harvesting either plants or game with sustained yield in mind: gathering and killing are indiscriminate. Even so, the ecosystem apparently goes on giving the Hadza adequate nutrition (in a survey of 62 children no evidence of kwashiorkor, marasmus, rickets, infantile scurvy or Vitamin B deficiency was seen), without undue effort on their part: an estimated average of 1–2 hours per day is spent in getting food. Extermination of game is to some extent presumably alleviated by the fact that only a small minority of the adult men do the hunting, and there is no pressure by men upon men to do it or be skilful at it, although keeping a wife may be difficult for an unsuccessful hunter. Further, gambling with metal-headed arrows is a favourite way of passing the time during the dry season and this probably relieves the hunting pressure on the animals.

Some contrast is offered by the subsistence patterns of the native inhabitants of the arctic regions of North America, of which the Netsilik Eskimos who inhabit the tundra regions north and west of Hudson Bay are a sample (Balikci 1968). Their base is essentially a marine-winter (seal) and inland-summer (caribou, salmon trout) movement with elements of substitution should one resource fail. For example, caribou would be hunted across the open tundra with bow and arrow should the normal method of killing them from kayaks at a river crossing fail. The critical period is the long winter, and caches of food for such a period are necessary. Population seems to have been severely limited to those who could be supported readily during the lean times. Thus female infanticide, senilicide and invalidicide were all practised when necessary, especially when travelling was essential. So over very large areas, the population density was quite low: in 1923, the Netsilik numbered about 260, in a region 480 × 160 km in size. In such a context, the harshness of the environment must have meant that the gaining of subsistence in the short term was a considerable struggle and the conscious manipulation of the ecosystem for the long term was scarcely likely. The advent of Western culture has altered the living conditions of most Eskimo, for they can now rely upon imported food from both trade and welfare programmes, and also have access to fossil fuel sources. In a group studied on Baffin Island, Kemp (1970) calculated that in one year the people gained 12,790,435 kcal of consumable food from wild sources. This was backed up by the outside world in the form of 7,549,216 kcal of store food, the equivalent of 8,261,600 kcal in ammunition, and 885 gal (2,815 litres) of gasoline for snowmobiles and outboard motors. In this area hunger is now virtually unknown, although it was in any case rarer than in the harsher terrain of the Netsilik.

In general, hunting and gathering seems to provide a very adequate way of life which can persist for centuries without radical alteration. This suggests that manipulation of ecosystems on a conscious level is rare; unconscious manipulation disturbs the system so little that fluctuations in yield or sudden adaptations to different food sources caused by catastrophes are virtually unknown. Thus obvious, and perhaps even borderline, malnutrition is rare. Even the minimal dietary requirements provided by hunting and gathering often allow such people to fare better than neighbouring groups who subsist on primitive agriculture or who are urbanized. Thus starvation is commonplace only in extremely rigorous climates where wild animals form practically the entire diet. Elsewhere, if there are any selective effects of shortages, they lie in the differential mortality of the old and infirm in the face of the water shortages which are more likely and more frequent than lack of food. Mortality from other causes is not particularly high among hunter-gatherers. Chronic diseases, traumatic deaths, accidents and predation vary in their incidence but are generally low (Dunn 1968). But in most such societies, social mortality has been part of the population–resources equation, with infanticide the most widespread practice. If, therefore, we have a tendency to regard hunter-gatherers as the members of the original affluent societies then it is because they did not attempt to populate their territories up to the limits of the carrying capacities of the lands (Deevey 1968). Either populations were kept down by systematic infanticide or else groups moved elsewhere (Birdsell 1968). Under such conditions, manipulation of environments, though not by any means impossible, becomes much less likely.

The evidence from modern hunters is so scanty and of such an indifferent kind for our purposes that it is scarcely possible to come to a firm conclusion about whether lands occupied by them are virgin lands, i.e. have unmanipulated ecosystems. In practical terms, since they are such small groups, it does not perhaps matter. Theoretically, however, there ought to be a point where the shift is made from man as an animal component of an eco-system to man the changer of the ecosystem. The factors involved are very diverse, but two have major significance: the population numbers and the fragility of the ecosystem. The importance of the first of these is seen in the population control mechanisms exerted by many groups. Quite possibly experience at a past time had shown them that to grow too large in numbers was to exert an influence on the local ecology which was inimical to future food supply. The fragility of the ecosystem is another variable: semi-arid and arctic areas are particularly vulnerable, whereas temperate zones tend to have greater powers of recuperation after man-wrought alteration. The overall picture presented is of a mosaic in which the presence solely of hunters cannot automatically be taken to imply unaltered ecosystems; but most of the evidence which would enable more precise investigations to be made has now been overlain or wiped out by later changes.

Unused lands today

The 'unused' or 'virgin' lands of the world at present can only be found where human settlement is sparse. Not only is absence of man, or his presence at a very low density, necessary but also his use of either a simple level of technology or a 'point' settlement which is self-contained or relies on outside sources for its materials.

Let us differentiate between two types of 'virgin' lands: those which remain wild because they are residual lands of no value to contemporary resource processes, and those where there is a deliberate preservation of the wild for its own sake or for some other non-exploitative purpose. This second category is often described as wilderness: a term which although equally apt for the first set of lands is perhaps more useful where a particular concept of the role of wild terrain in relation to human purposes is envisaged. We shall deal with these two sets of virgin terrestrial ecosystems separately; the most pristine set of ecosystems of all, the sea, is treated individually later in the book.

Sparsely settled biomes

The largest more or less continuous single area of 'unused' land not deliberately preserved belongs to the arctic and subarctic zones of Eurasia and North America. These lands are mostly in the possession of the USSR, Canada and the USA (Alaska), with contributions from Finland, Sweden and Norway. The region has only relatively recently emerged from glaciation and is often characterized by immature soils and poor drainage. The characteristic vegetation type is the tundra, although many wetland and mountain communities also exist. Southwards, a belt of hardy deciduous forest like the birch scrub of Lapland may intervene between the tundra and the coniferous woodlands of the boreal forest biome. The animals are all adapted to survival over a long and very cold winter.

Like the high arctic and polar lands of perpetual snow and ice beyond them, these northern territories are sparsely settled. Modern incomers mostly live at 'point settlements' supplied by air or sea; the native peoples have always been few in number, although more wide-ranging at ground level both inland and across the ice-covered seas than immigrant whites. Both groups have had some effect on the ecology of the northern wilderness, though of different types. The native populations were largely dependent upon animals such as reindeer, caribou and seals for their subsistence. The number of people was small and the herds of animals immense so that probably no permanent change was effected in the natural ecosystems unless the biota were at a low level: the decline of the musk-ox in the Canadian tundra may have been due to native overhunting, although protection has now allowed it to regain higher population levels.

The advent of industrial man to the north has meant both direct and indirect change. Direct alteration of areas comes from mining, trapping and logging, although the last two need not wreak permanent change on ecosystems if carried out with due regard for sustained yield; inevitably such policies have often been neglected. Indirect changes come from incidental operations: fires from logging which run up onto lichen-clad slopes and destroy the winter feed of caribou, for example. The explosions from seismic testing for petroleum scare away the arctic fox, according to many Eskimo, and there is now the possibility of large-scale oil contamination from the finds on the arctic slope of Alaska and Canada's North-West Territories. In such a cold climate, the longevity of spilled oil is not known and might persist for decades. The same development is producing plans for pipelines across the tundra carrying heated oil, and the effect this will have on the permafrost is not properly known. At point settlements such as drilling rigs, considerable erosion of the tundra can be caused by vehicles and temporary dwellings if the permafrost is not protected by a thick pad of insulating material such as gravel. The wastes from such places are also apt to attract scavenging animals such as polar bears which then tend to end up as rugs. The northern lands, therefore, are still vast wildernesses of mostly natural systems, but exploitation is eroding these wild areas, and agricultural expansion in their climatically more favourable parts is still an aim of some governments. The ecosystems are generally so simple and specialized that it takes very little to cause their breakdown: this can be seen to a minor extent in Iceland, where there has been no impact of heavy industry on the land to disturb the sparsely vegetated surface, but where sheep grazing has neverthe-less caused shifts in vegetation towards more open communities and hence an increase in the surfaces susceptible to sub-aerial erosion processes. We must conclude that the fragility of these northern areas needs careful consideration in any proposals to develop them, whether it be for minerals, biotic resources or tourism.

Similar in many ways are the high mountain areas of the world, such as the Rockies, Andes and Himalayas. In general the human impact has been very much less than in arctic and subarctic regions because high relief is added to harsh climate, but apparently unsettled lands may have undergone grazing by domesticated animals. This may produce the symptoms of overgrazing because the ecosystems are fragile and easily changed: so in the nineteenth century John Muir was moved to write of sheep in the Sierra Nevada mountains of California as 'hooved locusts' and to point out the soil erosion that followed in their trail. Today, recreationists may outnumber sheep, but their effect can also be strong. Numerous boot-clad feet can wear away mountain vegetation and allow erosion, and pack animals can do the same damage as other domesticated livestock. In winter, animals may be frightened away from their feeding grounds by motorized incursions on vehicles such as the snowmobile, which may also be used for hunting; by extending the range of hunters in winter it may help reduce the populations of some animals since they are likely to be in poor condition, although if predators like the wolf are killed then species like deer may expand beyond the carrying capacity of their habitat. In northern Ontario, some isolated lakes have been virtually fished out because of improved access during the winter by tracked vehicles.

Some forested areas of the world are also lacking in any density of settlement. The largest of such areas are the boreal forest zones of Canada and the USSR. This zone comprises several different vegetation types, ranging from an admixture of moss-floored forest and bog to an open forest with a dry lichen-heath ground layer. The short summer inhibits the activity of the soil fauna and flora and so a considerable depth of humus is characteristic of many parts of this formation. Along with fallen branches and trees, this layer is potential fuel for wild fires, and when set by humans or lightning these can destroy large areas of forest. They tend to be even more damaging when a management policy of instant fire suppression has been carried out for some years, since this allows the forest floor material to build up. Some populations of animals, such as moose, may build up to extremely high levels when a man-induced predator control programme is effective, as has been that of the wolf in Canada. The herbivores may then seriously affect forest regeneration and growth because of the intensity with which they browse. Even minimal human occupance can therefore lead to quite far-reaching ecological change.

In the remaining stretches of tropical forest considered 'natural', such as those of Amazonia and the highlands of New Guinea, the most disturbing influence has been shifting cultivation (see pp. 196–7). After abandonment, the plots recolonize with secondary forest and if not eventually re-used for agriculture then they become climax-type forest again. It is not certain whether the secondary forest ever regains the exact composition of its virgin state, but if not then reserves may eventually contain the only truly natural tropical forest and all the rest reflect the influence of an unconscious management system, as do most temperate forests even if they are apparently 'natural'.

Possibly the most 'unused' land of all is in the desert areas of the world. Their biological productivity is low, and apart from some hunting and pastoralism human use tends to be confined to mineral exploitation and especially in North America, recreation. Extraction of minerals such as petroleum is a 'point' activity and pipelines do not alter the desert very much, although the arid climate means that any hardware left lying around will persist for a long time, witness the tank hulks in North Africa and the beer cans in Arizona. Recreational use of deserts in the USA, especially in California and Arizona, centres around activities involving four-wheel drive vehicles and, in sandy terrain, 'dune buggies'. The former do not change the ecology very much themselves but import people into another type of fragile ecosystem where, for example, the trampling of succulents or the gathering of dried cactus 'skeletons' for firewood disturb large numbers of niches for a very long time, since plant growth rates are so low. Dune buggies may easily change unfixed dune systems quite radically, but the wind soon rectifies the situation; on the other hand, partially vegetated dunes are soon converted into 'blow-outs' after a few vehicles have torn up the root systems of the grasses binding them.

Islands, particularly those isolated in large oceans, might be thought to be likely candidates for pristine status, but this is rarely so. As Elton (1958) pointed out, such islands generally have a depauperate biota, with the result that unstable ecosystems change very rapidly as a result of direct human activity or the man-induced introduction of alien plants and animals. The coming of the pig and goat to many tropical islands resulted in a revolutionary destruction of vegetation; likewise the rat caused a large faunal shift in small coral-based islands. The innate instability of the latter is underlined by the anxiety which resulted from the population explosion of the large Crown-of-Thorns starfish. Such islands as remain in an unaltered state are highly prized for scientific purposes: Aldabra in the Indian Ocean is one example, containing rare fauna as well as an absence of anthropogenic effects (Stoddart and Wright 1967). The plan to build an airstrip there caused a considerable outcry from the international scientific community; it was, however, financial rather than ecological instability which defeated it in the end (Stoddart 1968).

There remain for discussion a few special cases of ecological systems which can be regarded as natural because they undergo constant renewal. Unfixed sand dunes, in an early stage of succession, are one example. Coastal systems such as the Sands of Forvie (Aberdeenshire, Scotland) are examples of such a condition; inland, the White Sands of New Mexico (part of which are under protection as a National Monument) provide another. Any activity of man generally proves very ephemeral in shifting dunes, but once they become fixed by vegetation then they are much more vulnerable to human activity, especially the specialized form of recreation which causes blow-outs. Tidal salt marshes which receive periodic inundation, and hence an input of silt and salt, might also be considered natural, although many of them are subject to grazing by domesticates; in the tropics the mangrove swamps occupy a similar niche, although without the sheep. Large paludal areas are often close to their virgin condition but are increasingly becoming altered by outside influences such as the influx of pesticides or eutrophication agents from their highly manipulated watershed areas.

Wilderness

In this section, some examples of the conscious and deliberate protection of large wilderness areas are discussed. It is difficult to distinguish these from the national parks and nature reserves described in the next chapter, but the main criteria are the large area (whereas parks and reserves can be of any size), the absence of deliberate management wherever possible, and the feeling of wholeness. The set of systems is preserved particularly because of its unity and not for any particular biota, landscape or recreational activity, as is so often the case with wildlife protection and landscape preservation areas (Plate 3).

Motivations

Ideally, wilderness areas should never have been subject to human activity which has resulted in manipulation, either deliberate or unconscious, of the ecology of the areas being considered. But in many cases our knowledge of land-use history is so fragmentary that we cannot honestly say other than 'it looks natural'. Research into Quaternary ecology and land-use history produces more and more evidence of the antiquity of man's imprint, and it becomes increasingly likely that some areas preserved for their 'natural wilderness' quality have in fact been altered by man at a pre-industrial or even pre-agricultural stage in the past.

The reasons given for the setting aside of wilderness areas vary from place to place and from culture to culture, but running through most of the legislation and regulations are a shared set of themes. There is often a declamation of the rightfulness of the independent existence of such areas: not all nature is to be perceived as a profitable or potentially useful resource and it should be allowed to persist on its own terms without any interference from man. In the last phrase is implicit the absence of any deliberate management of the areas designated and, like so many such hopes, this is often more pious than practical. This ethical strand of thought frequently stems from or is accompanied by religious motivation.

The most persuasive non-scientific argument in Western countries has been the advocacy of the spiritual aura of such lands. It is evident that their nature is changed by the incursion of large numbers of people, so their virtues reside either in their being experienced by small numbers of people as a special form of recreation which is basically spiritual refreshment, or in being symbolic. Then they do not need to be visited, they are just there as 'the wilderness beyond'. At one extreme, wilderness advocates may insist that experience of great natural areas is a spiritual essential for every person. This is unlikely and, nowadays, impractical. A more balanced point of view regards wilderness as being just as much a state of mind as a condition of nature; the beholder's response becomes paramount and hence the type of person determines the necessity or otherwise of wilderness experience. Although a pristine condition is a requirement of consciously preserved wilderness areas, the desire of people to visit them soon leads to ecological changes, and this possibility brings about conflict with another major set of reasons for wilderness protection, which are scientific in origin. There are three main strands to these propositions. There is firstly the need to keep a gene pool of wild organisms, both plant and animal, to ensure present and future genetic variety. Circumstances under which new strains may be needed cannot be foreseen and by

Plate 3 A wild area under protective management: Mount Hood, Oregon, USA. Habitats such as this mountain meadow may experience recreational pressure severe enough to impoverish the biota and spoil the aesthetics; thus restriction of access becomes essential to prevent certain types of change. *(Grant Heilman, Lititz, Pa)*

reducing diversity the possibilities for future choice are much restricted. Large wild areas ensure that a reservoir of potentially useful sources of breeding material for human use is preserved. Secondly, there is an emphasis upon the maintenance of animal communities in their natural surroundings in order to facilitate research upon their behaviour. In changed habitats the animals act differently and the chance to study specialized patterns as the product of a particular ecological niche is lost. This argument is similar to that advanced for many national parks and nature reserves, but here the emphasis is on the large area of the wildernesses and the increased chance that the whole life-span and seasonal cycles of the animal are completed in undisturbed conditions. Thirdly, sharing the last set of motivations and constraints, is the absolute necessity of protecting undisturbed ecosystems of all kinds for research in ecology. Many of man's activities consist of tinkering with his environment, and the prime requirement of successful tinkering is keeping all the parts. Much useful research is done in smaller areas, but large wildernesses are essential not only for pure research but also for applied work. Efforts to increase the productivity of crops, for example, may gain much from an understanding of the functioning of natural ecosystems.

As some of the examples will show, different reasons have been responsible for the legal designation of wildernesses in different places. In some, such as Antarctica, scientific reasons have been dominant. In the case of the National Wilderness Preservation System of the USA, the recreational-aesthetic reasons won the day. Also, some wildernesses may be called by names such as National Parks; in differentiating them from the areas to be reviewed in Chapter 3, we shall try to follow the criteria of size, lack of settlement, and absence of management policies and practices.

The USA and other nations

'The Wilderness' has always played an important part in the symbolic life of North Americans (R. Nash 1967); the rapidity with which the continent was settled and exploited meant the disappearance of most virgin land except in marginal environments. Even here, in remote forests, unyielding deserts and high mountains, the determination to log, mine or graze was often successful even if only temporarily so. The erosion of the wild led to a rising groundswell of public opinion which resulted in the passage through Congress of the Wilderness Act of 1964 (Simmons 1966). This immediately established a National Wilderness Preservation System and placed in it 54 wildernesses, wild and canoe areas, totalling about nine million acres (36,450 km²). All additions to the System have to be approved individually by Congress: by 1970 the System totalled about ten million acres (40,500 km²). The areas thus set aside are to have no economic uses, except where mining has been previously allowed, in which case it has to be removed by 1983; the President may allow other economic uses but only in times of considerable emergency. The criteria for establishment include a normal minimal size of 80 mi² (207 km²) and the Act's formal definition of ecological condition requires

> . . . an area where the earth and its community are untrammelled by man, where man himself is a visitor who does not remain . . . [and] without permanent improvements. . . .

The wilderness areas are to contain no roads, nor use of motor vehicles and aircraft except in an emergency; wilderness users were divided in one survey about the desirability of telephones for emergency use, and none have yet been installed. The terrains designated are mostly in the west of the USA. This is where the wild country is, and where the Federal Government, especially the Forest Service of the Department of Agriculture, has its largest holdings. The wildernesses are mostly forested at their lower elevations but with an alpine terrain of high peaks, cirques and snowfields at the upper levels. An exception is the Boundary Waters Canoe Area in the Quetico-Superior area of Minnesota-Ontario. Here a maze of natural waterways intersects coniferous forest, and canoe travel is the only method of transport permitted.

The Act makes it quite clear that the wilderness areas are recreative in purpose as well as scientific, for it speaks of 'outstanding opportunities for solitude or a primitive and unconfined type of recreation' as well as 'features of scientific, educational, scenic or historical value'. Thus, although wilderness and ecological purity are equated, there is a considerable amount of human incursion either on foot or with pack or riding animals. The convention of wilderness recreation seems to be that the area is crowded if you see people other than those of your own party, and so the constraints on carrying capacity are narrow. Even with such small numbers of users, management of the wildernesses may present problems. For example, natural lightning fires are probably a regular feature of the ecology of western coniferous forests, but these can of course engulf people. Should such forest fires (as distinct from man-set ones, if the distinction can easily be made by a dragged-out-of-bed Ranger who has to decide whether to call in the fire-fighting services) be suppressed or let alone even if there is risk to human life? These and other difficulties, such as refuse and sewage disposal, and the overgrazing of fragile mountain meadows by pack stock, pose formidable problems for those whose task it is to keep the wildernesses wild, for even low levels of use is scientific in purpose, and for example the helicopter used to ferry people, together such as the suppression of fire or the construction of primitive camp sites. Only where the use is scientific in purpose, and for example the helicopter used to ferry people together with their gear and food, can the USA wildernesses be likely in the long run to remain truly inviolate in an ecological sense. Rationing of recreational visits to wilderness areas is now being practised in some of the most popular areas of the Western Cordillera.

Some other examples of the conflict between designated wilderness areas and the need to manage visitors are provided by some of the mountain National Parks of Sweden and Czechoslovakia. In Sweden, the northern wild Parks, administered by the Forest Service, are probably not totally natural since their lower areas are Lapp territory. Nevertheless an information brochure states,

> they must not be visited in such a way that . . . the land loses its unique character, and that any of what we can perhaps best express by the word 'mood' is lost.

Inaccessibility is a feature of Parks such as Sarek (470,490 ac/1905 km²) where provisions for a week have to be carried, while access is forbidden to parts of the forest land and mire complex of Muddus National Park (121,577 ac/492 km²), especially to protect bird life. In the Tatra National Park, jointly managed by Poland and Czechoslovakia, the high innermost zone can only be entered on certain paths and these must be kept to. Again, such areas were set aside with proper wilderness intentions, but their very designation has probably attracted some of the people whose numbers make management necessary.

Antarctica

The world's southern extremity is perhaps the best example of a deliberately protected wilderness (Plate 4). For many years following the early explorations it was an unconsciously preserved wilderness owing to its hostile nature, although the establishment of an increasing number of scientific bases by many nations meant that some destruction of biota ensued. The great impetus given to international scientific co-operation by the International Geophysical Year (1957–8), when research and observations in Antarctica played an important part, led the nations with territorial interests in Antarctica to conclude the Antarctic Treaty in 1959 (Heatherton 1965, Roberts 1965, Holdgate 1970). Even before the treaty the basic conditions for wilderness were in fact met: all settlement is 'point' settlement, supplied from

Plate 4 Antarctica: the last great wilderness. Even this remote region is not immune from residual pesticides and its research-orientated function is being complicated by the advent of tourism. (*Aerofilms Ltd, London*)

outside, and much transport is by air; none of the local resources is used for food or building purposes except in an emergency. None the less, even this remote polar ice-mass is not totally exempt from man's less disinterested activities. Tourist visits to Antarctica are becoming common, and the body tissues of the penguins contain DDT which has presumably come via oceanic food chains. In addition the major commercial resource of Antarctica, the pelagic whales of its waters, are exempt from the Antarctic Treaty.

The Treaty itself affirms the principle of international co-operation in occupance of the continent for scientific purposes. There is to be no military use or training, although military equipment may be used to aid research; no nuclear explosions or dumping of nuclear waste are to take place. No specific provision, however, is made for any terrestrial commercial resources should they be found: coal is the most likely, although this is highly baked and of a marginal quality. The protection of the ecosystems comes in the Agreed Measures which are annexed to the Treaty and which aim at minimizing any disturbance to the plants, mammals and birds of the Treaty Area. No mammal or bird may be killed, wounded or maimed without a permit, for example; dogs must be inoculated against, *inter alia*, rabies and leptospirosis, and are not allowed to run free. Helicopters are not to approach large concentrations of animals, and all the signatories agree to try to alleviate pollution near the coasts and ice-shelves which are the sites of most of the bases. Particularly noteworthy is the prohibition of the importation of non-indigenous species, except for laboratory use. There are also Specially Protected Areas where no vehicles are allowed and where even plants may not be collected 'except for some compelling scientific purpose', and Specially Protected Species, such as fur seals and the Ross seal, which are thought to be especially deserving of preservation. Overall, therefore, the Measures aim at the perpetuation of the variety of species and the maintenance of the balance of the natural ecological systems. The extent of their success is difficult to estimate but is probably high, since no large-scale ecological changes in the Antarctic appear to have taken place.

A wider context

It is unequivocally clear that the amount of 'unused' land in a 'natural' state is declining, and the rate of its disappearance is quite fast although precise data are lacking. The preservation of virgin land must therefore be a deliberate act, thus bringing it into the cultural-perceptual phase of resource allocation. The 'wilderness' idea is obviously culturally relative: many cultures see no virtue in the preservation of a large area of wild terrain just for its own sake. In many cases it is clearly a 'fringe benefit' for richer countries which poorer ones cannot afford if there are any resources at all in the wild areas. Are there, then, any strong reasons for the protection of wilderness areas other than those which are extensions of the arguments put forward for the designation of land as parks and nature reserves? Apart from the genetic pool idea, a suggestion which seems to have a world-wide validity is the role of wild areas, especially those with a high biological productivity, as 'protective' ecosystems which counterbalance the less stable 'productive' systems, a classification suggested by E. P. Odum (1969) and further discussed near the end of the book (pp. 367–9). A similar role has been postulated for the oceans. The exact role of these biomes is not known, but if there is any possibility that these wild ecosystems might be crucial then no deleterious action should be taken until more knowledge is available. The firm pressures of the numbers of people and their demands for materials militate against such action, for few nations or indeed individuals subscribe to Henry David Thoreau's motto for the preservers of wilderness, that,

> . . . a man is rich in proportion to the number of things he can afford to let alone.

Further reading

BRYAN, R. 1973: *Much is taken, much remains.*
ELTON, C. S. 1958: *The ecology of invasions by animals and plants.*
LEE, R. B. and DE VORE, I. (eds.) 1968: *Man the hunter.*
NASH, R. 1967: *Wilderness and the American mind.*
ODUM, E. P. 1969: The strategy of ecosystem development.
PARKER, B. C. (ed.) 1972: *Conservation problems in Antarctica.*
ROHMER, R. 1973: *The arctic imperative.*
SATER, J. E., RONHOVDE, A. G. and VAN ALLEN, L. C. 1972: *Arctic environments and resources.*

3

Protected ecosystems and landscapes

In the previous section we considered that change was an accidental, if widespread, feature of wilderness areas and unused land. Since management was reduced to a minimum the ecosystems were insulated from anthropogenic changes. We now discuss certain classes of ecosystems where change is acceptable and management a necessary feature but where there is protection from certain kinds of alteration. Such action generally results from a desire to keep an ecosystem or set of systems in a valued state, and so is very much dependent upon cultural factors. The aim may be to preserve a species, assemblage or habitat which is rare, or typical, or symbolic, or perhaps to keep unchanged a traditional landscape because it occupies a high place in the values of those who see it or are responsible for it. Such ecosystems are usually wild rather than obviously man-made. Plants, animals, water and soil are, or are thought to be, relatively undisturbed and the terms frequently used of such areas are 'natural' and 'semi-natural'. In fact, a significant number of protected landscapes are cultural landscapes which exhibit distinctly the work of man, but this need not prevent them from being valued highly.

The desire to protect wild species and favoured landscapes usually resolves itself into two practical elements. The first group is nature protection (for which wildlife protection/preservation/conservation, nature conservation/preservation are synonyms) in which it is desired to perpetuate either a taxon or a group of taxa, or a particular habit. Species protection has a tendency to concentrate on the rare and unusual and habitat conservation upon the typical, but many exceptions can be found. The desire for protection is especially strong if the species is endangered (IUCN 1970, Fisher *et al.* 1969). The second element may be termed landscape protection where a particular view or piece of country is protected from undesired despoliation or simply where change of any sort is restrained. These areas are sometimes used also for outdoor recreation, but that set of activities often requires much more manipulation and is considered separately in Chapter 4. As with wilderness, scientific and educational reasons are often advanced for the protection of biota and landscapes, partly for their study value as relatively undisturbed systems from which we may learn the better to manage intensively used systems, and partly for their role in maintaining the stability of the biosphere. Spiritual and aesthetic, even ethical, considerations also lie behind many protectionist movements: there is no denying the pleasure which many people gain from seeing wild rural landscapes, from Kinder Scout through Yosemite Valley to Fujiyama, and the popularity of bird-watching is such that in some crowded parts of Europe the great migration stopovers sometimes attract as many people as birds. Neither can economics be omitted: the public will line up to see rare fauna, as demonstrated by the nest of the Loch Garten ospreys in Scotland (free, in fact, but donations welcome), and in scenically beautiful areas they spread a lot of cash around the periphery in payment for souvenirs, film, food, lodging and public toilets. In a few instances, such as the CSSR, the right of the people to enjoy unspoiled nature and to see beautiful scenery is enshrined in the constitution of the Republic. In the capitalist world the statement of national purpose is rarely as explicit, but is implied in many legislative acts to create nature reserves and protected landscape areas.

Nature protection

Nature protection stems from a desire to perpetuate certain biota indefinitely (Dorst 1970, IUCN 1971). The object of concern may range from a single species living in a very restricted area to a set of complex ecosystems covering a large tract like a mountain range. Such a continuum can only be divided arbitrarily, but for this discussion a differentiation will be made between species protection, where the resource manager aims to keep a viable population of a particular taxon, and habitat protection, where the whole is more important and fluctuations in the populations of component species or in features of the inanimate environment are not considered detrimental. A capricious feature of wildlife conservation is nomenclature: nature reserves, game reserves, national parks, nature parks and several other terms are used by the private and governmental organizations which manage land and water resources with the purpose of perpetuating wild nature. For example the term National Park covers systems managed for many diverse purposes, all the way from wilderness to intensive outdoor recreation. In this account the purpose of management will be stressed rather than the details of designation.

Species preservation

Nature reserves are usually designated in order to give protection to a species of plant or animal which is rare (on a variety of scales from the regional to the global) and which it is thought can be preserved in this way. Animals, especially birds and large mammals, are most often thought of in this connection, but plants may qualify for the same treatment, especially in densely settled lands where many of the wild mammals have disappeared. Typical early instances of such reserves are the nesting sites of rare birds, although general legislation preventing the killing of particular species is commonly passed before the setting up of reserves. In Britain, for example, a law protecting seabirds was passed by Parliament in 1869 and wild birds generally in 1880, but there were no National Nature Reserves until after the founding of an appropriate government agency, the Nature Conservancy Council, in 1949. Privately owned preserves such as those of the Royal Society for the Protection of Birds were earlier in the field (Fitter 1963). Single-species conservation in Britain is dominated by plants and there are reserves owned or leased by the Nature Conservancy or bodies such as the County Naturalists Trusts or the National Trust which are dedicated to protecting, for example, a good fritillary meadow or particularly rare buttercup (Stamp 1969). In the field of animals, the Farne Islands off the coast of Northumberland are a sanctuary for the grey seal: these islands have a long history of management for the benefit of wild creatures, starting with St Cuthbert in the seventh century AD.

Elsewhere in the world, animals tend to dominate single-species preservation mainly because they dominate worldwide concern, largely of a sentimental nature. In northern Alberta and the North-West Territories of Canada, for example, the Wood Buffalo National Park preserves in a wild and almost roadless terrain one of the few remaining herds of North American bison. The herd is culled regularly in order to keep it within the carrying capacity of the National Park area and also to try and keep down the diseases to which the herd is subject. Elsewhere, many other sanctuaries exist and it is often the first step in protection measures taken by undeveloped countries: two small islands in Sabah, Malaysia, protect frigate birds, for example; in north-east India the Kaziranga Sanctuary preserves the Great Indian rhinoceros; and the last 25–40 Javan rhinos are in a reserve at Udjung Kulon-Panailan in western Java, established in 1921 (Talbot and Talbot 1968).

Management of such reserves is usually limited. Where possible a fence is put up, a warden or ranger installed and the area left alone. Where management is practised then it is usual to manipulate either the habitat or the population of the protected species. At Havergate Island in Suffolk, England, the RSPB have created pools in stretches of shingle in order to extend the conditions favourable for the breeding of the avocet, a bird rare in Britain. Further north, the National Trust periodically culls the grey seals of the Farne Islands in order that mortality said to be due to overcrowding should be reduced, and to keep down damage allegedly done to local salmon fisheries. The usefulness of this management policy has been strongly questioned, since others (Coulson 1972) hold the view that natural mechanisms can be relied upon to keep the populations stable.

The protection of assemblages

Rather more common are reserves to protect an assemblage of species. These merge imperceptibly with those in which a whole habitat or set of habitats is preserved, but a distinction can perhaps be made on the arbitrary grounds of size: habitat reserves are large relative to the assemblage ones. The assemblages may have some linking affinity: wildfowl refuges, for example, which cater for the nesting or migration of many species of ducks, geese and waders (Plate 5). High mountain reserves often protect a very diverse suite of alpine plants, sometimes with their attendant fauna. Although wild terrain is often sought for such reserves, the behaviour of wild animals often makes it necessary to set aside man-made habitats and quite frequently suitable places are of commercial value. The case of wetlands which are sought for reclamation as industrial land, airports or garbage dumps can be seen in many parts of the world: the value of the tidal marshes of Essex, England, as a wildfowl habitat rather than as the basis of the third London airport was strongly argued in 1971. Tidal estuaries are also among the most productive ecosystems in the world and clearly deserve special attention on this account.

The USA has a system of National Wildfowl Refuges which are placed on or near the major flyways which run north–south across that continent (Fig. 3.1). They are designated

Plate 5 Wildfowl. Unpriceable but invaluable? *(Grant Heilman, Lititz, Pa)*

in concert with Canada, on whose northern lands (along with those of Alaska) many of the birds nest. Their management is designed to provide maximum cover and food supply for the migrating birds and to provide refuge from hunting so that while sufficient numbers reach the waiting guns to satisfy the hunters (who pay for 'Duck Stamps' and a tax on all equipment in order to finance research and land-acquisition programmes), there are sufficient escapees to return to breed in the following year. Some limited hunting may be allowed on the Refuges along with a restricted variety of other recreational activities. Experience has shown that most populations of ducks and geese can replace hunting losses quite satisfactorily provided the cropping levels are planned in accordance with the breeding success. This necessitates a fairly sophisticated cropper who is able to distinguish between one species and another and between males and females, which surveys by management authorities have shown not to be axiomatic. Plant assemblages are often protected in reserves, especially where some of them are rare on a regional or national scale. In the

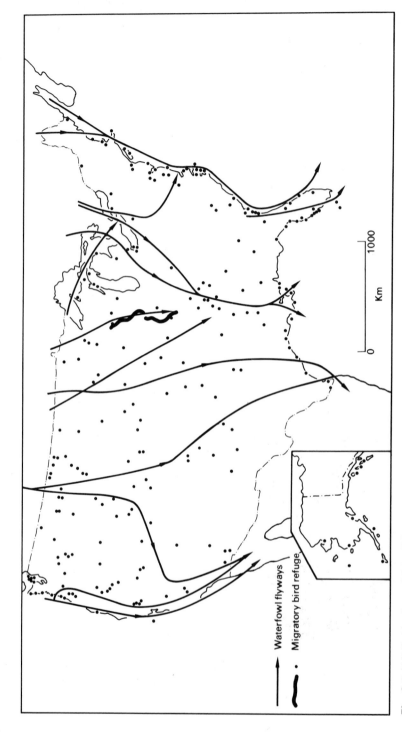

Fig. 3.1 Wildfowl refuges in the USA and the main 'flyways'—the annual migration routes of these birds. The refuges are principally aimed at perpetuation of a particular assemblage of avian species.
Source: Dasmann 1972

Upper Teesdale area of northern Britain, an assemblage of arctic-alpine plants, most of which are found relatively frequently in the Scottish Highlands and commonly in the Alps and Scandinavia, but not elsewhere in England (Piggot 1956), was designated first an SSSI (Site of Special Scientific Interest) under the authority of the National Parks and Access to the Countryside Act of 1949, and then a National Nature Reserve. Because of other interests in the land (especially grouse shooting), management will consist mostly of the traditional practices which include regular firing of heather (*Calluna vulgaris*) which is the food of the grouse. Experimental enclosures which relieve grazing pressure by sheep and rabbits first give a tremendous surge of the rare flora, but this then tends to be suppressed by the vigorous growth of the accompanying plants, often very common grasses. Land-use practices may therefore have been strongly influential in the continued existence of some elements of this flora, and complete protection by withdrawal of other land uses would be likely to entail the loss of some plants by competition. A piece of woodland thought to be typical of a region is also a candidate for preservation, especially if it is thought to be substantially unmanipulated. This is particularly so in Europe, where most woodlands have been either removed to make way for agriculture or intensively managed for centuries. In southern Bohemia, for example, the ČSSR has designated as a reserve the last fragment of beech-spruce *urwald* at Boubinsky Prales. A fence has been erected to keep out deer; the result has been rapid regeneration of the beech but not the spruce, and so other management devices are clearly necessary. The difficulties of ensuring regeneration in small woodland fragments are also illustrated by some of the relict pinewoods of Scotland in the care of the Nature Conservancy. Regeneration of the dominant *Pinus sylvestris* is confined to woods on bouldery slopes; elsewhere the raw acid humus appears to inhibit the seedlings. Here again is a case of *laissez-faire* being unsuccessful in perpetuating a particular plant.

Habitat preservation

Reserves which are large and diverse enough to protect whole sets of ecosystems which are either rare on a national or world basis, or thought to be especially typical of the country where they occur, are often designated as National Parks, although nature protection is often not the sole purpose of such places.

Few reserves in Britain are able to qualify for this category. The possible exceptions are some National Nature Reserves in Scotland such as the Cairngorms, Beinn Eighe and the Isle of Rhum. The first two are mainly mountainous terrain, with grasslands, mountain heath, and relict pinewood on the lower slopes. The red deer is the largest mammal and is in general too high in numbers for the amount of winter feed. But the Nature Conservancy is unable to carry out effective management policies since its leases do not confer complete control over animal management and because animals transgress the boundaries of the Reserves. This is not true of the Isle of Rhum, where it controls the grazing: the sheep which were overgrazing the open moorlands have been removed, and planned management of a herd of red deer substituted. One result has been an increase in the yield of animal protein per unit area together with a recovery of the pastures (Eggeling 1964). Some of the National Parks of the USA are devoted mainly to conserving a series of wildlife habitats. This is particularly true of the Everglades National Park in Florida, which comprises a complex of wetland areas such as coastal mangroves, tropical saw-grass marshes and 'hammock' forests on the slightly drier areas a few centimetres above flood level. The 4,856 km² (1,200,000 ac) park supports a wide variety of animals also, such as the rare Everglades kite, the roseate spoonbill, alligators, manatees and the many fish that are the basis of a sizeable industry. Until recently management was confined to the channelling of the ever-increasing numbers of visitors, and to measures like the protecting of alligators from would-be makers of handbags. But the large size of the Everglades and its proximity to the popular holiday area of Florida mean that pressures to alter the ecology are intense. Apart from proposals (which were allowed to lapse after a considerable controversy but which in 1973 showed signs of reviving) to build an airport on one fringe, the main threat has been the loss of its freshwater input and thus the possibility of the wetlands drying out. The main water source is Lake Okeechobee and the water in this lake has been cut off from the Park in the name of flood control further north; surplus water was released into the ocean instead of into the Everglades. Pressure from concerned people has allowed the tapping of an aquifer and the restoration of some of the lake water, but the future of the Everglades as a set of natural ecosystems remains in doubt (Dasmann 1968, Harte and Socolow 1971).

On a still larger scale are some of the National Parks and Game Reserves of eastern, central and southern Africa, in such countries as the Republic of South Africa, Tanzania, Zambia, Uganda and Kenya (Fig. 3.2). Here the desire to ensure the survival of the fauna, especially the large mammals, is reinforced by two strong economic considerations. Firstly, most of these countries (especially the newly independent republics) make a great deal of foreign currency from tourism; for some it is their largest earner, and the visitors nearly all come to see the animals. Secondly, it has been shown that controlled harvesting of wild animals not only helps to ensure their preservation, since their ranges are being restricted by various forms of development, but also that the wild game can yield more protein per unit area than domesticated animals and with less damage from overgrazing. This is a fairly revolutionary concept and is not widely acceptable at grassroots level. Groups such as the Masai of Kenya, for example, are reluctant to give up their tradition of cattle-herding since the animals are not only meat and milk but also money to them (Pearsall 1957, Huxley 1961). The potential of controlled cropping is discussed in Chapter 5.

Asia too has many parks devoted to protecting mountain and forest areas, along with the associated fauna, in a natural state. Even countries like South Viet-Nam had two National Parks. The large one, of 78,000 ha at Bach-ma Hai-Van, near Hue, was of virgin monsoon forest (Nguyen-van-Hiep 1968). It is presumably necessary to use the past tense when referring to these Parks, and probably those of some other south-east Asian countries also. The course of shifting cultivation and logging have also injured many park areas in Asia where insufficient park personnel and wild terrain mean that control of these inimical land uses is scarcely possible. A further reason for preservation of upland forests is found in their protection of watersheds: if deforested they add to the flood hazard of urban and agricultural lands downstream and increase the silt burden as well. They also form reserves for research into management of Asian wild lands, and although they are not yet tourist attractions on the scale of the African parks, there can be little doubt that their turn will come in the course of the upsurge of world tourism (Talbot and Talbot 1968).

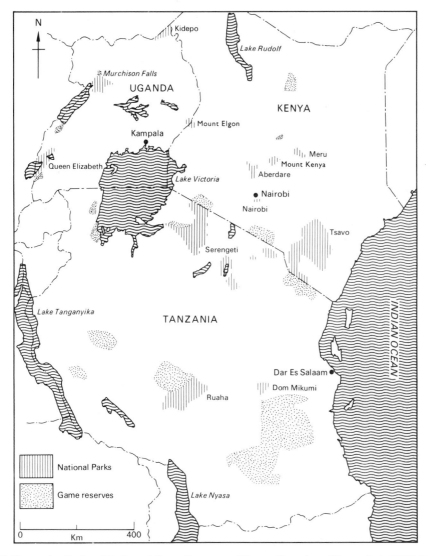

Fig. 3.2 The major National Parks and Game Reserves of Kenya, Uganda and Tanzania in 1970. The large areas which they occupy are symbolic of their role in the economy of the nations concerned as well as environmental considerations.
Source: Morgan 1972

The preservation of habitats is also the main function of the natural areas of the USSR which are withdrawn from economic utilization for scientific research and for cultural-education purposes. In 1966 there were 68 of these *zapovedniki*, totalling 4,300,000 ha, and the predominance of scientific research as their main purpose was well established, in such fields as the breeding and propagation of animals that are rare or threatened with extinction, the study of both unusual and typical vegetation types, the investigation of the total ecology of particular regions, and the preservation of unique geological or archaeological features. Certain 'open' *zapovedniki* accommodate tourism, but they are limited in number and recreation appears to be a secondary consideration. A long-range plan for new reserves was presented in 1957, but so far few of its recommendations have been implemented (Pryde 1972).

Difficulties

The preceding paragraphs have given particular instances of difficulties associated with the management of ecosystems for nature protection, and some of these have a more general applicability. As with wilderness areas, deliberate designation is necessary but mere legislative enactment is insufficient. Apart from the obvious protective measures such as the prevention of poaching or picking, there are more subtle ecological interactions. For example, the removal of a particular type of pressure from a desired species may cause it to 'bloom' in an explosive fashion and crash thereafter. The mule deer of the Kaibab Plateau of Arizona are one much-chronicled example (Fig. 3.3). In an effort to increase their numbers, predator control was introduced and numbers of wolves were exterminated. The deer herd rapidly grew in size and outstripped its food supply, with a subsequent population 'crash' down to very low numbers (Dasmann 1964b). Similar difficulties have been

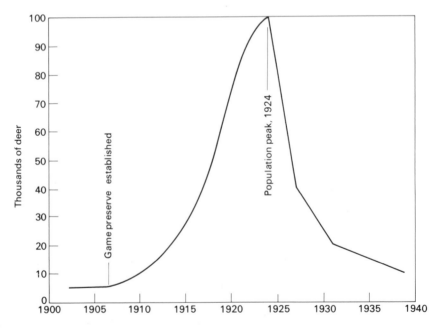

Fig. 3.3 The population expansion and 'crash' of the deer of the Kaibab plateau of Arizona, following the application of predator control.
Source: Dasmann 1964b

experienced when the enclosure of rare plants has been followed by the discovery that they have survived because grazing pressure has kept down competing species. An example of this is given by some species of orchids in the chalk grassland of southern England. In the absence of sheep this plant association soon becomes long grassland and then scrub, so that the orchids characteristic of the short-grass stage disappear very quickly once succession starts to take place. In this case, management measures for the preservation of orchids consist either of re-introducing sheep or of mowing the nature reserve. A classic instance of the imperfections of designated reserves occurs when an animal spends part of its yearly cycle outside the reserve. A large mammal may spend its winters in a reserve where predators are protected but the rest of the year on a range outside the reserve which it shares with domestic livestock and where predator control, as of the wolf or the coyote, is maintained. The populations of the mammal are thus liable to build up to levels which cannot be supported by the winter feed, and the predators are incapable of trimming the population sufficiently. In such cases, management must be undertaken, either by culling a number of beasts or by feeding them artificially. The elk of Yellowstone National Park in the USA have had to be treated in this way: in this instance culling by the Park staff is undertaken, much to the chagrin of local hunters.

Such problems basically arise from the fact that legislative boundaries rarely coincide with the natural spatial limits of the ecosystems which it is desired to protect; this may also be manifested in the operation of watershed influences which originate beyond the limits of the reserve but which penetrate into it. An obvious case would be the spraying with a persistent insecticide of agricultural land upstream from a protected lake. Similarly, the addition of large quantities of chemical fertilizer would probably result in the eutrophication of the lake. If the protected system is a forest, then commercial logging up to the boundaries of the reserve may possibly mean that the remnant area is too small to function as a natural unit—e.g. there may be insufficient territories for a viable population of a particular species. As a further example, in connection with the establishment of a Redwoods National Park in northern California in 1968, the Secretary of the Interior is authorized to enter into agreements and easements with the owners of the watersheds whose ecology affects that of the Park, in order to protect certain features of the Park itself (Simmons 1971). Apparently destructive influences such as fire and flood, whose origin is frequently outside the reserve area, often pose problems for the managers of protected ecosystems. Fire may in some places be a part of the natural ecology, especially in coniferous forests where it seems to have an important role in mineralizing organic matter piled up on the forest floor, and in aiding tree regeneration. (Several species of conifers have cones that only open and release their seed after subjection to very high temperatures.) The giant redwood (*Sequoia gigantea*) of the western slopes of the Sierra Nevada in California is a case in point. Nearly all the remaining specimens of this tree are in State or National Parks, but regeneration has been sparse since the seedlings of the tree were shaded out by faster-growing competitors. Following the realization that lightning-set fires had been a normal component of the local ecosystem, managers began programmes of controlled burning. Along with some restrictions on access to prevent trampling, these appear to have encouraged some regeneration of this rare and exceptionally impressive tree.

Although the presence of wild nature is becoming more and more valued, it does not yet take precedence over more directly economic uses of land and water resources, and so conflicts over the conversion of use arise. The most common of these is the encroachment of industry on formerly wild lands which may have been under protection. Examples of this are particularly common on tidal lands and freshwater wetlands, both of which are commercially cheap and easily 'reclaimable'. Wetlands are especially vulnerable when surrounded by agricultural land, owing not only to substances dissolved in the drainage water, but also to the need to drain the agricultural land. If a 'perched' water-table is to be achieved in isolation from the surrounding drier lands, then considerable engineering works are a necessary prelude to management. This has been achieved by the Nature Conservancy at Woodwalton Fen in eastern England, where a remnant of original fen vegetation is maintained as an island in a sea of intensively farmed agricultural land (Duffey and Watt 1971).

Purposes

The aim of much nature protection is the avoidance of species extinction at one or more scales, and we may legitimately ask whether the disappearance of a species represents an inevitability or merely a failure on man's part to be sufficiently sensitive to the web of living organisms of which he is a part. Scientific reasons for the perpetuation of such organisms exist in terms of interest and possibly of short- or medium-term 'usefulness': it may be very helpful in terms of agricultural development to know how a rare species has adapted itself to a very hostile environment such as a saline desert. On the other hand its very scarcity means that the disappearance of a rare component is unlikely to cause instability in the ecosystems of which it was a component unless it is a key species of the type described by Paine (1969). However, Western culture recognizes that the quality of our lives is enhanced by having around us a rich diversity of organic life, including rare, strange and beautiful forms. Another 'useful' purpose perhaps needs to be stressed most. In Westhoff's (1970) words:

> nature conservation itself has one main end: preserving the stability of the ecosystem where such is required and thus maintaining the diversity of biotic communities, which is necessary for preserving all organisms living on Earth.

To this end, the designation of nature reserves is an initial step.

The protection of landscapes

The placing of whole landscapes under some form of legislative or regulatory protection comes from the desire to maintain or enhance a scene which is of great value, often for various types of recreation or for aesthetic purposes, and so emotive and symbolic values are of considerable importance. Highly valued landscapes do not have to be 'natural'. Some of them are mostly virgin terrain, for example the National Parks in the western cordillera of North America like the Yellowstone and Rocky Mountain Parks in the USA and the Banff-Jasper Parks in Canada. Others are landscapes which are thought to be natural but which closer investigation reveals to be man-made, even if they are extremely wild, like the moorlands of England and Wales. Lastly there is the frank preference for the man-made landscape which exhibits aesthetic qualities that makes it worthy of special attention. The combination lake, wood, field and village in parts of Denmark, the small-scale neatness of rural England, the patterned richness of Lancaster County, Pennsylvania, the staircase of rice paddies flanked by cherry trees in rural Kyushu, all exemplify this type. The perception of the landscape, and the value then attributed to it, are obviously all very important in the decision to protect it. Management may (or may not) thereafter be carried out on scientific principles, but the initial motivation is inspired by a particular set of cultural values.

National Parks

One expression of the desire for protection is the designation of entire landscapes as 'scenic areas', 'areas of natural beauty' or 'national (state, regional county, country) parks' in such a way that the dominant purpose of management becomes the preservation of the qualities of the scenery. This 'total protection' is most often done with natural landscapes, since the lack of other uses produces fewer conflicts than in areas with more directly economic utilization. The legislation is therefore necessarily strong, since it must confer upon the manager the power to exclude all manipulations and changes which are deemed to be inimical to the perpetuation of the values of the landscape. In practice this usually means government ownership of the land and its recources, and the outstanding example of this category is the National Parks system of the USA (Fig. 3.4). Not only does it exemplify the way in which protection has taken place, but it also illustrates some of the conflicts which may arise within the framework of protection, even after the decision to remove the park resources from the ambit of commerce has been taken.

The first of the National Parks, Yellowstone, was designated in 1872. Others followed and the system grew to the point where an Act of the Federal Government was necessary to establish a National Parks Service to administer the system. The wording of the organic Act of 1916 enshrines the purpose of the Parks as being to:

Conserve the scenery and the natural and historical objects and the wildlife therein and to provide for the enjoyment of the same in such manner and by such means as will leave them unimpaired for the enjoyment of future generations.

The system has grown to include not only the National Parks which are the chief concern of this section, but National Monuments, National Recreation Areas, Seashores and many other features. National Parks are, however, still being added (e.g. Utah Canyonlands in 1964, Redwoods and North Cascades in 1968), although it was intended to complete the system by 1972. In 1970 there were 35 National Parks, with a total area of 59,086 km² (14·6 million ac), of which the Federal Government owned over 90 per cent, the difference being accounted for by privately held inholdings within the park boundaries. The types of terrain enclosed in the system are those generally acknowledged to be outstanding examples of the American scene: Yellowstone, Glacier, and Rocky Mountain National Parks in the Rockies, for example; Shenandoah and the Great Smoky Mountains in Appalachia; Grand Canyon, Bryce Canyon, Zion, and Canyonlands in the arid south-west; Yosemite, Kings Canyon-Sequoia, Lassen, Crater Lake and Mount Rainier in the far western ranges of the cordillera; and many more, including the Florida Everglades discussed earlier in this

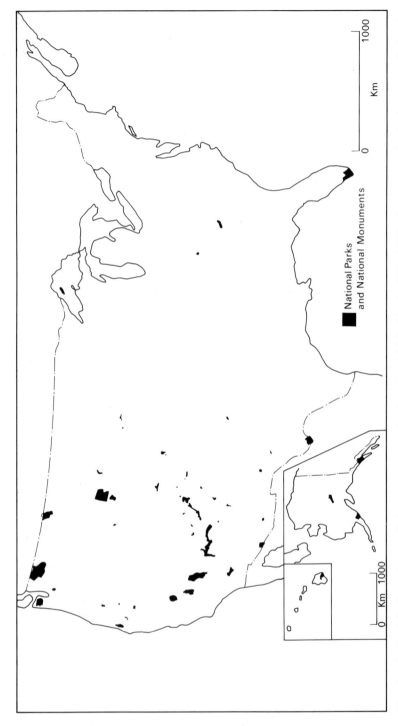

Fig. 3.4 National Parks and larger National Monuments (such as Death Valley) in the USA, 1970. The concentration in the west underlies the class of resource under this type of management, but the very small proportion of the nation so protected is evident.
Source: US National Parks Service 1970: *Areas administered by the National Park Service and related properties as 1 January 1970*. Washington, DC.

section. Hunting is not allowed, but the Parks are popular for many other recreational activities, of which the main one is the viewing of the scenery and its component natural elements which are the *raison d'être* of these Parks. Their popularity is such that visitor numbers have been rising by about 10 per cent each year, i.e. doubling every seven years.

In spite of these pressures, active manipulation of the Parks has been limited to relatively small areas. Forests and water-courses are little altered and there is neither grazing nor mining. In surroundings with such little change, wildlife is comparatively abundant, although sometimes the protection leads either to an overall superabundance, as with the Yellowstone elk, or to undesirable concentrations, as where a species turns to scavenging upon the leavings of the visitors and occasionally predating upon the visitors themselves, as has happened with grizzly bears (*Ursus horribilis*). Because most of the visitors stay close to the roads, campgrounds and other 'developed' parts of the Parks, wilderness can also be a feature, and most of the Parks have large back-country areas which are only infrequently visited since they have to be traversed on foot or horseback. Inevitably, the more accessible areas are the most popular and here the demands of visitors have in large measure been met: there are car parks, campgrounds, stores, hot showers, cabins, nature trails and other interpretive facilities. Fishing is so popular that all the streams have had to be kept stocked. The story is told of the angler in a National Park who had fished for five days and caught nothing. In a similar situation was another angler. When the first expressed disgust at his lack of fortune and said he was leaving the area, the second is reputed to have said, 'Well, I'm stayin'. Tomorrow's the day they put the fish in.' The catering to visitors extends in many parks to a hotel or park lodge and in some to a luxury version, like the Ahwahnee hotel in Yosemite National Park. To go with such developments there may be a golf course and for many long years summer nights in Yosemite were momentarily enlivened by the famous firefall, when glowing ashes from a large wood fire were pushed in an incandescent stream over the edge of a highly U-shaped valley. It was an unusual, if over-rated, form of scenic *divertissement*. With so many functions to perform it was inevitable that conflicts between them arose, especially under the relentless escalation of visitor numbers. Under the politically useful if ecologically contradictory slogan 'parks are for people', many developments were made which threatened wilderness values, such as roads into remote parts. More campgrounds intruded into wildlife foraging areas, sometimes those of easily angered animals such as bears, and the problems of sewage and garbage disposal from the campers and day-visitors in a few places resembled those of a small town (Bourne 1970). Such conflicts were the subject of a special advisory committee to the Secretary of the Interior (A. S. Leopold 1963). Their special concern was wildlife, but their report had far-reaching effects upon the long-term purposes of the Parks. They concluded that the management goal should be

> to preserve or where necessary to re-create, the ecologic scene as viewed by the first European visitors, . . . in order to . . . 'enhance the aesthetic, historical and scientific values of the parks to the American public, vis-à-vis the mass recreational values'.

In line with these aims, a new set of policies appeared, designed to avoid land-use conflicts arising from confusions of purpose (National Park Service 1968). Three major types of area within the National Parks system have been designated (natural, recreational and historic) and the administrative guidelines for the 'natural areas' emphasize the protection of the ecological systems, in such terms as,

(1) Safeguarding forests, wildlife and natural features against impairment or destruction.

(2) The application of ecological management techniques to neutralize the unnatural influences of man, thus permitting the natural environment to be maintained essentially by nature.

(3) Master planning for the appropriate allocation of lands to various purposes in a park and location of use areas as needed for development.

Some of the measures taken to achieve these ends included the formulation of control programmes for ungulate populations, the use of prescribed burning to pre-empt dangerous wildfire, and the gradual removal of service facilities outside the park boundaries. In due course the motor car is to be restricted: in the summer of 1970 an area of Yosemite Valley was sealed off and a minibus service substituted and further plans envisage a 'de-development' at popular areas such as the Old Faithful geyser at Yellowstone National Park. It remains to be seen whether the public image of the National Parks as all-purpose scenic-recreation-resort areas is maintained or whether their avowed role as the jewels in the crown of protected lands with a special, even élitist, role can be substituted. Their remarkable nature and distinctive purpose (it must be remembered that the USA gave the world the National Park idea) requires a farseeing intellectual effort on the part of managers and an understanding attitude from the visiting public. As Darling and Eichorn (1967) conclude,

> certain forms of decorous behaviour should be accepted and not questioned. . . . The national parks . . . represent the glorious creations of nature and no expediency or misconception of their beauty must endanger the world heritage of which they are so shining a part.

Protected landscape areas

The amount of land that can be placed under restrictions of the kind reviewed in the previous section is, by present cultural criteria, limited. Elsewhere, economic considerations may apparently dictate land and water use. Some of the landscapes created by economic usage are nevertheless highly valued, and the desire arises to prevent changes which threaten the areas which have evoked such reactions, for some landscapes exhibit in their aesthetic dimensions a quality which adds to their conventionally utilitarian worth. The type of protective measure which seeks to protect such landscape values while not interfering with the farming or forestry or other commercial use could perhaps be described as 'cosmetic', since it deals with the treatment of details of the surface, rather than with the underlying structure. A more conventional term is 'development control'. Development control seeks to minimize conflicts between the normal processes of economic use and the principally aesthetic appeal which the landscapes hold. Thus control conferred by legislation or by agreement seeks to preserve the familiar and well-beloved by preventing change which is deemed to be ugly, and by clearing up unwanted relics of the past. As examples, we may quote the banning of advertising billboards along roads in Denmark, the control exercised over certain types of agricultural buildings in parts of England and Wales, and the grants available in many countries for the camouflaging of auto junkyards in rural areas and on urban fringes. There are basically two ways in which such controls can be applied: by wholesale prohibitions and regulation over the whole of an administrative area; or by designating certain regions with a distinctive character and concentrating on the protection of that particular place. In the case of the latter, some distinguishing title, such as Protected Landscape Area, Area of Outstanding Natural Beauty, or even National Park, is given.

The control of outdoor advertising is one of the fields in which cosmetic control is exercised. Although the USA is frequently excoriated for this contribution to the scenery, it is worth noting that by 1968 some 31 states had enacted legislation controlling billboards, neon signs and similar paraphernalia outside the commercial zones of towns and cities. Vermont and Hawaii have banned all off-premise outdoor advertising signs, and the city of Aspen, Colorado, has installed a successful sign wall to replace billboards along a State Highway. The constitutionality of restricting outdoor advertising has been affirmed by courts in the states of Washington and Hawaii, and the pursuit of high aesthetic standards as a community goal has thus been endorsed (US President's Council on Recreation and Natural Beauty 1968).

In the case of areas of a particular character which it is desired to protect *in toto* from certain landscape changes, the two main aids are development controls and the provision of governmental aid to clear up detrimental features (Plate 6). Thus one of the major aims of the National Parks and Access to the Countryside Act 1949 of England and Wales was to secure control over most types of development such as non-agricultural buildings, advertising, and caravan sites, in the areas which were to be designated (Fig. 3.5) as National Parks (Darby 1963). Money for clearing up eyesores, mainly wartime remnants, was also available to planning authorities. Regions of slightly lower value, Areas of Outstanding Natural Beauty, have also been designated. As it has turned out, the major landscape changes in the National Parks to which many people have taken objection are exempt from the provisions of the Act. These were large-scale afforestation with coniferous trees, reclamation of open moorland for agriculture and the erection of large-scale farm buildings to take advantage of new developments in intensive farming. Because of the importance of retaining the economic life of the National Parks, even the Countryside Act of 1968 did not provide for control of these changes.

In Denmark, the protected landscape may, if small, be part of the system of nature reserves. Larger units are called 'Naturparker', and the aim is to preserve a total environment or milieu with both cultural and natural features in which the Dane will feel at home. As Bjerke (1967) puts it:

The individual forms his own impression of the Danish landscape, and this impression is influenced by impressions from the landscape of his childhood and later connections. ... The impression of landscape formed by an individual rests upon past experience, and often also upon knowledge of the dynamic composition in what was experienced. Expectations are thus generally limited to existing landscape forms and often restricted, when compared to the expectations an individual may have towards landscapes in other countries.

Plate 6 Derwentwater in the English Lake District. Apart from the lake this is largely a cultural landscape, but one so valued that it enjoys protection from certain kinds of change by virtue of its designation as a National Park. As can be seen from some of the mountains, afforestation is not subject to control. *(Aerofilms Ltd, London)*

The formation of a 'Naturpark' takes place under the 1969 Preservation of Nature Act which makes possible the designation of large areas (10–15,000 ha, for example) in all parts of the country. The chief aim will be the preservation of current characteristics, and to that end farming and forestry will continue, with new buildings and other developments strictly controlled. Management aims will allow the integration of recreation areas where these are compatible with the primary purpose. An early example of a Naturpark is the Tystrup-Bavelse area of Zealand, known as 'Sjaellands grønne hjerte'. It is an area of

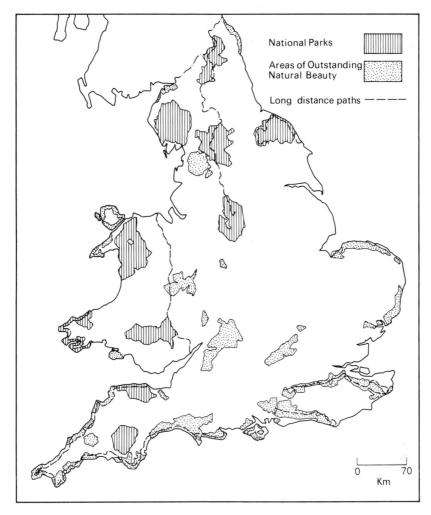

Fig. 3.5 National Parks and Areas of Outstanding Natural Beauty in England and Wales (1972), where strict development control is practised. Although a large proportion of the land surface is protected by these designations, economic activities are supposed to continue unabated.
Source: Countryside Commission of England and Wales 1972: *Annual Report 1971–72*

farmland, woods and villages comprising 12,000 ha around a lake, the Tystrup Sø. Until the 1969 Act it was not possible to pay compensation to landowners materially affected by the emparking, and the character of the area was maintained largely by voluntary agreements, but this legislation has made the position of both government and landowners clear.

Needless to say, there are many problems associated with the preservation of landscape values. Take for example the implication that a landscape should be kept as it is. Unless it is a totally natural landscape, then it has come to its present state in response to operation of past economic processes. If the needs now change, why should not the landscapes alter? What justification can be found for fossilizing a cultural landscape as it is now? The answer that present values demand it raises the question of whether such values are permanent, which they clearly are not. If we agree that uncontrolled alteration of landscapes in response to every economic whim of a *laissez-faire* economy is unacceptable, but that fossilization is also undesirable, then we have to find criteria for distinguishing allowable change from that which must be stopped (Simmons 1967). Although development policies can be defined and adopted democratically (or autocratically), not every demand for change will fall neatly into an allowable or prohibited category, so that many *ad hoc* decisions have to be taken. In the face of pressures for a new industrial development such as a newly discovered mineral deposit, it is almost impossible to uphold a protective set of regulations, witness the controversies over the North York Moors National Park (Statham 1971), and the concern over the copper and gold extraction explorations of RTZ in the Snowdonia National Park in the early 1970s. Sometimes the viewers of the landscapes create the greatest problems, especially if they are present in sufficiently large numbers (Duffey 1967). The unwitting damage which they then do, such as trampling and the scattering of litter, is made worse by the presence of numerous vehicles (Bayfield 1971, Streeter 1971). These not only damage the ecology unless properly managed: in open areas they represent a highly unaesthetic intrusion. But only small numbers of careless or malevolent visitors are needed to create damage of a vandalistic kind. Examples of this are very familiar, and include direct economic loss to farmers as when stock are allowed to stray or are harassed by dogs; or when palatable but lethal rubbish such as some types of plastic are left behind for domestic animals like cattle to eat.

Ideally, the protected landscape is a non-consumptive resource: the crop is of a visual nature, and when this has been taken by the onlookers, the resource remains; the aim of management is to perpetuate this attribute.

Conflicts

The mention of landscape-protection areas which embrace forestry and farming provokes the discussion of the possibilities of multiple-use schemes which embrace a measure of wildlife or scenic preservation. Clearly, given goodwill and the possible loss of income from compromising with that aim, farming and forestry can be carried on along with nature parks, National Parks and the like. Any severe restrictions, such as the control of agricultural buildings or the enforced planting of hardwood screens around conifer plantations, need compensation payments if they are to be reasonably willingly adopted. Recreation and watershed management may also usually be integrated into scenery preservation if firm control can be exercised over the siting of developments. Reservoirs may of course come into the category of unacceptable alterations of the landscape: tastes vary from country to country. Nature protection often fits well, as when small reserves are embedded in a matrix of preserved landscape. Some resource uses are decidedly incompatible with the protection of landscapes: military use almost invariably results in considerable damage, and industrial plants can rarely be given sufficient screening to render them unobtrusive. Large quarries are generally inimical developments, producing dust and noise as well as large holes, and even solution mining of minerals such as potash causes large scars in wild country where the pipelines are buried. Processing plants are likewise highly intrusive and often sources of environmental contamination. So while landscape protection and nature conservation elements can and should be a part of every development scheme, rural or urban (as it is in the Netherlands where the Forest Service has a national responsibility for landscaping), the opposite case, where the valued scene and wildlife are the primary objectives of management, needs careful attention.

The effects of increasing human populations are both direct and indirect. Directly, there are more people, usually with more vehicles either public or private, wanting to visit the protected places, and they are often concentrated at especially popular times like the summer weekends and holidays. This intensifies their impact upon the ecological systems which form the landscape, and in large enough numbers they become a feature, usually undesired, of the landscape itself. Indirectly, more people want more jobs, more housing, more water and the like. Even when regional or national planning is efficient, these pressures cannot be for long diverted from valued landscapes. The patterns of world trade and interdependence exert effects too, so that agricultural development in LDCs* stimulates demand for fertilizer production in DCs, whose industrial anabasis in turn requires more water and hence more reservoir construction in areas of high landscape value which inevitably will sometimes be in areas of considerable scientific interest, with an area of flora and fauna being threatened with damage or extinction (R. Gregory 1971). Despite considerable opportunities for creative planning and public education there remains among resource managers, in the West at least, no doubt that landscapes and nature can in the end be kept untrammelled only by restrictions on the number of people who come into their presence and by the slowing down or cessation of the competing demands for space created by higher populations with rising material expectations.

* Throughout this book the abbreviations LDC (less developed country) and DC (developed country) will be used.

Further reading

BUSH, R. 1973: *The National Parks of England and Wales.*

DASMANN, R. F. 1964: *Wildlife biology.*

DUFFEY, E. and WATT, A. S. (eds.) 1971: *The scientific management of animal and plant communities for conservation.*

FRASER DARLING, F. and EICHORN, N. 1967: *Man and nature in the National Parks: some reflections on policy.*

GREGORY, R. 1971: *The price of amenity.*

IUCN 1970: *United Nations list of National Parks and equivalent reserves.*

JARRETT, H. (ed.) 1961: *Comparisons in resource management.*

KRUTILLA, J. (ed.) 1972: *Natural environments.*

PRYDE, P. R. 1972: *Conservation in the Soviet Union.*

4

Outdoor recreation

The urge to spend leisure time in rural surroundings, thus creating a demand for the use of land and water resources, even if not exclusively for that purpose, has probably existed since the beginning of an urban way of life. In pre-industrial times, even the city dwellers were in relatively close contact with nature, but with the coming of the factory and the urban explosion of the nineteenth century, the working masses became confined to their towns except for holidays, for after the long hours of work there was time only for eating and sleeping. The waggonnette and then the train became cheap means of escape to seaside and countryside, and the working classes began to acquire that taste for fresh air and rural surroundings which hitherto only the rich had been able to enjoy. The developments of the twentieth century have further entrenched the recreational desires of all strata of society in the West (Revelle 1967), to the point where Gabor (1963) listed leisure among the dangers to civilization along with war and overpopulation.

Leisure, affluence and mobility in the twentieth century

At the turn of the century, the 60-hour working week was common in the West. In Holland and Denmark, for example, this was the usual figure, and similar hours were worked in most industrial countries. In the USA, for example, the fall in hours worked, along with increase in average daily leisure time, is given in Table 4.1. The present situation is summed up in Table 4.2, from a Danish source, which gives for slightly different dates (mostly 1964–6) the relevant figures. The daily hours of work, the annual holiday and the occasional free days mean that individuals are now able to plan a very different time-budget from that which was common earlier in the century. In 1900, Clawson (1963) reports, 26·5 per cent of the time of US citizens could be classed as leisure (time after work, sleep, housekeeping and personal care); by 1950 this proportion had risen to 34 per cent and is likely to rise to 38 per cent by the year 2000. In Britain, the 1967 proportion is about 31 per cent (BTA–Keele University 1967). The pattern of leisure that is developing seems to be common to most north Atlantic countries. Daily after-work or after-school leisure is currently least important for outdoor recreation, but its contribution is growing, especially with increase in second-car ownership; weekend and special holiday leisure is extremely important and contributes substantially.

Forecasts of work and leisure suggest a continuation of present trends. Sweden expects a 40-hour week by the 1970s with at least 4 weeks' vacation; in the USA, projections

TABLE 4.1   Work and leisure in the USA 1920–60

Date	Work hrs/day	Leisure hrs/day (averaged for year, including vacation)
1920	49·7	5·7
1930	45·9	6·4
1940	44·0	6·7
1950	40·0	7·4
1960	37·5	7·8

Source: Scheider 1962

TABLE 4.2   Working hours and holidays

Country	Normal weekly working hours	Yearly number of vacation days	Yearly number of free days (weekdays or holidays)
Denmark	42·5	18	9–10
England	40·0–42·5	12	6
Netherlands	45·0	12	7
USA	40·0	6–24	6–8
Finland	40·0–45·0	18	12
Sweden	43·3	24	11
Norway	42·5	24	10
Belgium	42·0–45·0	18	10
West Germany	40·0–42·0	15–18	10–12
France	40·0	18	5–10
Italy	44·0–45·0	12	16
Luxembourg	42·5–44·0	18	10
Iceland	44·0	18	?
Ireland	48·0	12	6
Spain	44·0	7–12	13
Switzerland	44·0–46·0	12–24	6–8
Australia	40·0	18	10
Israel	47·0	12–18	9–11
Japan	44·0–48·0	6–20	?
USSR	41·0	15–24	?

Source: Arbejdsministeriet Danmarks 1968

suggested by the Outdoor Recreation Resources Review Commission (ORRRC) in 1962 are given in Table 4.3. Other countries will no doubt follow at varying rates; lower-paid workers are usually willing to exchange leisure time for extra income and the proportions of different income groups among a population are therefore likely to influence the rate at which the 'standard' working week decreases in length.

TABLE 4.3   Projected working hours and holidays

Year	Weekly working hours	Weeks' holiday	Individual free days
1976	35·4	2·8	8·5
2000	30·7	3·9	10·1

Source: ORRRC 1962b

The basic richness of some industrialized countries is emphasized in Table 4.4, and together with the other criteria of leisure and mobility it enforces the view that the use of resources for outdoor recreation is primarily a phenomenon of industrial nations; particularly those of the West, along with Japan, some of the highly urbanized Asian states, and the richer nations of the southern hemisphere. For the present purpose the relevant part of the richness is the disposable income, and Table 4.5 shows the increase in disposable personal income in the USA and its forecast level for 1976. Within the disposable category, expenditure on recreation as a whole appears to vary only within the 4–7 per cent bracket and is surprisingly constant for all income levels. Definition makes difficult the separation of outdoor recreation expenditure, but it appears that in the US there is a steeper rise in the proportion spent on outdoor recreation than on recreation in general. Nobody expects that the rate of expenditure on leisure activities will do anything other than rise, war and monetary system collapse permitting. In Britain, for example, real income per head in 1985 is expected to be 175 per cent of the 1960 figure.

TABLE 4.4   Per capita GNP (mostly 1969 data; US dollars)

Western countries		Socialist countries		Non-Western countries	
Canada	2,650	USSR	1,200	Brazil	270
Denmark	2,310	Czechoslovakia	1,370	Nigeria	100
UK	1,890	Hungary	1,100	Indonesia	100
Netherlands	1,760	Poland	940	India	110
USA	4,240	Rumania	860	Japan	1,430

Source: Population Reference Bureau 1972

TABLE 4.5   Disposable personal income, USA (billions (= 000 million) 1959 dollars)

1946	1950	1957	1976
222·48	246·9	316·0	702·5

Source: ORRRC 1962b

As far as outdoor recreation in the West is concerned, possession of a private motor vehicle is a paramount factor in participation (Table 4.6). In eastern Europe and Japan, public transport is still the most important conveyor of recreationists, but in the West the outdoors is visited largely in the company of the internal combustion engine. Even if the gasoline engine becomes a museum-piece within the span of projections now being made, possession of private individual transport seems to be very firmly tied into the patterns of outdoor recreation which have become familiar and desirable to the inhabitants of the West.

TABLE 4.6   Passenger cars in use (thousands)

	1953	1963	1970	Persons per car 1970
Canada	2,513·8	4,788·9	6,602·2	3·03
Denmark	157·5	605·0	1,076·1	4·52
Great Britain	2,797·7	7,482·6	11,666·0	4·62
Netherlands	187·6	865·5	2,500·0	4·58
USA	46,460·1	68,683·0	88,840·5	2·28
Japan	114·7	1,234·0	8,779·0	10·18

Source: United Nations 1972

Activities

Outdoor recreation consists of leisure-time activities undertaken in relatively small groups, in a rural setting. The second two of these conditions are not capable of precise delimitation, for the number—units run from the solitary walker to the members of a sailing club. The major activities are included in Table 4.7.

Although some of these require considerable manipulation of the natural resource or heavy investment in equipment, it can be seen that an important element in every activity is a 'natural' substance, be it fields and forests, water or snow; this is the difference between these forms of activity and the nature-divorced pursuits such as bowls, cricket, and football of all kinds. Hence, extra-urban areas are the locations for the activities, particularly since just being out in rural surroundings doubtless forms a major source of attraction, although not one easily assessed by questionnaire survey.

In Western countries where surveys of participation in these activities have been carried out, we can gain an idea of the number of people who take part in outdoor recreation. Table 4.8 gives such data as are reasonably comparable. From the extensive list of activities and the relatively high proportions of people undertaking them, we can readily visualize that land and water resources are demanded by people for their leisure time. There has always been an element of this kind of 'non-productive' use in most places: in medieval England there were the Royal Forests, strictly preserved for the King, and areas of lower status like Chases and Warrens for the lesser aristocracy. Later, the great landscape gardens of

TABLE 4.7   Major outdoor recreation activities (no ranking is implied by the order)

Driving for pleasure	
Walking for pleasure/Hiking	This is a useful distinction—the latter is the serious version.
Outdoor games	These should be of an informal nature, requiring little or no fixed equipment.
Swimming	Includes sub-aqua activities. It is implied that a 'natural-looking' water body is involved, not a 'pool'.
Bicycling	
Fishing	
Nature study, archaeology	
Nature walks	Includes both guided walks and self-guiding nature trails.
Boating/Sailing	This category means motor-boats on inland waters and sea.
Canoeing	Inland water.
Sea sailing	Sail only.
Sightseeing	Of cultural interests rather than appreciation of views, etc.
Caving	Restricted to limestone pothole country.
Hunting	This is an American term, and is used there mainly for deer-shooting. For use in this book it will be taken to be synonymous with shooting and to exclude fox-hunting.
Horseback riding	Including pony-trekking.
Camping	Including 'day-camping', not easily separable from picnicking; also caravaning: difficult to separate in North America.
Picknicking	
Ice skating	Outdoor only, on naturally frozen water.
Tobogganing	
Snow skiing	
Mountain climbing	Synonymous with rock climbing: fell-walking and scrambling under hiking.
Motor sports	Hill trials, motorcycle scrambles over informal courses.
Water skiing	

Sources: ORRRC 1962a, BTA-Keele University 1967. This latter survey also includes activities such as archery, bowls, golf and athletics which are considered as urban phenomena and are not dealt with here.

the seventeenth and eighteenth centuries became backgrounds for the less lusty pursuits of the contemporary gentry. The ruling classes of most ages have had their resource-using pleasure gardens, whether rural or urban, as with the pleasure-dome of Xanadu, presumably a sort of early Havasupai City. By contrast with the requirements of the numerically insignificant rich, the demand to transfer resources into leisure use now emanates from a large proportion of the population in industrialized countries. Another way in which the dimensions of man–environment relations have altered with regard to leisure is the hardware involved. Once a pair of nailed boots and a woolly sweater (or solar topee in the tropics) sufficed. Now, trailbikes, dune buggies and snowmobiles extend mobility off the roads into most kinds of terrain; aqualungs allow penetration under water (there is a sub-marine National Park in the US Virgin Islands); and the humble tent is being ousted in favour of a caravan or an integral-chassis camper. In North America it is not uncommon to see a large integral camper with a boat on the roof, two trailbikes slung on the front,

Plate 7 Perhaps most people's ideal of outdoor recreation? An isolated lake and a lone fisherman-camper, communing with nature. *(Grant Heilman, Lititz, Pa)*

and a small Japanese motorcar being towed behind. The impact of all this technology upon some of the recreation resources can easily be imagined.

The types of ecosystems which people like to be in for their outdoor recreation are very varied, according to both taste and availability, but certain preferences emerge. Overriding them all is the attraction of water (Plate 7). The pull of the seashore or the sandy edge of large lakes needs no stressing, but the presence of a small inland lake or river adds immeasurably to the value of a recreation area inland. There is, too, a preference for wild or seemingly wild vegetation such as woods, dunes and heaths, providing that the woods have ample openings or 'edge'. In climates with inhospitable tendencies some sort of shelter is demanded, so that the picnic tables at White Sands in New Mexico have reflective shades over them; in part of the Netherlands a very popular region is that where forest is found in the lee of sand-dunes so that people can move inland if the weather turns chill. It is not of course the actual nature of the ecosystem which attracts people so much as their perception of it, and varying degrees of alteration and change are acceptable for different recreation activities. While it is usually only possible to describe outdoor recreation use of resources in objective terms, therefore, it must not be forgotten that just as important are people's ideas about the sort of surroundings they choose, or would choose if alternatives were available. For example, Lucas (1964) showed that the two major groups of users (those

TABLE 4.8   Comparisons of participation

	USA		Netherlands	Sweden	Canada	GB
Selected activities per cent of population						
Activity	1960	1965	1966	1963	1966–7	1960–4
Walking for pleasure	33	48	25	73		
Swimming	45	48	29	65	34	10[1]
Camping	8	10	11[2]	19	13	6
Sightseeing	42	49			29	
Driving	52	55	50	73	47	56[3]
Fishing	29	30	14	37	26	6
Hiking	7	9			11	5
Sailing[4]	2	3		24	7	6
Skiing	2	4		41	6	1[5]

[1] Will include some use of urban facilities.
[2] Includes use of country cottage.
[3] An estimate for Whitsun 1963.
[4] Not motorized (Sweden, motorists included); includes rowing where this is separated.
[5] All winter sports.
This table is compiled from a variety of sources.

with and those without motors on their craft) of a wilderness canoe area in Minnesota–Ontario have different perceptions of the amount of human interference with the forest and of the effect such alterations have upon their enjoyment.

Classification of outdoor recreation areas and users

One classification of outdoor recreation resources is in terms of their actual or potential use; this method was adopted by the ORRRC (1962a) of the USA and distinguished six types of area:

> *Class 1:* High Density Recreation Areas: areas intensively developed and managed for mass use
> *Class 2:* General Outdoor Recreation Areas: areas subject to substantial development for a wide variety of specific recreation uses
> *Class 3:* Natural Environment Areas: various types of areas that are suitable recreation in a natural environment and usually in combination with other uses
> *Class 4:* Unique Natural Areas: areas of outstanding scenic splendour, natural wonder or scientific importance
> *Class 5:* Primitive Areas: undisturbed roadless areas, characterized by natural wild conditions, including 'wilderness areas'
> *Class 6:* Historic and Cultural Sites: sites of major historic or cultural significance, either local, regional, or national

Another method takes account of social factors such as accessibility from the users, and the classification to be used here has been developed by Knetsch and Clawson (1967). It is basically a *user-resource* method in which the two major elements are the characteristics of the users in terms of the time when they use the resource—whether it be afternoon, day or weekend use, or in their longer vacations—and the physical and ecological characteristics of the resource, especially its degree of wildness and of manipulation away from the natural state. The classification has three categories: user-orientated, dealing with the shorter periods of use; resource-based, treating the longer holiday periods; and intermediate, not unnaturally discussing the class in between—mainly the weekend and short vacation periods.

User-orientated recreation resources

The recreation areas deemed to be user-orientated are characterized by being as close to the homes of users as possible, and thus make use of whatever resources are available. The activities become the most important feature and a great deal of alteration is acceptable, and often necessary to protect the area against the damaging effects of heavy use. Activities such as golf, tennis, swimming and picnics, walking and horse riding, small zoos and model farms or railways and general informal play are the most usually found. The intensive use of what are often quite small areas, at most a few hundred hectares, with many smaller units, comes after school or after work and at weekends. Such areas are commonly owned by city or county governments or their various equivalents. The city park forms the innermost element of the structure. Its nature is very variable and the present tendency is away from the starched formality of traditional city parks. The value of such areas of open space as Boston Common, Central Park in New York and the Royal Parks of London is probably best judged from the fact that they are still not yet built upon.

Examples of recreation areas near cities

Parks and recreation areas on city fringes are difficult to acquire because of the high cost of land which is also valuable for housing or perhaps industrial use; but some cities have happily acquired, been given or converted from dereliction suitable tracts of land and water. The Amsterdam Forest ('Het Amsterdamse Bos') on the south-east side of that city is a large (900 ha), totally artificial recreation area, converted from polderland. Since 1934 (Fig. 4.1) the major pattern is of woods with informal footpaths and cycleways interspersed with grass fields and water-bodies, some irregular and informal, others regular as in the case of a rowing course. The developed facilities include a sports stadium, riding school and open-air theatre. There are roads and car parks, but access by public transport forms the commonest pattern of use. In the same country, the theme of conversion is echoed by a water area just outside Utrecht, called Maarseveense Plassen. Under the auspices of the national authority carrying out land-consolidation plans, a former wetland area of peat cuttings and intervening baulks has been dredged out to form a swimming and boating lake. The margins are landscaped, either with woodland containing cycleways and footpaths or with lawns

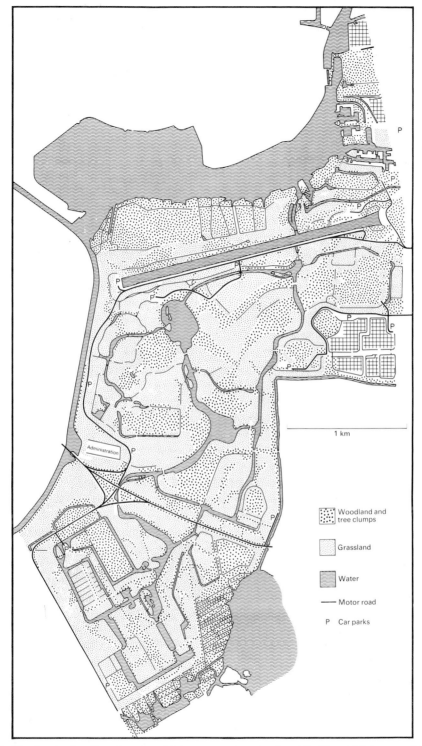

Fig. 4.1 The Amsterdam Forest: a completely man-made recreational facility which by use of trees and water creates a rural atmosphere in some parts. More urbanized and formal areas for games and a rowing course are also part of the area.
Source: Dienst der Publike Werken Amsterdam 1960: *Het Amsterdamse Bos*

leading from the facilities (toilets, changing rooms and café) down to the diving boards and shallow-water zone. Use is heavy, averaging some 30,000 people per annum in the first years of its use during the 1960s.

The valley of the River Lee slices through the eastern suburbs of London and here a scheme to develop a rather ill-assorted agglomeration of reservoirs, a canal, gravel pits, football pitches, refuse dumps and small industries like scrap-metal reclamation into a Lee Valley Regional Park has been initiated (Civic Trust 1964). The Park will have some nature reserves but will in general be highly developed, with playing fields, indoor sports halls, water-sport pools, restaurants, and possibly animal collections of special interest to urban children, like cows and horses (Fig. 4.2).

These are more or less spatially isolated instances, and actual park systems on the edges of urbanized areas are rarer. One example is the East Bay Regional Park District on the east side of San Francisco Bay in California. The hills behind cities such as Oakland, Berkeley and Albany are naturally grass- and chaparral-covered, with some redwoods, but since the nineteenth century eucalyptuses have become naturalized. In this setting, a series of parks has become established catering mainly for user-orientated recreation but admittedly overlapping into the intermediate zone. The most user-orientated parks in the system are Tilden Park and Redwood Park. In the valleys nearest to the cities, development of features such as a swimming lake, steam-powered railways, golf course, a carousel, a miniature farm, and riding stables has taken place. Further in is a less developed zone with picnic sites, group camp sites and a botanic garden of a relatively informal kind. Beyond these the park is largely wild in appearance, with a few trails striking off into the chaparral and wooded areas. Here, deer herds exist probably along with their natural predator, the bobcat or mountain lion. The development of Tilden Park, for example, shows a distinct series of development zones aligned parallel to both the topography and the adjacent cities (Fig. 4.3). Another unit in the system consists almost entirely of a swimming pool and adjacent facilities, open-air but formal in character, near to the edge of the Bay Area conurbation.

Possibly the largest class of user-orientated recreation areas are beaches at the seaward fringes of seaside cities. These are very cheap resources since there is generally perpetual renewal of the essential elements by the sea. Where this action breaks down then sand has to be brought in and an artificial beach maintained, which is costly but usually essential for the viability of the resort. In Japan, for example, a first priority in open-space acquisition for public use is the provision of beaches which will be easily accessible to the people of the great conurbations.

Changes wrought by recreational use

The designation of a unit of land or water as a recreation area within this present category usually means that changes will occur in the local ecosystems. At a deliberate level, most changes have to be made in order that the area can withstand the intensive use which it receives. Thus circulation routes are inevitably hard-surfaced, and it may be necessary to plant trees and shrubs which can withstand compaction of the earth over their roots and the loss of a branch or two by vandalism. Picnic tables if installed have to be specially strong, and concrete frames, if not tops, are common. Biota rarely receive management in

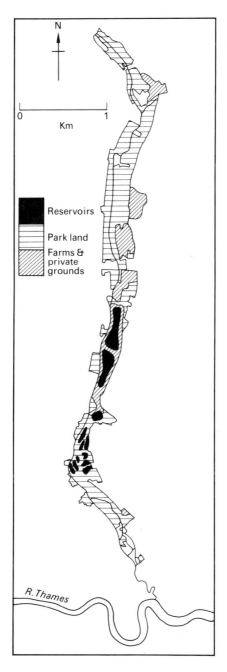

Fig. 4.2 The proposed redevelopment of the Lee Valley in east London: a mosaic of reservoirs, private lands and parklands for intensive use by the population of the urban areas which surround the valley. Source: Civic Trust 1964

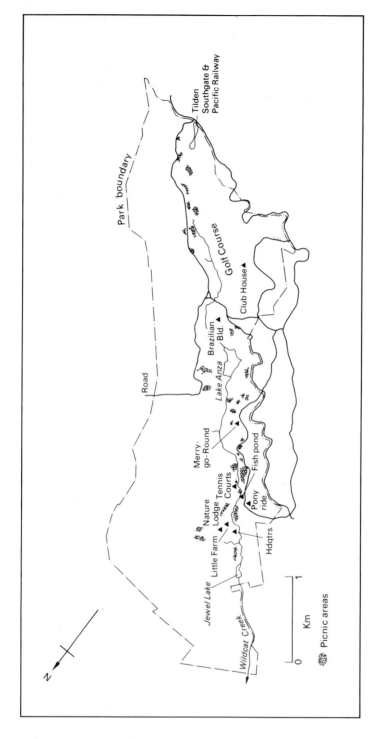

Fig. 4.3 Tilden Park, a component of the East Bay Regional Park District in California. To the east of the park is undeveloped watershed land, to the west the urbanized areas of the East Bay (e.g. Berkeley, Albany, Oakland). The concentration of developed facilities along the western edge is evident.

Source: East Bay Regional Parks District n.d.: *Charles Lee Tilden Park* (pamphlet)

such places, although a pair of nesting swans can be inimical to other uses of water-bodies in spring, and in many countries the numbers of pigeons and starlings attracted to such areas may be undesirable. Beaches may of course suffer from polluted water, and enlightened municipalities endeavour to remove the source of pollution, which may be not only unaesthetic but a positive danger to health.

Intermediate-type recreation resources

The zone of recreation resources available to the city-dweller for use on day outings and weekends is called by Knetsch and Clawson (1967) the Intermediate zone. The actual distance travelled by users will vary according to the road system, since transport by private auto is all-important for this type of use. Within the time–distance limitation, preference is shown for the best resources that are available, in terms for instance of scenery, water and forests. These are generally larger in size than the user-orientated areas, running from a few hundred to several thousand hectares. Emphasis is put on activities such as camping, picnicking, hiking, swimming, hunting and fishing, and there is also the pleasure of driving to get to the chosen location. Although public resources managed by governmental agencies are perhaps the most common feature of this category, the private sector is often involved. The degree of manipulation away from the natural state tends to be less than in user-orientated areas, and acceptance of quasi-urban features is lower. Insistance on a natural environment is of course impossible in continents like Europe and here high value is placed on areas which are obviously wild even if not natural, or on areas like heaths and moors which are popularly thought to be natural even though they are anthropogenic in origin. The pressures resulting from recreation may still be intense over a small area of the resource, but there is more often a large area of back country into which the less gregarious can escape.

National Parks in England and Wales

Although dealt with once under the heading of protected landscape, the National Parks of England and Wales come under this heading too (Darby 1963). People come to them not only to view the scenery, but for many active recreations as well. Driving for pleasure, walking and hiking, climbing, potholing, boating, natural history pursuits and many other activities are carried out in these 11 designated areas. Most of them are within the day-use zone of a major conurbation, yet several receive some usage of a resource-based category. Most of the valley land within the Parks is private and obviously so, which means that use is only by direct permission of the owner unless walking along a public right of way is contemplated. Even the owner may be under restrictions since, for example, the placing of caravans requires planning permission. The majority of farmers in the Parks do not welcome recreationists, however, because of the trouble caused by their ignorance of the working nature of rural areas. It is not surprising therefore that much recreation tends to be concentrated in the unenclosed zones which are altitudinally above the farmed lands. Such lands are often common land to which there is a *de facto* but not *de jure* right of public access (Fig. 4.4). It is here that most people like to set off on walks, to picnic or simply to sit in their cars. Since until the late 1960s there were few places where cars could pull off the usually narrow roads, such spots as there were frequently received very heavy pressure. The installation of car parks and toilets in many of the attractive villages that are found in the lower areas of the Parks has meant an alleviation of the congestion of narrow and picturesque streets by fleets of visitors' cars. In some of the Parks, the planning authorities have taken the lead in such actions as providing official but limited camp and caravan sites in order to prevent a rash over all the countryside. Experiments are being undertaken to control car access to some of the most popular but narrow roads in the interests of general public amenity: the Goyt Valley in the Peak District National Park is an example (Countryside Commission 1970).

Even with such measures, it is difficult to avoid the conclusion that at peak times some of the National Parks (the Lake District and Peak District especially) are reaching their carrying capacity for outdoor recreation. This is especially so for people with cars, but queues to climb particular crags and to descend certain potholes suggest that the pinch is also being felt in other activities. Under the aegis of the Countryside Act of 1968, county councils are empowered to designate another kind of Intermediate-class recreation area, the Country Parks. The degree of development of these facilities can be varied according to the circumstances, and it is hoped that the National Parks will be relieved of some of their recreational pressures and be visited more for their unique attractions rather than for activities which can be pursued equally well in other areas. The Country Parks will amplify a role already played in some parts of the country by the plantations of the Forestry Commission. During the last few years there has been a revolution in the policy of this body regarding recreation, so that picnic sites, camping sites, trails and visitor centres are now often found, as at Grizedale in the Lake District, Allerston Forest in North Yorkshire, and many other places. As these areas have distinct boundaries, it is often possible to make a charge for facilities and this is usually done. In this context, recreation presents fewer problems as an element of multiple use than with farming: young forests are very susceptible to damage but are not very attractive for recreation, and wildlife is not particularly abundant in monocultural coniferous forests.

The Dutch experience

The role of recreation in re-afforested parts of Europe is carried to a considerable length in the Netherlands, where 25 per cent of the area managed by the State Forest Service (Staatsbosbeheer, SBB) is managed primarily for timber production, and the remainder mostly for recreation and nature conservation, especially the former (SBB 1966). Apart from the customary facilities, the SBB has created large informal swimming holes out of sandy lands, an example is to be found at Nunspeet. In at least one case the hole represents the further use of a borrow-pit resulting from motorway construction. Most of the State Forests of the Netherlands come into the Intermediate category although some are near enough to towns to be thought of as user-orientated and development is correspondingly intensive. In both situations, however, the Dutch love of food is exemplified in the

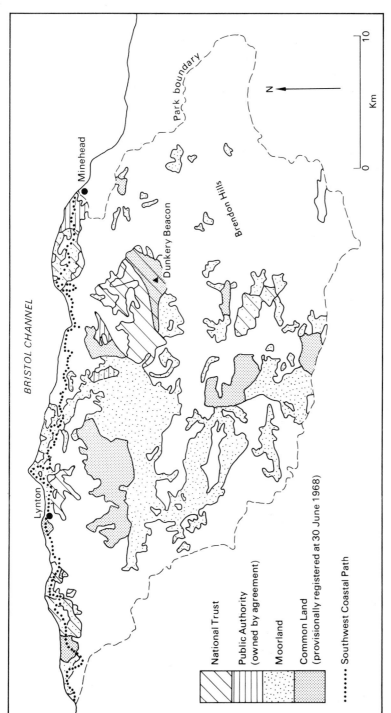

Fig. 4.4 Access land on Exmoor, one of the National Parks of England and Wales. *De jure* access is to National Trust and Public Authority land; *de facto* access exists to moorland and commonland but, strictly speaking, such access could be withdrawn. The Coastal Path is a public right of way for those on foot. Source: Patmore 1971.

provision of refreshment kiosks and restaurants in places where British and American experience and preference would find them a little intrusive.

State Parks in the USA

Most states have such a system of State Parks, but their effectiveness and range of utilized resources vary greatly. In general, the richer the state, the more complex the State Parks system will be: the states of New York, Michigan, Minnesota, Oregon and California are generally recognized to be the leaders. In all such systems these are areas of primarily historical or cultural interest (such as some of the Franciscan Missions in California), and in some the system embraces nature protection as well. For recreation, State Park systems usually enclose the best scenic and recreational resources which are not already within the Federal system and develop them to cope with heavy pressures, especially at summer week-ends; winter sports may also be catered for at selected locations. Nearly all outdoor recreations are carried on in these Parks, with some emphasis on camping, fishing and hiking. Hunting is rarely permitted in them. In states like California, with a high diversity of ecosystems, generalizations about the pattern of resource use are difficult to make. Forests have a clear attraction especially for summer shade, and in this connexion the northern coast redwood parks are popular as cool places quite apart from the magnificence of *Sequoia sempervirens*. Water is another attraction, whether on the few public beaches (those of southern California are very crowded in summer) or inland at reservoirs or natural lakes such as Clear Lake and Lake Tahoe, both of which have State Parks along part of their otherwise privately owned shores. The desert Parks are naturally popular in winter, as are skiing, tobogganing and other snow-based sports.

The second home

The possession of second homes in rural areas is a rapidly growing phenomenon in the West. In Europe it reaches the apogee of its development in Scandinavia, but it is burgeoning everywhere (Fig. 4.5). Weekend cottages, beach-houses, cabins, caravans and their kin are almost by definition part of the Intermediate zone; and because their owners wish to be in rural surroundings but also to have most home comforts such as electricity and mains drainage (or at least a cesspool or septic tank), they pose resource management problems. The aesthetic one of screening to avoid the appearance of a rather tatty suburb is one difficulty, and where zoning laws do not exist it is often impossible to prevent a variegated scatter of bungaloid growth in favoured spots. Economically they pose problems in terms of the services which their owners demand, while often paying relatively low local taxes. The communities in which they exist are therefore likely to have to subsidize them.

Ecologically their effects are most profound when a new area is opened up for cabins around a desirable place such as a lake. It is unlikely that regulations about waste disposal are in effect and so raw sewage will be discharged into the lake with consequent eutrophication and aesthetic damage. The actual placing of the cottages may have less effect since there is a desire to preserve trees and other biota.

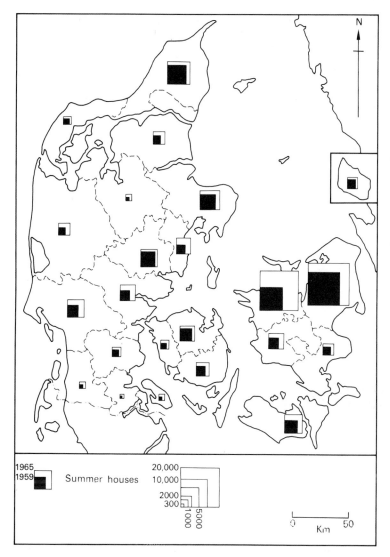

Fig. 4.5 Summerhouses in Denmark, by counties, 1959 and 1965. The concentration in Sjaelland (especially near Copenhagen) and in east Jylland is noticeable. Most of these summerhouse areas were not subject to planning control.
Source: Landsplanudvalgets Sekretariat 1965: *Strandkvalitet og Fritidsbebyggelse*

Resource-based recreation

In contrast to the previous two categories, resource-based recreation takes place where the outstanding resources are to be found, independently of the distribution of population. This may well be some distance from the majority of users, although some people may live in the backyard of an outstanding resource which others travel thousands of miles to visit. It follows that the longer vacation periods are the commonest use periods and that activities are consequent upon the resource offered: major sightseeing is perhaps paramount, along with scientific and historic interest, even if these latter two are very inchoately realized. Hiking and climbing, fishing and hunting may also be pursued because of the superlative qualities of the particular place; camping may be an end in itself or a cheap way to visit the resource area. The qualities of the attractive area are generally extensive: typically a resource-based recreation area may range from many thousands of hectares in size to ten times that magnitude. It is not surprising therefore that the resource is usually publicly owned and that the agencies of the national government are usually the managers. Exceptions to this are sometimes found in water frontages along large lakes and the sea.

As the environment is all-important, it should be a feature of the designated areas that human impacts resulting in alterations to the ecology should be minimized. This is generally so, except where visitor numbers are very high and require particular management responses. But highly developed zones are usually small in relation to the proportion of wild back-country.

National Parks in North America

The world's most famous examples of the designation of resource-based recreation areas are the National Parks of the USA and Canada, especially those of the western cordillera. The range of terrains is immense, but all the Parks share the property of being very wild and in most places natural or at any rate affected only by aboriginal economics in the form of hunting and burning. Economic activities on a large scale have never been permitted, although some early grazing may have left erosive scars, and there are numerous private inholdings which complicate management.

The major problems of the National Parks come from the great mass of visitors. In 1910, about 0·2 million people visited a US National Park system of about 9,308 km² (2·3 million ac), in the 1960s about 95 million a year went to a system that was still below 80,940 km² (20 million ac) in size. Such numbers initiate immense demands for roads (since most use private cars), for accommodation, food, gasoline, water and other services (Plate 8); in turn they produce sewage, garbage, litter, car exhausts and traffic jams (Cahn 1968). These effects, together with the presence in some National Parks of luxury hotels and golf courses, eventually led to the reappraisal of National Park policy in the USA described in Chapter 3, which has resulted in the designation of recreation areas within a park system whose function is primarily protective. Thus recreation is being de-emphasized, and eventually perhaps most developed facilities will be withdrawn beyond the park boundaries. Under the impetus of public opinion, the master plans for the National Parks of Canada include large wild areas and developed areas are being kept to a minimum (Fig. 4.6).

Even before such changes in policy, these National Parks were unequal to the recreation pressure they were being expected to carry. One result, analogous in function to the Country Parks in Britain, has been the development within the USA Federal system of National Recreation Areas. In 1971, there were 17 units comprising 14,164 km² (3·5 million ac), representing outstanding opportunities for resource-based recreation within the Federal

Plate 8 Perhaps most people's reality of outdoor recreation? The area near Old Faithful geyser in Yellowstone National Park. The Park Service now aims to 'de-develop' this part of the Park. *(Grant Heilman, Lititz, Pa)*

system at areas not suitable for designation as National Parks. The selection criteria involve consideration of the size of an area, its ability to provide a high carrying capacity for recreation, and a location usually not more than 400 km from large urban centres. A natural environment is not required and many of the areas are primarily for water-based recreation along artificial impoundments such as Lake Mead, Lake Powell, and the Shasta Dam and Lake in California.

Multiple use with recreation as a primary purpose of management is represented in the USA Federal system by the National Forests. Most of their 752,742 km² (183 million ac) are in the west and they often form the matrix within which the National Parks and National Recreation Areas are set. Since recreation is only one of the purposes of management (the others are wildlife, grazing, water and timber production), the multiple use tends to be a mosaic pattern, with developed recreational facilities and roads within a much larger area of undeveloped country. Even where campsites and picnic grounds are developed, they tend to be more simple than in National Parks and National Recreation Areas. Hot

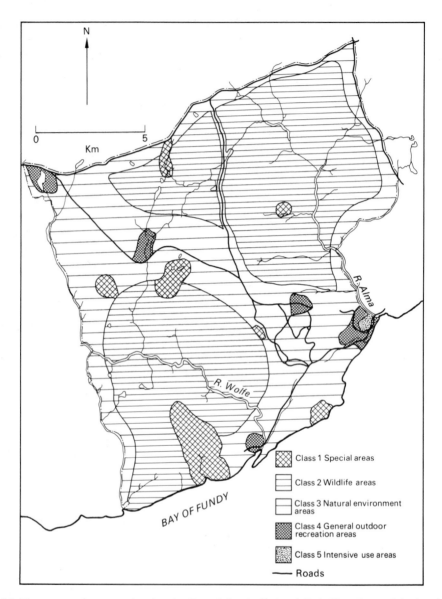

Fig. 4.6 The proposed master plan for the Bay of Fundy National Park, New Brunswick, showing the division of the park into zones. Developed areas are kept to a minimum consistent with the use of the park for recreation. Such a plan is a public document and the subject of public hearings.
Source: National and Historic Parks branch kit for hearings on Bay of Fundy National Park Master Plan, Ottawa, 1968

showers and launderettes are not found in National Forest campgrounds, and the deep-pit toilet replaces the flush type. Thus the local ecology is usually less modified than in the Parks and Recreation Areas, a feature which commends the National Forests to the more hardy campers. The National Forests in fact extend well beyond the forested zone in mountainous terrain and so enclose the alpine meadows and slopes and the high alpine country itself. Recreation activities are hence very varied in kind and range from the highly popular to the more eclectic such as river-rafting and wilderness back-packing.

Europe

In more densely settled parts of the world like Europe, resource-based recreation areas are harder to find and are mostly confined to high mountain areas such as the Alps, Pyrenees, Carpathians and the Norwegian *fjells*. Each of these regions attracts many people both winter and summer for recreation. Management varies, but in general there are a few areas within each region which are particularly designated for the protection of wildlife (e.g. the Tatra National Park in ČSSR–Poland, and the Swiss National Park) and then development of recreation in the rest is subject to the ordinary planning laws of the country.

Within Europe, one area with potential for resource-based recreation is Lapland. At present relatively few people visit it except for such specialized activities as bird-watching and tourism based on the few roads. The same can be said of Iceland. Both these places have very fragile ecosystems with short growing seasons, and any development must recognize this if irresponsible damage is not to be done. On a European scale it would probably be best to make most of both areas into formally protected wildernesses.

A small yet densely populated region like the British Isles fares badly for resource-based recreation, but fortunately the unequal distribution of population confers a sense of remoteness upon places like the Western Highlands and Hebrides of Scotland. The roadless nature and low population density confirms the 'otherness' of these areas and the result is their function as a resource-based recreation region. This has been emphasized by the development of the Cairngorms as Britain's leading winter sport area. Some of the Scottish National Forest Parks attract a nationwide clientele, and a study of the National Forest Park at Beddgelert in North Wales (Sinden and Sinden 1964) showed that many campers were taking their annual holiday, a pointer to one of the functions of the mountains of North Wales generally, although they are probably most heavily used as Intermediate areas by the population of Lancashire and the industrial Midlands.

An immense country like the USSR has enormous recreation resources; yet protected areas for recreation which have nationwide importance have been slow in coming. Pryde (1972) discusses the planned creation of two National Parks ('Russian Forest' south of Moscow, and Lake Baykal in eastern Siberia) which would be devoted primarily to vacation use by the Soviet people. Another 13 sites have been put forward as suitable areas, which would be at least 10,000 ha in size and would be divided into developed and undeveloped sections, with a central semi-wilderness having only trails and designated camping sites. The 'Russian Forest' Park, about 100 km from Moscow, will cater for more intensive use which will be combined with educative functions such as a demonstration forest.

Japan

In all essentials, Japan shares the West's tastes in outdoor recreation. Given a small country with a high density of population, particularly in the Tokyo-Osaka axis, there are large numbers of outdoor recreationists, whose quantity is increasing steadily with the advent of more leisure time and income. The only areas of the country which were specifically designated in 1972 as being available for outdoor recreation are the 26 National Parks and 46 Quasi-National Parks (QNPs), together with 286 prefectural parks; about 13 per cent of the surface of Japan is thus designated. The Parks function through all three user-resource recreation zones, but some especially are of the resource-based character. In these, the cultural attractions are generally less than in the intermediate zone, assuming not unreasonably that Fujiyama has a significance far beyond that of being a mountain. The resource-based National Parks are all distant from the major population axis of Japan; thus the Aso National Park and Unzen-Amakusa National Park in Kyushu, the Towada-Hachimantai National Park in northern Honshu, and the Daisetsuzan and Akan National Parks in Hokkaido are all composed largely of the natural environment of mountain, forest and lake. Nevertheless all the National Parks and Quasi-National Parks are probably accessible for weekend use if overnight trains or planes are used, and all are penetrated by public transport often to an intensity not now common in the West. In the case of Japan, the dilemma of development or preservation centres around two factors: the ownership of the land, and the application of zoning (Senge 1969). Where the land is in national ownership then it is frequently under the control of the Forest Agency, which places a high priority on economic timber production and tends to use clear felling as a method of harvesting; this conflicts at least temporarily with recreational activities as well as spoiling some of the visual attractions of the landscape. Thus the National Parks Agency is frequently at loggerheads with the Forest Agency over resource management in the National Parks. Where there are large areas of private land within the National Parks, the Parks Agency has little control over the development of hot springs, hotels and inns, restaurants, cafés and souvenir shops; these tend to be very frequent elements of the landscape at the nodal points of the National Parks, such as around Lake Shikotsu and Mount Showashinzan in the Shikotsu-Toya National Park in Hokkaido. Another example is at the transport-mode interchange station high on the slopes of Mount Aso in Kyushu. Under the impact of the recreation-seeking element of the population of Japan, there seems at present to be an impetus towards development, and the appreciation of the virtues of the natural environment as a milieu for recreation which has characterized recent movements in the West does not yet seem to have penetrated: there is consequently considerable ecological change wrought by developments made in the name of the provision of recreation facilities.

Changes caused by recreation

As with other types of recreation, the activities and development may affect the ecosystems within which the recreationists operate. At a conscious level, developments to cope with large numbers in popular areas are probably the most noticeable. In Yosemite Valley there is a small village catering to visitors; and in the Canadian Rockies earlier policies established two small towns (Jasper and Banff) which are currently suffering expansionist pressures. In such Parks there is then the somewhat incongruous sight of sewage works and solid waste disposal areas. As pressure increases so more management has to be undertaken, necessitating more notices, more hardtop and generally less nature. Another deliberate policy stems from the desire of some managers to make as much country as possible accessible to as many people as practicable. The building of roads is therefore undertaken, with considerable effects on drainage lines, soil stability and many other features. A road through tundra may have unstable banks which are then seeded with a commercial mixture containing exotics and so the potential for very large biotic invasions may be created. Trees may often be felled to give a clearer view; conversely, insecticides may be used to preserve trees which have a special landscape significance or other associations. Hardware such as gondola lifts require the clearing of a swathe of forest beneath them like a fire-break; and fire roads themselves may be cut for the maximum travel efficiency of fire-fighting crews rather than with regard for the ecology.

Unconscious effects are numerous. The effect of human feet is perhaps the most noticeable, especially where plant roots are susceptible to compaction of the upper layers of the soil, as happens with the California coast redwood. In this case, redwood bark chip mulches have to be laid along the major pathways. In many popular resource-based areas, one animal develops the role of scavenger, to become dependent for its food on the leavings of the visitors: yellowhammers at Tarn Hows in the English Lakes, brown bears in western America. Bears can be dangerous, if surprised or with cubs; harmless-looking animals like ground squirrels and chipmunks may have rabies. At the other extreme are creatures which are driven out of their habitats either because of alterations brought about by visitors or simply by the presence of large numbers of our species. Either way, the ecological patterns which are so valued in 'natural' resource-based recreation areas are disrupted. Plants may suffer even more and after a few years' use a forest campground does not regenerate: there are no seedlings and usually the surface is trodden too hard for germination to take place. A period of 'rest' with management techniques such as scarifying the soil and burning off excess litter (of the natural variety) may be necessary.

These few examples, and many more which could be quoted, serve to highlight the basic dilemma of resource-based recreation: that too great a number of people destroy what they come to seek. The resolution of this in the short term lies in better management of the visitors and, where possible, in the transfer of additional resources from other uses.

Outdoor recreation as an element of multiple use

The non-consumptive nature of most outdoor recreation activities means that it is sometimes possible to combine them with other resource uses. Multiple use may be of two types: either the use of one piece of terrain for several purposes, or a densely interwoven mosaic of different uses. Occasionally both can be found. In general, the compatibility of different use varies according to the intensity of the uses, i.e. the degree of ecological manipulation the systems have undergone. Thus generally compatible resource uses include watershed land, provided the recreation does not cause erosion leading to high silt yields. Water stored in reservoirs can also be used for most types of recreation, although swimming may be discouraged where the water is for drinking purposes and is near to its delivery point. Similarly, the preservation of scenery is usually compatible with recreation, except where extensive development of a visitor-orientated kind has to be undertaken. Nature conservation may be compatible with recreation, but there is a good deal of variation; and the fugacity of animals or the resistance to damage of plants and animals under protection differ in the amount of visitor pressure they can withstand without harm. But such compatibilities are not axiomatic, and careful distinction of the management aims of recreation areas from those of nature conservation and landscape protection are necessary: it is folly to lump them together under a single 'conservationist' label. Certain resource uses are clearly highly incompatible with recreation. The protection of delicate or rare species needs often to be accomplished in secrecy, not least to be hidden from keen botanists and birdwatchers. A more commonly irreconcilable land use at present is agriculture. The damage inflicted on farming operations by either malicious or ignorant visitors to rural areas is a constant complaint of farmers in industrial countries and the eradication of their just cause for concern is difficult. Education is one solution, but it is a long-term process; in the meantime, areas of very high agricultural productivity are probably best kept underdeveloped as far as recreation is concerned. It seems that farmers who suffer loss because of recreation, or who voluntarily manage their farms so as to take account of it, are increasingly likely to be compensated out of public funds, as are woodland owners in the Netherlands who receive freedom from certain estate duties if they maintain footpaths through their property. Obviously mineral extraction is inimical to all forms of recreation, but we may note that after-treatment of abandoned workings may bring them very successfully into resource processes. Landscaped wet gravel pits are very popular for sailing in many places; old quarries and dry pits may house car parks or sheltered picnic sites and day-camps, and with the queues at the bases of popular rock climbs there may be a demand to create new faces by management of suitable quarry walls. Lastly, the military use large areas of land and water which would otherwise be suitable as recreation resources. Heaths in the Netherlands and south-east England, wild terrain in Utah and south-west England, coastlines in most maritime countries, all form the habitat of *Homo aggressor* rather than *Homo ludens*. Pressures to move them on are occasionally successful and compromises over access can sometimes be reached (Please do not step on unexploded shells), but large areas are still devoted to the training of the military and appear likely to remain so.

Multiple-use schemes containing recreation, if carefully planned and managed by a body representative of all the interests concerned, can be highly successful. In industrialized countries where demand especially for intermediate and user-orientated recreation facilities is increasing so quickly, such schemes may represent, in the short term, the only way of providing anything like an adequate supply of resources and may in turn serve to take some pressure off the resource-based areas whose nature generally makes them very susceptible to damage. In recreation, damage is the only form of consumption, and the continuing pressures of use make reparation by natural processes very difficult.

Effects of increasing populations

Although in the short term more recreation resources can be created by shifts of land and water from other uses, this process cannot be carried on indefinitely. Other more basic demands like housing, industry and agriculture cannot be deprived of their share. Rising populations exert an increasing pressure upon resources because demand for recreation in industrialized countries appears to rise at approximately five times the rate of population growth. In poor countries fewer people participate and so the dimensions of the interaction are much smaller. An increase in the number of people hammering at the park gates is immediately caused to a great extent by increases in leisure, affluence and mobility, and in recreation areas they cause crowding with subsequent loss of satisfaction from the recreation experience; at popular times the peak loading causes tremendous management problems, and the intensity of use may lead to loss of biotic diversity. Environmental contamination may even result, since sewage and refuse disposal systems are unlikely to have been built to deal with such peak loads. People who come to enjoy wild places and rural environments seem inexorably destined to destroy them.

In a more long-term perspective, recreation and the protection of wild ecosystems are essential components of what industrial countries call 'environmental quality'. Inasmuch as the demands for material resources are, per capita, the highest in the world, and that such desires seem to conflict with the maintenance of environmental quality, it is not surprising that population growth has been called the fundamental cause of the overloading of park and recreation systems. It is argued that just as LDCs suffer from certain material or 'quantity' deficits, because of their increases in population size, so even the relatively slow growth of population in the DCs is fundamental to the steady attrition of environmental quality. Such a train of thought is hard to prove quantitatively, since so much can be done to alleviate the problems by allocating more resources and by improved management. But as populations and expectations continue to rise, it appears inevitable that competition for land and water resources, including those at present of value for recreation, will rise. The more basic demands are likely to prove victorious in any such conflict. Similarly, if the quality of recreation declines because of pressure, there are few substitutes that can be brought into this particular resource process. While it is scarcely possible therefore to argue that a cessation of population growth is essential for the persistence of outdoor recreation as a cultural activity, it certainly appears that slower growth with its consequent redistribution of age classes would make available a high quality of outdoor recreation experiences much further into the future than would be possible with a rapidly expanding population.

Further reading

ADAMS, A. B. (ed.) 1964: *First World Conference on National Parks.*
BRACEY, H. C. 1970: *People and the countryside.*
CLAWSON, M. and KNETSCH, J. L. 1966: *Economics of outdoor recreation.*
OUTDOOR RECREATION RESOURCES REVIEW COMMISSION 1962: *Recreation for America.*
PATMORE, J. A. 1970: *Land and leisure in England and Wales.*
REVELLE, R. 1967: Outdoor recreation in a hyper-productive society.
SENGE, T. 1969: The planning of national parks in Japan and other parts of Asia.
YOUNG, G. 1973: *Tourism: blessing or blight?*

5

Grazing

The products of this resource process consist of both edible and potable substances (meat, fat, milk, blood and various other delicacies) together with materials such as hides, wool and other minor non-edible items, and are taken by culling populations of domesticated or semi-domesticated herbivorous mammals. The planned cropping of certain wild mammal populations is also discussed at this point.

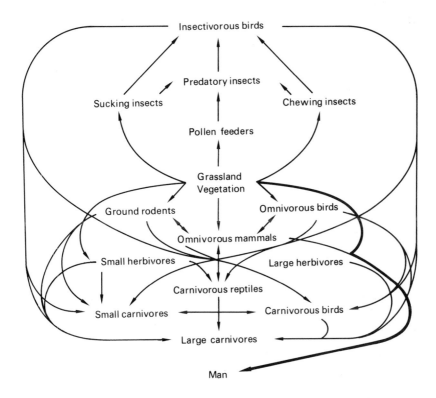

Fig. 5.1 A simplified food chain for a grassland system, with man's cropping pathway added and emphasized. In order to enhance his offtake, man will often eliminate other energy pathways and hence simplify the ecosystem.
Source: Lewis 1969

The grazing systems discussed in this section are divided from the utilization of herbivorous animals in an intensive agricultural context by the absence of deliberate nutrient return to the soils by the resource managers. The animals themselves may contribute to the biogeochemical cycles by way of excreta and the odd carcass, but most of the soil nutrients which reach the body of the selected animal are removed from the site of intake. Even though other manipulations of the local ecosystems may occur (either deliberately as with stock water management, or unconsciously as with gradual shifts in forage composition due to selective grazing by certain species), fertilizer input is unlikely except in the richest countries. This major criterion does not conflict with the definition of the grazing resource formulated by the American Society of Range Management (1964) as 'all land producing native forage for animal consumption and lands that are vegetated naturally or artificially to provide a forage cover that is managed like native vegetation'. Alteration of the ecology of areas utilized by pastoralists has often been slow and unconscious, thus earning its position among the less manipulated of the ecosystems discussed in this book. As Fraser Darling (1956) says, man's ecological dominance of wild lands through the medium of domesticated animals

> takes a long time to develop its expression, and is not always conspicuous in process, so that its influence is often unappraised in both biological and administrative assessments....

The most obvious form of deliberate ecosystem manipulation which takes place is the struggle against competitors for the crop of herbivores, or 'predator control'. This gives us the clue that although the food chain of plants–herbivores–man is very simple, it is in fact part of a more complex web (Fig. 5.1).

Biology of grazing

There is a high variety of biomes in which grazing by domesticated animals is important, although the various types of grassland (Fig. 5.2) form the main source of forage (C. W. E. Moore 1964). Of the total land surface, some 28 per cent is covered by forest which is grazed by wildlife and/or domestic stock for at least part of the year; and 47 per cent is suitable only for grazing by wild beasts or domesticated stock, having no potential for any more intensive use (Lewis 1969). FAO estimates of 'permanent meadows and pasture' give a rough indication of the continental distribution of grasslands (Table 5.1). On a world scale, it has been estimated that domestic stock get 75 per cent of their forage needs from such extensive grazing resources.

The ecology of extensive grasslands is complex. It is dominated by grasses and herbs, sometimes with trees or shrubs, especially at the transitions to forest or desert. The plants form a closely knit cover over the soil, with their roots penetrating to considerable depths. The sod thus formed protects the soil from physical removal although the root system may be inadequate to prevent podzolization in wet and cool climates. On the other hand, where evaporation exceeds precipitation, minerals move up the soil profile: the humus content and the presence of upward-moving calcium carbonate give the chernozem, a most characteristic grassland soil, its particular qualities including a pH in excess of 7·0. As Fig. 5.1 shows,

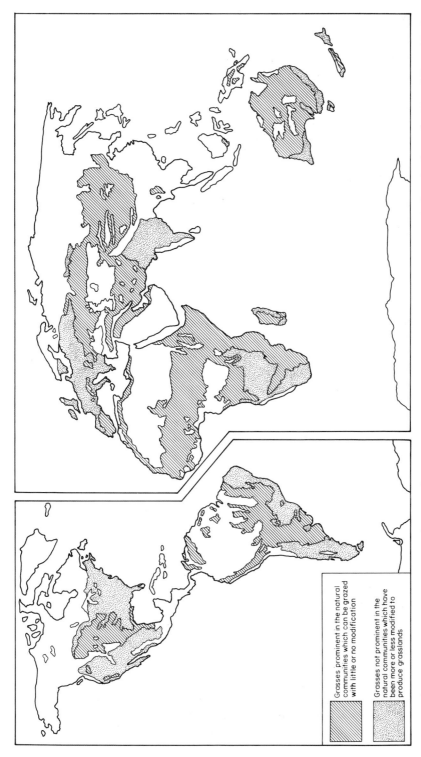

Fig. 5.2 A world map of grassland types. Some of the 'modified community' grasslands are used intensively (e.g. in Europe) and so fall outside the definition of the grazing system used in this chapter, which thus deals mostly but not exclusively with the 'natural community' grassland. Source: C. W. E. Moore 1964

Grasses prominent in the natural communities which can be grazed with little or no modification

Grasses not prominent in the natural communities which have been more or less modified to produce grasslands

TABLE 5.1   Geography and biology of grazing

	Grasslands by continental distribution (1,000 ha)	
	Land area	'Permanent meadows and pastures'
Europe	493,000	93,000
USSR	2,240,220	374,000
North and Central America	2,241,000	372,000
South America	1,784,000	413,000
Asia	1,797,000	322,000
China	956,100	177,000
Africa	3,030,000	844,000
Oceania	851,000	464,000
World	13,392,000	3,059,000

Source: FAO *Production Yearbook No. 25* (1971), Table 1

this vegetation is the starting point of a complicated ecosystem of which the grazing sub-system is the part in which man is primarily interested, to the point of trying to eliminate wild mammals which are also grazers and which he perceives as competition for the forage. The primary productivity of the grasslands is of course the key feature of the system whether it is being valued for its natural or man-managed features, and it is highly variable,

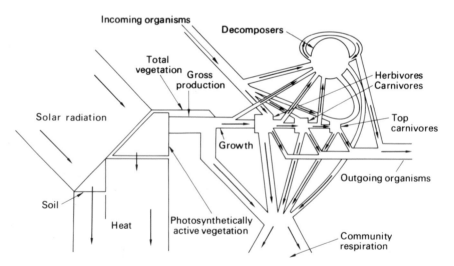

Fig. 5.3 A diagram of a Lindemann model representation of a natural grassland ecosystem. The usual features of such models are present, including the considerable losses (as heat) at the primary producer stage and the overall conversion of concentrated energy to the dispersed form of heat. A special grassland feature is the importance of the decomposers, and boundary difficulties are acknowledged by the presence of flows from incoming and outgoing organisms.
Source: Lewis 1969

being dependent upon minerals, water, climate and other factors. Much of it goes into subterranean parts which are not available to most grazing animals: in *Andropogon* prairie in Missouri, USA, the energy production for the above-ground parts of the grassland was 1.962×10^6 cals of biomass/yr, whereas the below-ground portions yielded 2.389×10^6 cals biomass/yr (Kucera *et al.* 1967). On a world scale grasslands do not come very high in biome productivity ranking (see p. 19) and a single instance illustrates this (Table 5.2). The low production of the grassland compared with the other forms, all within the same environment, is emphasized by Ovington *et al.* (1963) when they point out that the greatest mass of potential food for grazing, and hence the highest rate of secondary production, is in the savanna because the shelter of the scattered trees resulted in a very high primary productivity at ground level. Here can be seen a fundamental reason for the high densities of wild animals in African savannas, particularly when specialist grazers of swamps and tree tops are added to the ground-level suite. Because they are adapted to use a greater proportion of the forage than domestic livestock, the biomass of wild herbivores on extensive grazings is nearly always greater than domestic stock, a fact which will be referred to again later in this section (Plate 9).

TABLE 5.2   Comparative production of some
North American ecosystems

Cedar Creek, Minnesota, primary productivity $(kg/ha^2/yr)$		
	Max.	*Min.*
Prairie grasslands	9,700	6,100
Savanna	63,200	54,400
Oak forest	257,100	224,200

Source: Ovington *et al.* 1963

In a grassland, as in other ecosystems, the cycles of water, carbon, oxygen, nitrogen and other kinds of matter are very complex but stable. Energy flows through the system at a rapid rate and through many strands of the web, yet all the energy is dissipated in the life processes of the living components of the ecosystem (Fig. 5.3). The way in which the energy flows of a grassland are tapped by domesticated beasts is little quantified. One of the best studies for our purpose is that of Macfadyen (1964), who attempted to quantify the energy exploitation of a reasonably fertile grass field under British conditions. It thus belongs rather more to an intensive agricultural system than to real pastoralism, but it will serve as a guide which will point to features of grazing systems, and Fig. 5.4 shows his results, using the Lindemann structural model of ecosystems, and Standard Nutrition Units as measures. Some of the main features of the diagram will be expected from the discussion of ecosystems on pages 6–12: the fact that, out of 2,500 SNU/ha/yr of incident radiant energy, only 40 SNU/ha/yr appears as grass will not be surprising. The very low proportion (0.2 SNU/ha/yr) appearing as beef stock is worthy of more comment. Bullocks select only about

Plate 9 A natural grassland in South Dakota, grazed by the aboriginal large mammal herbivore, the bison. Most major grasslands had a similar mammal or marsupial in such a niche. Compare the condition of the sward with Plate 10. *(Grant Heilman, Lititz, Pa.)*

one-seventh of the available herbage, reject about two-thirds of the ingested food as faeces and respire 90 per cent of what they assimilate. If the stock becomes unhealthy all the desired crop may go to the decomposers. So if the initial grass production is of the order of 5,000 cal/m²/yr, then a successful resource manager is going to harvest only 30 cal/m²/yr. In a commercial (as distinct from subsistence) system much of that will be unusable products such as hoof and bone. An annual-type California range studied by W. A. Williams (1966) exhibited an energy flow of the same order, where over a 3-year period the efficiency of conversion of solar energy in the vegetation was 0·09 per cent and in animal stock 0·004 per cent (Table 5.3). Another outstanding feature of Macfadyen's diagram is the accumulation of organic matter in the soil, mostly at its surface. This is mainly humus from the grasses, but animal excreta are an important component too. This large amount emphasizes the importance of soil flora and fauna, especially micro-organisms, in mineralizing this matter and making it available again for uptake by the grasses. Macfadyen (1964) says that it is the activity of the decomposers which limits the productivity of the whole system and so clearly this 'hidden' factor must be taken into account when assessing rangeland or diagnosing its ills. Quantitative budgets of nutrients in contrasted grazing systems are also difficult to find. One example is the work of D. T. Crisp (1963) in a Pennine moorland catchment. Here the input and output of key nutrients into a peat-covered watershed of 83 ha at about 600 m ASL with a rainfall of 2,130 mm/yr was studied. Especially noteworthy was the immediate loss of most of the nutrients in runoff, but by contrast the proportion of the nutrients which was removed in the form of the sheep, which were the

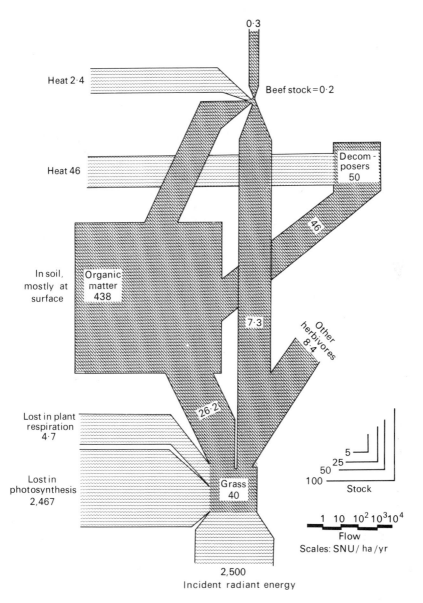

Fig. 5.4 Schematic diagram of energy flow in an intensively managed grassland-cattle ecosystem, expressed in SNU/ha/yr, where 1 SNU represents adequate caloric nutrition of 1 person at a rate of 2,460 kcal/day (900,000 kcal/yr). The darker shading represents flows and storages of organic matter, the lighter shading being flows of radiant energy or heat. The low quantity of incident radiation which becomes beef stock is apparent, as is the importance of the decomposer level at the soil surface, as suggested in Fig. 5.3.
Source: Macfadyen 1964

principal grazing animals of the watershed, was very small, about 1/200 of the incoming phosphorus, for example, being taken off in this manner. Pastoralism here is obviously an insignificant part of the ecosystem in terms of nutrient loss, although the sheep may alter the system in other ways, as by altering the species composition of the vegetation. In eco-systems with lower inputs of nutrients from precipitation, the removal of animals may constitute a higher proportion of the budget of essential elements.

TABLE 5.3   Energy flow and conversion in a California range

	kcal/m²/yr	%
Total incoming solar radiation	1,600,000	100
Available solar radiation of suitable wavelength	700,000	44
Net primary production[1]	1,410	0·09
Net secondary production	69	0·004

[1] Before the introductions of legumes and fertilization with sulphur, net primary production was 0·04 per cent.
Source: W. A. Williams 1966

These studies, doubtless to be amplified by results from International Biological Pro-gramme (IBP) research, point to certain generalities about pastoral grazing systems. Most striking is the generally low efficiency of the process. The large domestic herbivore appears to be an inefficient converter of greenstuff to animal protein: it is too selective in its intake of forage, it passes out too much of it as faeces and dissipates too much of the assimilated energy by running about. On the other hand the tissue produced is high in animal protein, the insufficiency of which is often the cause of malnutrition in humans. With such con-straints it is not surprising that commercially produced protein is expensive, and so other sources must be found for those malnourished because of its lack. Animals which are omnivorous scavengers or detritus feeders (such as pigs and molluscs) become ecologically if not culturally more attractive propositions for development.

The crop of domesticated animals

The ubiquity and absolute numbers of domesticated animals, including the grazers, are such that accurate statistics are not to be expected. The FAO figures given in Table 5.4 allow some estimate of the overall totals for different beasts, but they include animals from intensive agriculture systems and of course represent numbers of animals and not numbers killed for produce. They do total the number of beasts which are utilizing the grazing resources of the continents, and include a large number of work animals used in agriculture which may consume extensive grassland resources close to the land upon which they work.

The major extensive grazing animals are distributed largely in accordance with the

TABLE 5.4   Major livestock numbers 1970–71 (millions)

	Horses	Mules	Asses	Cattle	Pigs	Sheep	Goats	Buffaloes	Camels
Europe	7·7	1·1	1·7	122·6	139·4	127·5	12·6	0·3	—
USSR	12·8	—	0·6	99·1	67·4	137·9	5·4	0·5	0·2
North and Central America	14·2	3·1	3·6	172·0	95·2	26·8	13·6	—	—
South America	18·0	6·0	5·4	203·3	83·3	123·5	28·0	0·1	—
Asia	8·4	0·7	8·1	288·9	49·1	210·4	146·5	92·9	4·1
Africa	3·2	2·2	10·8	158·4	6·9	140·4	119·4	2·1	10·0
China (mainland)	5·3	1·6	11·7	63·2	223·0	71·0	57·5	29·4	—
Oceania[1]	1·3	—	—	33·7	3·5	237·2	0·2	—	—
World	66·3	14·7	41·9	1,141·2	667·7	1,074·7	383·0	125·3	14·6

Source: *FAO Production Yearbook No. 25* (1971), Table 104A

[1] Australia, New Zealand and the islands of the Pacific

availability of pasture, competition from other land uses and cultural preferences. As stated before, many of the Asian cattle do not enter resource processes except as symbols, but such animals are not users of extensive grassland areas.

The general inadequacy of animal protein supplies in the LDCs and the high cultural demand for meat in DCs has led to an ambitious programme for livestock being incorporated in the Provisional Indicative World Plan (IWP) of the FAO (FAO 1970). The basis of their proposals is the calculation that although by 1975 90 per cent of the projected demand for animal protein will be met, by 1985 (the last year of the IWP period), only 77 per cent can be catered for. The shortfall is caused partly by factors such as the poor suitability of forage and the bad management of herds: on the savanna of Guyana the cattle : land ratio is 1 animal : 17 ha; and on African savannas as a whole it is c. 1 : 8–10. In Tanzania, for example, only about half the cows calve annually, and about 50 per cent of the calves die shortly after birth. Malnutrition of the animals themselves, disease and bad herding practices are all important. External economic factors also loom large in this system. Demand is high and rising as overall prosperity in DCs increases, but the grazing system has been unattractive to investors in LDCs because of the low turnover and return on capital. Rates of increase would therefore have probably been very low, even supposing environmental limitations were exerting no constraints.

In determining the IWP objectives, religious customs were stressed as far as culturally inedible animals like cattle in India and pigs in Islamic countries are concerned. These factors, together with the low efficiency of the ruminants, have meant that a great increase in production of poultry is suggested (Table 5.5), since it is a very efficient converter of a great many types of foodstuff, and the same can be said of pigs for the non-Muslim areas. Thus intensive production of animal protein by moving from an emphasis on the grazing system to the agricultural—or even industrial as is happening in DCs at present—is proposed. Nevertheless, protein deficiencies in LDCs by 1985 are still likely, and the

TABLE 5.5   Proposed growth rates in output of livestock products[1] 1962–85 (per cent p.a.)

Region	Ruminant meat	Pork	Poultry meat	Total meat without offals	Milk	Eggs
Africa, south of Sahara	3·1	4·1	6·3	3·4	2·4	4·9
Asia and Far East	2·2	4·4	5·6	3·5	2·8	5·9
Latin America	2·9[2]	3·5	4·7	3·1	3·1	4·1
Near East and north-west Africa	2·9	− 1·8[3]	7·0	3·2	2·6	4·4

[1] These growth rates exclude retention of stock to build up inventories.
[2] This figure rises to 3·2 per cent if Argentina is excluded from the analysis.
[3] This decline is attributable to the fact that pork is only eaten in non-Moslem communities and in some of the countries (particularly in north Africa) such communities are expected to decline in numbers during the lifetime of the Plan
Source: FAO 1970, ∎

DCs are probably going to be short of beef and veal, so that the relatively unconventional methods of protein production and the harvest of the seas are clearly going to suffer no diminution in importance.

Ecological shifts caused by grazing

In the absence of deliberate management of pastures, changes in vegetation and subsequently in other ecosystem components are likely. The plants which prove most palatable to the stock are grazed frequently, and those weakened by cropping are replaced by species which are able to withstand such attention. These are taxa capable of rapid immigration into areas of lessened competition and which escape being eaten because of features such as low stature, a short season of growth, low palatability, poisonous properties, or spines (Klapp 1964, Moore and Biddiscombe 1964). Concomitant changes involve the reduction of the mulch cover of the soil. The microclimate then becomes drier and more severe, and so many invaders are plants of xeric habit: in semi-arid areas they are frequently plants of the desert biome such as succulents and thorny shrubs. The absence of humus cover may mean that the mineral soil surface is heavily trampled when wet, producing puddling of the surface layers, which in turn reduces the infiltration of water into the soil and accelerates its runoff, producing drought. These changes all contribute to the reduction of the rate of energy flow, and the disruption of the stratification and periodicity of the primary producers results in a breakdown of the biogeochemical cycles, especially those involving water, carbon and nitrogen. A final stage of total system breakdown may occur where a very dry microclimate is accompanied by extensive water and wind erosion.

The advent of domestic flocks onto extensive pastures formerly grazed only by wild animals may alter the vegetation completely. In New Zealand, for example, the aboriginal vegetation of the plains of South Island was tussock grassland dominated by species of *Poa* and *Festuca*. The introduction by Europeans of grazing animals such as sheep, rabbits, red deer and goats, and the use of fire as a management technique, has resulted in a more or less complete replacement of the native flora. The chief forage is now introduced grasses such as *Anthoxanthum odoratum*, *Festuca rubra* and *Holcus lanatus*, and on the whole this type of vegetation cover is now less complete than formerly. Introduced wild animals have also destroyed the natural stability of their new habitats, especially forests and alpine grasslands, rendering these lands unsuitable for the grazing of domesticates and accelerating erosion. Table 5.6 gives some information on the species ranked as 'problem animals' (Howard 1964). As another instance we may quote the deforestation of Iceland in the course of sheep grazing, which has meant the denudation of 30–40 per cent of the soils; the annual loss of soil and vegetation cover is still greater than that regained through plant recolonization and management efforts (Thorsteinsson *et al.* 1971).

Shifts within a native flora are also common. The deforestation of the Scottish Highlands produced a moorland vegetation of hedges, grasses and heather. The selective grazing of sheep leaves ungrazed material which has to be burnt off, and together with the differential effects of the foraging habits of the animals this produces a change from the mixed vegetation to one in which *Nardus stricta* and *Molinia caerulea* are dominant. The first is unpalatable and the second deciduous. The xerophytic *Erica tetralix* then becomes important and finally the useless *Scirpus caespitosa* dominates the vegetation. Thus the calcicoles have disappeared, the herbage is deficient in minerals and protein, yet the attempt continues to extract protein directly as meat and wool (Fraser Darling 1963, McVean and Lockie 1969).

Intensive grazing which results in increased areas of bare soil creates a new habitat in which burrowing animals may flourish. In North America, mice, jackrabbits, gophers and prairie dogs all probably benefit from overgrazing; predator control applied to wolves or coyotes may also have released their numbers and so the levels of these rodents reach almost epidemic proportions. In their increased burrowing they render sterile thousands of hectares of forage land, and control measures aimed only at their direct extermination are clearly ecologically unsound. Although there is no direct evidence, we may also speculate about the connection between intensive grazing in semi-arid areas and locust plagues. The presence of loose sandy soil is necessary for oviposition in locusts and heavy grazing produces such conditions. Thus the pastoralists of antiquity may have been creating some of their own plagues rather than having Jehovah do it for them.

TABLE 5.6   Browsing mammals established as 'problems' in New Zealand

Species	Origin	Date introduced	Abundance	Degree of damage
Brush-tail oppossum (*Trichosurus vulpecula*)	Australia	1858	Abundant	Acute
European hare (*Lepus europaeus*)	Europe	1867	Abundant	Acute
Goat (*Capra hircus*)	Europe	18th century	Common	Acute
Thar (*Hemitragus jemlahicus*)	Asia	1904	Common	Moderate
Chamois (*Rupicapra rupicapra*)	Europe	1967	Common	Acute
Red deer (*Cervus elephas*)	Europe	1851	Abundant	Acute
Pig (*Sus scrofa*)	Europe	18th century	Common	Acute

Source: Howard 1964

We can see that the potential of pastoralism for vegetation change of a deleterious character is great (Plate 10). Beyond a certain intensity, the pressure of grazing animals produces effects which are labelled 'overgrazing'. These changes are very varied in nature, and this term may apply to the forage resource or to some symptoms exhibited by the stock itself. As far as the grassland is concerned, 'overgrazing' consists of an intensification of the trends already noted. The incidence of such overgrazing may not be uniform in a given area: within a mosaic a particular species may be grazed out; equally a seasonal overgrazing may occur as when the first flush of spring grass or post-rains grass is immediately

Plate 10 Cattle on an overgrazed range. Virtually all the available forage has been grazed or browsed out and patches of bare soil can be seen. Invasion by xerophytes and soil erosion are both likely in such circumstances. *(Grant Heilman, Lititz, Pa)*

totally consumed. In such conditions, there are likely to be stock 'crashes', when catastrophic declines in the animal population may be observed: these may be absolute in terms of numbers no longer pasturable, or actually dying, or relative in terms of low gain or malnutritive disease. Beyond this stage, an environmental 'crash', in the form of accelerated soil erosion, is the most probable eventuality. Wind erosion produces scoured areas where the bedrock or its upper weathered layers form the ground surface, and the transported material accumulates elsewhere as drifts or even dunes of sandy material. Water erosion produces sheet-wash areas as well as the familiar gullies. In high-latitude and high-altitude areas, overgrazing may remove insulating vegetation cover to the point where freeze–thaw processes are accelerated and heaving then becomes more widespread, increasing the coverage of bare ground at the expense of plant material. Some of these phenomena may of course be produced at the analogous point in agricultural ecosystems by the process of overcropping. The problems associated with severely eroded land do not stop with its abandonment. Siltation of water courses ensues, as in the case of the Mangla Reservoir in

Pakistan, whose planned life of 100 years as an irrigation reservoir has been cut by half due to silt input from the watershed (Brown and Finsterbusch 1971).

Recovery from man-accelerated erosion requires either a long 'fallow' period in which the cause of the erosion is removed and natural processes allowed to heal the scars, or a considerable input of matter and energy by man: the fundamental cause of the erosion must be eliminated as well (L. N. Costin 1970). Natural healing is invariably lengthy since succession has to start from the bare ground stage and a gully system may have acquired an erosive momentum which, following the laws of the development of drainage systems, is unlikely to stop short of its energetic equilibrium point. In the case of Mr Zabriskie's Point, for example, this is well after the forage resource has disappeared. Man-directed schemes of erosion control for grazing lands share some characteristics of those for agricultural systems, but engineering works are less usual owing to the lower return on investment from grazing systems. Wind-eroded areas, however, can usually only be re-seeded if the hard surface ('scalded' is a term sometimes used) is subjected first to a mechanical treatment such as ripping or ploughing. The stabilization of mobile material is akin to the management of coastal sand-dunes and requires a pioneer species which can withstand alternating burial and exposure. If grasses can be successfully planted then the material can be stabilized, and even if good forage does not develop for some time, loose material is at least prevented from burying useful areas elsewhere. In water-eroded areas, the aim of a managed grass cover is to minimize surface runoff and soil loss. To this end grasses with a dense, compact growth habit are most desirable, and their establishment may be aided with cheap mechanical devices such as straw mulches, wire netting and bitumen. The cost of such processes and the technical expertise required ensure that their application is limited relative to the extent of the initial erosion.

Range improvement

The degradation of pastures is a regression to an early phase of succession. The opposite is a progression to a condition of higher secondary production and, on a sustained yield basis, can be induced by manipulation of various components of the grazing ecosystem. Such treatment may be applied either to a more or less virgin system in the hope of increasing the potential crop, or to a degraded area by way of rehabilitation. Geology and landforms may be taken as immutable factors, but climate at the local scale can sometimes be altered by cloud seeding; the certainty of success is not high and there may be difficult legal problems, but experiments at three rangeland sites in Kansas which cost $0.10/ac ($0.25/ha) to produce 0·5-in (12·7 mm) increase in precipitation showed benefit/cost ratios of 22 : 1, 6 : 1 and 25 : 1 respectively (Hausle 1972).

The alteration of components such as the plants, soils and consumer organisms offers most hope for the resource manager wishing to increase his output and at the same time consider the long-term biological productivity of his range, and the management of the crop herbivores themselves is an obvious first stage. The actual species used can be selected if alien species can be brought in: most of the domestic herbivores have been introduced to parts of the world in which their ancestors were not native. Beyond this elementary

TABLE 5.7   Some manipulations of range ecosystems for increased efficiency of energy utilization

Factors	Manipulation
Controlling factors	
Climate	Weather modification, burning
Geological materials	Water spreading, land levelling, terracing, fertilization, ground-water recharge, drainage
Available organisms	Species elimination, introduction and improvement
Dependent factors	
Consumers	
Native biota	Grazing management, wildlife management, insect and rodent control
Livestock	Grazing management, livestock management
Vegetation	Plant control, hay management, plant disease control, revegetation
Soil	Mechanical treatments, nitrogen fertilization
Decomposers and transformers	Antibiotics, growth stimulators (?)
Microclimate	Shades, shelters, mulch manipulation
Human factors	Objectives, management, use of goods and services, economics

Source: Lewis 1969

consideration lies the grazing management techniques applied to the selected animal; these are the heart of successful range management. Thus the numbers of animals, their species and strain, their proportions if pastured in mixed herds, and their distribution in space and time, control the species of plants which are grazed, the time in their life cycle at which they are cropped, and the frequency with which they are eaten. The manager selects his species in the light of the available forage, the preferences of the animal and the prevailing economic factors. He may control their grazing distribution by providing water points, salt licks or specially fertilized patches of grassland. Above all, he may be able to fence or herd animals. All such measures are designed to spread the animals to the optimum density for utilizing the forage. In Australia, one study found that the net primary productivity was greatest at a stocking density of Merino sheep at 20 sheep/ha and least at 10 sheep/ha; at 30 sheep/ha, productivity was slightly higher than the rate for 10 sheep/ha (Fig. 5.5), but seasonal fluctuations were greatest at the highest stocking rate. This suggests there are optimum stocking densities for maximum net primary productivity of grazed grasslands in temperate zones, but that they vary according to the time of year (Vickery 1972). Many plants are easily damaged by being grazed too soon after they have started their growth, yet it is during periods of fastest growth that they are most nutritious. Thus grazing systems (Table 5.8) must be elaborated, either by folk knowledge as in relatively simple societies or by complex socio-legal arrangements as in the Grazing Districts of the United States of America. If a system other than continuous grazing is employed, then additional water developments are usually necessary, as is the fencing of the range into units with

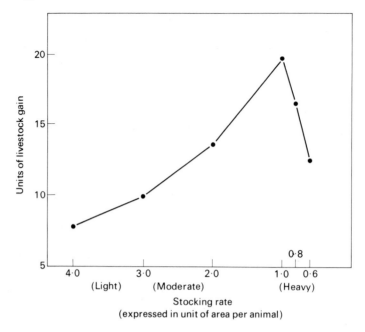

Fig. 5.5 Livestock gains for different stocking rates in the south-west USA. Gains are higher at increasingly heavy grazing densities until a critical value is reached, beyond which there is a 'crash' in production. These results suggest the ease with which the grassland ecosystem can be over-exploited by managers of domesticated animals.
Source: A. B. Costin 1964

more or less equal stocking potential. Scientific range management becomes a very intricate matter in which the cowboy's hip is more likely to be decorated with a sampling quadrat than a Colt ·45.

TABLE 5.8   Classification of grazing systems

I. All sub-units grazed one or not more than two periods per year	
A. Continuous occupation by grazing animals during the same grazing season each year	Continuous grazing
B. Grazing deferred on one or more sub-units	
1. Deferment not rotated	Deferred grazing
2. Deferment rotated	
a. Grazed sub-units continuously occupied	Rotational deferment
b. Grazing rotated in sub-units	Deferred rotation
II. One or more sub-units rested	
A. Rest not rotated	Rest
B. Rest rotated	Rest rotation
III. All sub-units grazed more than two periods per year	Rotational grazing

Source: Lewis 1969

The bringing about of changes in vegetation is another method of manipulating grazing systems, but one which involves longer time-spans than the attraction of stocking rates. The aims are to produce a high proportion of palatable plants, preferably with a spread of maximum growth periods so as to provide a long grazing season, and to reduce the proportions of open ground, unpalatable shrubs or scrub and poisonous or injurious plants. Mechanical control by chaining and cabling may reduce the proportion of juniper and mesquite in places like Arizona, USA; fire may be employed with some success, for mesquite and cactus kills of 50 per cent have been reported; and chemical treatment is increasingly favoured, especially with hormonal herbicides such as 2,4-D and 2,4,5-T. These latter are not without dangerous side-effects, however and the use of 2,4,5-T has now become very restricted in developed countries. Range seeding may seem an attractive proposition where aids such as light aircraft are available, but success appears very variable. A sequence of burning, then seeding coincident with the high rainfall season, and thereafter applying chemical weed control has been followed with some advantage in California and Israel. Similarly, parasite and disease control of range plants may be possible in rich countries with a highly developed infrastructure capable of delivering the correct dosage of a specific pesticide more or less to the correct place.

The soil itself is more difficult to alter than animals or plants but is not beyond treatment. Mechanical treatment such as discing, subsoiling and contour furrowing may help to improve runoff characteristics or provide a niche for more desirable forage species, but improvement of the nitrogen status of the soil is one of the most usual desirabilities. Crops and tame pastures of the world contain about 200 leguminous species, whereas wild range and forest ecosystems have c. 12,000, of which 90 per cent have nodule-bearing roots; thus the encouragement of leguminous species helps to counteract the loss of soil nitrogen. Furthermore, some soils appear to be deficient in mineral elements such as copper, cobalt and molybdenum, which are essential for the nutrition of animals, so that fertilization of intensively used grasslands generally has taken place since the nineteenth century (Barnard and Frankel 1964) and the light aeroplane has extended the practice to extensive forage resources. One edaphic element which cannot easily be directly manipulated is the soil flora and fauna. The importance of these biota was stressed earlier (pp. 13–15), especially in the detritus food chain which is critical to nutrient circulation. Most other management techniques will affect these biota, some adversely.

Many of the management arrangements described above are clearly applicable to both simple societies and more complex, industrially based ones. But many of the most effective are available only to high-energy and high-material-input societies. This limitation needs keeping in mind when improvements to the grazing system are considered, for many of the world's forage resources are outside that particular ambit.

The cropping of wild animals for food

Most domestic animals are very selective in their use of forage; by contrast, many wild animals of potential use for food, particularly ungulates, are much more thorough in their use of the available herbage; even if one species is very selective, it is likely to exist as part of a suite of animals whose combined cropping effectively utilizes the range. The faunas of the savanna and grassland biomes of east and central Africa are the outstanding example of this characteristic, and a considerable amount of research has been done on their ecology (Fraser Darling 1960, Dasmann 1964a, Talbot 1966), although Parker and Graham (1971) point out that such cropping is more talked about than done, and suggest that the case for utilizing wild animals is not so strong as that for improving domesticates.

Africa

A high biomass of wild animals is partly a consequence of the variety of habitats within the biome: although large areas of uniform landscape such as *Acacia* savanna exist, they are broken by swampy zones, by dense bush and other terrain types (Fig. 5.6). Within these units, certain animals are specialized, whereas others move throughout a number of them in a purposeful seasonal or diurnal sequence. The sitatunga, for example, is confined to perpetually inundated swamps, whereas the lechwe ranges from the edge of that habitat through to the outer margins of seasonally flooded riverine plains. Likewise, the klip-springer scarcely ventures forth from rocky hills, whereas zebra will forage in most types of grassland, bush and wooded savanna, though venturing rarely into dense bush. The gross anatomy of species helps to spread their foraging habits: the giraffe is the obvious example, enabled by its long neck to browse off the canopies of trees otherwise inaccessible unless pulled down. At a less obvious level, browsers such as the black rhino stay in bush and wooded areas, thus avoiding competition with the grazers of the open grassland such as the white rhino. Even where the same grass species is a preferred element of several animals' diet, grazing is staggered to avoid competition. The red oats grass (*Themeda triandra*) is a very important part of the intake of wildebeests, topis and zebras. The wildebeests eat the fresh leaves of the grass only, until they are about 4 inches long, avoiding stalks and seed heads. Zebras prefer more mature forage, eating longer leaves together with stalks and heads; however, they avoided the grass when it was dry. The topis exhibit a distinct preference for dry red oats grass, usually at a mature stage and with a large proportion of stalks and heads.

The result of the interaction of a variety of habitats, species and habits is a high herbivore biomass (Fig. 5.7), in which very large numbers are found of some species (hartebeest, wildebeest, zebra) and in which some species (hippopotamus, elephant, rhinoceros) are very large. As expected, predator numbers and biomass are much lower but nevertheless add up to a relatively high density of such creatures: a particularly important feature when the tourist-trade value of the game areas is considered. Table 5.9 considers some data for year-long biomass of the wild faunas of grasslands and savannas and compares it with some figures for domestic stock in similar environments. The poor animals, from badly managed tribal grazing systems, reach at best one-fifth of the biomass of the wild population, and even European management can scarcely bring the proportion to one-half. The discrepancy between wild and domestic beasts in Africa can be further seen from figures for liveweight gain. Species such as eland (0·33 kg/day), wildebeest (0·185–0·28) and topi (0·15–0·19) contrast with domestic sheep (0·05) and cattle (0·13). Cattle reach marketable size in 5–7 years, whereas the flesh of Grant's gazelles and impalas could be marketed in 18 months,

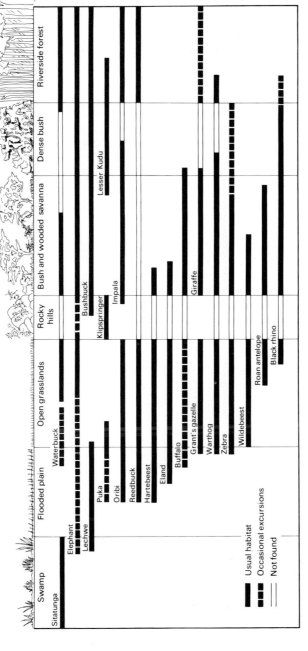

Fig. 5.6 The savanna provides a variety of habitats, some of which are the only forage areas of a particular herbivore, whereas others are utilized by a wide variety of the fauna, which sometimes crop different levels of the vegetation, e.g. the giraffe and black rhino do not compete for forage in bush and wooded savanna.
Source: Reader's Digest Publications 1970

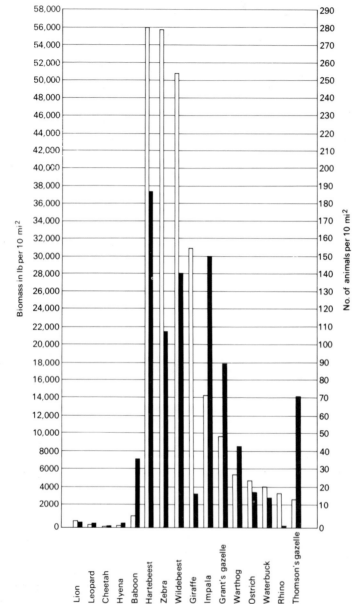

Fig. 5.7 The biomass of animals in Nairobi National Park. The open column represents the weight per unit area and the black column the number of individual animals per unit area. The relatively large herbivore population needed to support a few predators is clearly shown, as is the very high biomass of certain ungulates which might be cropped for food (lb/10 mi^2 equals approximately kg per 5,000 ha; 10 mi^2 = 2,590 ha).
Source: Reader's Digest Publications 1970

and wildebeests in 2·5–3 years. Furthermore, the marketable proportion of the carcass is higher for wild animals, they contain more meat and less fat, and the proportion of valuable hind-quarter is also higher than that of cattle raised on the same lands. Transport and marketing generally present the most difficult problems (Talbot and Talbot 1963). The meat of all species of wild ungulates is eaten by Africans and Europeans, although there are some local taboos. Dried meat (biltong) is also a useful product, and experiments with canning hippo have been tried. By-products can also be valuable if properly handled: zebra skins and elephant tusks are but the most obvious examples.

TABLE 5.9   Comparison of biomass of wild and domesticated animals

| Animals | Range type and location | Year-long biomass | |
		lb/mi²	kg/ha × 10⁵
Wild ungulates	Savanna, east Africa	70,000–100,000	82·2–117·5
Domestic livestock	Tribal savanna, east Africa	11,200–16,000	13·2–18·8
Cattle	European-managed savanna, Africa	21,000–32,000	24·7–37·6
Domestic livestock	Virgin grassland, western USA	26,700	31·3
Bison and ungulates	Prairie, USA	14,000–20,000	16·4–23·5
Red deer	Deer forest, Scotland	4,373	0·14

Source: Talbot and Talbot 1963

Cropping programmes require sophisticated knowledge of the ecology of the animals involved and especially their social structure, so that discriminating culling can be practised: it is a different matter shooting young males of a pair-bonded species, for example, from culling spare males from territorially based harem groups kept together by one male. The role of hunter and predator has to be carefully evaluated, as has the contribution of species such as the elephant which, by virtue of its size and habits, strongly affects the development of habitats. On the one hand, they make forage from high trees available to other species by pulling them down, and they also dig water-holes: on the negative side, they will damage large areas of otherwise edible bush by trampling, will pull up trees which are the habitats of birds, for example, and at high densities wreak a general damage to the environment. Culling of elephants has often been a first step in good game management.

As well as the gains so far mentioned there is the income from tourism, which is the major source of foreign exchange for many east and central African countries. Here is a growing industry, and shooting animals with cameras does not conflict with the use of the game populations for meat. In Kenya, for example, tourism netted $52·5 million in 1971 and is predicted to yield $105 million/yr by the end of 1974; in 1966–7 the rate of return on government assets was a very high 20–30 per cent, and the employment of 20,000 people in 1971 is expected to double by 1975 (Swank 1972). In spite of this, huge game-extermination programmes have been carried out in Africa in the probably forlorn hope of exterminating tsetse fly. Cattle are often then brought in and if managed inefficiently contribute to ecological degradation. Their concentration around water sources means puddling of soils, especially in the wet season, with subsequent soil erosion. This is exacerbated by the use of fire to encourage early growth at the start of wet seasons (Talbot 1972, West 1972). By contrast, native ungulates only degrade environments if their densities are too high, as has happened with hippo and elephants that have moved out of 'reclaimed' areas.

Grazing as an element of multiple use

Although livestock production is the major aim of most range managers, from Arabia to Alberta, other goods and services are also potential crops. Forest lands, for example, often support grazing animals. Advantages which may accrue to the forest manager are the reduction of inflammable undergrowth or the checking of some species competitive with his desired species such as leafy shrubs in a softwood forest, and sometimes the animals are beneficial in scarifying and manuring a clear-felled area before it is re-seeded. Yet there are numerous disadvantages to this form of multiple use (FAO 1953), since damage to the forest stands may take place because of the elimination of seedlings or their deformation, and mature trees may be injured by being debarked. Goats especially can reduce woodland to scrub or completely open land, and sheep are only a little slower. Cattle are much less dangerous and it is said that pigs bury acorns as well as eat them. Grazing in forest lands must be controlled with some care, lest overstocking eventually produces watershed deterioration and soil erosion.

As has been seen from the African examples, wildlife and domesticated animals may be highly incompatible, but under some conditions, sophisticated management may realize that very little competition for grazing resources may occur between, for example, sheep and deer since there is 'forage separation'. In such instances income from game and associated recreation facilities has, in rich countries like the USA, exceeded that from the grazing livestock. The winter or other off-season is generally the critical time when competition for forage may occur and the manager who would have both sheep and deer must face the fact that sometimes the deer's predators will like a change of menu.

Hunting of wildlife is a form of recreation towards which the grazing manager is likely to feel ambivalent. He can raise money from it; but on the other hand hunters are not always careful in their treatment of his fences and water-holes, nor, in the last analysis, of their targets. Tom Lehrer's bag of 'two game wardens and a pure-bred Guernsey cow' is probably not too great an exaggeration. Other forms of outdoor recreation tend to conflict with range management: the hill lands of Great Britain exemplify the problems. Fires, destruction of fences, leaving gates open, worrying by dogs, fouling of water and edible but lethal litter are everyday complaints by farmers. Carried out with due care for the countryside, many outdoor activities do not, however, conflict with grazing. In semi-arid areas with low stocking rates, recreation may well be a compatible use, and carries considerable potential for expansion, as in Australia, where the traditional beach recreation is becoming overcrowded: in 1967 there were 40,000 tourists to the Northern Territory (Box and Perry 1971).

Many grazing lands are also used as watershed lands, and overgrazing reduces their use for this purpose just as it will for further grazing. In particular, high silt yields fill up reservoirs, while poorly vegetated areas produce flash floods and then dry up quickly instead of yielding a steady flow of water. Remedial measures, as with other overgrazed areas, are often expensive and long-term.

Potentials and possibilities

The overriding aim of rational management of the grazing resource is simple: the maintenance of a permanent productive capacity at a level which not only precludes the possibility of decline but also contains the seeds of further improvement. Secondary purposes include the use of forage areas so as not to exclude other uses such as water catchment for which fewer alternative areas are available, or perhaps nature conservation. No changes should be irreversible.

To this end, various measures have been suggested. The detailed range improvements discussed above are very important, for in a world context it seems more profitable to improve existing grasslands than to try to find new ones: indeed the Indicative World Plan for Agriculture (IWP) of the FAO suggests a decline by 2 per cent (25 million ha) in the total grazing resource land during the 1972–85 period. Besides their major features, there are many other components, of the grazing ecosystem, both social and biological, that can be changed. The control of the currently rife overgrazing is a clear priority. The replacement of some phases of the wild grassland grazing with feed-lot ingestion of fodder crops might help with this problem, but prejudice against cereals as fodder crops is strong in many places, and it is scarcely to be expected that such people would take easily to the use of concentrated feeds, even if they could afford them. Similarly, problems of land ownership and tenure may be critical. The minimum economic size of enterprises (in the British uplands no less than in the arid lands of Africa) needs careful consideration. In many places the forage resource is a commons, with all that implies by way of potential for misuse by individuals. Apparently rational developments may in reality be inimical to each other: the encouragement of nomadism and transhumance to avoid overgrazing (Fraser Darling and Farvar 1972, Heady 1972), for instance, is scarcely compatible with the development of an infrastructure that will allow such people to market perishable products like milk and meat. Yet again, diseases act as a drag on animal productivity and we must consider the economic and ecological implications of tsetse which reinforce the idea that wildlife grazing is the proper use of such lands (Lambrecht 1972), and features like the need to eradicate foot-and-mouth disease in the flesh-producing countries of Latin America.

Not so far discussed are the possibilities of domesticating new animals. The present meat-producing domesticates are all members of the order Artiodactyla, and that same order has perhaps the greatest potential for new domestications (Jewell 1969). There are 192 species in the order, of which 92 are African, but even outside Africa there is considerable potential. The various deer are the obvious candidates since they can crop the shrubs, lichens and mosses of the tundra, taiga and boreal forest which are otherwise inedible by man. Of the African species, the most notable example of an attempt at domestication has been the eland, both in South Africa and in the Ukraine. The eland

(*Taurotragus orys*) can thrive in a domesticated state when food, water and tsetse fly make cattle a very poor prospect. Jewell calls the domestication of the African buffalo (*Synoceros caffer*) 'long overdue', and even the warthog has its potential since it is unaffected by the African swine fever which may make pig farming difficult.

We should note in passing that domestication of such wild species will very likely bring about physical and behavioural changes in the animals, so that it cannot be considered a way of protecting wild species which are otherwise threatened with extinction.

The effects of increasing human populations

As far as subsistence graziers are concerned, the effects of an increasing number of mouths to feed is relatively simple: more beasts are depastured (especially on forage resources held in common), there is a lower-quality animal product, and all the effects of overgrazing described above become manifest (L. H. Brown 1971). Basically, the increased number of people help to contravene the rules of successful pastoralism which revolve around the maxim 'once over, lightly' (Fraser Darling 1955). Structural alterations in the system, such as the importation of animal foodstuffs, may alleviate some difficulties, but the important cultural shift is to an acceptance of the possession of fewer animals. Since in many pastoralist societies the beasts possess a value far beyond that of their products, this has proved almost uniformly impossible: death control applied to men and animals in societies based on grazing systems has not been accompanied by the cultural changes which would have prevented widespread ecological degradation.

Commercial extensive pastoralism is less likely to fall into the overgrazing–poor beast syndrome, for its existence depends upon a high-quality product. Higher demand for animal protein caused by both increased populations and raised levels of living will in general mean higher prices, so that greater profits and investment will lead to more efficient production within the ecological limits of the system. Eventually the high prices commanded by animal products may cause subsistence pastoralists to re-evaluate their position and move into a form of commercial pastoralism. Their cultural conservatism can sometimes be changed if the new systems are presented so that they become desirable, and increased nationalism has also been cited as an aid to changing traditional resource processes (L. N. Costin 1970, Semple 1971).

One of the arguments in favour of the grazing ecosystem is that it brings into resource processes all sorts of primary productivity, from lichens to desert halophytes, which would otherwise be uncropped by man. But as experiments with leaf materials (p. 215) have shown, this may not always be so, and in time the direct extraction of useful foodstuffs from present forage resources without the interposition of the animal may be commonplace.

Further reading

BARNARD, C. (ed.) 1964: *Grasses and grasslands.*

DASMANN, R. F. 1964: *African game ranching.*

FAO 1970: *Indicative World Plan for Agriculture.*

FRASER DARLING, F. 1956: Man's ecological dominance through domesticated animals on wild lands.

LEWIS, G. M. 1969: Range management viewed in the ecosystem framework.

MACFADYEN, A. 1964: Energy flow in ecosystems and its exploitation by grazing.

MCVEAN, D. N. and LOCKIE, J. D. 1969: *Ecology and land use in upland Scotland.*

SWANK, W. G. 1972: Wildlife management in Masailand, east Africa.

TALBOT, L. M. 1972: Ecological consequences of rangeland development in Masailand, east Africa.

6

Water

Water occurs naturally in gaseous, solid and liquid phases; man's use of it is nearly all concerned with the last state and is also dominated by his demand for water relatively low in dissolved salts, i.e. fresh water. Of the various conditions in which free water exists, salt water in the oceans claims 97 per cent, in absolute terms $1 \cdot 31 \times 10^{24}$ cm^3. The remaining 3 per cent is fresh water, but three-quarters of this is virtually immobilized as glaciers and ice-caps. Of the last quarter, most is ground water, so that at any instant in time surface fresh water (lakes and rivers) accounts for only 0·33 per cent of all fresh water, and the atmosphere 0·035 per cent (Barry 1969; Fig. 6.1). Since our demands, like those of nearly all terrestrial living things, are for fresh water rather than salt, we deal with only a tiny fraction of the total water volume of the planet; yet the absolute amounts are large, and the energy relations of the various phases are such that human intervention is often no easy matter and water management can be very expensive.

The water that is not locked up as permanent ice is continually moving through various pathways in the atmosphere, biosphere and lithosphere, and this set of natural flows is called the hydrological cycle. A pictorial representation of its qualitative aspects is shown as Fig. 6.1. From the point of view of water resources, the quantity of water in each major unit of the cycle and the rapidity of flux between each becomes the important consideration. The cycle can therefore be regarded as a series of storage tanks, interconnected by the transfer processes of evaporation, moisture transport, condensation, precipitation and runoff. Fig. 6.2 presents a simple model of the quantitative flows within the cycle (Barry 1969). It takes as its starting point the mean annual global precipitation of 85·7 cm (33·8 in) and calls this 100 units. Evaporation and transpiration then provide the sources of input into the atmospheric part of the cycle: 84 per cent comes from the oceans and 16 per cent from the continents. The average water content of the atmosphere if rained out all at once would provide a global fall of 2·5 cm (1 in) and *de facto* constitutes about 10 days' supply of rainfall (Barry 1969). Ten days is also the average residence time of a water molecule in the atmosphere. This points at once to a rapidly fluxing cycle of evaporation, runoff and precipitation: the annual precipitation over land surfaces alone is about 30 times the moisture content of the air over the land at any one time.

As far as most water resources are concerned, precipitation onto land surfaces is a critical component of the system since much fresh water falls onto the oceans where there is no possibility of garnering it. Over land the distribution of the various forms of precipitation is uneven and on a world scale, but four outstanding features of the pattern may be noted: firstly, the equatorial maximum, which is deflected into the northern hemisphere;

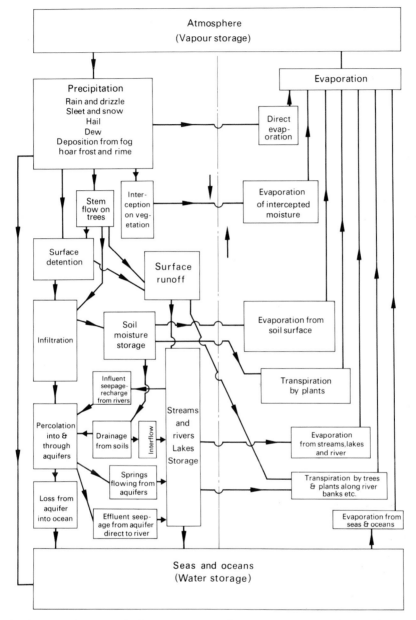

Fig. 6.1 A schematic diagram of the hydrological cycle. The boxes represent both the major storage zones and the transfers between the storages.
Source: Barry 1969

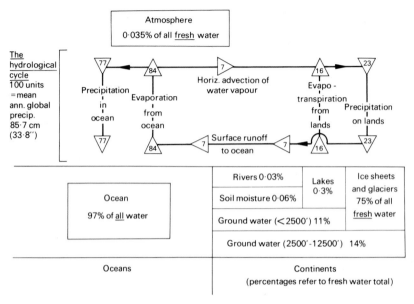

Fig. 6.2 A quantitative diagram of the proportions of total water at various stages of the hydrological cycle. In the top part of the diagram 100 units represent the mean annual global precipitation; the lower part shows how the planet's water is divided up: the fresh water (right-hand boxes) is only 3 per cent of the total water, and 75 per cent of it is locked up as ice sheets and glaciers.
Source: Barry 1969

secondly, the very reliable falls upon the west coasts of continents in the middle latitudes: thirdly, the arid areas of subtropical cells of high pressure where rainfall is not only sparse but sporadic from year to year; lastly, high latitudes become 'arctic deserts' because of the low precipitation from the cold dry air of these regions. The natural flow of water once it has reached the ground is of importance from the resources point of view. Some is re-evaporated, some runs off by way of rivers to the oceans, and a third component enters the ground-water system. If the precipitation falls as snow, then until melting occurs there is a lag between precipitative input and its re-distribution. Globally, water retention on the land surfaces is highest in March–April when there is extensive snow cover and freezing of lakes and rivers in the northern hemisphere. In October there is a rise in sea level of 1–2 cm, when an estimated extra 7.5×10^{18} cm^3 of water are present in the oceans. Water normally spends between 10–100 days on land, unless it enters ground-water circulation, in which case it stays much longer. In the great Artesian basin of Australia, some water in the aquifers has apparently been there for 20,000 years, but both younger and older sources have been found (Barry 1969).

Human use of water

There are two types of 'use' of water. In the first, water is used as a carrying medium in which materials or objects are carried either suspended in the water, or in solution, or by flotation. The last of these, theoretically, leaves the water in an unchanged condition, and from the former the water can be reclaimed by treatment. On the other hand, the use of water may result in its evaporating into the atmosphere and so passing at least temporarily out of a resource process, or being incorporated with some other material to make a new product. Then the use can be said to be consumptive, since the water is effectively removed from the resource process, even if not permanently. Uses of both types are multifarious, since water is one of the most versatile as well as necessary of man's materials. The most basic need is our own metabolic requirement: men die of thirst long before they succumb to hunger. Since our bodies are 60 per cent water, those of politicians and professors included, a daily intake of about 2·25 litres is needed. To this must be added the residential demands of our species. In the LDCs this may not be very great (90 litres/day for the inhabitants of Karachi), but in industrialized countries the amount is much higher: figures of 160 litres/day in the UK and 635 litres/day in the USA are commonly quoted. Activities thus covered include washing, the preparation and cooking of food, and the disposal of household wastes and sewage. Such patterns comprise both consumptive and non-consumptive uses, with some emphasis on the latter. Industrial use of water reaches immense proportions in the DCs. A typical factory will probably use 45–70 litres/day for each of its employees, apart from its needs for industrial processes which include the use of water for energy conversion as in boilers (including those of ships) and especially in the generation of electricity from fossil and nuclear fuels. High pressures ($> 1,000$ lb/in^2; 70 kg/cm^2) call for water of a very high quality free from dissolved solids and silica, and high capital costs demand minimum stoppages for cleaning and descaling. In an industrial country such as the UK, demands on quantity (about 2,300 mgd (million gal per day)/$10\cdot4 \times 10^6$ kilolitres in 1968) and quality are therefore very high (Institution of Civil Engineers 1963, Water Resources Board 1969). Water is also much in demand for cooling, since it is the cheapest available substance for the transfer of heat. Even though recirculation is widely practised, the Central Electricity Generating Board of the UK loses an average of 40 mgd ($0\cdot18 \times 10^6$ kilolitres) to the atmosphere (Water Resources Board 1969). Quality here is not quite so critical as in boiler use, but scaling and corrosion are inevitable consequences of water that is less than pure. Hot water returned to a river alters the ecology for some distance downstream; this is called calefaction or thermal pollution. Industrial processing often requires high-quality water, but the nature of each individual product is critical. Washing of materials and equipment, conveyance of solids, dilution, and the scrubbing of gases to remove unwanted elements are all important here. Water which is incorporated in a product usually needs to be very pure, especially in food, drink and pharmaceutical industries. Some contaminations are, however, permitted in special products as in the case of peat in whisky manufacture and the special qualities of the River Liffey in the case of Guinness. Most modern techniques require a very high water input per unit of product output: for example, 1 ton (1,016 kg) of cement requires 800 gal (36 kiloltres) of water; 1 ton of steel, 25,000 gal (113 kilolitres); and 1 ton of paper, 60,000 gal (272·5 kilolitres). Even a gallon (4·5 litres) of beer uses 350 gal (1,590 litres) of water, much of which appears to remain in the product.

The flotational use of fresh water is largest in timber-producing countries and in industrial waterways. Hence the rivers of Finland form 400,000 km of floatway for logs, conveying 3 million m³ of timber annually; the St Lawrence Seaway is a major traffic artery in North America and in 1966 was used by 60·7 million mt of cargo, while the Rhine is another outstanding industrial waterway, conveying 230·6 million mt in 1965. Such a use is theoretically non-consumptive, but the general contamination caused by shipping (sewage, oil, solid waste and garbage) generally renders the water unusable for other purposes without treatment (Beckinsale 1969a).

A genuinely non-consumptive use of water is the generation of hydro-electric power. This method of electricity generation is extensively used in some LDCs as well as in the West and the socialist countries (Beckinsale 1969b). In Peru, for example, 68 per cent of all electricity comes from this source, and in Colombia 63 per cent. Canada is very dependent with 81 per cent, but Norway heads the list at 99·8 per cent. Although the use is non-consumptive, considerable man-directed intervention in the hydrological cycle at river-basin scale is required (p. 156).

Plants are dependent upon water for their metabolism, and those in the direct service of man as in crops and managed forests no less so. The transpiration from several 'tame' plant communities appears to be of a similar order: 470 mm/yr from short grass, 580 mm/yr from a tall crop and 480 mm/yr from a pine plantation have all been reported from the UK. The absolute amounts depend principally upon climate, and here the supply of water for irrigation may become important. In California, irrigation use may rise to 500–635 mm/yr, and even in Great Britain it has been estimated that 600,000 ha would benefit from supplemental irrigation (Prickett 1963). At the equivalent of 2·54 mm, this would require a water supply of $1·3 \times 10^6$ kilolitres (3,000 mgd) which is similar to the demands of an equivalent area of a densely built-up city. Non-irrigated agricultural use of water is also very high: one pound (0·45 kg) of dry wheat needs 60 US gal (227 litres) for its production; 1 lb rice between 200–250 gal (757–946 litres), and 1 quart (0·9 litres) of milk 1,000 gal (3,785 litres) of water. Neither can the water consumption of animals be dismissed as negligible. A pig of body weight 75–125 lb (34–57 kg) needs 16 lb (7–25 kg) of water per day; a pregnant sow 30–38 lb (14–17 kg) and a lactating sow 40–50 lb (18–23 kg). A lactating Jersey cow requires 60–102 lb (27–46 kg) per day in order to produce 5–30 lb (2·25–14 kg) of milk. By contrast sheep are very abstemious, for on a good pasture they need little if any free water, and on dry range only 5–13 lb (2·25–6 kg) of water per day; on salty range they can be kept happy with a daily input of 17 lb (8 kg) (US Department of Agriculture 1955).

The recreational use of water is analogous to flotation in the sense that it is not consumptive at all except where pollutive contamination occurs. Again, many recreational activities involve floating (more or less) of people or boats. Only sport fishing involves a consumptive crop and even that is sometimes returned to the water. The use of water as a wildlife habitat is non-consumptive too when the wildlife is for scientific purposes or for observational recreation. Fish and fowl for consumption are important as well: fresh-water fish formed 14 per cent of the world's fish catch in 1966 (Beckinsale 1969a).

One theme runs through all these uses: the greater amount demanded in the DCs. It is in these areas that we expect to find the greatest manipulations of the hydrological cycle at whatever scales are manageable with the available technology. In the LDCs the demands are also high in particular sectors, but the development to match these requirements with the supply is often lacking so that large rapidly growing cities especially may suffer inadequacies of both quantity and quality.

Ecosystem modification for water control

In order to divert water from the natural hydrological cycle to his own purposes, man must intervene at those places where technology makes it feasible and where the ratio of benefits to costs is deemed to be favourable. Most phases of the cycle are prone to intervention but naturally the runoff and storage phases of fresh water are the most usual. Others, however, need consideration.

Weather modification

The difficulties of manipulating the atmospheric phase of water are such that, compared with attempts to regulate water flow in other parts of the cycle, its practice is both very recent and small in scale. The methods employed have been dominated by cloud seeding. The statistical significance of results is hard to assess, but one example from Australia shows a benefit of $A2 million to wheat growers who produced an extra 1·8 million bushels (63.4×10^6 kilolitres) after a 6-month seeding programme had increased precipitation by 13–25 mm (A. B. Costin 1971). None of the studies mention the fate of the silver iodide used to provide condensation nuclei, but the most immediate difficulties are legal rather than ecological. If precipitation is induced at area A, then area B downwind is unlikely to receive the precipitation it might otherwise have had. At intranational levels this is a fruitful source of profit for lawyers (Maryland has made weather modification a crime, and Pennsylvania gives counties the option of making it so), but internationally it is conceivable that it could be used as a long-term weapon to subdue an enemy by desiccation (MacDonald 1968, Sargent 1969). Ecologically, the effects of one-shot 'weather modification' are unlikely to be serious, but persistent interventions come more into the category of 'climatic modification' and hence shifts in species are likely. Gross vegetation shifts are of course possible, but even more rapid would be those of rapidly disseminating species such as fungi and insects, some of which are bound to be 'pests'. So even meso-scale changes which are artificially induced are likely to produce serious and unpredictable biological consequences; should the technology for larger-scale changes become available, then the prospect is full of hazard.

Watershed management

Once precipitated, water in its liquid form is much more amenable to management. The portion not immediately re-evaporated goes largely through the pathways of the vegetation (transpiration), into water courses (runoff) and into ground-water storage at various levels (Fig. 6.3). In the first two categories, the most usual manipulations involve firstly the alteration of the vegetation of a catchment area or watershed, in order to produce more runoff, and secondly the increasing of the storage capacity in the runoff phase so that water may be held for use in dry seasons or to prevent floods.

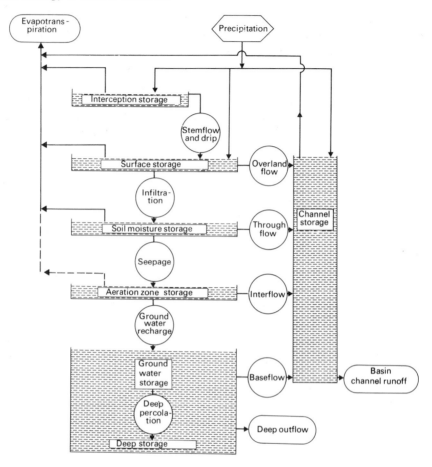

Fig. 6.3 Schematic relationships of the components of the hydrological cycle at the scale of a single basin. Interception storage refers principally to vegetation above the ground but might presumably also comprise buildings in an urban context.
Source: More 1969

The runoff characteristics of catchments are affected by many variables such as slope, soil type and depth, and vegetation cover, of which the last is the easiest to alter. In general, the higher the vegetative biomass the higher the transpiration and hence the greater the water 'loss'. Other factors such as the aerodynamic roughness of the vegetation may be important, but a forest normally transpires much more water than a grassland. On the other hand, a deforested watershed or a grassy catchment may yield greater quantities of unwanted silt than the forested zone, so that the optimal balance point between high water yield and high water quality must always be sought. Flood peaks are usually higher in unforested catchments unless the soil is unusually deep or unusually retentive as with blanket peat on British uplands. Forested mountains are often critical watershed areas because they may accumulate snow during the winter, the melt from which forms a major source of water for lowland areas. Management aims at increasing the depth of snowpack but delaying the melt so as to produce a steady and prolonged yield. It has been found in the western USA that snowpack depth is lowest in the centre of dense coniferous forests and highest (by increases of 15–30 per cent) in openings and lightly wooded areas such as aspen stands. Management techniques used include logging narrow strips on an east-west axis across the watersheds, which may produce 25 per cent more snow (30·5 cm water), and shading the trees over the narrow strips to delay melting; fencing on open watersheds may also increase the depth of snow. A major economic difficulty is that the benefits of such management may not accrue to the landowner but to the down-stream user and so adequate costing is rather difficult; this makes the technique especially suitable for high terrain in public ownership (Martinelli 1964). In brushlands and other semi-arid vegetation, the removal of scrub may increase water flow but the quantity of silt may increase dramatically, and wind erosion may also result unless seeding to grass is successfully employed. The removal of riparian vegetation can be a useful ploy which increases channel flow but affects silt yield very little. In the San Dimas experimental watersheds of southern California, for example, a flow of $86·3 \times 10^3$ m³/day was produced during a wet season instead of $49·3 \times 10^3$ m³/day before the removal of riparian vegeta-tion. The stream flow also continued all year round instead of drying up for the summer months. Such treatment is most effective in semi-arid and arid areas where phreatophytic vegetation (with species such as tamarisk) transpires large quantities of water (Hopkins and Sinclair 1960). Watershed management by vegetation control is not yet an exact science, but computer modelling and simulation are rapidly bringing about a situation where the optimum cover for a given mix of resource uses can be predicted and the major obstacles to successful implementation may then be institutional and social constraints.

Intervention in surface and immediate sub-surface flow

A primary aim of managing water flow over land surfaces is to get rid of any excess. Drainage is therefore important in questions of water supply, although it is not usually done with the object of providing a higher downstream flow. Nevertheless, different methods of drainage will affect many aspects of river regimes, as well as contributing to the quality of the water. Loss through evaporation must have been reduced by the advent of under-draining of fields, and large-scale drainage of wetlands such as the Fens of eastern England must have altered the regime of the rivers of the region. Urbanization has also produced its complex of effects, including the rapid runoff from impervious substances which is partly balanced by high potential evaporation from these surfaces.

Once the runoff from both rural and urban areas becomes committed to a flow channel or a lake, management and offtake become feasible. In effect, streams and lakes are moving storage cells of water, especially since many lakes are temporary widenings of rivers. On a world scale the amount of fresh water stored in lakes and rivers is dominated by the lakes of Africa, which amount to 30 per cent of the world's liquid fresh water at the surface; they are followed by the lakes of North America with 25 per cent, and Lake Baykal (USSR) with 18 per cent. Smaller lakes and the world's rivers comprise the remaining 27 per cent. River channels themselves are distinguished by a relatively rapid flow of water, but as storage cells they are held to be insignificant on a world scale. A world isochronal volume of water in river channels was estimated to be 1,200 km³, compared with 125,000 km³ of fresh water in the world's lakes and 124,000,000 km³ on the world's land areas as a whole, a total which includes some saline water in inland seas. This emphasizes the minute proportion of the planet's water with which man is concerned when he manipulates the river systems, although at regional and local scales the absolute amounts may be very important indeed. The storage capacity of rivers can be marginally enlarged by engineering works such as the deepening of channels and the regulation of flow: these are generally carried out as part of flood-control schemes but may have a secondary effect. Rivers are often the immediate source of water for the world's irrigated areas, which comprise about 202,500 km², although pumped ground water is a significant component as well. Manipulation for irrigation is dominated by mainland China, followed by the USA and USSR, and indeed some 80 per cent of all irrigated lands are in Asia (excluding the USSR). Thus few irrigated lands, actual or potential, occur in very arid regions. Here, and to a lesser extent elsewhere, evaporation losses from the open channels used in most irrigation schemes can assume very high proportions (Beckinsale 1969b).

The technology involved in manipulation for irrigation is very variable, depending upon the access to energy resources of the society involved. At one level are the man-powered devices for lifting water into irrigation channels (e.g. the shadoof), and the small earthen dams or minor streams which merely divert the flow into irrigated areas such as rice paddies; at the other extreme are the giant multi-purpose dams of the world.

Water storage

There can be no doubt that the dam is the most popular of all devices for controlling water supplies on a large scale. The effect is to create a lake whose discharge can be controlled according to the demands placed upon the resource manager (Plate 11). The lake itself may create secondary benefits in the form of fisheries or recreation space to offset the value of the land which is drowned in its creation. The earliest dams, such as the tanks of ancient India and Ceylon, were built solely for water storage, so that water collected during a rainy season could be stored and used during dry periods for irrigation or human consumption. Such a function remains one of the primary purposes of the large-scale control schemes much in evidence today. Even in relatively wet climates, there are advantages in smoothing out river regimes, for example so as to avoid a summer low-flow period when the river may be unable to carry its downstream effluent loads without serious disturbance of its biological communities, and when its dissolved oxygen levels may also be very low. Where a river forms the major source for an industry then it is vital that a year-round supply is ensured so that the processes are not interrupted; the same applies to domestic supplies. The evening-out of the flow may also contribute to the solution of flood-control problems. Particularly in areas with rapid runoff, flash flooding causes serious damage and loss of life, but a dam may retain such waters and thus obviate their damaging effect. Sometimes the efficacy of dams in this respect obscures the need for more rational management of the catchment areas that are contributing the rapid runoff. A steady release of water for irrigation is one of the greatest benefits conferred by storage. In seasonally dry climates it

Plate 11 The traditional way of garnering water for industrial and urban purposes. In this Welsh example, the effect of the reservoir in drowning the sheltered valley lands of the farms can be seen, as can the apparent lack of recreational facilities which might have been a minor consolation. *(Aerofilms Ltd, London)*

may be possible to utilize year-long sunshine for multiple cropping on land formerly rendered agriculturally unusable by aridity. The control of the Sacramento River in the Central Valley of California by the Shasta Dam and associated works of the Central Valley Project has facilitated treble and even quadruple cropping of some fruits and vegetables in the southern half of the Valley. Storage requirements per unit area of land increase in regions of climatic variability, so that per acre of irrigated land Australia stores 6·9 acft (1 acft = 1,233·5 m³), the USA 31 acft, and India only 1·7 acft (A. B. Costin 1971). The generation of electrical power from falling water is much enhanced by the construction of large dams. In industrialized countries there is the frequent advantage that the power can be sold to industry in order to pay for the cost of construction and hence agriculture is made more efficient by its linkage with industry. It is one of the less happy features of some major dam projects in LDCs that no market exists for the power that could be generated.

The numerous purposes to which a large dam can be put, together with its visible presence as a symbol of modernity and apparent mastery over nature, has meant the construction of some very large edifices, together with huge impoundments. Of the 20 largest dams in the world, only one pre-dates 1950, and the Hoover Dam's (1930s) 221 m is dwarfed by several at 300 m. Kariba is the largest impoundment (130 million acft/159·9 × 10⁹ m³), followed by High Aswan (127·3 million acft/156·6 × 10⁹ m³) and Akosombo, Ghana (120 million acft/147·6 × 10⁹ m³), and 13 others above 20 million acft (25 × 10⁹ m³). Areally, the USA now have a greater surface of man-made than natural lakes, if Alaska and the Great Lakes are excluded.

The benefits to be gained from manipulation of the river flow usually overwhelm any suggestion that significant secondary costs might be incurred; indeed much water power is very cheap because the social and ecological costs are rarely reckoned up in the accounting of projects. The effects of large impoundments are wide-reaching and affect the hydrology, the terrestrial system and the aquatic systems of the basin in ways which have not always been beneficial (Lagler 1971). The hydrology of the basin is most altered downstream from a dam, especially if the dam is completely closed during the filling period. Thereafter, the volume of discharge and the current velocity downstream are most obviously altered, with a concomitant reduction in river turbidity. Basin evaporation rates rise, especially in arid and semi-arid countries, leading to the trial of surface films which will transmit oxygen and carbon dioxide, resist wind, be self-restoring after disturbance and be non-toxic. The alcohols octodecanol and hexadecanol from monomolecular films and on small stock dams in Australia have reduced evaporation by 15–70 per cent, decreasing to 15–20 per cent as the impoundment area increases (A. B. Costin 1971). Downstream from a dam, the water temperature may be affected severely if water is drawn off below a thermocline, and the quality of the water will also be changed if the impoundment is chemostratified and draw-off comes from only one depth in the lake. There is also the possibility that large dams may trigger seismic movements, especially in highly faulted regions (Rothe 1968). Silting reduces the life-span of a large impoundment and where possible a silt trap is built into the design; if the sediment piles against the dam, it may be periodically flushed out, with disastrous effects on the ecology of the river downstream. Silt removed by an impoundment may represent a loss of nutrient input to lands lower down and have to be replaced by chemical fertilizer; projected dams on the rivers of northern California would deprive some of the coast redwoods (*Sequoia sempervirens*) of their periodic injection of nutrients and probably prevent them reaching their enormous height (up to 112 m) which is their major aesthetic and commercial attraction. Control of river regimes may also lead to a net loss of soil moisture downstream, although it is sometimes predicted that lateral percolation from the impoundment may increase the groundwater supply to quite distant points.

When the initial flooding takes place there is a biogeochemical enrichment of the water, usually resulting in an explosive growth of phytoplankton and other producer organisms. Some of these are floating water plants such as water hyacinth (*Eichhornia crassipes*), salvinia (*Salvinia auriculata*) and water lettuce (*Pistia stratiotes*). These weeds transpire water which would otherwise remain in the catchment: they and ditchbank plants together transpire $2 \cdot 3 \times 10^9$ m^3/yr, worth about $40 million, in the 17 western states of the USA. The cost of clearing them is likewise high: only the expenditure of $1·5 million/yr on herbicides has enabled the Sudanese to prevent the spread of water hyacinth from the White to the Blue Nile. In this region, the loss of water from *Eichhornia*-covered lakes is $3 \cdot 2$–$3 \cdot 7$ times that from a free surface. The weeds also prevent algal photosynthesis and hence lead to serious depletion of fisheries. On Lake Volta, water lettuce serves as a habitat for the larvae of several mosquitoes, including the vectors of encephalomyelitis and filariasis (Holm *et al.* 1969). Submerged weeds may create difficulties, especially in irrigation systems, as with the introduction of *Myriophyllum spicatum* into North America from Europe. With other similar plants it causes losses in fishing, hinders navigation, interferes with recreation use, clogs water intake points, smothers shellfish beds and provides habitats for mosquito larvae. Control by herbicides is often used, but it is very expensive and a constant vigilance is necessary: the cessation of spraying of the Congo after the post-independence wars allowed water hyacinth to clog it again very quickly, and some herbicides are also toxic to fish. Mechanical removal is slow and costs 10 times as much as herbicides. Biological control depends upon finding an animal with a voracious appetite for a particular plant: some snails are the subject of experiment, and the sea-cow or manatee is a possibility if enough of them can be found, since conversion into pelts is currently a profitable exercise. The white amuo fish and a wingless aquatic grasshopper (*Paulinia acriminate*) are also specialized feeders, the latter eating only *Salvinia*.

Downstream, the stabilized stream flow favours the survival of sedentary and rooted organisms but disrupts species of fish which spawn in flood water or whose eggs or fry depend upon the occurrence of a nutrient-enriched zone of inundation. Adult fish may be catered for by fish passes round dams, but these have not been universally successful, and young fish going downstream sometimes find them difficult to traverse.

A concatenation of the unforeseen effects of river impoundment have all been observed on the Nile as a consequence of the construction of the Aswan High Dam. The removal of silt has taken away a natural source of nutrients which must be replaced by buying chemical fertilizers, and off the delta, the stoppage of nutrient input into the Mediterranean has caused a decline in fishery yield to Egypt since the sardines have disappeared. In 1962 the Egyptian fish catch was 30,600 mt, but this was reduced by 18,000 mt by 1965. The fishery of Lake Nasser is expected to reach 10,000 mt by the mid-1970s, but this figure probably represents an initial 'bloom' and will stabilize well below that figure. The productivity of the delta lakes has fallen owing to fish kills caused by biocide runoff, and by accelerated eutrophication (George 1972). The Nile delta itself is now in retreat due to lack of building material. The extension of perennial irrigation is instrumental in extending the range of blood-fluke diseases such as bilharziasis which now infects 100 per cent of the population of some areas; it is virtually impossible to cure, and control measures such as improving sanitary conditions, drug therapy or snail control have all been ineffective because of their expense or their incompatibility with cultural patterns (Schalie 1972).

This example could be buttressed with many others where unforeseen effects of impoundments have been detrimental. The W. A. C. Bennett Dam in British Columbia removed the spring flooding of the Peace–Athabasca delta, and thus the muskrat resources upon which the native population depended; a similar project to raise the level of South Indian Lake and drown some Indian settlements became an election issue in Manitoba; the Quebec government's James Bay project (the largest hydro-electric power project in the world) will drown one year's production of timber from the province and many Indian and Eskimo resource areas, but the political symbolism of the project and the chance of selling the electricity to the USA are primary considerations. The examples show that the damming of rivers may have many beneficial results, but that the consequences of the alteration of the many ecosystems to which the river acts as a common thread have rarely been explored and scarcely ever incorporated into the reckoning of costs and benefits.

Floods

One normal condition of the hydrological cycle has been perceived as abnormal by man and labelled as floods. Poor watershed practices have often exacerbated and in some places have been the cause of floods, but it remains true that most rivers have floodplains which get inundated from time to time with varying depths of water and at low levels of predictability. For human purposes, as in Eliot's impression of the Mississippi, quantity is high and quality is low:

> ... implacable
> Keeping his seasons and rages, destroyer, reminder
> of what men choose to forget. ...
> Like the river with its cargo of dead negroes, cows
> and chicken coops.

Human adjustment to flood hazard (White 1964) may take the non-ecological form of moving smartly away, lock, stock and barrel, or *inter alia* of pressuring the appropriate governmental agency to remove the threat by environmental intervention. Flood-control dams are one remedy as are channel widening, channel straightening and deepening, and the construction of by-pass channels. Apart from the three-dimensional aspect, the problem is rather like traffic engineering, but new freeways only create more traffic and concrete riprap does not reforest an urbanized watershed. In sum, flood-control measures rarely control beyond certain well-defined limits at certain places and do not look at the cause of the flood or the real reasons (usually to be found in ecologically unsuitable land-use patterns) why they cause damage and loss of life.

For all-round ease, manipulation at this surface-water phase of the hydrological cycle ranks first. But the essentially limited amount of water at this stage, together with the fact that most of it is not of the desired quality unless treated, means that nations with access to advanced technology are assessing their deep underground aquifers more keenly.

Intervention at the ground-water phase

Relative to other sources of fresh water, ground water is an important phase of the hydrological cycle. One estimate suggests that about 7×10^6 km^3 of such water is recoverable (about half the total thus stored) and indeed ground water comprises about 0·5 per cent of total planetary water, compared with 1·9 per cent (26×10^6 km^3) as ice and 0·0001 per cent in rivers (Nace 1969). Though ground water is essentially a storage phase, it appears to have two components: cyclic ground water, which passes in and out naturally within the space of a year, and inherited ground water, which appears to have a much longer storage period.

One of the most important roles of ground water so far as man is concerned is its role as the major contributor to the base flow of rivers. Without this regular input, the reliability of rivers as resources would be much diminished. Of greater importance regionally is the pumping out of water for all purposes and this is done on many scales: dense networks of pumped wells serve towns and industrial areas in many parts of the world, as they do some major irrigated areas where river storage is not feasible. On the other hand, a single wind-driven pump watering a livestock trough or an isolated farm is a common enough sight in semi-arid parts of the world. Pumped wells have their disadvantages because it is often difficult to estimate the quality and quantity of water available, and, like oil, recovery may be uneven. Near the coast, overpumping beyond a certain level may allow the influx of saline water into the aquifers, rendering them useless for a sustained yield of water. Artificial recharge is one response: water is spread into the aquifer by forcing it down through pumps, but achieving a reasonably even spread of the water through the rock can present problems. Nearer the ground surface, the Dutch, for instance, spread polluted waters from the Rhine system over the coastal sand-dunes, which act as a filter, and the water collected beneath is to some degree purified. Deeper recharge schemes often have the aim of allowing the period of percolation through rock to remove contaminants. Purification depends largely upon porosity, and if a high rate of flow is desired then a high-porosity rock needs to be chosen, which will mean a low efficiency of purification. The inverse relation between flow and purification appears to hold for most types of rock, so that ground-water recharge is not always a great success. Nevertheless, many overpumped aquifers such as the Chalk under London are now subject to recharge schemes.

Intervention at the saline phase

The limitation upon the human use of 98 per cent of the world's water is its content of mineral salts. Comprising all except 1 per cent of that proportion, sea water commonly has

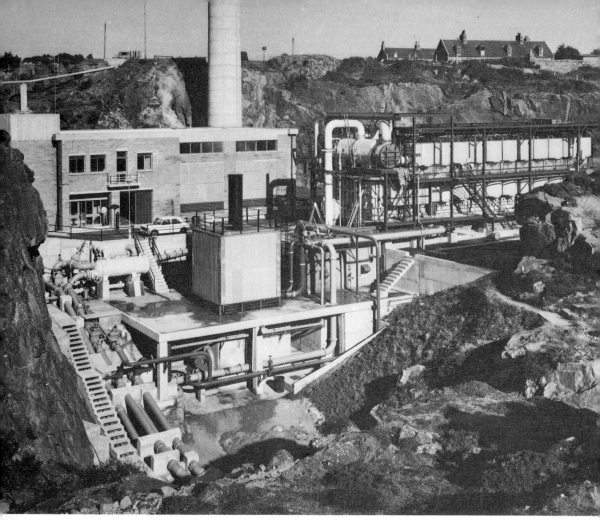

Plate 12 A small desalinating plant in the Channel Isles, UK. Such plants are very useful on small islands low in ground-water resources, especially where there is a peaking of demand caused by a seasonal influx of tourists. *(Senett and Spears Ltd, Jersey)*

35 g/litre of salts, and there are many brackish waters inland with contents above about 2 g/litre which make them useless for most purposes except flotation. In view of the increasing demands for water which is low in mineral salts as well as free from particulate matter, harmful organisms and toxic substances, it is not surprising that attention should have been turned to methods of demineralizing salt and brackish waters (Plate 12).

About 50 plants are currently in use in the world, of which the largest are in places such as Aruba, Curacao and Kuwait. These use multiple distillation of sea water as their extractive technique: one plant in Kuwait produces 6 million gal/day at $US1.76/1,000 gal (4,542 litres) and costs may in similar plants fall to $US1.40/1,000 gal with this method. Multiple-stage flash distillation appears to be cheaper, and a plant in Guernsey, Channel Islands, which is used for 'topping up' during the holiday season produces at 45c/1,000 gal (Pugh 1963); there is a similar plant at Oxnard in California. Another promising method is electrodialysis, in which a series of membranes allows migration of the water but not the dissolved salts. A good yield can be obtained but the price is high: a plant using brackish ground water at Coalinga, California, has a production cost of $7/1,000 gal. The prices quoted are all high compared with the current costs of supply from ground and surface resources: a comparable figure would be 20c/1,000 gal from traditional supplies.

Other methods tried include freezing, using butane as a liquid refrigerant; exchange resins, which will work only up to a salt content of 5 g/litre; and solar distillation, the drawback of which is the large area needed to collect the sun's energy; and plants using natural freezing have been designed in the USSR (Pryde 1972).

Apart from the heavy cost of plant involved, the cost of energy for separating salts from the water is critical, and so nuclear energy is often thought of as a principal source of power for demineralizing water in the near future. One idea is the 'nuplex': this envisages the development of an arid region based upon a 3,000 MWe nuclear reactor to which is coupled a desalination unit, a fertilizer plant producing nitrogen and phosphorus fertilizers for local use and export, electrochemical and electrometallurgical industries, and fisheries, in all supporting a population of 250,000–400,000 (Meier 1969). Such a plant would take about 8 years before it came into full operation and it would be 20 years before any profit was realized. Locations such as Sinai and the Gulf of Kutch have been suggested, and there are problems of the social impact of such a development, particularly since its protagonists consider its main virtue to be a freedom from the institutional and social constraints the region might otherwise possess. The output from distilled sources might not be required immediately it is produced, but in order to be economic a distillation unit would have to be constantly on stream. Thus there would be considerable water losses during periods of storage and stages of transport. Since the water may well be expensive to begin with (one proposal envisages a cost of 28·6c/1,000 gal, another 17c/1,000 gal, but a higher interest rate would force these up to 67c and 32c respectively), then its loss during phases of storage and transport, together with extra energy costs of lifting the water away from the shore-lines where it would be produced, might well make the economics of the whole project unviable; for example, to lift water 500 ft (152·4 m) would cost $3.50/acft for energy and $3/acft for construction. Water which cost, for instance, 60c/1,000 gal at the plant would in reality cost 90c/1,000 gal delivered to the field (Clawson et al. 1969). If water were to be lifted for urban and industrial use, one estimate suggests that a payment of 1c/100 m of lift/1,000 litres of water would be necessary, so that Lubbock, Texas (population 150,000, elevation 1,000 m), would have to pay $5 million/yr for lifting, plus $5 million for the horizontal delivery costs (van Hylckama 1971). The type of areas which would both benefit and be able to afford desalination are therefore restricted in number. Urban and industrial areas in high-technology countries may be one of these, but it may be noted that a plant in southern California to be built under a low interest rate (3·5 per cent) and a guaranteed market for 90 per cent of its water and power (150 mgd/0·681 × 10⁶ kilolitres/day and 1·8 million KWe) was deemed uneconomic. If nuclear plants are not viable in such places, where might they be so? The use of desalted water as a catalyst for agricultural and in-dustrial development in poor and arid areas is an exciting prospect, but as the cost of demineralized water is at least one whole order of magnitude higher than present supplies, it seems unlikely to be a cornucopia at any rate until virtually unlimited supplies of extremely cheap energy are available; even such a project would have to reckon with the ecological costs of the return to the sea of immense quantities of hot concentrated brine.

In from the cold?

Van Hylckama (1971) suggests that since icebergs contain so much fresh water they should be considered as resources. The average Greenland iceberg has an initial volume of 15×10^6 m³ or enough to supply a city of 60,000 people for one year. Their shape would make them difficult to tow, but the flat-topped antarctic bergs might be easier: an iceberg of dimensions $3,000 \times 3,000 \times 250$ m might be towed to Australia in 1 month for a cost of $US1·5 million. Even if half of it melted there would still be 1×10^9 m³ of water or enough to supply 4 million people for one year at an average cost of $1.50 per annum. Even better figures might be obtained for the dry west coast of South America, where ocean currents might be used to aid transport. Early in 1973 the USA Government was reported to be setting up a feasibility study of towing icebergs from Antarctica to the west coast; it was criticized on the grounds that lines of weakness in the bergs would cause them to crumble long before they reached their proposed destination.

Scales of manipulation

The simplest and earliest forms of intervention in the hydrological cycle were at a series of single points. Wells, shadoofs, Archimedean screws and similar devices tapped the water at one place and it was then borne to the site of use by pipe, container or channel. It is a measure of their effectiveness and of the recency of much water-control technology that they are still found around the world, though often with a motor attached to reduce the labour. At a high intensity, such as closely spaced pumped wells, the effect on the water storage can be very great; point manipulation in rivers affects flow rather less.

Another scale of manipulation involves much more intervention, but the control is confined to one basin. Dams for irrigation, flood control and the various other purposes discussed above, irrigation schemes fed from wells or impoundments, and underground transfer lines such as the *qanats* of the Middle East (especially Iran) are examples of this scale of diversion (Beaumont 1968). As the effectiveness of technology increases and planning sophistication soars, so the proportion of water under control in the basin becomes greater so that multiple-use schemes for whole basins of varying sizes become feasible. The Tennessee Valley Authority scheme (quoted still so often as if it were the only example of a multi-purpose basin development) is one example, and those prepared for the Jordan basin and the lower Mekong others; the last two are problematical because of the political boundaries which transgress the natural water-control unit. The creation of large fresh-water lakes behind barrages at coastal estuaries is another major intervention that is especially popular in low-lying countries without steep-sided inland valleys to flood. The IJsselmeer and Delta schemes of the Netherlands and the studies for Morecambe Bay, the Wash and the Solway Firth in Britain are contemporary examples.

A still larger scale is the transfer of water between river basins, sometimes involving an ascent stage which necessitates pumping. The earliest examples of such interbasin transfers were usually to ensure a good head of water behind a particular dam which was being used for power production or irrigation, or both. The Conon Valley scheme in Scotland (Fig. 6.4) is a scheme designed to develop power from the flow of tributaries in the same basin

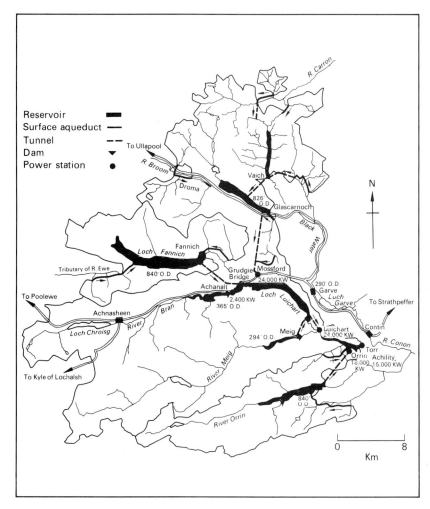

Fig. 6.4 The Conon Valley scheme in Scotland. Transfers within the basin (e.g. from Glascarnoch to Mossford) as well as from outside it (e.g. from tributaries of the River Ewe into Loch Fannich and from the headwaters of the River Carron to those of the Black Water) are used to provide the maximum head of water for hydropower generation.
Source: Aitken 1963

by tunnelling water across watersheds, and also bringing it by tunnel and surface aqueduct from other basins: water from the Ewe (which drains to the west coast) is tapped for Loch Fannich which drains to the Moray Firth. Glascanoch water is piped into Loch Luichart, its parallel eastward-flowing system. Of the scheme's total catchment area of 119,140 ha, 5,957 ha belong entirely to other basins (Aitken 1963). The road to the isles nowadays is accompanied by the skirl of a different sort of pipe.

A larger-scale set of diversions can be seen in schemes planned for Alberta and north-east England. In both there is relatively ample water in the north and a thirsty south, with

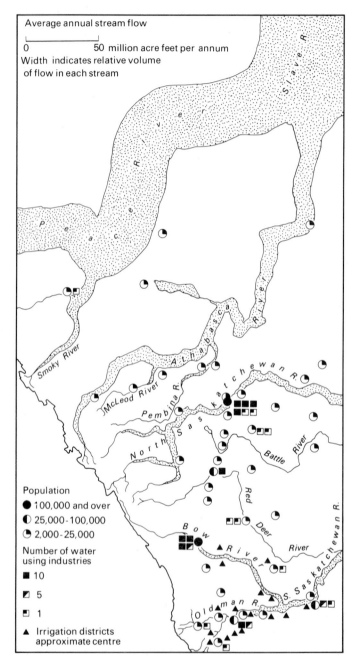

Fig. 6.5 The volume of prairie rivers in relation to user groups. The spatial discrepancies provided the impetus for a scheme of interbasin transfer, progressively transferring water southwards. This scheme (PRIME) has now been incorporated into a larger project.
Source: Province of Alberta 1969

parallel west–east rivers. Plans exist therefore to transfer water from the northernmost stream via intermediate rivers to the middle reaches of the southernmost artery. In the case of north-east England the transfer is from the north Tyne via the Wear to the Tees (Water Resources Board 1970). Alberta was the centrepiece of PRIME (Prairie Rivers Improvement Management and Evaluation), in which the great untapped flow of the Peace River (Fig. 6.5) was to be the northernmost source of a set of interbasin transfers. Water from the Peace was to be fed via Lesser Slave Lake to the Athabasca and thence to the north Saskatchewan; there was also a transfer planned further west between the Athabasca and the north Saskatchewan, and water was to be fed from the north Saskatchewan to the Red Deer River as well. In the south of the province many tributary streams of the south Saskatchewan will have dams in order to supply irrigation districts (Province of Alberta 1969). This scheme has been subsumed into a much larger project for the whole of the Saskatchewan-Nelson basin which is the fourth largest basin in Canada (Saskatchewan-Nelson Basin Board 1972).

Such schemes are puny compared with some of the ideas put forward for large continents, particularly where a small number of political units is present. The USSR is an obvious

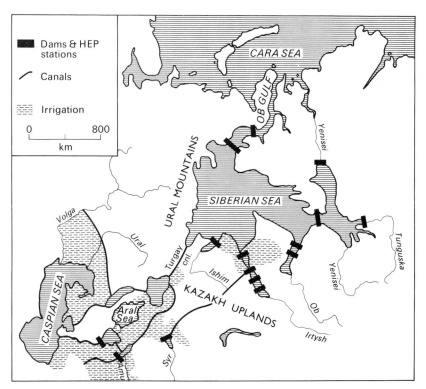

Fig. 6.6 A plan for the use of Siberian rivers to irrigate large areas of central Asia and also to generate hydropower. Considerable controversy has arisen over such massive schemes because of the quantity of land drowned and because of possible changes in climate.
Source: Simons 1969

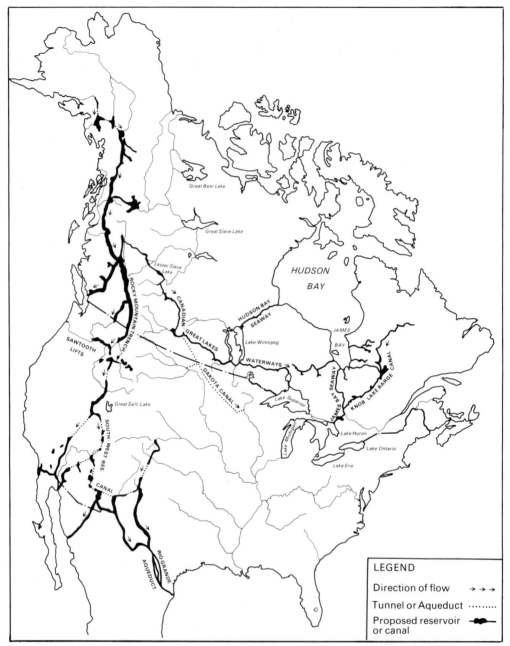

Fig. 6.7 The North American Water and Power Alliance (NAWAPA) scheme which would divert water from northern Canada and Alaska and use it to supply southern California, northern Mexico and the upper Great Lakes region. Navigation projects are also proposed. The effects of drowning the Rocky Mountain Trench upon wildlife, recreation, forestry, communications and earthquake frequency are hard to predict. Source: Province of Alberta 1968

instance, and here engineers have suggested diverting the northward flowing Ob, Yenesei and Irtysh rivers to the south in order to irrigate large areas around the Caspian and Aral Seas (Fig. 6.6). A major problem would be the repercussions upon the climate of 60,000 km² south of the Steppes, where there would be a net loss of heat to plants and where the continentality of the climate would be reduced, and the west Siberian water-table would doubtless rise to the point where large areas would become swamplands (Micklin 1969). However, the discovery of oil and gas in areas which would have been flooded has caused the apparent dropping of the scheme. Another example of continental plumbing is the Parson's Company plan for taking 'unused' water from the northern rivers of Canada and feeding it as far as the Great Lakes, New York, Los Angeles (inevitably) and Chihuahua in Mexico (Fig. 6.7). Virtually all the western rivers of North America would be reservoirs or strictly controlled, and the centrepiece would be a flooded Rocky Mountain Trench in Montana and British Columbia, 914 m ASL (Province of Alberta 1968). The objections range from the geological doubts about the ability of the Trench to withstand such a weight of water to the complaints on aesthetic grounds that the great playground of North America would not have a wild river left and that much wildlife habitat would be destroyed. Figs. 6.8 and 6.9 also show some 'geographical engineering' projects for North America. At 1966 prices, the NAWAPA (North American Water and Power Alliance) scheme was estimated to cost $800 million; an even more potent objection, however, is the rising Canadian nationalism, which seeks to free Canada from economic dominance by the USA. Like many such schemes it presupposes that urban/industrial growth is an ever-expanding consumer which must be supplied, and that it is more necessary to take the water to the sites of use than *vice versa*. Apart from its engineering *folies de grandeur*, NAWAPA appears to be devoid of useful thought about water resources.

Economic and social constraints

More than most resource ecosystems, the water crop is subject to difficulty by virtue of economic pressures. These often derive from the status of water as a free good in economic terms. It costs nothing itself, but manipulating it and treating it may be very expensive: a typical municipal scheme may incur costs of land acquisition and compensation at the site of a headwater reservoir, dam construction and maintenance, pipelines to the city, treatment plants, storage space near the city and distribution costs within the city itself. Inevitably, the greater the distance from source to user the greater the costs; not only is the initial supply system expensive, but its maintenance is likely to absorb large quantities of money. In the south-west of the USA water costs 5–15c per 1,000 gal (4,542 litres) per 100 miles (160 km) to transport, thus making some 'project water' sell at $1 per 1,000 gal, compared with the usual price of 50–70c for industrial water and 5–10c for agricultural supplies. Small wonder that many authorities try to generate power at their dams in order to sell the electricity to pay for the costs of the water-supply system. In the face of supply shortages and rising costs, the search for effective methods of cleaning effluents from water so that it may be re-used downstream is an important development, as is the technology for recycling water used at one site, for example as a cooling agent in an industrial

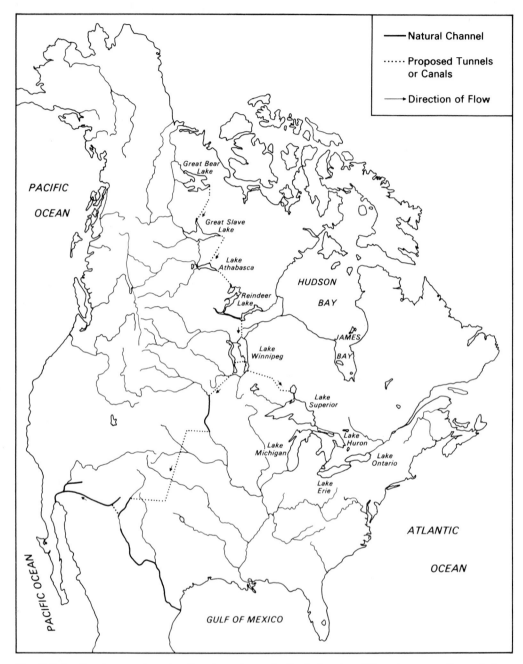

Fig. 6.8 Another large-scale water diversion scheme for North America. Although on a smaller scale than NAWAPA (Fig. 6.7), its magnitude is nevertheless impressive in conception.
Source: Province of Alberta 1968

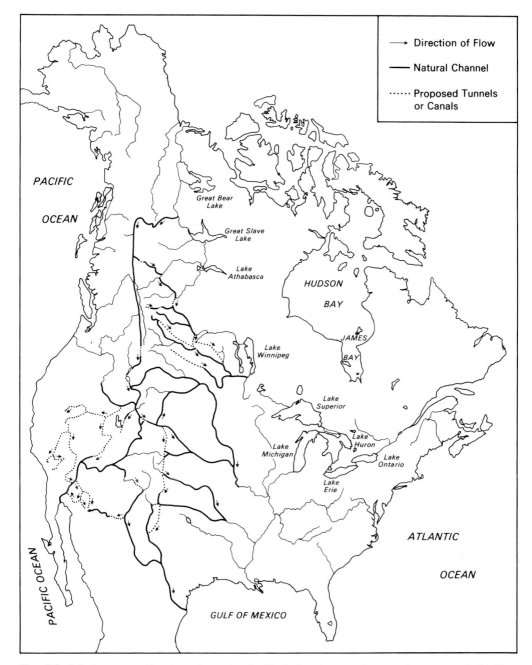

Legend:
→ Direction of Flow
— Natural Channel
⋯⋯ Proposed Tunnels or Canals

PACIFIC

OCEAN

Great Bear
Lake

Great Slave
Lake

Lake
Athabasca

HUDSON

BAY

JAMES

BAY

Lake
Winnipeg

Lake
Superior

Lake
Huron

Lake
Michigan

Lake
Ontario

Lake
Erie

ATLANTIC

OCEAN

PACIFIC OCEAN

GULF OF MEXICO

Fig. 6.9 A further water diversion scheme for the North American continent, to be compared with Figs. 6.7 and 6.8. None of these three schemes has as yet proceeded towards any form of implementation. Source: Province of Alberta 1968

plant or thermal power station. On the River Trent in England, water containing sewage effluent can be used by power stations for cooling, and it is successively re-used by power stations downstream at intervals of 16–32 km. The operations have to be regulated so that the river temperature does not exceed a prescribed limit of 30°C. Cooling towers themselves achieve re-use within a power station: the water is cooled partly by evaporation, which means a loss of just over 1 per cent of the amount of water being circulated through the tower. This amounts to 14 mgd (0.066×10^6 kilolitres/day) for a 200 MW power station and is usually made up from a riverine source. The large bulk of water required for nuclear power stations has meant that coastal sites have been favoured, bringing them into conflict with recreational and wildlife resource uses.

Treatment of waste waters is more fully dealt with in the section on water pollution (pp. 295–7), but the economic constraints appear in the costs of the full treatment needed to return water from, say, domestic sewage to a high degree of purity. The necessity for the introduction of full treatment can be deduced from the fact that such processing is usually five times as cheap as the supply of new water. Here therefore is a major source of supply of potentially high-quality water: theoretically a town could recycle its own fluids on a closed-system basis. This argument can probably be applied to many polluted waters, particularly if the authorities responsible for sewage charge the true costs of treating industrial effluents.

The different values put on different uses of water or catchment areas often exert a social constraint on water manipulation. The most frequent instance of this is a controversy over the loss of land under a reservoir impoundment. Settlements may be lost, as in the Tsimlyansk reservoir in the USSR which necessitated the relocation of 159 towns, villages and hamlets (Pryde 1972); or the loss may be cultural as with the Abu Simbel temples which would have drowned beneath Lake Nasser in Egypt, but were saved by international action; it may be more narrowly economic as with the disruption of farm units when bottom land is drowned in upland Britain; it may be scientific as with the Cow Green reservoir in Upper Teesdale (northern England) where part of an assemblage of arctic-alpine relict plants was destroyed; or it may be scenic as with the drowning of Glen Canyon in Arizona, and the proposals to put dams in Bridge Canyon and Marble Canyon near the Grand Canyon of the Colorado River. In all these cases, and many others, there has been fierce opposition to the proposed water-management scheme, and the opposition to the building of dams especially has become vocal and well informed. In industrial countries, therefore, we are likely to see social pressures influencing large manipulation schemes to a greater extent than hitherto and hence accelerating the move towards closed-cycle re-use. If the benefits of wild country and natural ecosystems are considered at their true value, then the case against some impoundments may be stronger.

The effect of increasing human populations

The very vastness of the quantity of water on the planet gives it an aura of an illimitable resource. Regionally this is clearly not so, but is not the total amount so great that improved distribution would bring about plentiful supplies for every purpose? But only 3 per cent of this great amount of liquid is fresh water, and obstacles exist to the use of the salted variety. In the industrialized nations particularly, vast quantities are needed to sustain the urban-industrial life-cycle. In the USA, for example, Wollman (1960) estimates that 15,000 gal/day/person ($68 \cdot 1 \times 10^3$ litres/day/cap) are used, out of a total resource of 28,000 gal/day/person (127×10^3 litres/day/cap). Projections of demand for the near future reveal vast increases in the quantities of water required, much of it of high quality (Table 6.1). At the current rate of use in the USA, even if all the nation's water resources were utilized, a population above 230 million (1970 level: 210 million) would begin to notice losses in water quality. Regional shortages are already apparent and are the moving force behind some of the continental plumbing schemes like NAWAPA.

TABLE 6.1   Estimated water withdrawn and water consumed, USA 1980 and 2000 (mgd—1 million gal = 4,542 kilolitres)

Use	Withdrawn		Consumed	
	1980	2000	1980	2000
Municipal (public supplies)	29,000	42,000	3,500	5,500
Industrial	363,000	662,000	11,000	24,000
Agricultural	167,000	184,000	104,000	126,000
Local uses, e.g. hatcheries, wetlands	—	—,	71,000	97,000
Totals	559,000	880,000	190,000	253,000

Source: Wollman 1960

On a world scale all known sources of fresh water have been estimated to total $4 \cdot 5 \times 10^{13}$ imperial gal or 20,000 km³. At a present per capita use this could support a world population of 20,000 million, a number arriving in about AD 2040 from a growth rate of 2 per cent p.a. (Simons 1969). The slightly larger estimate for the earth's annually renewable waters of 37,000 km³ (Kalinin and Bykov 1969) only alters the prospect slightly. They suggest that, by the year 2000, half of the above total will be in use by men (Table 6.2).

Within the envelope of these global limits much can be done to procure essential water supplies. New technology will probably reduce demand in some industrial processes, as in the halving of water used per KWH generated in England between 1900 and 1965. Much pure water is now used for purposes which do not require such pristine conditions, as in carrying industrial effluents and domestic sewage for example; and the provision of separate supply channels for pure and not-so-pure water, as already happens for effluent in the Ruhr area of West Germany where one river is maintained clean as a recreational stream and urban supplier while a parallel water-course acts as the regional cloaca (Fair 1961), is a development which may have wider application. The purification of contaminated water would provide a major source of supply possibly equal to half that needed by industrial nations.

TABLE 6.2   Annual world water requirements by 2000 A.D. (km³)

Usage	Total	Lost by evaporation
Irrigation	7,000	4,800
Domestic	600	100
Industrial	1,700	170
Dilution of effluents and wastes	9,000	—
Other	400	4,000
Total	18,700	5,470

Source: Kalinin and Bykov 1969

We must not lose sight of the possibility that water supply could be a limiting factor on population levels, especially at a regional scale. Even given unlimited re-use the time taken to recycle would be critical, and use of all known sources for economic purposes (including, as Borgstrom (1965) suggests, the large quantities needed for producing food) would cut across the rising expectations of those who demand water for recreation and wildlife, or for its scenic value, particularly where it is untouched by man. If shortfalls begin to occur, whether of quality or quantity, we must remember that technological substitutes for water are not very likely and it does not appear to exist in recoverable quantities on other planets even if the cost of space water-carts could be borne. We must at the very least disprove the validity as far as water is concerned of the Chinese proverb:

> Water and words . . .
> Easy to pour
> Impossible to recover.

Further reading

CHORLEY, R. J. (ed.) 1969: *Water, earth and man.*

CLAWSON, M., LANDSBERG, H. H. and ALEXANDER, M. T. 1969: Desalted water for agriculture: is it economic?

HOLM, L. G., WELDON, L. W. and BLACKBURN, R. D. 1969: Aquatic weeds.

VAN HYLCKAMA, T. E. A. 1971: Water resources.

LAGLER, K. F. 1971: Ecological effects of hydroelectric dams.

SMITH, K. 1972: *Water in Britain.*

US DEPT OF AGRICULTURE 1955: *Water.*

7

Forestry

About one-third of the world's land surface (4,028 million ha) is covered with forests (whose continental distribution is outlined in Table 7.1), which we may intuitively define as eco-systems dominated by trees, reflecting the status of some of those organisms as being among the biggest living things in the world: both species of redwood are examples, and the bristlecone pines of California are certainly the oldest living organisms in the world at about 4,600 years. The size of trees subjects all the other elements of the forest system to a hegemony which is reflected in the organization of the layering of the forest plants: the canopy of the dominant trees may be penetrated by only a limited amount of light to be absorbed by shrubs; patches of light on the forest floor allow the growth of shade-intolerant elements of the ground flora. In deciduous forests a temporal element may be noticed in the herbs that flower, shed seed, and die down before the trees come into leaf.

TABLE 7.1   Forest lands (000 ha)

Europe	140,000
USSR	910,009
North and Central America	815,000
South America	908,000
Asia	458,000
China	76,600
Africa	639,000
Oceania	81,000
World	4,028,000

Source: FAO *Production Yearbook 25*, 1971. See also Fig. 7.1.

The leaves of the trees themselves are the fundamental element in the system since they are the site of photosynthesis. Growing in Switzerland, spruce trees (*Picea abies*) need 2,300 kg (fresh weight) of leaves to produce 1 m³ of freshwood, and the average dry weight of leaves in measured forests is 7,000 kg/ha (3 tons/ac) (Ovington 1962). These organs are also important in the food webs of woodlands, since the stem of the tree contains few nutrients and is physically intractable to many animals as food. The nutrient-rich leaves and twigs hence form the first level of most of the food chains of the forest, both predatory and saprophytic: defoliating insects thus have an important role to play in natural forests.

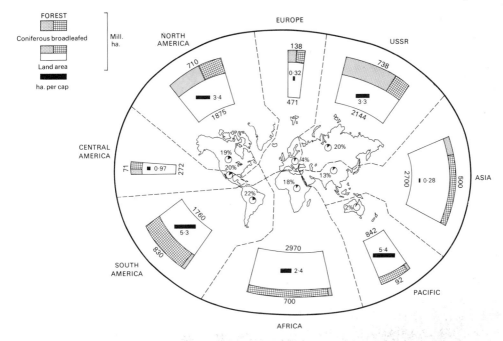

Fig. 7.1 A diagram of forest area and distribution in the world. The divided circle located in each major region indicates the proportion of the land area devoted to forest. The outer segments show (reading outwards) the total land area (million ha), the number of hectares of forest per person, the division of forest between conifers and broadleaved types, and the total forest area. The area of the segment itself is proportional to total land area, subdivided into forest and non-forest sectors. The predominance of the USSR and North America in terms of the coniferous trees so much in demand for paper and paper products will be noted. The dependence of Europe on outside resources in this field (as in so many others) can easily be inferred.
Source: FAO 1963

It follows that the biota of the forest floor are very important factors in the dynamics of forests, for they exist mainly among the leaf and twig litter and are responsible for its mineralization and re-use by the tree and for providing some of the energy pathways through the ecosystem. In temperate woodlands, for example, they decompose 3,000–4,000 kg/ha of autumnal leaf fall by the next spring (Ovington 1965), and in evergreen tropical forests their activity keeps the ground surface virtually free of dead organic matter. Larger animals, too, may have vital roles in the ecology of the forest: the populations of small mammals, which feed on for example acorns and beech mast, will affect recruitment to the next cohort of young trees and so the populations of the predators of these animals such as owls can also be critical. An overpopulation of deer can damage and disfigure a whole generation of young trees by browsing off the leading shoots, while a population explosion of insects can strip a forest of its leaves and alter the ecology of a woodland for many years.

A forest is one of the most complex of natural ecosystems, and in man's use of natural forests and his attempts to imitate or improve on them these intricacies must be borne in mind, since manipulation of the ecosystem for resource purposes can easily bring about deleterious effects which were not foreseen.

Energy flow and nutrient circulation in forests

Because forests are so interesting and because the accumulation of organic matter in the tree stems forms the most important forest resource, more studies on woodland energetics have been done than on many other ecosystems. Forests are reputed to be very efficient users of incident solar energy because of the stratification of photosynthetic surfaces and the high density of chlorophyll-containing tissue. The maximum thermal efficiency of photosynthesis here, as elsewhere, is about 14 per cent, however, and of the net radiation received, a tree expends 60 per cent in transpiration, and the actual processes of photosynthesis account for only 1·5 per cent (Ovington 1962). The balance between photosynthesis and respiration determines the accretion of organic material in the tree, and this depends not only on the season but on the age of the tree. The rate of accumulation of organic matter is greatest at the dense pole stage of young forest, becoming slower in mature woodlands. A climax forest may attain 400,000 kg/ha of dry matter; in energy terms, forest plantations have been found to contain $22–156 \times 10^{10}$ cals/ha. Animal biomass is much lower and probably does not exceed 1,000 kg/ha in the temperate zones of the world (Ovington 1962). Table 7.2 shows the annual energy budget for a plantation of Scots pine.

TABLE 7.2   Annual energy budget for Scots pine (*Pinus sylvestris*) plantation 26 years old

	1×10^8 calories per hectare
Income of short-wave radiation	76,700
Net long-wave radiation loss	32,000
Net radiation assuming a reflection coefficient of 0·25	25,500
Energy flow through organic matter	
Captured during photosynthesis of trees and under-storey plants	1,890
Released by respiration of trees and under-storey plants	890
Contained in organic matter produced by trees and under-storey plants	1,000
Accumulated in tree stock	339
Accumulated in under-storey plants	6
Accumulated in A_0 horizon	32
Removed in trunks of harvested trees	172
In roots of harvested trees	72
Released by litter decomposition	378

Source: Ovington 1965

The processes of the biota cannot be considered separately from those of the soil, since there is a reciprocal relationship. The importance of soil organisms is corroborated by the fact that the overwhelming energy use in the soil is in the breakdown of organic matter.

Nevertheless, the soil humus is an important store of energy: in Devon, England, the annual leaf fall was calculated at 4,000 kg/ha (Ovington 1962), and in very wet climates the depth of organic matter in needleleaf forests (such as those of the west coast of North America) may be so great as to form a peat. Weathering processes in soil rank second in their consumption of energy, followed by the hydrothermic cycle and the transport of substances in the soil profile.

In summary, most of the incident radiant energy is used in the metabolism of the tree. A small proportion (1–3 per cent according to Ovington (1962)) is used for the critical phase of accumulating the organic matter which is the basis of both the forest resource and the forest food web. The subsequent pathways are dominated by the stem and by forest humus, which both accumulate energy over long time-spans, and by the leaves, which have a shorter turnover period and a lower energy content. Some actual figures which demonstrate this are shown in Table 7.3.

As with energy studies, quantitative investigations of the circulation paths of essential elements, such as calcium, potassium and nitrogen, have been undertaken in many different types of forest. The basic flow consists of inputs from rain and subsoil weathering, circulation within the forest–soil–animals system, losses by way of crops of plants or animals, and runoff in both dissolved and particulate forms. The exact quantities in each pathway vary greatly according to the species involved and environmental factors like precipitation. In wet climates, for example, there is often a high input of certain cations from rainfall, but rapid runoff removes much of this quite quickly. Fig. 7.2 shows some pathways of potassium in two different kinds of British woodland. Different rates of processing mean that essential elements need not be distributed evenly in both parts of the forest–soil system. In tropical forests, for example, the amount of calcium in plant shoots is 20 times greater than in the roots, and phosphorus 10 times greater. In temperate forests the order of difference is usually 2–3 times, and in a strand of Corsican pine in Scotland the nitrogen content of the trees was estimated to be only 0·4 per cent of the total nitrogen content of the ecosystem (Ford 1971). So the tropical forest is regarded as having evolved a circulation system which reduces nutrient loss from leaching and runoff by keeping most of the minerals locked up in the vegetation. The total nutrient budget is high in such places: tropical forests have been estimated to accumulate 2,000–53,000 kg/ha of minerals, whereas dry savannas reach only 1,000 kg/ha (Bakuzis 1969). The long-term stability of the forest ecosystem depends upon a successful balance between output and input of nutrients. If there are high losses these need to be replaced, but it is more common to find that they are small in undisturbed forest. A small area of New Hampshire with an average slope of 26 per cent, which included some slopes of 70 per cent, lost on average only 14 mt/km²/yr of nutrients. Clear felling accelerated the nutrient drain by factors of ×3 to ×20 for various cations, and in the first year after felling an amount equivalent to a whole year's turnover of nitrogen was lost (Bormann *et al.* 1968). Within the forest itself the cycling of nutrients involves uptake by the plants, storage within the organisms, and return to the soil via dead organic matter. The quantities of nutrients at various stages are important in resource processes because they determine the quantities of minerals removed if the tree is harvested and taken elsewhere. Table 7.4 shows some comparative data for different European species, from which it can be seen that storage is the smallest of these stages and

TABLE 7.3   Plant biomass of woodlands

Trees	Pinus nigra	Pinus sylvestris	Betula verrucosa	Quercus borealis	Picea abies	Nothofagus truncata	Pseudotsuga taxifolia	Evergreen gallery forest
Location	North-east Scotland	Eastern England	Moscow, USSR	Minnesota, USA	Sweden	New Zealand	Washington State, USA	Thailand
Status	Plantation	Plantation	Natural	Natural	Natural	Natural	Natural	Natural
Age of trees (years)	48	55	67	57	58	110	52	n.a.
Tree height (m)	14	16	26	17	17	21	17	29
Number of trees/ha	1,112	760	n.a.	800	924	490	1,157	16,200
Oven-dry weight (000 kg/ha)								
Tree leaves	5·6	7·2	2·8	3·5	9·1	2·7	12·0	19·0
Tree branches	11·2	12·3	11·3	49·5	14·3	42·0	17·9	50·0
Tree trunks	95·1	96·7	156·7	111·9	85·2	224·8	174·8	225·2
Shrubs and herbs	7·0	2·6	2·0*	0·6	1·0*	0*	0·1	0·2
Roots	34·0	34·1	43·1	15·0	60·0*	39·2	12·3	88·5
Dead branches on trees	10·0	10·0	2·0*	21·9	2·6	1·1	11·2	n.a.
Organic matter on ground	22·0	45·0	3·0	36·7	78·0	16·7	117·3	3·0
Total	184·9	207·9	220·9	239·1	250·2	326·5	345·6	385·9

* Estimated from other woodlands
Source: Ovington 1965

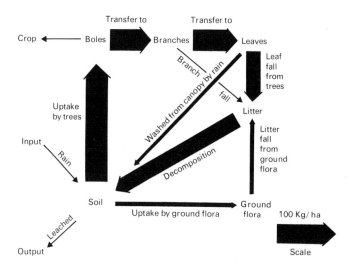

Quercus robur aged 47 years

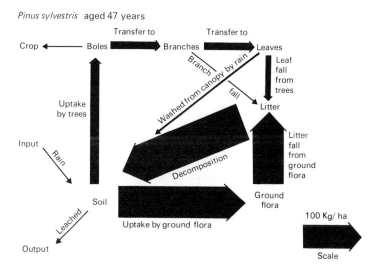

Pinus sylvestris aged 47 years

Fig. 7.2 The circulation of potassium in adjacent woodlands under similar conditions, showing the dominance exercised by the trees over the movement of essential elements. The oak trees, for example, take up much more potassium than the pines, where the ground flora (in this case, of bracken fern) is considerably more important in its flow.
Source: Ovington 1965

TABLE 7.4   Annual cycling of nutrients in forest stands (kg/ha)

Process	Species	Nitrogen	Phosphorus	Potassium	Calcium
Uptake	Pine	45	5	7	29
	Beech	50	13	15	96
	Oak	87	6·5	79	95·1
Return	Pine	35	4	5	19
	Beech	40	10	10	82
	Oak	55·6	3·1	58·6	82·8
Storage	Pine	10	1	2	10
	Beech	10	3	5	14
	Oak	27	3	13·9	0·8
Removed by thinning	Oak	5·1	0·4	6·5	10·5

Source: Bakuzis 1969

hence cropping of the stem, which in turn has the lowest proportion of nutrients, involves the least of these elements. See also Fig. 7.3.

The nutrient flow of the forest may be summarized by emphasizing that under natural conditions it is cyclic and loss is nearly always in balance with gain. If forests are to be used as crops, then an ecologically sound resource process must ensure that this cycle is perpetuated; artificial forests must either establish their own cycles or be aided to do so by forest management. In all cases, the soil fauna and flora are a little-noticed but vital part of the mechanism of nutrient flow in the ecosystem: this is exemplified by the findings of Stark (1972) on the role of soil fungi as nutrient sinks for different kinds of forest (see p. 13).

In spite of the effects of man, enough forest remains to give us a clear idea of the nature and functioning of the natural forest. Some details of the diverse forest types of the world therefore form a necessary background to an understanding of their potential as a source both past and present. This information is summarized in Table 7.5. The nature of the forests is perhaps epitomized in the values for diversity and biomass, which decline poleward as climatic conditions become less favourable for tree growth. The tropical forests have easily the highest production of organic matter, but the forests of the subtropics and temperate zones do not greatly lag behind; the boreal conifer forest has a lower productivity, but even so it is higher than non-forest vegetation types such as savannas (66,000 kg/ha), tundra (5,000 kg/ha) or shrub desert (4,300 kg/ha) (Rodin and Bazilevic 1966).

Man's demand upon the forests can be divided into two categories, of which the first comprises the direct uses of the wood itself, gathered almost entirely from the stems of the trees. The second category consists of indirect uses such as water yield and animal products which have come from the forested area and in whose ecosystems the trees have played an important part. The cropped forests of the world have an annual growth potential of 4,500 million mt, of which 1,626 million mt are estimated to be harvested (Weck and Wiebecke 1961). In Europe the deciduous trees appear to have the most efficient foliage,

TABLE 7.5   Some characteristics of the world's main forest types

Forest type	Regime	Structure[1]	Typical dominants	Spp/ha	Tree biomass[2] (kg/ha)	Typical fauna	Soil type	Uses
Moist tropical forest (e.g. Congo; Amazon basins)	Evergreen broad-leaved	3TL OSL OGL climbers, epiphytes	Mahogany Ironwood *Morea*	200	500,000	Stratified: Canopy: flying squirrels, monkeys Trunk: martens, baboon Ground: tapir, anteater, deer	Variable. Nutrient-poor	Selected hardwoods, e.g. mahogany; shifting cultivation; clearance for agriculture; simplification, e.g. rubber
Subtropical broad-leaved forests	Deciduous broad-leaved	2TL 1SL 1GL	Teak Pyinkado	n.a.	410,000	Canopy: monkeys, civets Ground: tiger, elephant	Variable. Nutrient-poor	Dominants, e.g. teak, have commercial value; shifting cultivation; clearance for agriculture; watershed protection
Temperate zone coniferous forests	Coniferous needle-leaved	1TL 1SL 1GL	Douglas fir Redwood	1–5		Black bear	Leached brown-earth	Dominants have commercial value; clearance for agriculture; watershed protection; recreation;
Temperate zone deciduous forests	Deciduous broad-leaved	1TL 1SL 1GL	Oak Beech Lime Chestnut	20–40	370,000–400,000	Deer; small rodents; owls; insect-eating birds	Brown-earth; leached brown-earth	Dominants have commercial value; clearance for agriculture; watershed protection; recreation; simplification for plantation, e.g. oak, beech; grazing of cattle, pigs
Boreal forest	Coniferous needle-leaved	1TL 1GL	Spruce Firs Pines	1–5	200,000	Moose; wolf; woodland caribou; reindeer	Podzol	Dominants have commercial value: recreation

[1] TL = tree layer; SL = shrub layer; GL = ground layer.
[2] Source: Rodin and Bazilevic 1966

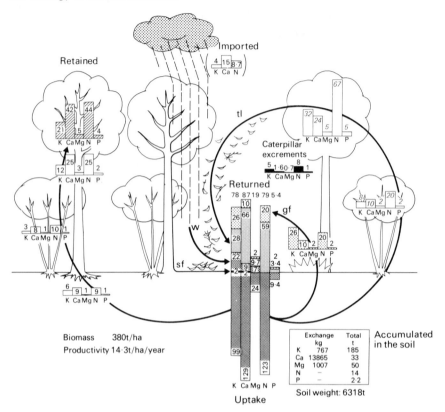

Fig. 7.3 The annual cycling of selected minerals (in kg/ha) in a Belgian forest of oak and ash with an understorey of hazel and hornbeam. The retention of the elements is in the annual wood and bark increment of both roots and above-ground portions of the trees and the 1-year-old twigs. The pathways of return are tree litter (tl on the diagram), ground flora (gf), washing and leaching of canopy (w) and stem flow (sf). Imported flow is from rainfall. The italic figures on the right of the diagram are for crown leaves at full growth in July, at which time defoliating caterpillars are an important part of the return flow. Uptake is equal to the sum of the retained and returned portions of the circulation. (The tons (t) are metric tons.) At harvest, it is largely the stem component of the larger trees which is removed.
Source: Duvignéaud and Denaeyer-De Smet 1970

for 880 kg of fresh foliage will produce 1 m³ of solid merchantable wood; even-aged spruce stands require 3,000 kg for the same production and Scots pine 1,200 kg (Bakuzis 1969). Table 7.6 shows the area and growth potential for the various forest types of the world. The dominance of the lowland equatorial forests is apparent, as is the subordinate status of the rest: possible exceptions are the summergreen (i.e. temperate deciduous) forests and mountain conifers, but an order of ×2 separates them from the tropical rain forests. This growth potential is not equivalent to harvesting potential since species diversity and accessibility are very important too. The latter is self-explanatory; with regard to the former it must be remembered that the number of species per unit area in tropical forests is so much higher than in the boreal conifer forests that harvesting is costly. By contrast, the

immense stands of one or two species of pine and spruce in subarctic Canada provide a
uniform product much more evenly distributed.

TABLE 7.6   Estimated forest area and estimated growth potential[1] for different
formation classes of the forests of the world

| Formation class | Estimated area | | Estimated growth | | |
	Million ha	%	mt/ha yr	Total million mt/yr	%
Equatorial rain forest, lower range	440	18	3·5	1,540	35
Equatorial rain forest, mountain range	48	2	3·0	144	3
Monsoon forests and humid savanna	263	11	1·8	474	11
Dry savanna and dry mountain forests in tropics	530	21	1·0	530	12
Temperate rain forests and laurel; precipitation below 1,000 mm	20	1	7·2	143	3
Sclerophyllous forests	177·5	7	1·0	178	4
Summergreen forests and mountain conifers	393	16	2·2	865	19·5
Boreal conifers	605·5	24	0·9	556	12·5
Total	2,477			4,430	100

[1] In tons of dry matter production per hectare and per year.
Source: Bakuzis 1969

Wood

Fig. 7.4 sets out the main uses of forests. Among the high number of direct uses, the use of
wood for fuel has probably been the most significant until relatively recently. The average
figures for the 1960s show that industrial wood (i.e. all uses except fuel and products such
as cork and waxes) accounted for 54 per cent of the world's crop, so that fuel is slightly
overshadowed (FAO 1969). Nevertheless it remains an enormous consumer of forest and one
in which there is little selectivity, for almost the whole tree can be used. It can be removed
from its growth site, so any return of mineral nutrients to the soil is precluded, and
although some trees are better fuel wood than others, in places of scarcity any tree or bush
will be utilized (Openshaw 1974). In many countries the wood is converted to charcoal
before being sold: India and Japan are instances, and in rural Japan a large proportion of
domestic heating still comes from the charcoal-burning *hibachi*. Table 7.7 states baldly the
magnitude of recent increase and the proportion of industrial wood, and Table 7.8 the
regional components of the total production. Of the uses of industrial wood, lumber is the

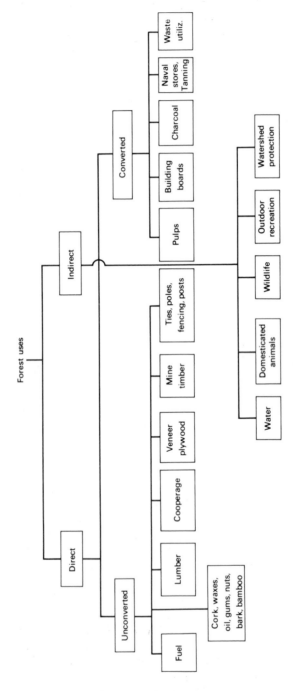

Fig. 7.4 A diagram of the major uses, direct and indirect, of forests

TABLE 7.7   Removals of wood 1959 and
1969 (000 m³)

Year	Total wood	Industrial wood
1959	1900·1	1009·0
1969	2184·7	1219·4

Source: FAO *Yearbook of Forest Products 1969–1970*

TABLE 7.8   Total wood production 1969 (000 m³)

Area	Quantity
North America	448,030
Western Europe	243,511
Developed Oceania	20,510
Other developed areas	60,541
Central America	41,285
South America	233,025
Africa	237,231
African Near East	21,560
Asian Near East	30,892
Far East	213,244
Developing Oceania	4,713
Eastern Europe	628,624
USSR (1968)	380,400
Other centrally planned economies	175,675
World	2,184,739

Source: FAO *Yearbook of Forest Products 1969–1970*

most important, especially in the construction of housing, and the furniture industry is also a major market for both soft and hard woods. Other industrial uses include cooperage (a declining use due in part to the regrettable rise of beer sold in glass or metal kegs), veneer and plywood which consume about 10 times less wood than lumber but are a very large industry on a world scale, mine timber, railway sleepers or ties, posts, poles, fencing and various minor products such as cork, waxes, nuts, resins and bark. The uses of converted wood are dominated by the practice of converting wood to pulp in order to make paper. In 1968 a total of 90,409,000 mt dry weight of pulp was produced. By far the largest proportion (80,034,000 mt) came from the market economies of the West and Japan, with the centrally planned economies following at 8,576,000 mt, and the developing countries producing relatively little at 1,799,000 mt (FAO 1969). The rank order of the major producers of pulp in 1968 was USA, Canada, Sweden, Japan, Finland, USSR. The consumption of paper and paperboard products in the Western-type economies is enormous (Table 7.9), and increased 50 per cent during 1955–67. Most of it is converted eventually to ash and CO_2 and recycling has been little practised outside a few environment-conscious cities in Europe and North America. The profligacy of use is illustrated by the story of the

TABLE 7.9   Per capita consumption of paper and
pulpboard products

		1967: mt/1,000 cap	
USA	226·3	Denmark	115·4
Sweden	168·9	UK	115·2
Switzerland	126·8	Norway	110·0

Source: FAO *Yearbook of Forest Products 1969–1970*

little old lady in Idaho who came across a recently logged forest. As she walked among the debris of the former woodland, seeing the great stumps of decapitated trees, she wept. She cried so hard that she used up a whole box of Kleenex tissues. Among the other uses of converted wood, the various kinds of particle board and building board have a very high growth rate. Not only is waste from lumber used up in this way but trees which have a relatively low market value as lumber can be used too, providing industry for places that might otherwise be economically remote. The whole question of waste utilization is important: sawing lumber produces large quantities of sawdust, and up to 35 per cent of total harvested timber may in fact be waste which at present is often used as a fuel at sawmills but which may be converted into a saleable product in future. The leaves of the trees are traditionally not used. They contain much protein, however, and experiments have been conducted into the feasibility of harvesting them for food, discussed in Chapter 8. The roots are never used and may either be left *in situ* or gathered up. The trunk of the tree is thus the source of nearly all the forest products which are harvested directly.

As the major consumer of wood, the West's tastes and technologies obviously affect the ecology of the forests which they use. Some changes in demand may eventually be reflected in the types of forest which resource managers try to produce. Modern housing, especially apartments, uses less sawn lumber than individual houses, so that the trend of the 1960s, when half the new housing in Europe (except the UK) was apartments, is towards a lower demand for sawn wood. Similarly, particle boards are absorbing much of the market for sawn wood in the housing and furniture fields. Mining timber output is falling, but the same kinds of wood are being absorbed into the enormous increase in pulp production. In Europe during the period 1950–75 the proportion of logs used for pulping will rise from 18 to 44 per cent, and as high as 50 per cent for smaller logs. These trends have their repercussions in the move to the planting or manipulation of forests to bring about pure even-aged stands of fast-growing trees such as poplars, certain conifers, teak and eucalypts. Such forests are of course monocultures and, while possessing the economic cheapness associated with uniformity, are also subject to the ecological instabilities and aesthetic inacceptabilities which accompany a lack of diversity.

Crop ecology

The use of the forest for wood inevitably removes energy-rich material from the site on which it has grown. However, this loss to the local ecosystem is probably not of great consequence provided regeneration eventually takes place. In nature the removed tree trunks would eventually provide energy for decomposer organisms whose populations are probably linked to the available organic detritus and so fluctuate within wide limits. Thus the food webs based on the flora and fauna of the litter horizons must be deprived of energy by the practice of forestry. It has already been noted that forest trees utilize only 1–3 per cent of total incident energy for the production of matter; at harvesting a lot of this is left on site as litter, seeds and roots. The proportion of incident energy which is cropped is thus very small, and so forests are certainly not efficient ways of gathering winter fuel. Industrial users of wood are not of course interested in its energy content; but of the total assimilated matter of the forest, only about 32 per cent appears as usable wood even under very good conditions, since respiration accounts for 45 per cent, litter 16 per cent, roots 3 per cent, seeds 1 per cent, and 3 per cent is lost in logging and transport (Polster

Plate 13 Modern forestry has strong ties to industrial energy sources as seen in the heavy equipment portrayed in this photograph from the USA. Although most of the nutrient-rich parts of the tree are being left on site, the bark is being removed. The traditional suitability of winter for forest operations is confirmed here, as is the commercial suitability of relatively uniform stands of coniferous trees. *(Grant Heilman, Lititz, Pa)*

1961). This last figure is much higher in places with a tradition of inexpert logging and in the Soviet Union has been placed at 33 per cent, including 50 million m³/yr wasted at the cutting areas (Pryde 1972). So the final crop of wood from a mature forest (a fast-growing one is accumulating energy as organic matter more rapidly) is of the order of 0·1 per cent of the incident solar radiation (Plate 13). Mineral nutrients in the natural forest are cycled, so cropping in this case may remove elements in short supply from the plant–soil system. Losses through harvest are highly variable, according to Duvignéaud and Denaeyer-De Smet (1970), and vary with the type of tree: 100-year-old stands of some European species had different amounts of certain nutrients in their trunks (Table 7.10). These data show broadly that a good proportion of the nutrients in the forest are removed by stem harvest but equally that the leaving on-site of much of the crown provides a source of organic matter to be recycled. What is not shown by figures is whether any particularly scarce element in the ecosystem is removed which cannot quickly be replaced by subsoil weathering or precipitative input. There is at present no evidence to suggest that this is so, but the base status

TABLE 7.10   Nutrients in 100-year-old forest stands

	Kg/ha in trunks and roots, and total for stand					
	Calcium		Potassium		Phosphorus	
Deciduous hardwoods	257	1,283	121	320	20	70
Conifers other than pines	129	676	102	375	10	70
Pines	84	283	45	138	8	30

Source: Rennie 1955

of the local rainfall and soils must inevitably be critical. Forestry operations may involve the elimination of designated trees (selective logging) or the removal of whole stands (clear-cutting), although the so-called Montana definition of the former is, 'You select a forest and then you log it.' Clear-felling has been unequivocally shown to accelerate silt and nutrient loss into the streams of the forest. In a New Hampshire deciduous forest nutrient loss was accelerated by several methods (Bormann et al. 1969). Transpiration was reduced so the amount of water passing directly through the ecosystem was increased, root surfaces able to remove nutrients from the leaching waters were reduced, and in some cases more rapid mineralization of added organic matter increased the loss. (Microbiological processes in the soil may also lead to an increase of dissolved nitrate in waters and eventually exceed levels of 10 ppm in the runoff, thus causing algal blooms, i.e. bringing about eutrophication.) In many forests, however, the immediate losses of precipitative input in rainwater and the possibilities of luxury consumption by trees suggest that harvesting may not in the long term be deleterious to the ecosystem providing that the input in precipitation can be intercepted and stored in the soil, and that nutrient-rich but unwanted parts of the tree are left to mineralize on site; Likens and Bormann (1971) show that, for example, 36 per cent of the total calcium in the deciduous forest they investigated is incorporated in the stem bark of the trees. Forest practices which are inimical to such processes need to be eliminated, and in any case monitoring of the nutrient flows of all exploited forest is essential if sustained yield is to be maintained. Existing forests may be very strongly manipulated in order to increase their yield of desired benefits, especially in the case of timber production where man-directed inputs of energy and matter may be of an almost agricultural intensity. Attention to the trees themselves involves 'weeding', i.e. the elimination of species which might compete with the seedlings of desired species; thinning, i.e. the eradication of individuals of the same species; and brashing, i.e. the removal of leafless lower branches especially in conifers. These levels of control are applied only in intensively managed forests, but other influences may affect extensive tracts of more or less natural forest. Chief among these is the application of chemical technology against insect parasites and damaging fungi. Beginning with tar washes and Bordeaux mixture earlier this century, the advent of the aircraft and the organic pesticide has escalated warfare against creatures such as the spruce budworm to a very high degree. Some of the spraying has had untoward side-effects, along with many other uses of persistent pesticides. Fire control has also been ruthlessly practised on all forms of forest despite the fact that in many coniferous forests fires appear to be a normal part of the ecology. The cessation of fire due to a policy of suppression may produce two major effects in fire-adapted ecosystems. The first is to bring about a shift in species composition. This may favour trees less attractive from a commercial point of view, or, to take an example from the field of nature protection, the remaining trees of the fire-tolerant *Sequoia gigantea* more or less ceased to regenerate because their saplings were shaded out by competitors which were not fire-resistant and which would have been destroyed if fires had taken their normal course. A second consequence may be the piling up of humus and litter to great depths on the forest floor. When such a thickness is ignited the temperatures are very high, and 'jumping' to produce a crown fire which is the most destructive form of forest fires is likely. More regular burning of a thin layer of humus and litter does not lead to such damage. One result of these discoveries has been the careful introduction of prescribed burning into some sophisticated forest management schemes. Such a practice may well be much cheaper than fire suppression: the US Federal Government spent $186 million in 1968 on suppression but an average of 1·9 million ha still burn every year, and in 1968, Alaska suffered 1·7 million ha of burnt forest (Oberle 1969). Even spatially minor forest exploitation works may have effects on the forests. Roads for logging are one example: if badly sited they act as channels for water and eventually as initiators of gulley systems in steep terrain. Together with careless logging and fire, enough silt may be shed into streams to render them aesthetically unattractive, kill the fish populations (especially salmonids), and contribute markedly to the silting-up of impoundments.

The net effect of manipulation of natural and semi-natural forests for timber yield is generally to simplify them by reducing undergrowth, eliminating 'weed' species and controlling herbivorous animals who feed directly upon the trees. The ecological analogy of an intensively managed forest is an agricultural crop like grass, and indeed cropping such a forest is very much like grazing with domesticated animals.

On the other hand, the new forests which are the result of the afforestation of previously unforested land are analogous to crop agriculture. The ground is carefully prepared by ploughing and perhaps by applying chemical fertilizer; the trees are planted as seedlings from nurseries, weeded and carefully protected from grazing and browsing animals, sprayed with insecticides and generally pampered. The reasons for establishment of such forests are generally either production of cheap softwood or soil conservation, or both. Countries like Denmark and Britain which down the centuries had become denuded of forests undertook extensive planting of new forests, generally of native or imported (usually North American) conifers. In Britain the intention was principally to build up a strategic reserve of timber after the 1914–18 war, a reason only officially abandoned in 1972. In the south-eastern USA, great areas of pine plantations have stabilized some of the soils most affected by erosion following overcropping for tobacco and cotton, and they form the basis of pulp and furniture industries. In New Zealand about half the indigenous forests of the islands were removed in the century 1850–1950 (12·1 million ha to 5·7 million ha) and the establishment of large forests of exotic species, mainly pines, was undertaken after 1896 with the result that, by 1950, 360,450 ha of exotic forest had been planted, half by the State (New Zealand Forest Service 1970).

New forests are usually highly productive because the species have been chosen for their suitability for the prevailing climate, their ability to grow fast and their conformity to market demands. Some doubts about their long-term efficacy as wood producers still remain. One of these is the worry that the establishment of monocultures (necessary for the reduction of short-term costs) may make the forests prone to particular types of ecological instability. For example, small environmental shifts may allow new pests to spread rapidly and become rife. Their uniformity also means a constant fuel supply for an established fire. In addition, the short cropping cycle of 30–40 years on which forests for pulp production are maintained may take away too many nutrients for production to be sustained, especially in cool temperate latitudes where podzolic soils are part of the coniferous forest ecosystem. In such cases chemical fertilization will become a standard procedure, showing these forests to be indeed a form of intensive agriculture.

Forestry as a land use

The external and reciprocal interconnections of forest land with other land uses are of interest and significance. Its relation to agriculture and pastoralism, for example, is and has long been ambivalent. As Sears (1956) phrases it:

> The forest . . . was prized for the material it yielded and for some of the functions it performed, but it was also regarded as a rival to the space needed for crops and flocks. This two-mindedness about the forest has continued to confuse humanity down to the present day.

On the one hand, therefore, agricultural pressures have meant the clearing of forest, whether it be the great medieval clearances of Europe, the opening up of the interior of eastern North America, or the patchwork of shifting cultivation that covers so many hillsides in Asia and South America. The forest removal may be temporary, as in shifting cultivation on a relatively long rotation period, or permanent as in Europe. The result may be the substitution of a stable ecosystem such as European agriculture, or total ecological collapse through soil erosion. By contrast, forests have taken over from agriculture in some places. The abandonment of fields in Black Death Britain or twentieth-century Sweden allows forests to recolonize, and on a larger scale commercial forestry may become competitive with agriculture on marginal land during a period of agricultural intensification. Thus in upland Britain or on the sandy moraines of Denmark, farms are being replaced by forest.

The key to the interchangeability of forest and farmland may lie partially in the nutrient distribution within the natural system. In temperate latitudes where a good proportion lies in the soil and litter, stable agriculture may often replace forests provided due care is paid to the nutrient and organic matter status of the cropped soils. In the tropics, however, an ecosystem deprived of its forest vegetation loses most of its mineral nutrients and those that are left are rapidly leached away or converted to laterite. Successful 'development' of tropical forests has been largely confined to replacing a type of mixed natural

TABLE 7.11   Amount (kg/ha) of mineral nutrient required to produce 1 ton of forest and agriculture crop

	Nitrogen	Phosphorus	Potassium	Calcium
Forest	4–7	0·3–0·6	1–5	3–9
Field crops	10–17	2–3	8–26	3–8

Source: Bakuzis 1969

forest with a less diverse man-made one: rubber is the obvious example; the maintenance of a simplified forest ecosystem will also allow some cultivation beneath the dominants. Most attempts at agriculture on the European pattern have failed, since without trees the richness of the equatorial lowlands appears to be illusory. Although we cannot do without our crops, we might recall the efficiency of the forest relative to agricultural land as an energy fixer and add to that the information that trees are conservative users of minerals (Table 7.11). In time to come, this thrifty habit may find a new relevance.

The structure of the forest, and the relatively little damage that can be done to it (compared with field crops for example), have encouraged resource managers to think of multiple use as a normal aim of woodland management. Some of the possible combinations are set out in Table 7.12, which also attempts to assess the compatibility of the various components. Water is probably the most important accessory use, since undisturbed forest catchments have low silt and mineral yields and hence give water which requires little treatment. These considerations have to be balanced against the enhanced losses from transpiration, and the balance of benefits and costs probably depends upon the other uses of the forests. Domesticated animals may be grazed in forests provided that the numbers are kept to a level which does not inhibit regeneration and that areas planted with young trees are fenced.

TABLE 7.12   Compatibilities of elements of multiple use in forests

	Grazing	Water	Hunting	Wildlife observation	Recreation
Logging	Not compatible at immediate site	Long-term compatibility OK	Not compatible at site, long term OK	Not compatible	Not compatible
Grazing		OK	Not compatible	Not compatible if predators	Compatible
Water catchment			OK	OK	OK
Wildlife hunting				OK but difficulties	Difficulties but separation possible
Recreation					

The use of the forest for recreation is one of the fastest-growing demands made upon the resource. A notable example of this is the Netherlands, where the State Forest Service now manages about 75 per cent of the area of its larger forests primarily for recreation, nature protection and landscape enhancement (Staatsbosbeheer 1966). Small blocks of forest have also been planted in the Netherlands purely for landscape and recreation purposes in such places as the shores of newly embanked land in the Delta project and on the edges of agricultural land in the new polders of IJsselmeer. More commonly recreation is one element of multiple-use schemes. If it is to be compatible with the other functions, it seems essential that mass recreation should be managed as part of a mosaic of different uses of the forest rather than as one of several uses of the same stand of trees. Recreation affects forest ecology in many ways, the most noticeable of which are the increased number of fires and decreased incidence of regeneration. In spite of such difficulties one study indicated that a forest area in California could increase its recreation capacity 10 times and suffer a loss of timber production of only 13 per cent (Amidon and Gould 1962). If such a conclusion were to be true of most forests, the outlook for compatibility of these two resource processes is very good.

Established forests act as a reservoir of wildlife, both plant and animal. Although the animal biomass is not very high in relation to that of the plants, some of it is very visible in the shape of birds and of mammals such as deer. Natural and semi-natural forests with plenty of glades and 'edge' habitats are particularly valuable from this point of view. Forestry operations are rarely deleterious in the long term to such animal populations, unless very large areas are clear-felled. The exceptions are the rare cases where an animal cannot tolerate humans anywhere in its vicinity: the California condor now confined to the Los Padres National Forest in California is an instance, and special status has been given to the forest land around its remaining eyries. Reciprocally, wildlife populations such as deer must usually be managed if they are not to endanger tree growth. Browse-lines are a common sight in forests where there is perhaps insufficient predation, and in such cases controlled culling is essential.

Forest policies

The importance of forests and their products is such that many countries have adopted national forest policies, and even in the LDCs one of the better legacies of the colonialist era has often been a technically competent forest service. However, it is the DCs which have on the whole evolved the more detailed national schemes.

In the USA, for example, the Forest Service of the Department of Agriculture operates principally under the Multiple Use–Sustained Yield Act of 1960. A mosaic of uses is maintained, with accessibility by motor car the determinant of facility development. The Forest Service operates only on land belonging to the Federal Government: 75·7 million ha, out of a total of 186·3 million ha, is commercial forest area. The national resource process is thus dominated by private landowners, whether in the shape of giant timber corporations or woodlots attached to farms. Both state and Federal governments influence private owners however, through taxation structures and forest practice legislation. In such a large country, with complex patterns of ownership and fragmented levels of legislation, an overall picture is impossible except to say that in general the large forest landowners are very conscious of the importance of their management programmes, and that in this they are influenced by an articulate and concerned public which expects the Forest Service to set the standards for the nation (Frome 1962).

In New Zealand, the national forest policy concentrates on the long-term management of both indigenous and exotic forests for timber production, recreation and water yield (New Zealand Forest Service 1970). In addition, however, the Forest Service is responsible for control programmes exercised on 'noxious animals'. The principal offenders are deer, whose large populations eradicate mountain vegetation and induce serious soil erosion (see p. 126). The Forest Service is also concerned with the reclamation of sandy areas, and co-operates with the National Parks Authority to preserve examples of natural forest eco-systems and scenic reserves. One sanctuary of 5,112·5 ha contains the rare kauri, and kiwi and blue-wattled crows are similarly protected by the Service. Countries with low population densities and large areas of forest need devote little attention to development for recreation. An example is Finland, where policy is to develop timber production and at present allow the recreation to look after itself. In the subarctic part of Finland, for example, there are 55 million m³ of timber with an annual growth of 870,000 m³. This growth is quite slow and regeneration uncertain in the northern part of Finland, so that investigations of climatic fluctuations, the encouragement of regeneration and the selection of suitable strains all become critical, especially as timber is the major export of the nation. Seeding using selected strains may become important even in wild terrain like Lapland (Mikola 1970). Another aim of the national policy for the northern forests is the maintenance of reindeer grazing, which plays an important role in the northern economy. A different example is the Sudan where, apart from in the south, forests do not grow easily, where the overwhelming demand upon trees is for fuel, and where government policies must be directed at securing an orderly flow of trees for this use at a reasonable price. In the 1960s a typical annual consumption of firewood and charcoal was 42 million m³, contrasting with a sawn timber production of 153,000 m³. Continued pressure on the woodlands and savannas of the Sudan is causing soil and wind erosion, sandstorms and the encroachment of the desert (Faris 1966). A major product is gum arabic, of which the Sudan is an important exporter (production in 1968 was 58,000 mt, of which 50,736 mt, value $22 million, was exported). Fortunately, gum trees (*Acacia senegal*) are regarded as 'garden' trees and are mostly grown in rotation with crops, so they share the protection afforded to agricultural crops.

As a last example we may discuss the USSR, an industrial nation with strong centralized control of resource processes. The forest lands belong collectively to a State Forest Reserve of 1,238 million ha, of which 738·2 million ha are actually tree-clad and 171·8 million ha are burned and unreforested logged areas. There are three categories of forest: group I (5·6 per cent of the total) which enjoys maximum protection and preservation and is often largely for amenity and shelter purposes; group II (7 per cent) which consists of forests covering important watersheds and woodlands in lightly forested areas of European Russia; group III (87·4 per cent) are the main productive forests subject to intensive timber harvest, and are mostly in northern European Russia, the Urals, Siberia and the Far East.

The forests are controlled by the State Forestry Committee, and out of a resource of 76×10^9 m^3 an annual cut of $350–400 \times 10^6$ m^3 is taken. According to Pryde (1972) there is a lack of effective sustained-yield harvesting practices, and overcutting is noticeable: a cut of 150–200 per cent of the annual growth is not uncommon in group III forests. In 1960 it was said that 10 million ha which had been cut in the previous decade had no regrowth. Forest land is also lost to fire (1 million ha/yr), insects, and reservoirs (a total of 18 million ha), as in many other countries. In spite of a centralized bureaucracy, the control exerted upon the field managers appears to be insufficient to inculcate modern forest management methods, especially in the face of what locally must be perceived to be an inexhaustible resource.

Effects of increasing human populations

Population pressure upon the world's forests is inextricably linked to scale, and three areas of concern at different scales will be examined. The first of these is the local scale in LDCs, where the pressure of population growth results in extensive deforestation. Woods are cut for fuel and building material, cleared for agriculture and subject to attrition from grazing by domestic animals. Forest policies at any scale are often absent and if they exist are unenforced. The relationships of the DCs to their forests at the national scale are rather different. Fuel needs are at present catered for mostly by fossil hydrocarbon and hydro-electric power, so that the forest becomes a supplier of timber, pulp and a desirable environment. In many places secondary forest becomes a desirable habitat for suburban houses: New England is a prime case. Virgin forest is even more desirable for second houses in the mountains or by lakes. Thus not only the trees but the whole forest ecosystem enters the economic-social-political realm and conflicts over priorities of use and manipulation assume large dimensions, especially since publicly owned forest lands become subject to pressures from all the citizens who consider they have a right to say how they should be used. Approximately 70 per cent of the world's forests are currently in public ownership (FAO 1963), although the extraction of their resources may frequently be in the hands, legal or otherwise, of individuals and companies.

If substitutes for timber are likely, but for paper less so and forest recreation not at all, then the pressures on the forests of DCs will come mainly from the conflicts between recreational use of forests and the short-cycle uniform softwoods needed for pulping. If spatial zoning can be achieved, so much the better; but the size of management units is crucial, particularly where some of the nations of Europe are concerned.

On a global scale, forests are responsible for about half the photosynthesis of the world, which means a much higher proportion of the terrestrial photosynthesis. If, as seems very likely, the balance of gases in the atmosphere is a biological artefact then the role of the forests in absorbing CO_2 and producing O_2 is very important. Just how the increase of CO_2 in the atmosphere (see pp. 283–4) and the decrease of forest area affect this balance is not known, but it seems likely that forests have an important place in the carbon and oxygen cycle of the planet. No suggestion is made here that a breakdown is imminent, but careful research into the global importance of forests is an obvious necessity. There seems to be no shortage of practical reasons for at least maintaining or at best enhancing the forest area of the planet even without acknowledging intangible values such as those exemplified by Charles Darwin in his *Journal During the Voyage of HMS Beagle*:

> Among the scenes which are deeply impressed on my mind, none exceed in sublimity the primeval forests undefaced by the hand of man. No man can stand in these solitudes unmoved and not feel that there is more in man than the mere breath of his body.

Further reading

BAKUZIS, E. G. 1969: Forestry viewed in an ecosystem concept.

DUVIGNÉAUD, P. (ed.) 1971: *Productivity of forest ecosystems.*

HOLDRIDGE, L. R. 1959: Ecological indications of the need for a new approach to tropical land use.

FROME, M. 1962: *Whose woods these are.*

MEGGERS, B. J. *et al.* (eds.) 1973: *Tropical forest ecosystems in Africa and South America: a comparative review.*

NEW ZEALAND FOREST SERVICE 1970: *Conservation policy and practice.*

OVINGTON, J. D. 1965: *Woodlands.*

PRYDE, P. R. 1972: *Conservation in the Soviet Union.*

REICHLE, D. (ed.) 1970: *Analysis of temperate forest ecosystems.*

RICHARDS, P. 1952: *The tropical rain forest.*

RICHARDSON, S. D. 1970: The end of forestry in Great Britain.

WESTOBY, J. C. 1963: The role of forest industries in the attack on economic underdevelopment.

8

Food and agriculture

Humans need food as a source of energy and for tissue replacement, like any other animal. Unlike them, our intake can be divided into metabolic food, necessary for the maintenance of the organism, and cultural food where preferences, taboos and excesses are manifested. The nutritional requirements of *Homo sapiens* vary according to size, age, and the kinds of activities which each individual undertakes: Table 8.1 shows the range of energy requirements for various tasks in an industrial society, and Table 8.2 the areal energy expenditures of some subsistence agriculturalists. If the individual is to function successfully an adequate energy intake must be complemented with sufficient protein to ensure the continuous replacement of tissues and, at certain times, to enable growth to take place. Some vitamins and mineral salts also appear to be essential, and water too is an indispensable part of the human diet. Table 8.3 sets out some recommended daily allowances for various ages and conditions. Such figures must be treated with caution, since it appears that some people are quite healthy even when receiving much lower amounts, especially of energy-yielding foods: nevertheless the figures are indicative of the level of intake considered necessary by Western nutritionists.

Cultural food is the translation of our metabolic requirements into such foods as are available and, for areas where food is plentiful, into choice between different kinds of food even to the point of the onset of diseases of obesity rather than dietary deficiency. On the other hand, people receiving barely adequate nutrition will avoid certain potential foods (Kerala exports millions of protein-laden frogs' legs every year) and prehistoric hunting societies may have limited their populations to the number that could be supported by the preferred food supply rather than by the total available nourishment (see Chapter 3). Our species also ingests various organic substances derived from natural or man-made ecosystems but which are not strictly food, such as medicinal and social drugs.

TABLE 8.1   Energy requirements (kcal/hr)

Writing	20	Cycling	180–600
Dressing	33	Coal mining	320
Ironing	60	Sawing wood	420
Walking	130–240	Walking upstairs	1,000
Polishing	175	Running quickly	1,240

Source: Pyke 1970a

TABLE 8.2   Energy required for agricultural tasks (kcal/ac)

The Tsembega of New Guinea, 1962–3	
Clearing underbrush	56,628
Clearing trees	22,650
Fencing garden	34,164
Weeding and burning	18,968
Placing soil retainers	14,476
Planting and weeding until end of harvest	180,336
Other maintenance	46,000
Sweet-potato harvest	44,835
Taro harvest	5,608
Cassava harvest	2,184
Yam harvest	15,700
Cartage	119,764

Source: Rappaport 1971

TABLE 8.3   Daily dietary allowances

	Energy-yielding foods (kcal)	Protein (g)	Others
Man, 25 yrs	2,900	65	
Woman, 25 yrs	2,300	55	Calcium, iron
Woman, pregnant	2,700	80	Vitamins A and D, Thiamine, ribo-flavin, niacin, ascorbic acid
Children, 4–9	kg × 110	kg × 3·5	
Boy, 16–20	3,800	100	
Girl, 16–20	2,400	75	

Source: Pyke 1970a

Sources of food

The source of much of the food consumed by man is terrestrial agriculture. This represents the most manipulated of all the non-urban ecosystems, in which the energy and matter pathways are directed almost entirely to man and where he maintains a high level of input of matter and energy to keep the system stable in order to yield his preferred crop. Fig. 8.1 shows a schematic representation of the energy pathways in an agricultural society. Not only is the ecosystem man-made, but the plant and animal components of it have usually been genetically altered by man in the course of their domestication. There are two main types of agriculture: crop agriculture, in which the plant production is harvested for use by man either directly or after processing; and animal agriculture, where a crop from a

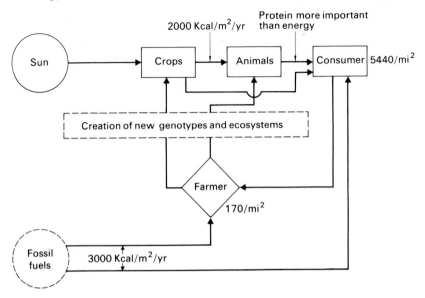

Fig. 8.1 The major flows of energy in modern agriculture. The flow of fossil power is not only applied directly by the farmer; it also fuels other activities of the consumers which result in feedbacks such as fertilizers, pesticides and improved varieties. With the aid of the fossil fuel subsidy, this agriculture can support a population density 32 times that of the farming people (1 mi² = 2·59 km²).
Simplified from H. T. Odum 1971

highly manipulated ecosystem is fed to domesticated animals. (Herein lies the difference from grazing systems, where the forage is more or less wild vegetation.) Ecologically, terrestrial agriculture presents man either as a herbivore or as a third trophic level carnivore, and Fig. 8.2 shows the energy harvest from different ecosystem levels.

Considering the importance of agriculture, it appears surprising at first sight how little of the surface of the continents is cultivated (Table 8.4). Closer inspection reveals the relatively small areas of land which can be subject to the manipulation required by agriculture and still remain as stable systems; furthermore the tolerances of domesticates are inevitably rather narrow, although increasingly accurate breeding methods may aim at widening them. The proportion of land under cultivation, which includes rotation grassland and fallow, is not an infallible guide to the production of agricultural crops since multiple cropping may be possible in tropical and subtropical latitudes.

Terrestrial agriculture is not our only source of food: grazing (Chapter 5), the oceans (Chapter 9) and the so-called 'unconventional' foods (pp. 214–18) are all important, but the relative proportions vary enormously with locality. Together with terrestrial agriculture these sources also supply 'industrial crops', consisting of non-food materials such as pyrethrum, sisal, ornamental flowers and pearls. This section is concerned entirely with food, and will concentrate largely upon terrestrial agriculture and 'unconventional foods'. In passing, we should note the sometimes important but usually unquantified contribution of 'wild' foods in some societies, usually rural, although the blackberrying and bilberrying of urban Europeans forms a traditional exception.

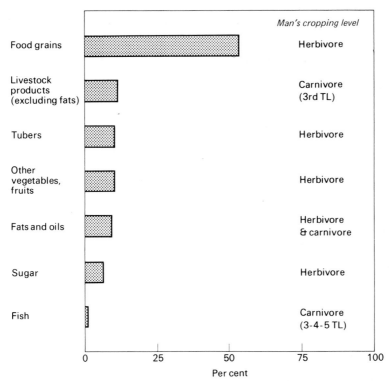

Fig. 8.2 Man's cropping level for food: his harvest is dominated by grains since wheat and rice each supply a fifth of his food energy, but offtake from other trophic levels is also common, including very high carnivore levels in the case of some fish. Yields are low compared with crops at the herbivore level. (TL = trophic level)
Source: L. R. Brown 1970

TABLE 8.4   Agricultural land (000 ha)

	Continental area, incl. inland water	Arable land, incl. fallow, non-permanent grassland, shifting agric.	% arable
Europe	493,000	14,500	29·4
North and Central America	2,242,000	27,100	12·0
South America	1,783,000	8,400	4·7
Asia	2,753,000	463,000	16·8
USSR	2,240,000	227,600	10·1
Africa	3,031,000	214,000	7·0
Oceania	851,000	47,000	5·5
World	13,393,000	1,457,000	10·8

Source: FAO *Production Yearbook 26*, 1972

The ecology of contemporary agriculture

Basic types

Agricultural systems today exhibit a major division into shifting and sedentary types. In the former, total manipulation of the natural system is practised over a limited area but for only a short (1–5 years) period of time. Thus the agricultural path is spatially and temporally enclosed by wild vegetation. Sedentary agriculture, on the other hand, aims at a permanent replacement of the natural systems by the man-made ones. Partial reversions may occur in the shape of fallow periods, but a pioneer stage of recolonization is usually all that is achieved especially if domesticated beasts are allowed to use the fallow land for grazing.

Shifting cultivation

Shifting agriculture today is largely confined to tropical forests, savannas and grasslands, although its demise in temperate zones is not particularly ancient. Its ecology has been conceptualized by Geertz (1963), who visualizes it as a miniature imitation of the closed plant community which it temporarily replaces, and this is especially so of the forest clearings. The crops are planted in a mosaic of different heights and times of fruition so that the plant cover of the soil remains as complete as possible throughout the year in order to reduce the leaching effect of heavy rainfall. The importance of mineral nutrients is emphasized by the burning which follows the clearing of the natural vegetation, for this mineralizes organic matter and allows its uptake by the crops. In virgin tropical forests most of the mineral nutrients at any one time are in the vegetation, and so 'slash and burn' provides a method of translocating some of these elements to the soil. The drain of nutrients by leaching and crop removal is traditionally the reason for the abandonment of the plots, although competition from weeds may be a more immediate factor (Cassidy and Pahalad 1953, Watters 1960). The natural diversity of the forests is imitated by the variety of crops which are grown by some shifting cultivators. Conklin (1954) describes the Hanunoo of the Philippines as recognizing 430 cultivates, of which 150 specific crop types were found in the first year of a slash-and-burn plot. Tropical crops favoured include rice, beans, root crops, shrub legumes, tree crops, yam, taro, sweet potato, vines, bananas and sugarcane, together with European-contact crops such as maize, groundnuts, tomatoes, melons and pumpkins. This cornucopian productivity is not maintained everywhere that shifting cultivation is practised: in the highlands of New Guinea, for example, there is a considerable dependence upon the sweet potato (*Ipomea batatas*), to the point where it usually provides 77 per cent of the calorie intake and 41 per cent of the total protein. Where a mixture of crops is grown then the food supply is abundant and varied, as Conklin (1957) says,

> over the first two years, a new swidden produces a steady stream of harvestable food . . . from a meter below to two meters above the ground level. And many other vegetable, spice and non-food crops are grown simultaneously.

The major disadvantage of such a system seems to be the inability to store surpluses, even when partly processed to paste and flour form. The grains are more stable but highly vulnerable to insects, bacteria and scavenging rodents. Buffering against a poor season is made very difficult by the lack of technology and even worse for groups who have come to depend largely upon one crop. In normal years, calorie intake is sufficient but there may be protein deficiency, especially in newly weaned children (2–3 years) and in adolescents: the groundnut was introduced in order to help combat this problem, especially since animal protein (pig) usually forms only 3 per cent of their protein ingestion (Conklin 1957). Breakdown of this agricultural system appears to occur when plots are re-cultivated too soon or when the system is extended into less humid areas where trees cannot re-establish themselves and a grassland establishes itself as the fallow vegetation. In both cases the mineral nutrient cycles never build up to their former levels and fertility is lower when the plot is cultivated again. The breakdown manifests itself in either or all of three ways: in malnutrition of the people, in emigration from the district, and in ecosystem disintegration particularly in the form of soil erosion. The population levels at which such a breakdown occurs are of considerable interest, but few generalizations can be made. In the forest area of Ghana, Hunter (1966) has estimated that emigration occurs when densities exceed 363–88/km², but 259–518/km² and even 777/km² appear to be carried in the New Guinea study areas. In Java, 20–50/km² has been quoted. Local circumstances vary greatly, but the general conclusion is irresistible: that shifting cultivation is an ecologically well-adapted system in forested lands where the trees regenerate easily when the plots are deserted, and where an equilibrium population has been established. Given a rapidly expanding population, the system cannot cope with the more intensive crop production needed and will either break down ecologically and socially or undergo transformation into a basically sedentary system.

Sedentary cultivation

Sedentary agriculture represents the permanent manipulation of an ecosystem: the natural biota are removed and replaced with domesticated plants and animals (Plate 14). Competition by the remnants of the original biota or by man-introduced organisms may still remain, and considerable effort may be needed to keep these weeds and pests at an acceptable level. In dryland agriculture the soil assumes an importance which it did not have in shifting systems, for it now becomes the long-term reservoir of all nutrients and is constantly depleted as crops are harvested and removed. The nutrients must be replenished either by the addition of organic excreta or chemical fertilizers. The former have the additional advantage that they usually help maintain the crumb structure of the soil as well as adding the elements necessary for plant growth. In contrast there is the important paddy-culture of rice, where the soil is very largely a mechanical rooting medium for the plants and the water supplies the essential mineral nutrients; it often contains blue-green algae which fix nitrogen, for example. Essentially this is an aquarium system with the boundaries made of earth instead of glass; it works particularly well when the catchment areas of the streams which feed the paddies drain from nutrient-rich rocks or soils. Thus paddy rice can be grown on a substratum which is very poor in essential elements and productivity can be maintained for long periods of time, since the cycle of cultivation practices ensures the replenishment of the mineral nutrients (Geertz 1963). The variety of crops grown under the various forms of

TABLE 8.5   A classification of farming systems

	Tree crops		Tillage with or without livestock	
	Temperate	Tropical	Temperate	Tropical
Very extensive Examples	Cork collection from Maquis in southern France **2**	Collection from wild trees, e.g. shea butter **1**	—	—
Extensive Examples	Self-sown or planted blue-berries in the north-east USA **2**	Self-sown oil palms in west Africa **2**	Cereal growing in Interior Plains of North America, pampas of South America, in un-irrigated areas, e.g. Syria **4**	Unirrigated cereals in central Sudan
Semi-intensive Examples	Cider-apple orchards in UK; some vineyards in France **4**	Cocoa in west Africa; coffee in Brazil **4**	Dry cereal farming in Israel or Texas, USA **4**	Continuous cropping in cor gested areas o Africa; rice in south-east Asia **4**
Intensive Examples	Citrus in California or Israel **4**	Rubber in south-east Asia; tea in India and Ceylon **4**	Corn belt of USA; continu-ous barley-grow-ing in UK **4**	Rice and vege-table-growing in south China sugarcane plar tations througr out tropics **4**
Typical food chains (see p. 201)	A	A	A, B	A

Ecosystem type: **1** Wild, **2** Semi-natural, **3** Man-directed, temporary, **4** Man-directed, permanent. Based on Duckham and Masefield 1970

sedentary cultivation is very high, and changing patterns of agriculture together with shifting trade flows and altered rates of consumption make a world kaleidoscope of infinite variety (Laut 1968). Table 8.5 reproduces one classification of farming systems, together with the degree of ecosystem manipulation they represent and the economic context (sub-sistence or commercial) in which they occur. This pattern is dominated by certain elements and Table 8.6 sets out the major crops from each of the main groups of foods and beverages, together with the totals for the group where appropriate.

Alternating tillage with grass, bush or forest		Grassland or grazing of land consistently in 'indigenous' or man-made pasture	
Temperate	Tropical	Temperate	Tropical
Shifting cultivation in Negev Desert, Israel **3**	Shifting cultivation in Zambia **3**	Reindeer herding in Lapland; nomadic pastoralism in Afghanistan **1**	Camel-herding in Arabia and Somalia **1**
	Shifting cultivation in the more arid parts of Africa **3**	Wool-growing in Australia; hill sheep in UK (sheep in Ireland); cattle ranching in USA **2**	Nomadic cattle-herding in east and west Africa; llamas in South America **1**
Cotton or tobacco with livestock in the south-east USA; wheat with leys and sheep in Australia **4**	Shifting cultivation in much of tropical Africa **3**	Upland sheep country in North Island, New Zealand **2**	Cattle and buffaloes in mixed farming in India and Africa **4**
Irrigated rice and grass beef farms in Australia; much of the eastern and southern UK, the Netherlands, northern France, Denmark, southern Sweden **4**	Experiment stations and scattered settlement schemes **4**	Parts of the Netherlands, New Zealand and England **4**	Dairying in Kenya and Rhodesia highlands **4**
A, B, C, D	A (C)	C (D)	C

The table confirms what has already been hinted at in the discussion of domestication and what we should expect from the trophic structure of ecological systems. Firstly, in spite of an overall diversity of crops a very few of them dominate the agricultural production: the three major cereals comprise seven-ninths of the world grain crop and the three major oil-seeds likewise provide seven-ninths of the world output of this group. Secondly, meat is a very much scarcer product because it comes mostly from domestic herbivores which are inefficient users of energy, whether cropped from pastoralism or from more intensive

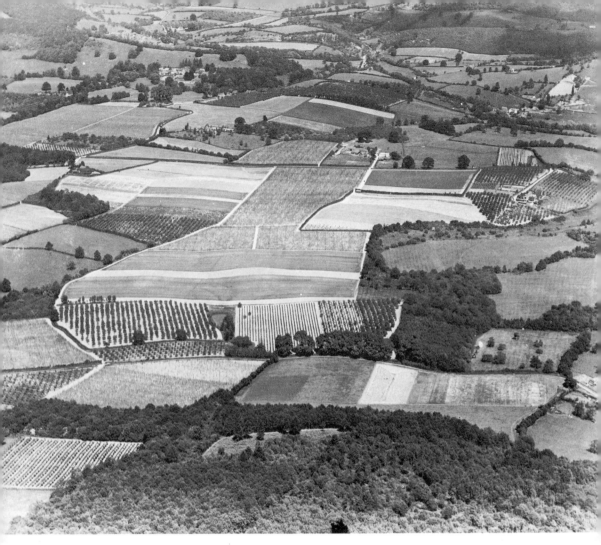

Plate 14 An agricultural landscape of high diversity near Cradley, Herefordshire, England. Fields, woods, orchards and hedgerows provide not only aesthetic pleasure but an ecological buffering system as reservoirs of predators upon the pests of man's crops. *(Aerofilms Ltd, London)*

agricultural systems. The world's dependence upon these few major crops in which there is at present a great deal of variety of plant type and technical practice to suit local circumstances is probably increased by current agricultural trends. Comparison with shifting agriculture of the numbers of people supported by sedentary agriculture is scarcely possible since so much trade is carried on. One of the most intensive of all, wet-rice paddy, appears however to be capable of supporting 2,000 persons/km² under subsistence conditions in favourable areas like Java. Odum and Odum (1972) calculate that the requirements for an American diet need 1·5 ac/cap, which would mean a density of 166/km².

TABLE 8.6   Estimated world production of certain agricultural commodities (million mt)

Average 1961–5[1]; 1972					
Wheat	228	*348*	Soya beans	32·5	*53·0*
Rice	242	*295*	Cotton-seed	20·1	*24·1*
Maize	207	*301*	Peanuts	15·9	*16·8*
Total grains	924	*1,275*			
Potatoes	237	*280*	Coffee	4·3	*4·9*
Sugar (cane)	471	*581*	Tea	1·0	*1·3*
Citrus fruits	23	*35*	Cocoa beans	1·2	*1·4*
Milk (cow)	327	*375*			
Meat (beef, mutton, pig)	68	*88*			
Eggs	15	*22*			

[1] Grains for 1961 only
Sources: Duckham and Masefield 1970; FAO *Production Yearbook 26*, 1972

Agriculture as food chains

General

A simple way of viewing agriculture ecologically is to use the model of a food chain with man as the end member (Duckham and Masefield 1970). There are four of these, of which chain C (Fig. 8.3) represents the grazing ecosystem dealt with in Chapter 6. The others are chain A: tillage crops—man; chain B: tillage crops—livestock—man; and chain D: tillage crops and grassland—livestock—man. Fig. 8.3 shows the inputs of energy and matter for each of these chains and the alternative pathways through which the energy-rich organic matter comes as food to man. Examples of chain A are cereals, potatoes and sugarbeet; of chain B, bacon pigs and barley-fed beef; of chain C either a nomadic pastoralist group or an intensive beef herd on carefully managed pasture; and of chain D, a mixed farm with dairying as the main enterprise. The economics and research input of agriculture have made it possible to compare the energetics and output of each of these chains, and some information is shown in Table 8.7. The general notions about trophic structure discussed in Part I are borne out here: man as herbivore in chain A has access to far higher quantities of energy and plant protein than when he acts as a carnivore in the other chains. In these, milk is the most 'efficient' product in terms of both energy and protein, and meat is obviously a great waster of energy and a relatively poor source of gross protein, although the special nutritional qualities of animal protein make it particularly valuable. The table also hints at the basic problem of agriculture, which is that none of these chains is very efficient at energy conversion, and Table 8.8 shows some food outputs as a proportion of energy input from solar radiation; it is evident that even the

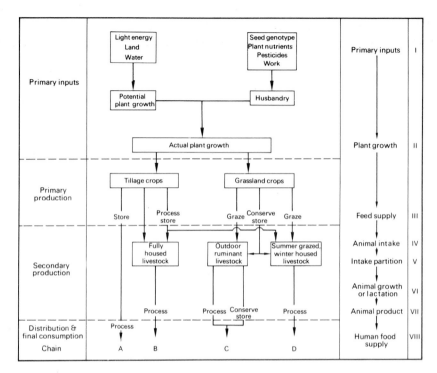

Fig. 8.3 The four food chains which characterize agriculture, with the basic stages set out on the right of the diagram. Where chain C derives its plant growth from grasslands not intensively managed then it falls into the class of the grazing system (Chapter 5). In the case of chain A, the absence of a box at the secondary production stage means that direct cropping by man at the herbivore level is practised. Source: Duckham and Masefield 1970

TABLE 8.7   Relative outputs of food chains in UK

Chain	mcal of food per 100,000 mcal solar radiation	mcal of food per acre (= ×0·405 mcal/ha)	Edible protein lb/acre (= ×0·184 kg/ha)
A (Tillage crop—man)	200–250	4,600–6,500	230
B (Tillage crop— livestock—man)	15–30	440–840	55–80
C (Intensive grassland— livestock—man)			
Meat	5–25	200	20
Milk	50–80	2,250	250
D (Grassland and crops— livestock—man)			
Milk	30–50	800	90

Source: Duckham and Masefield 1970 (1 mcal = 1,000 kcal)

herbivore chain is losing a potential energy yield, as would be expected, by respiration loss and by photosynthesizing for only part of the year. The harvest from indoor livestock and intensive milk production comes from the close attention paid to the feeding of pigs and their penning so as to avoid energy loss by movement, a feature also of intensive cattle-rearing, as is the avoidance of animal crop loss by disease, in which antibiotics play a large part.

TABLE 8.8   Energy production as a percentage of annual solar radiation

Chain	Production	Percentage of solar radiation	
A	Rice: Egypt	0·17	
	Cereals: UK	0·16	
	Potatoes and		
	sugarbeet: UK	0·21	Energy inputs on UK farm:
B	Pig meat	0·03	Manpower: 0·001%
C	Fat lambs	0·01	Power and electricity: 0·017%
	Summer milk on		
	experimental farm	0·08–0·15	
D	Summer and winter milk	0·05	

Source: Duckham and Masefield 1970

Individual chains

Since man is acting as a herbivore, chain A should be the most efficient at producing food. The gross energy disposal of a potato crop in the UK, excluding disease and wastage, is as follows (Duckham and Masefield 1970):

Total organic dry matter formed per acre	24,750 mcal	100%
Respiration loss	9,000 mcal	37%
Unharvested vegetation	3,750 mcal	15%
Post-harvest loss	2,250 mcal	9%
Household waste	2,250 mcal	9%
Net human food (1 mcal = 1,000 kcal)	7,500 mcal	30%

The 30 per cent of the photosynthate which becomes available as human food represents about 0·22 per cent of the total solar energy received. With such losses it is scarcely surprising that agricultural development strategists for areas of nutritional stress concentrate if possible on multiple cropping as the sure way to increase energy uptake. The potato crop referred to above was used in the UK, and therefore a lot of cultural waste occurs which might be obviated in poorer countries: peeling the tubers is quite obviously wasteful, and the above-ground parts are burnt.

Turning to chain C, a much lower efficiency is observed, as would be expected from the trophic structure of ecosystems. This example (Duckham and Masefield 1970) is an intensive grass crop grazed for beef production:

Total organic dry matter formed per acre	28,000 mcal	100%
Respiration loss	9,000 mcal	34%
Unharvested roots and stubble	3,000 mcal	11%
Uneaten grazing	4,000 mcal	14%
Faecal and urine loss	4,000 mcal	14%
Animal metabolism	5,000 mcal	17%
Tissue conversion loss	1,000 mcal	4%
Slaughter and household waste	500 mcal	2%
Net human food (1 mcal = 1,000 kcal)	1,500 mcal	4%

So this chain, cropped at carnivore level, yields 4 per cent of total photosynthate as food, which represents about 0·02 per cent of the solar energy received. Chains B and D show comparable efficiencies: pig meat from chain B may represent about 0·03 per cent of total solar radiation; milk from chain D, 0·05 per cent. All these are considerably more efficient than modified range ecosystems, where yields of 0·004 per cent of solar radiation as cattle have been found by W. A. Williams (1966).

In attempts to increase the yields of food, inputs of energy from human and fossil sources and from abiotic substances such as fertilizers and pesticides are almost universal.

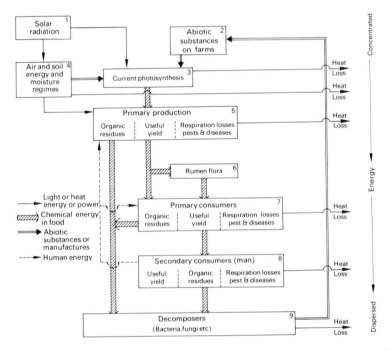

Fig. 8.4 Qualitative flows of energy and matter in a simple farming system in Uganda. In this case the crop is taken at a carnivore level via domesticated animals. Compare with Fig. 8.5, where equivalent boxes have the same numbers in them.
Source: Duckham and Masefield 1970

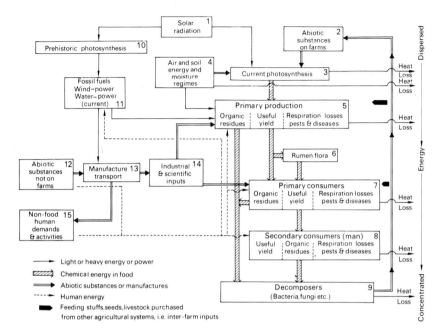

Fig. 8.5 Qualitative flows of energy and matter in a complex farming system in the UK. The greater complexity derives mainly from its linkage with the urban-industrial economy as shown on the left of the diagram. Inputs from other farms are represented by the two broad arrows on the right.
Source: Duckham and Masefield 1970

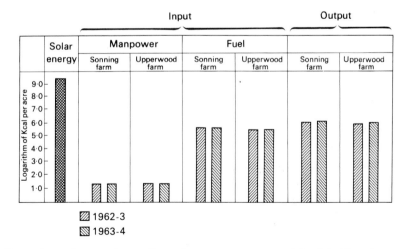

Fig. 8.6 Comparison of energy inputs (from the sun, manpower and fossil fuels) and output from two intensively managed farms in the UK for two successive years. (The vertical scale is logarithmic.) The role of fossil fuels is clear.
Source: Duckham and Masefield 1970

In a simple farming community in Uganda there is little input from outside the system: there are no fossil fuels nor any interfarm transfers of energy-rich substances like animal feeds (Fig. 8.4). In an industrial society, the farm's energy and matter relations are more complex, and the input of fossil fuels, animal feeds, pesticides and fertilizers is of considerable importance (Fig. 8.5). The latter system is much more efficient: whereas one family took 3·2 ha to feed itself in the Ugandan system, 8 workers on 178 ha in the industrialized farm produced enough food, including a high proportion of animal products, to feed 220 families (Duckham and Masefield 1970). The farm's dependence upon fossil-energy supplies for this high yield is very strong, and the relationship of manpower and fuel inputs to food output is shown in Fig. 8.6.

Constraints and buffers

Constraints and buffers operate at all scales, adding further to the diversity of agricultural types in the world. The possible constraints are both natural and man-made and the biggest is probably climate, which forms an overall frame of reference for the tolerances of the plants and animals selected and, in some areas, for the agricultural operatives too. Within the bounds of a climatic type, daily weather is also of importance in determining the crop to be taken from an agricultural system, for a deviation from the expected at a critical time in the life-history of a cultivar may be instrumental in delaying growth or even causing death. The unusual occurrence of a spell of bad weather at the time of parturition in a free-ranging domestic animal is an instance. Except in technologically complex societies the means of forecasting such eventualities are lacking, and even in the industrialized countries some farmers prefer aching toes to inaccurate broadcasts. Diseases and pests are another constraining factor which it may take large amounts of energy and matter to combat. Fossil supplies of the former are increasingly used to apply the latter, as in mechanical spraying, but the traditional energy inputs of a small boy waving his arms, or the contribution of the wind as exemplified in the *haiku* of Hagi-jo,

> His hat blown off . . .
> How pitiless the pelting
> Storm on the scarecrow

are still important in subsistence agriculture. Human constraints are of many types, most more appropriately discussed in economic or culturally oriented work, but infrastructural elements should perhaps be mentioned: if, for example, there are no roads to a farm, it is unlikely to produce cash crops or to make use of an industrial infrastructure which might make fertilizers and pesticides available. Simple economic problems may present themselves, as in the widespread case of the lack of purchasing power of the urban poor in underdeveloped countries. Thus not only do they remain malnourished, they do not stimulate increased production from traditional agricultural systems. Lastly there may be constraints resulting from the lack of knowledge of the farmer, his poor cognition of the limitations (or potentials) of farming in his locality, or simply prejudice against change.

In LDCs, food losses after harvest may significantly reduce the amount available to people. Estimates must of necessity be viewed with caution, but micro-organisms have been held to account for the deterioration of 1 per cent of the world's grain after it has been gathered. Insects are particularly likely to feed upon grains during storage, and in east Africa, corn losses of 9–23 per cent during 6–7 months' storage have been reported, along with 50 per cent losses of sorghum in the Congo during 12 months' storage and 25 per cent of rice in Sierra Leone, also during 12 months. Rodents are voracious feeders upon harvested crops, and it is suggested that 3·55 per cent (33·5 million mt) of the 1961–2 world grain-crop was lost to them; in India a loss of 20–30 per cent of stored grain from the same cause is reported. Mechanical damage is also of significance, as is the activity of mycotoxins such as those which produce aflatoxins in peanuts, possibly as an antidote to the allegedly aphrodisiac qualities of peanut butter which caused some concern in South Africa in 1971. One overall estimate suggests that if only half the post-harvest loss of food grains were prevented, the additional food would be an adequate source of calories for 500 million people in LDCs (US President's Science Advisory Committee 1967a).

To be put against these problem-inducing elements is a whole set of developments which buffer agriculture against such difficulties and stretch its capability. Energy inputs by man were the first of these and remain important, especially in some intensive systems such as paddy rice. Even here, however, the advent of the internal combustion engine has produced considerable change, and some of the crops of the 'Green Revolution' (p. 212) are heavily dependent, as is practically the whole of Western agriculture, upon fossil fuels. Storage is another buffer with an ancient history and one in which the technology is constantly being improved to prevent loss or deterioration of the crop. Not only man's food, but that of animals of lower stages in the food chains, can be stored against a rainy day or a very dry one. Dehydration, heat sterilization, radiation, fermentation, brining, smoking, freezing and chemically controlled ripening all spring to mind in this context. Continuous work on plant and animal breeding constitutes another attempt to improve the 'stretchability' of agriculture. Higher yielding strains, varieties higher in protein content (see Shapley (1973) for developments in sorghum), individuals more resistant to weather or pests, and even intergeneric hybrids like Triticale (wheat × rye), are all part of a post-Neolithic programme given added impetus by the discoveries of genetics. Molecular biology too may yield important advances in such botanical fields as the fusing of desired genetic characteristics (e.g. nitrogen fixation or resistance to a disease) into a receptor plant which then retains these important features. The use of messenger RNA to induce the high peroxidase levels which are associated with disease resistance in plants is an example of the early work (Galston 1971) which may be of considerable future significance, since such 'boosted' plants would be self-sufficient with regard to either fertilizers or pesticides and thus alleviate pollution problems such as eutrophication and the build-up of toxins. Machinery of all kinds has helped to improve agricultural production nearly everywhere, not the least being well-drilling equipment, which has made possible the extension of agriculture at the expense of other ecosystems and a greater intensity of production. Some undesirable results occasionally come to light, as in the breakdown of soil structure in European countries under a regime of continuous cereal cropping with the use of physically heavy machinery. Notwithstanding such objections, present levels of nutrition could not be achieved without the great inputs of fossil energy which is canalized through machines.

CROP PLANT ——— protoplasts ⟍
                              ⟩hybrid —————— NITROGEN-FIXING   1
LEGUME ——————— protoplasts ⟋   CROP

CROP PLANT ——————————————— high peroxidase —— DISEASE-RESISTING   2
                     | levels   CROP
        mRNA injection

The selection of a stable agricultural system for any one place must, as with all resource processes, satisfy three main conditions. Firstly, it must be ecologically feasible in the long term and must not lead to degradation of the ecosystem by means of such processes as soil erosion or structural breakdown. Secondly, it must be economically gainful to the operator: either he must make money at it, if it is a commercial enterprise, or he and his dependants must not die of starvation if it is a subsistence farm. Lastly, the system must be culturally acceptable both to the operator and to the society in whose context he farms. He may not adopt a new system because he fears the wrath of the gods, or the spirits of his ancestors, or the chilly disapproval of his neighbours. In these days of instant communication, neighbours may extend to non-farming people: witness for example the disapproval of 'factory-farming' systems which has sprung up in some Western countries: this may have persuaded a few farmers not to switch to such enterprises. The sifting produced by each of these variables should in theory produce a stable, economic and culturally accepted agricultural system in each part of the world: perhaps the most remarkable fact is the number of places where it has done so.

Food shortages and agricultural responses

Calorie and protein deficiencies

In the case of an insufficient amount of production from the other parts of the ecosphere discussed in this book, the remedies are fairly simple: give up that particular crop (e.g. cease seeing wildlife), accept a lower-quality product (a more crowded beach) or find a substitute material (silver instead of gold). But with food, the first and last possibilities do not exist since we are dealing with a metabolic resource for which there can be no substitute. Moving to a lower quality of nutrition is a possibility, one forced upon many people with varying frequencies: it usually means a diet which may be adequate in calories but deficient in protein, especially animal protein. Beyond lower-quality food lie severe malnutrition, undernutrition and starvation. The fact that food shortages exist is undisputed, but their extent in terms of population, of temporal duration and of their relation to the needs of the deprived people rather than the possibly artificial norms of Western observers is not so well accepted. Shortages of vitamins and mineral elements such as calcium seem to be due to lack of education rather than any real deficiency in most parts of the world, although the lack of iodine (causing goitre) in some areas could only be cured by importing the element. Deficiencies in calories are difficult to pin down because of the different requirements of different people and a certain (limited) ability to adapt to lower intake levels. FAO have estimated a norm at an average of 1,990 kcal/day for LDCs and 2,520 kcal/day for DCs, but even these have been disputed as too high. The effects of deficiency of calories are sluggishness and probably a reduced resistance to disease, but fertility appears to be unimpaired. In the 1962 base year of the IWP only Japan among the A zone countries was calorie deficient, and this has now doubtless been altered by the new strains of rice. The C zone countries, the LDCs, had an overall deficit of 6 per cent for calories. North Africa had only 88 per cent of its needs, central Africa 91 per cent and east Africa 93 per cent, India was lower at 90 per cent and Pakistan very poorly supplied at 85 per cent. Other areas of the world had only small deficiencies such as west Africa at 97 per cent and Africa south of the Sahara at 95 per cent, or a surplus such as South America at 106 per cent and, highest of all, Oceania at 124 per cent. Probably about 20 per cent of the population of LDCs are undernourished in terms of calorie supply, according to FAO.

More serious shortfalls are in protein supply, the lack of which leads to deficiency diseases of which kwashiorkor is the best known. The average shortage of protein in C zone countries is 7 per cent, in which central Africa features as being able to supply only 68 per cent of its requirements. India and Pakistan are also low, at 86 per cent and 89 per cent respectively; Asia generally has a shortfall of 12 per cent. Oceania again scores highest with 127 per cent. The totality means that one-third to one-half, perhaps even 60 per cent, of the population of the LDCs suffer at some time from protein deficiency. Since proteins are less abundant in foods than starches, oils and fats, and particularly because some amino-acids (notably methionine, threonine and tryptophan) are present in large quantities only in animal proteins, they must be cropped from a higher trophic level. Production of extra protein therefore presents more difficulties than extra carbohydrate.

FAO has estimated that by 1975 the shortfalls in calories and protein for the LDCs (given certain assumptions about population trends and income levels but taking into account improved cereals) will equal 30 kcal and 4 g of animal protein per day. Thus stated the amount sounds small, but the latter estimate is equivalent to 3·6 million mt of animal protein, more than was eaten in 1962 by all the inhabitants of the EEC nations. Rising populations and higher incomes have led FAO to call for an overall increase in food production in the LDCs of 140 per cent by 1985 over 1962: an annual rate of increase of 3·9 per cent. At the end of 1972 a maximum overall rate of 2 per cent had been achieved in the LDCs; per capita production had declined, especially in the Far East.

All the evidence, however, points to malnutrition as a multifactorial problem whose causes have local variations. In some places the diet is well balanced but inadequate in quantity; in others there is a seasonal deficiency of protein; and in any of them endemic disease may prevent absorption of available nutrients. Elsewhere the social structure of a community may direct the available protein away from children and the poorer people. The complexities of malnutrition will be solved only by understanding the social and behavioural environment of the consumers as well as the provision of more calories and protein (Payne and Wheeler 1971).

Extension of agriculture

The extension of the world's agricultural area seems an obvious way to resolve some of the problems. Improved machinery, irrigation, better roads, reclamation from the sea, trans-

TABLE 8.9   Effect of various combinations of factors limiting food production

Individual factors	Land area adapted to food production: 109 ac (1 ac = 0·405 ha)	%
Adequate sunlight	35·7	100
Adequate CO_2	35·7	100
Favourable temperature	29·5	83
Favourable topography	22·7	64
Reliable rainfall	16·6	46
Fertile soil	16·3	46
Adequate rainfall	15·5	43

Combinations of factors		
1. Adequate rainfall + sunlight + CO_2	15·5	43
2. Adequate and reliable rainfall + CO_2 + sunlight	12·2	34
3. Temperature + adequate and reliable rainfall + CO_2 + sunlight	11·4	32
4. Topography + temperature + rainfall + CO_2 + sunlight	7·4	21
5. Fertile soil and all others	2·6	7

Based on data in Pearson and Harper 1945

TABLE 8.10   Selected sub-regional totals for potential arable land

	Arable land 1962 Percentage of potential arable land	Proposed arable land 1985 Percentage of potential arable land	Potential arable land	
			Million	% of total area
Central America	64	76	46	19
South America	19	26	524	30
North-west Africa	100	100	295	6
South Asia (excl. Sri Lanka)	93	96	201	48
South-east Asia (incl. Sri Lanka)	44	57	47	47
Far East	81	97	4	28

Source: FAO *Indicative world plan for agriculture* 1970, **1**

formation of other ecosystems, all ought to provide a greater agricultural area. Inspection of the potential reveals, however, a relatively small area of 'virgin' land suitable for modern agriculture. On a world scale, the ecologically limiting factors are set out in Table 8.9. All the world has adequate sunlight and CO_2 for some form of photosynthesis, but when all other necessities like topography and soil are considered the proportion of the terrestrial surface suited to agriculture falls to 7 per cent. This is probably a pessimistic estimate since *de facto* about 9 per cent appears currently to be thus utilized, but some of it doubtless would be more stable as forest or grassland ecosystems. Regional estimates for the expansion of arable land in the LDCs are given in Table 8.10. The increases are mostly modest but greater than the expectations of the previous table, owing to advances in agricultural technology and resource appraisal. Nevertheless in three regions the 1985 total is at or near to the limit of potential and so further expansion will be nearly impossible. Again, the expansions suggested may need considerable cultural adjustments such as the resettlement of graziers and nomads as well as the relatively easier tasks of drainage or tsetse eradication. Irrigation will of necessity play a large part in agricultural expansion, and if schemes are not to end up choked with salt and silt then considerable technical skill in both planning and day-to-day management is required. Irrigation already accounts for 11 per cent of the world's cultivated land, and two-thirds of the world's population live in the diet-deficient countries which contain 75 per cent of the irrigated land, so that its importance to the malnourished is greater than world statistics imply. IWP envisages a faster growth rate for new irrigation schemes than for non-irrigated harvested lands, together with equally important investments in modernizing existing schemes. All such expansions, in the words of the Indicative World Plan, are unlikely to be 'easy, rapid or cheap'.

Intensification

Most authorities agree that this process holds most promise of improving food yields from existing cultivated lands. It is a complex sequence of events which brings a low-yielding traditional agriculture into connection with the technology and economics of industry. Thus a great deal of capital and management skill are needed for success in applying developments such as irrigation, flood control, drainage, erosion control, mechanization, fertilizer and biocide use and the raising of improved varieties of plant and animal (Plate 15). The keys to intensification are energy availability, both on-site and in the places where tractors, pesticides, pumps and the milk are made; a steady effective demand for the products of the farming system; and good communications between the source of supply of the input, the farm, and the consumers. The doubling of agricultural production in the LDCs in the period 1966–85 will require an increased application of plant nutrients from 6 million mt to 67 million mt, and from 120,000 mt to 700,000 mt of pesticides, representing capital outlays (in 1966 US dollars) of 17×10^9 and 1.87×10^9 respectively (US President's Science Advisory Committee 1967b). This assumes the availability of the appropriate materials: in discussing phosphates Eyre (1971) notes that 80 per cent of the phosphate fertilizer was used in western Europe, North America and the USSR in 1968–9, and that north German agriculture received twice as much as the combined systems of

India, Pakistan and Indonesia. 'One must doubt,' he says, 'the feasibility of so expensive a commodity being made available in vast quantities to poor countries.'

The best-known intensification is the so-called 'Green Revolution', the development of new high-yielding and high-protein crops of basic cereals, especially the wheats bred by the International Corn and Wheat Improvement Center in Mexico and rice strains evolved at the Institute of Rice Research in the Philippines (Harrar and Wortman 1969). Of these the development of IR-8-288-3 ('miracle rice') is the most famous. The highly bred grain matures early after rapid growth and is insensitive to day length so that in the tropics and subtropics two to three crops per year become practicable; resistance to lodging is another important characteristic. IR-8 was developed from a cross between two *Indica* rice strains, and matures in 120–30 days. Its top yield averages 1,067 kg/ha (5,800 lb/ac) compared with the 368–405 kg/ha (2,000–2,200 lb/ac) of its parents and 239–331 kg/ha (1,300–1,800 lb/ac) of most local varieties in the Philippines. IR-5 is also an important new variety

Plate 15 An agricultural landscape of low diversity in the Noord-Ost polder of the IJsselmeer scheme of the Netherlands. This also shows one of the major sources of creation of new land for agriculture—from the sea. *(Aerofilms Ltd, London)*

since it cooks dry and fluffy, whereas IR-8 tends to become soggy as it cools and thus is culturally less acceptable in some places (zu Lowenstein 1969). Such yields can only be obtained with careful cultivation. Fertilizers are the key element: IR-8 needs 13·0–16·5 kg/ha (70–90 lb/ac) of nitrogenous fertilizer applied at particular times, together with a continuous water supply, and the use of biocides; the traditional criteria for harvesting time have also to be abandoned. In spite of these sophisticated requirements the spread of new varieties of cereals has been rapid, as is shown by the estimated figures for Asian acreages planted to all new grain types (Ehrlich and Ehrlich 1972).

1964–5	200 ac	81 ha
1965–6	37,000 ac	14,985 ha
1966–7	4·8 million ac	1·9 million ha
1967–8	20 million ac	8·1 million ha
1968–9	34 million ac	13·7 million ha
1969–70	44 million ac	17·8 million ha

Equally important is realization of higher yields per capita (Table 8.11), although sober reflection reveals the harsh fact that population can expand far more steadily than any agricultural output, which tends to come in surges with development of new technologies.

TABLE 8.11   Impact of production using new seeds

	Annual production of selected cereals using new seeds (lb/person of total population (1 lb = 0·4536 kg))			
	India, wheat	Pakistan, wheat	Sri Lanka, rice	Mexico, all cereals
1960	53	87	201	495
1961	55	83	196	496
1962	59	87	213	525
1963	51	86	218	546
1964	46	83	213	611
1965	56	90	150	639
1966	46	71	188	649
1967	49	80	216	655
1968	76	116	247	680
1969	80	121	n.a.	n.a.

Source: Brown and Finsterbusch 1971

Two biological dangers are inherent in the 'Green Revolution', both of which stem from the lack of genetic diversity in new crops. Hitherto, individual farmers selected their variety according to their own idiosyncrasies and so a mosaic of different strains was produced. With the new types large contiguous areas are planted to one strain and so pathological susceptibility is multiplied. A small change in climate allowing the expansion of the range of an insect or a new strain of rust would cause a major disaster: the new wheats of India, Pakistan, Iran and Turkey might all fail at the same time, although more likely are less extensive failures such as the failure of 10 per cent of the hybrid corn in the Middle West in 1971 because of southern corn leaf blight (Dasmann 1972). Also, the breeding of the new strains means that the genetic diversity present in the old varieties is in danger of being lost, and a programme of cultivation and storage of seeds of all geno-types is absolutely essential (Frankel 1969). If such fears do not materialize then production will be very high indeed, and many modifications to current marketing practices, pricing structures and trade patterns must be made: what, for example, will become of the tradi-tional rice-exporting nations of Asia? On the one hand the potentials unleashed are immense; on the other the price paid for the increased production is an enhanced risk of widespread catastrophe, particularly if the cornucopian aspects are used as an excuse to lessen the emphasis upon population control programmes in cereal-dependent nations (Wharton 1969). Socially, the introduction of the new varieties in a nation like India have swept away a great deal of conservatism on the part of farmers, but the selective impact of the agricultural changes has created unrest on the part of the many who want to be part of the new deal but cannot find the means to get started. Problems of land tenure have also been exacerbated, since rents have often risen as high as 70 per cent of the new crops and some owners would now like to get rid of tenants altogether. The introduction of a technical revolution without understanding of its cultural context is always likely to be fraught with problems (Ladejinsky 1970). There needs to be effective demand from consumers: the penniless cannot buy all the IR-8 in the world. And beyond this there is the concomitant problem of how all the people displaced by even moderately efficient agriculture are to be employed: industrialization to give them all jobs would have to be on a totally unprecedented scale, although the development of a mechanized, industrially based agriculture could come to involve 30 per cent of the working population as it does in the USA (Paddock 1971).

New sources of food

Biological resources

Even if the rapid development of conventional agriculture is sustained, most authorities agree that protein deficiencies will continue to exist. A search for supplementary sources of both plant and animal proteins is therefore in progress, with some emphasis on the latter since their amino-acid make-up is closest to man's requirements. Animal flesh has the further advantage that it is usually the more easily assimilable, since the plant proteins are locked away behind a cell wall of cellulose not easily broken down by the action of the human stomach. Animals have thus been a means of harvesting the plant protein in a digestible form, and so have considerable dietary advantages in spite of the energy losses due to their position in the trophic structure of an ecosystem: looked at economically, the livestock industries of DCs are gigantic welfare societies for domestic animals which return only 10 per cent of the energy invested in them by way of foodstuffs. If animals are to be avoided, a food source which will yield plant protein in a digestible form or from which the majority of cellulose has been removed is clearly attractive. Fungi appear to be easily assimilated and contain a good deal of protein by comparison with some other sources (Table 8.12). Other advantages are that they do not absorb much human or fossil energy in production, can be grown independently of environmental factors in places such as caves and abandoned railway tunnels, can readily be stored in dried form and require little sophisticated knowledge or technology (Pyke 1970b).

TABLE 8.12   Comparative yield potential of mushrooms

	lb/dry protein/ac/yr (× 0·184 kg/ha)
Conventional methods of beef production	70
Fish farming	600
Mushroom growing in UK	60,000–70,000

Source: Pyke 1970b

Requiring rather more technology but readily available are leaves which are not normally cropped or which are fed upon by animals. Within their cells is a considerable harvest of protein if this can be separated from the fibrous material of the leaf and made palatable. Pirie (1969) notes that protein was extracted from leaves as early as 1773, but that the effort devoted to it by modern research is minimal. Leaves which are the by-products of another crop could be used and the fibre returned to the soil as a texture-maintaining essential, or otherwise unused grasses, shrubs or marginal aquatics might be harvested. Thus any leafy plant becomes a potential protein source, providing it is susceptible to propagation and harvesting. The potential of the tropics is especially high and the cropping of leaf protein would make attractive the retention of much of the forest cover, and help to prevent ecological degradation. Apart from harvesting, the major industrial input required is processing the extract to the point where it becomes palatable either by itself or as an additive to other foods. This need not be difficult but inevitably adds both to the cost and to the number of trained technicians who are needed (Pirie 1970). The potential is immense and probably greatly undervalued, since protein yields of 1,200 kg/ha/yr have been obtained with legumes in Britain, and 3,000 kg/ha/yr should be possible in the tropics; these harvests could be raised to 2,000 kg/ha/yr and 5,000 kg/ha/yr respectively if nitrogen fertilizer were added to the appropriate ecosystem (Arkcoll 1971). Algae are groups of plants which have received a good deal of attention as possible sources of food, especially the noncellular varieties which under optimal conditions have exceptionally high rates of primary productivity. 5 m² devoted to algae production could feed one man 10^6 kcal/yr, whereas it would take 1,200 m² of grain and 4,000 m² of pork to reach the same level. Since algae would be cultured in tanks, non-agricultural surfaces such as rooftops might become food-producing. The potential yields have, however, been stressed at the expense of the drawbacks. Production of algae would be a very technical process, requiring stirring, bubbling of carbon dioxide, sophisticated machinery and skilled manpower (Pirie 1969). All things considered, the net energy input might be higher than the output and only if this were an acceptable price to pay for protein would the process become economically gainful; unquestionably it would depend upon the continued supply of cheap fossil-energy supplies. Algae are demonstrably not the panacea that has been claimed for them, especially in terms of dependence as in Nigel Calder's book, *The environment game* (1967).

Energy-wasters though they are, animals retain many desirable characteristics as cellulose-converters and as saliva-inducers. That so few species have become domesticated is often a source of wonder, and only recently has the potential of many wild animals been realized. If sustained-yield practices are adopted, together with minimal amounts of processing, many wild animals come within the ambit of possibility: most are eaten somewhere. Birds such as young colonial seabirds, reptiles and amphibians are probably under-utilized, and a larger beast like the aquatic manatee which might feed on such nuisances as water hyacinths is also a feasibility. The large South American rodent *Capybara* (about 1·3 m long) which feeds on aquatic weeds is another candidate of Pirie's (1969). New domestications, among which the eland and the African buffalo rank as favourites (Jewell 1969), would be useful too, particularly if they ate plants which currently go unharvested.

Fresh-water and brackish-water fish are other sources capable of development, especially in the tropics (Tables 8.13 and 8.14), where high yields are taken from fertilized ponds (Table 8.14) (milkfish in the Philippines are a good example). Israel and the USSR are also intensive raisers of fresh-water fish, whose protein content is very high (Hickling 1970).

TABLE 8.13   Comparisons of milkfish (*Chanos chanos*) yields (lb/ac (× 0·184 kg/ha))

Country	Milkfish total	Fish total	Total edible protein (dry weight) %	
Java	180	280	15·1	Unfertilized
Taiwan	958	958	51·7	Fertilized
Philippines	300	300	16·2	Unfertilized
Agric. land: swine		450		
cattle		250		

Source: Walford 1958

TABLE 8.14   Yields of milkfishes and various shads (000 mt)

Country	1964	1966
Taiwan	30·7	19·0
India	9·9	8·5
Pakistan	7·1	4·7
South Korea	2·0	6·4
Philippines	62·7	146·0
USSR	324·0	344·6

Source: FAO *Yearbook of Fishery Statistics 28*, 1969

In Asia, yields seem to be declining, possibly as a result of pesticide runoff and of conversion of the ponds to rice-growing; fish were harvested from rice paddies under some traditional systems of agriculture, but multiple cropping has cut into the life cycle of the fish and so this additional protein source is no longer available. In Hong Kong, small ponds have suddenly begun to be very popular with farmers, who also keep ducks which enrich the water and are marketable as well. The remaining aquatic source of food, detritus feeders, is dealt with in the chapter on the sea.

Where industrial technology is available, the choice of organisms for food can be widened, since close control of growth conditions and subsequent processing can be achieved. A first stage in industrialized food is the processing of otherwise unpalatable materials to yield either desirable food or a neutral substance which, if not exactly mouth-watering, is at least not repellent. For example, the soya-bean is high in protein and also highly adaptable, so that its content of plant protein can be disguised as (inter alia) turkey or pork sausages via flavouring, colouring and texturizing. It is also cheaper than another alternative, Fish Protein Concentrate. Many unmarketable fish can be defatted, deboned and dehydrated to a white tasteless powder that can be further processed or sprinkled on food as a powder additive. Its disadvantages include a complex and expensive processing procedure, but even so the marketed product is cheap if it can be got to places where it is needed without increasing its cost unduly.

Industrial food

Production of food by industrial processes which altogether sidestep contemporary photosynthesis offers new possibilities. Bacteria and fungi form the basis of the technique, with yeasts as the group upon which most work has been done. The substrates upon which yeasts can be induced to grow under industrial conditions include waste whey, some sugar waste, sulphite liquor and sewage. The cellulose in paper and sulphite liquor could be used to grow yeasts: one-third of the paper waste of the USA could supply one-third of its calories, but protein yields are less satisfactory (Mateles and Tannenbaum 1968). The most satisfactory substrates so far tested on an industrial scale have been the hydrocarbon by-products of petroleum. These are available in large quantities and not being agricultural products are relatively constant in supply and price. Yeasts grown upon them can be processed to a powder of dead cells containing 35–75 per cent of crude protein. Lysine content is adequate or even high, although methionine and tryptophan are relatively low: rumen bacteria offer future possibilities here because of their high content of these amino-acids. The two hydrocarbons which have been selected for yeast production are gas oil and n-paraffins. Gas-oil-grown yeasts give a product which is 70·5 per cent dry weight of crude protein and also contains 2,550 kcal/kg; n-paraffins yield 65 per cent dry weight of protein and 2,550 kcal/kg. (The FAO standard for a 25-year-old 65-kg male is 3,200 kcal/day, so the product is clearly not likely to be a major energy source.) The basic requirements for the process are pure water as suspension medium, the hydrocarbon substrate, access to balanced concentrations of mineral ions and certain trace ions, continuous supply of oxygen and eliminations of excess carbon dioxide, a pH in the range 3·5–6·5 and a controlled temperature of $30° \pm 2°C$. Constant stirring is necessary to mix the hydrocarbons, the water and the oxygen, so that this has to be supplied; however, the consumption of the substrate is correspondingly reduced: 1 kg of sugar will produce 0·5 kg of yeast, whereas 1 kg of hydrocarbon will yield 1 kg of yeast. The gas-oil variant of this process must be associated with an oil refinery, but the n-paraffin substrate can be used wherever the raw materials are available so it would be theoretically possible to site it near a market. A refinery-based plant in France is producing 16,000 mt/yr of feed-grade protein (Champagnat 1965; Mateles, Baruah and Tannenbaum 1967; Shacklady 1969). Useful as this process is, it is tied to industrial technology and skill together with fossil-energy inputs, and so the problems of providing cheap protein for those most needing it are very considerable and will not be quickly overcome. Nevertheless cheap sources such as these yeast flours, currently being produced largely as animal foodstuffs for non-ruminants like pigs and chickens, offer large-scale possibilities for food fortification programmes. Together with other concentrated sources of food they can be added to traditional diets which are low in protein or added to 'luxury' items such as carbonated soft drinks which are sought by even the poorest people. In such supplementation and fortification schemes, amino-acids produced purely by industrial synthesis are also important, especially lysine; most bread in Indian cities has such an additive, as does 30 per cent of the bread used in Japanese school-lunch programmes. The cheapness of industrially synthesized amino-acids means that they can be fed to poultry and non-ruminant animals instead of conventional animal foodstuffs, soya-bean or FPC products (Pyke 1971). Industrially processed high protein foods may be used: Incaparina has been successfully sold as an infant and child food in Latin America. It consists of cotton seed and maize flour plus vitamins and minerals, and has 28 per cent high-quality protein enriched with lysine. Another product for infants is Duryea, a blend of degermed high-lysine maize flour, soya flour and non-fat dry milk; this costs only half as much as milk protein. The US Government distributes overseas CSM and WSB, which are foods on a corn or wheat basis plus added vitamins, minerals and protein, usually of the order of 20 per cent. Most of these foods and additives have been developed in the West; few LDCs have their own plants for such products (Altschul and Rosenfeld 1970).

The effect of increasing human populations

Population growth is more often considered in terms of the future availability of adequate nutrition than any other factor. The result is a complete lack of unanimity in forecasts, from famine in 1975 to enough and to spare. The effects of the Green Revolution and of industrial sources of food production cannot yet be assessed with any long-term meaning, and as C. Clarke (1967) demonstrates, if nutrition patterns are reduced from the US level to the Japanese standard then it ought to be possible to feed a lot more people. The surpluses of Europe and North America might by 1980 amount to 10 per cent of world food production and be used to make good some of the deficiencies in Asia, provided it was politically acceptable. Such a contribution, either as aid or trade, could only make an impact for a

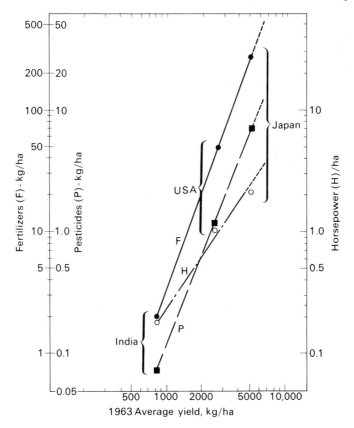

Fig. 8.7 Relationships between yield of food crops and requirements for fertilizer (F), pesticides (P) and horsepower (H) used in cultivation and harvest of crops. Doubling the yield of food requires a 10-fold increase in the use of fertilizers, pesticides and animal or machine power.
Source: E. P. Odum 1971

limited period given a rise in Asian populations of 2 per cent a year: as soon as 1980, four-fifths of the increase in world population will be in LDCs where the food situation is already bad. To these additional people must be added an escalation of demand from developing societies whose better standard of living generates higher expectations, and of those whose aspirations are fuelled by worldwide electronic communications and better levels of literacy; Brown (1971) suggests these may be more potent than population growth. In the face of rapidly expanding food requirements, agriculture must be the main source of food in the foreseeable future, despite contributions from industrial and marine sources; but expansion of production is beset with difficulties both ecological and cultural (Farmer 1969, Hendricks 1969). Extension of the cultivated area is constrained largely by problems of stability of the new systems, where soil breakdown and erosion are common. The greatest reserves of potential agricultural land are in sub-Saharan Africa and the Amazon basin, if the successful management of tropical soils can be achieved and if these lands are not more valuable on a world basis as protective ecosystems; but even in technologically advanced countries like the USA and USSR soil erosion is a problem. In the latter, 30–35 million ha of arable land are affected by water erosion, and 20–25 million ha of cropland are subject to wind erosion; 1·8 per cent of all arable land is classified as 'very heavily eroded' (Pryde 1972). With intensification, the main process is the linkage of agriculture to the industrial world, and some results can be seen in Table 8.15. This comparison is to some extent invalidated by the more recent advent of the new varieties of cereals, but it stands as an example of the differences between an advanced agriculture and a simpler system; in more general terms, the statistics of Table 8.16 show that the production of a fossil-fuel-subsidized agriculture is able to support a much greater number of people than

TABLE 8.15   Comparison of agriculture in Japan and India, 1960

	Yield (kcal/cap/day)	Value of agric. output (US $)	Chemical fertilizers used (kg/ha)	% urban pop.	Tractors per 1,000 ha	Biocides applied (mt)
Japan	2,360	961	303·7	18	1·55	150,000
India	2,060	91	2·3	64	0·21	10,000

Source: Dasmann 1972

TABLE 8.16   Outputs of agricultural systems

System	Yield (kcal/m²/yr)	Persons/mi² supported On farm	Persons/mi² supported In cities
Tribal agriculture	20	50	0
Unsubsidized agriculture	245	600	100
Fuel-subsidized agriculture	1,000	150	2,350
		(1 mi² = 2·59 km²)	

Source: E. P. Odum 1971

one in which there are no ties with the world of industry. Such increases in output are not achieved without costs of various kinds; intensification is expensive for, as Fig. 8.7 shows, a doubling of agricultural output per unit area requires a tenfold increase in the inputs of fertilizers and pesticides. Apart from their monetary cost, such heavy use is likely to create dependence upon an advanced country for supplies which may bring political strings with them. Biologically, the new system will be monocultural and hence prone to instability, and the runoff of surplus fertilizer and pesticides (not always used exactly according to the manufacturer's instructions) creates problems of eutrophication and toxification. In some LDCs the latter may reduce protein supplies, as has happened in Asia, where fish yields of 30–145 kg/ha from unfertilized rice paddies have been wiped out or made unpalatable by the use of γ-BHC to control the rice stem borer (Kok 1972).

Intensification also depends upon a series of inputs of the type described by L. H. Brown (1971) as 'non-recurring improvements'. For example, the ability of plants to respond to fertilizer has an upper limit, as does the capacity for faster growth conferred by hybridization; soya-bean cannot be hybridized and shows a limited response to nitrogenous fertilizer. An inevitable result of any intensification programme is, therefore, an S-shaped yield curve, sometimes for economic reasons like the cost of energy or input materials, sometimes the result of technical considerations like the genetics of a particular crop plant. As a context to the whole development, food prices become critical, especially in relation to the costs of energy, fertilizers, water and pesticides. The role of properly trained personnel at all levels is also an important part of intensification and can sometimes be a limiting factor, as can the gap between the promise of a crop in an experimental farm and its performance under the less controlled conditions up-country. In addition, Borgstrom (1965) has pointed

TABLE 8.17   Water requirements in food production: temperate climates (lb H_2O per lb organic matter) (1 lb = 0·4536 kg)

Millet	200–250
Wheat	300–500
Potatoes	600–800
Rice	1,500–2,000
Vegetables	3,000–5,000
Milk	10,000[1]
Meat	20,000–50,000[1]

[1] Includes water needed for production of foodstuffs.
Source: Borgstrom 1965

out the possibility that water may be a limiting factor on agricultural production: it takes 35 US gallons (132·5 litres) to make a slice of bread, and as Table 8.17 shows, other food crops are high water users as well. To these amounts should be added the water needs of industrially based inputs such as fertilizers where 1 ton (1,016 kg) requires 150,000 US gallons ($56·8 \times 10^4$ litres) of water in its production, and food processing where 1 ton of edible oil requires 35 tons (35·5 mt) of water (Paddock 1971).

While photosynthesis is the dominant process in supplying our food, there must be an overall limit to the number of people that can be fed: there is considerable scope for trying to improve both the efficiency of photosynthesis and the proportion of it which we garner, but an overall limit must be present. Feeding even larger numbers of people approaching both the present and potential limits, without a considerable safety margin, would seem unwise. The perspective of ecology upon food production thus becomes less 'Can we feed the population we have and are likely to get, given also their rising expectations?' (to which the answer is 'Probably, yes'), but rather 'What are the ecological consequences of doing so?' (H. Brown 1970). Every move towards simplification of ecological systems produces higher chances of wider fluctuations and thus greater risks, many of which inevitably fall upon the LDCs, whose ability to cope with them is less buffered than that of the technologically advanced nations. In the DCs the intensive agriculture which is so successful has suffered from overcropping, and is a source of contaminants via animal waste, fertilizers and pesticide residues. And even assuming success in feeding immensely greater numbers of people (and pessimism is still prevalent (Wade 1973)), there is a fundamental question of purpose: do we want the planet's management to be geared almost entirely to the production of food?

Further reading

BRADY, N. C. (ed.) 1967: *Agriculture and the quality of our environment.*
BROWN, L. R. and FINSTERBUSCH, G. 1972: *Food.*
DASMANN, R. F. *et al.* 1973: *Ecological principles for economic development.*
DE WIT, C. T. 1967: Photosynthesis: its relation to overpopulation.
DUCKHAM, A. N. and MASEFIELD, G. B. 1970: *Farming systems of the world.*
GEERTZ, C. 1963: *Agricultural involution.*
GOUROU, P. 1966: *The tropical world.*
HENDRICKS, S. B. 1969: Food from the land.
LOW, P. F. 1972: Prospects for abundance: the food-supply question.
PIRIE, N. W. 1969: *Food resources: conventional and novel.*

9

The sea

The world's greater water bodies are perhaps less affected by man than any of the terrestrial ecosystems which have been treated so far. Byron could write:

> Roll on, thou deep and dark blue ocean—roll!
> Ten thousand fleets sweep over thee in vain;
> Man marks the earth with ruin—his control
> Stops with the shore.

and we can generally agree, with the proviso that if control stops with the shore, nowadays the ruin certainly does not; but it decreases quite quickly away from it. There are large areas of the oceans unfrequented by man because of their very size: approximately 71 per cent of the globe's surface is composed of the oceans together with the enclosed and fringing seas; volumetrically, this means about 1.5×10^{18} mt (330 million mi³) of water. The frozen water of the polar ice-caps forms some of the remaining land, although in this case the water is fresh and not salt.

A structurally important feature of the oceans is their depth. Whereas only 2 per cent of the land is over 10,000 ft (3,048 m) above the sea, 77 per cent of the ocean floor is more than that depth below sea level; the great trenches of the Philippines and the Marianas have a depth of 35,000 ft (10,668 m) and hence are deeper than the highest terrestrial mountain. Beyond the coastline there are three main zones: the continental shelves, descending gradually to about 650 ft (198 m) below sea level and the site of most human effects upon marine ecosystems; the continental slope, falling steeply from the edge of the shelf to about 8,000 ft (2,438 m); and beyond that the deep ocean. Being most accessible to the land masses as well as the shallowest part of the ocean, the continental shelf is most often emphasized in studies of marine resources.

The salt nature of the water of the oceans appears to be derived from inwash off the land masses in which soluble minerals and particulate matter contribute to the salinity, which is thought to have been at a virtually stable level during the last 2,000 million years. The organisms of the sea must therefore play an important role in removing minerals from the liquid-soluble phase, otherwise a secular increase in concentration would be expected. The present-day average salinity at −1,000 ft (−305 m) is 35 parts per thousand; nearer the surface there are regional effects such as the high evaporation rate and lack of freshwater inflow that produce salinities of 45/1,000 in the Red Sea, or the opposite situation which produces values as low as 10/1,000 in the Baltic. The chemical elements which produce this salinity are endlessly varied, since if an element is present on the land it will sooner or later find its way into the sea. There are, however, enormous differences in concentration, from chlorine as sodium chloride at 166,000 lb/million gallons ($19 \cdot 8 \times 10^3$ kg/10^6 litres) down to gold at 0·004 lb/million gallons (0·001 kg/$3 \cdot 7 \times 10^6$ litres). The commonest elements are of course the most important, since it is to their presence and concentrations that marine life has had to adapt, and it is they, together with offshore deposits of certain kinds, that constitute the inanimate resources of the oceans. Other resource processes for which the oceans are used include the harvesting of fish, shellfish and other marine life, including water fowl; recreational activities and the provision of aesthetic pleasure; navigation, the dilution and dispersal of wastes, and to a limited but increasing extent the extraction of a domestic and industrial water supply.

Mineral resources

The sea's mineral resources can be divided into three categories: those which are dissolved in the water itself; sediments present on the sea-bed at various depths; and those present at some depth below the sea-floor, beyond the sediments of relatively recent origin.

At present the utility of the dissolved elements is in direct proportion to their abundance and to the relative cost from terrestrial sources. Table 9.1 shows some of the commonest elements present and the 1968 values of the minerals that could be extracted. Common salt immediately springs to mind as one of the resources that has been utilized since prehistoric times for its value in flavouring and meat preservation. At present only salt, magnesium and bromine are being extracted in commercial quantities and the sea does indeed seem to be inexhaustible for these elements: presumably replenishment is taking place at an equal if not higher rate. The first few elements in Table 9.1 offer the highest chances of economically feasible recovery processes, but others lower down, even when they are sought-after metals such as zinc, do not seem a very likely prospect except in the direst of circumstances. For example, 9,000 billion gallons ($34,065 \times 10^9$ litres) of sea water, equal to the combined annual volume of the Hudson and Delaware Rivers, would yield 400 (406·4 mt) tons of zinc. In 1968, 122,400 tons (124,358 mt) of that metal were used in the USA alone (Cloud 1969). It may be possible to lower feasibility thresholds by investigating the capacity of marine organisms to concentrate desired elements (this is done *de facto* for nitrogen used in the form of fish-meal fertilizer and in sea-bird guano), and in the possible exploitation of zones along the sea-bed where fractures allow the escape of unusually high concentrations of mineral ions. As far as minerals are concerned the oceans are more like *consommé* than Scotch broth, and the technology of handling the appropriate volumes of water is poorly developed, but presumably the economic perception of the minerals would be greatly changed by advent of the cheap and ubiquitous power envisaged by Weinberg and Hammond (1971).

Sediments and sedimentary rocks on the continental shelves are sources of certain materials. Placer deposits contain workable quantities of gold, tin and diamonds, and other sediments which may be amenable to exploitation include sand, gravel and shells. The land-use problems created by their extraction from the land would largely be obviated by the use of the sea as a source, provided that the ecosystems of the oceans were not too

TABLE 9.1   Concentration and value of the elements in sea water

Element	Concentration lb/10⁶ gal (kg/8·34 × 10⁶ litres)	As	Value $/10⁶ gal (10⁶ gal = 3·785 × 10⁶ litres)
Chlorine	166,000	NaCl	924
Sodium	92,000	Na_2CO_3	378
Magnesium	11,800	Mg	4,130
Sulphur	7,750	S	101
Calcium	3,500	$CaCl_2$	150
Potassium	3,300	K_2O (equiv)	91
Bromine	570	Br_2	190
Carbon	250	Graphite	8×10^{-5}
Strontium	70	$SrCO_3$	2
Boron	40	H_3BO_3	3
Silicon	26	—	—
Fluorine	11	CaF_2	0·35
Argon	5	—	—
Nitrogen	4	NH_4NO_3	1
Lithium	1·5	Li_2CO_3	36
Rubidium	1·0	Rb	125
Phosphorus	0·6	$CaHPO_4$	0·08
Iodine	0·5	I_2	1
Barium	0·3	$BaSO_4$	0·01
Indium	0·2	In	4
Zinc	0·09	Zn	0·013
Iron	0·09	Fe_2O_3	0·001
Aluminium	0·09	Al	0·04
Molybdenum	0·09	Mo	0·004
Selenium	0·04	Se	0·2
Tin	0·03	Sn	0·05
Copper	0·03	Cu	0·01
Arsenic	0·03	As_2O_3	0·002
Uranium	0·03	U_3O_8	0·3
Nickel	0·02	Ni	0·02
Vanadium	0·02	V_2O_5	0·04
Manganese	0·02	Mn	0·006

The elements are listed in order of abundance; those in italic type have concentrations valued at $1.00 or more per million gallons of sea water. All others are < 0·02 lb/10⁶ gal.
Source: Cloud 1969

greatly damaged by the recovery processes, which create great quantities of silt and also eventuate imbalance in the sedimentary systems of the sea-floor. Phosphates are found as nodules and in crusts where the operation of natural concentration processes brings their recovery closer to economic feasibility. A further resource of the continental shelves is fresh water: large quantities of artesian water may be found in certain aquifers, and although such supplies are currently costly compared with terrestrial sources, a demand may arise for their use in relatively humid lands, just as they are already tapped around some islands and being sought in the Mediterranean. Finally there are petroleum and natural gas, which are already exploited in many offshore waters up to depths of 2–2·5 km, which is the current limit of the techniques used. The minerals of the deep ocean basins are difficult to appraise. The most extensive are the pelagic sediments, which are particles of biological, aeolian or chemical origin that have settled out on the ocean floor. They contain enormous quantities of certain metal elements, but only if they could be easily subjected to enrichment would they enter resource processes under current conditions. The most discussed of them is manganese, which forms in large nodules and crusts in which other metals like nickel, cobalt and copper are incorporated; they occur as a veneer with a mean depth of 4,000–5,000 m, coming up as shallow as 200–1,000 m off North Carolina, but their true extent is unknown, and large-scale methods of extracting the metals from the silica in which they are embodied are as yet undeveloped (Cloud 1969).

In 1964, about 5 per cent of the world's production by value of geological wealth came from the sources discussed above, mostly from oil and gas. That this proportion will increase is not in doubt, but the idea of an unending cornucopia is obviously false. The cheapest source, sea water, contains few elements demanded by modern industry in high concentrations, and access to the other sources is difficult. Any discussion of the extraction of these resources must reckon with the external costs in terms of impact upon the ecology of the seas, for inevitably there would be a risk of destruction of biological resources of considerable value and perhaps greater indispensability.

Biological resources

It is commonplace to see calls for greater use of marine biological resources for food. Yet there are severe limiting factors on biological productivity in the sea. The euphotic zone in which photosynthesis can occur is only about 60 m deep, since from there to 520 m there is only blue light, the other wavelengths having been absorbed. There are very few terrestrial areas where the photosynthesizing zone is 60 m deep, but the primary producers of the sea are scattered very thinly through the water; if they were more concentrated then the euphotic zone would be shallower and so the level is self-limiting. Also limiting is carbon dioxide: as in fresh water, this tends to be scarce and the amount dissolved is dependent upon mixing at the interface between the water and the atmosphere.

In spite of such limitations, the sea supports a great diversity of living forms existing in complex interactive systems; there is in fact no abiotic zone. Figs 9.1 and 9.2 summarize, very generally, some of the main food-chain characteristics in which a number of features stand out: firstly the length of the major predator chain, which has two 'top carnivores', by which stage energy is getting very scarce; secondly, the drifting nature of the first two trophic levels: neither phytoplankton nor zooplankton is able to control its regional movements; and thirdly, the importance of detritus feeding in the continental shelves and in the deep oceans. The primary productivity upon which the life depends is not uniform over the whole ocean area; the open oceans are the least productive and are in fact something of a biological desert, largely because of the small size of the autotrophic zone in relation to the

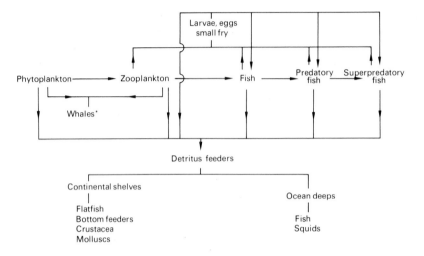

Larvae, eggs small fry

Phytoplankton⟶Zooplankton⟶Fish⟶Predatory fish⟶Superpredatory fish

Whales*

Detritus feeders

Continental shelves

Ocean deeps

Flatfish
Bottom feeders
Crustacea
Molluscs

Fish
Squids

* Some whales are predators upon
organisms like squids, not
plankton feeders

Fig. 9.1 Diagrammatic representation of the main food chains of the oceans: the high number of steps in the predator chain is a characteristic feature, as is the importance of the detritus chain on the continental shelves.

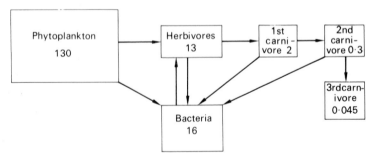

Phytoplankton 130 ⟶ Herbivores 13 ⟶ 1st carnivore 2 ⟶ 2nd carnivore 0·3

3rd carnivore 0·045

Bacteria 16

Units are billions of metric tons of organic matter/year

Fig. 9.2 Simple food chain in the oceans showing estimated production (not standing crop) of organic matter/yr at each level (1 billion = 1,000 million).
Source: Ricker 1969

heterotrophic zone in which the cycling of nutrients takes place. The distribution of productivity (Table 9.2) suggests that nutrients may be limiting factors in the ecosystem, which appears to have adapted itself by means of rapid mineral cycling with almost immediate uptake. The most important producer organisms are probably the nanoplankton (2–25 μ in size) which have a short biomass turnover time and rapid nutrient cycling. Corals are also efficient at retaining, for example, phosphorus, presumably because it is recycled between the plant and animal components of the colony. The coastal zone has a higher productivity because of its proximity to the sources of mineral nutrition, and upwelling zones share similar characteristics. Tidal estuaries and mudflats are among the most productive ecosystems in the world. The interpretation of estimates of yearly productivity must take into account the fact that the standing crop is very much lower: in the case of phytoplankton the biomass is probably about 1 per cent of the yearly turnover (Ryther 1969). This contrasts with the terrestrial ecosystems, where biomass of the standing crop may be roughly equal to yearly production as in grasslands and crops, or greater than that measure as with forests

TABLE 9.2   Estimated primary productivity of the oceans

Area	Size (10^6 km²)	Net primary productivity (gm/m²/yr)	Total for area (10^9 mt)	Annual energy fixation (10^{18} cals)
Reefs and estuaries	2·0	2,000·0	4·0	18·0
Continental shelf	26·0	350·0	9·3	42·6
Open ocean	332·0	125·0	41·5	109·2
Upwelling zones	0·4	500·0	0·2	1·0
Total	361·0	155·0	55·0	160·8

Source: Leith 1972

and desert shrubs. Even if all the phytoplankton were present in the top m of the sea, their average density would be 0·5 gm/m³ of water. Where the actual figure exceeds this greatly, as it does at certain places in particular seasons, direct harvesting by man is technically difficult and hence costs are high. The product is intractable not only on account of cultural factors such as taste and texture, which could be improved by industrial processing, but because of high salt and silica contents. Large-scale direct cropping of phytoplankton does not yet seem to be a very feasible food or fodder source, although use by man at the herbivore level should theoretically give high yields of energy and protein. The removal of organisms would mean taking away nutrients and these would have to be replaced, just as if it were an agricultural system.

As in all ecosystems, productivity falls at higher trophic levels; zooplankton presents similar cropping problems to phytoplankton, and man harvests very little of it. Most of his crop comes at the level of secondary and tertiary consumers, a few species of fish and some molluscs coming from the first trophic level of consumer organisms. The third trophic level yields a great number of the desired species, such as flounders, haddock, small cod, herring, sardines and whalebone whales, while some highly demanded species

Plate 16 Although contemporary fisheries are dominated by the deep-sea fleets with modern equipment, the fish protein supplied to many nations comes from small inshore fishermen operating in a traditional fashion, unlinked to fossil fuel power, as in this part of the New Territories of Hong Kong. *(I. G. Simmons)*

such as halibut, tuna, salmon, large cod, swordfish, seals and sperm whales are yet further along the food chain. At each stage there is competition for the production from taxa which are not important resource species for man: sharks, dogfish and seabirds, for example. A further harvest comes from detritus feeders which scavenge the sea-floor: many flatfish and crustacea belong to this group. World biological production at the levels mostly used by man is estimated variously at about 244–325 million mt fresh weight, mostly of fish. Estimates of the sustained annual yield of the seas vary from 55–2,000 million mt of fish; Ryther (1969) suggests that the length of food chains and the trophic levels at which man crops the oceans will limit the yield to about 100 million mt/yr, an estimate criticized by some authorities (e.g. Alverson *et al.* 1970) as too low. The constraints imposed by economic factors probably mean that the upper range of the various estimates will never be achieved: of the actual capture 80–90 per cent is at depths of less than 200 m and it seems unlikely that commercial trawling could ever extend much beyond 1,000 m. Beyond this level the animals are so scarce in relation to the volume of water that it is probably better to harvest predators which go down to such depths to feed, as do sperm whales on large deep-water squids.

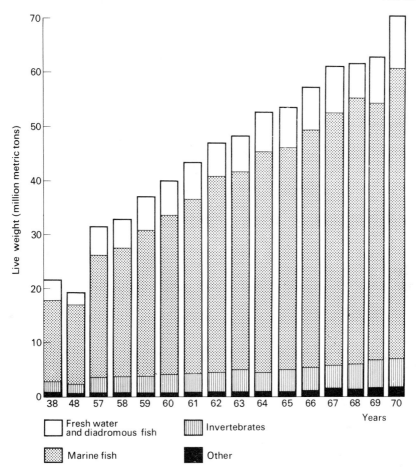

Fig. 9.3 The world fish catch 1938–70. Approximately half the crop is consumed directly by humans, the rest being used as livestock feed (1971 = 69·4 million mt).
Source: Holt 1971, with later additions from FAO data.

In 1971 world fish landings ran at 69·4 million mt (Fig. 9.3), a rate which has risen at about 8 per cent p.a. during the last 25 years, a doubling time of about 9 years. Nationally, Peru and Japan lead, followed by the USSR, China, Norway and the USA; other nations are some way behind. Consumption per person, however, is dominated by Japan, a fact as obvious to the viewer of the wax models outside restaurants in that land as to the avid *sashimi* enthusiast. The averaged figures also conceal the fact that several other Asian nations, such as Burma and Thailand, rely on fish for much of their animal protein (Plate 16). The discrepancy between the landings of Peru and the low overall consumption in Latin America is in part caused by the export of most of the anchovy catch to Europe as animal feed. According to Dasmann (1972) the Peruvian catch could provide a minimal protein intake for 413 million people, although when the Humboldt Current is displaced by the warmer El Nino Current, as happened in for example 1957, 1965 and 1972, the fishery yield is very small and so creates difficulties for Peru, since 40 per cent of her foreign earnings come from fish meal. Domestic consumption has been increasing too, especially since a meat shortage in 1972 necessitated a ban on the sale of beef in the first half of each month. Apart from particular regional and national situations, Tables 9.3

TABLE 9.3   Fishery statistics

1. World catch 1970 (million mt live weight)

Total for world	69·3 (exc. whales)		
For human consumption		42·8	
Fresh marketing			19·0
Freezing			9·5
Curing			8·1
Canning			6·2
Other purposes		26·5	
Reduction to meal and oil			25·5
Miscellaneous			1·0

2. Catches by nation 1970 (million mt live weight)

Peru	12·6	Spain	1·4
Japan	9·3	Canada	1·3
USSR	7·2	Denmark	1·2
China	5·8 (est. for 1960)	Thailand	1·2
Norway	2·9	Indonesia	1·2
USA	2·7	UK	1·0
South Africa	1·5	Chile	1·1
India	1·7		

3. Catches by fishing area 1970 (thousand mt live weight)

Inland waters	7,620	Indian Ocean	2,780
Atlantic Ocean	23,610	Pacific Ocean	35,330

Source: FAO *Yearbook of Fishery Statistics 1970*

TABLE 9.4   Regional consumption of fish, 1965 (kg/cap)

North America	14·5	USSR	13·1
EEC	12·1	Other central and eastern Europe	6·1
North-west Europe	20·5	China	6·9
Southern Europe	17·2	Latin America	6·0
Japan	53·7	Sub-Saharan Africa	8·2
Oceania	10·7	Near East and north-west Africa	3·2
South Africa	21·3	Asia	7·3

World average   10·3

Source: FAO *Indicative world plan for agriculture*, 1970, **1**

and 9.4 show that consumption per head of fish is highest in the developed countries, and since their livestock is also a major user of fishmeal, much of the world's catch is devoted to the industrial nations.

Extension of fisheries

The potential for extending fisheries comes from three sources: the utilization of untapped species, the cropping of hitherto unattractive areas, and the development of more novel methods of culture and harvesting. During recent years a number of new fisheries have started to flourish, such as Peruvian anchoveta, Alaska pollock, Bering Sea flatfishes and herring, and several more. The future for extensions of traditional fishing methods lies, for example, in the cool temperate parts of the southern hemisphere, which only produce about 10 per cent of the world's fish catch (2·7 million mt in 1962 against 25 million mt for the northern cool temperate seas). There are disadvantages, such as the small areas of continental shelf and the lack in some areas of suitable species, but it seems likely that considerable extension of fisheries could be wrought. Even in heavily fished northern areas there are abundant but little-used species: grenadiers in the north-west Atlantic, sandlance, anchovies and sauries in the Pacific, and small sharks like the dogfish in both areas. Even where fish are found that are not very useful for direct human consumption, large-scale catches may mean that they are useful as 'industrial' fish. A protein-rich concentrate can be made that is currently used, for instance, in the broiler-chicken industry. If further processed it can be made palatable and added to protein-deficient diets; at present this could cost less than dried skim milk (Ricker 1969).

Krill

Antarctic whaling has reduced stocks to about one-tenth of their former size and so the presumably uneaten food of the whales is theoretically available to man. Approximately 80 per cent of the prey of blue and fin whales, and even more of humpbacks, is krill, the shrimp *Euphausia superba*, up to 60–70 mm long and 1 g in weight, with a net weight content of 7 per cent fat and 16 per cent protein (Moiseev 1970). Rather rough calculations suggest that between 1964–6, whales ate 148×10^6 mt of krill in antarctic waters, and that the yearly production of nine-tenths of this amount should now be surplus. How much is consumed by other predators is unknown, but no surges in the populations of seals, birds, fish and minke whales have been recorded (Mackintosh 1970); fish and squid may have been the chief benefactors. Since biomass and productivity are not yet known, the sustained yield cannot be calculated, but USSR vessels are already catching and processing krill. Its potential may be very high, even in the same order of magnitude as the Peruvian anchoveta fishery (FAO 1971).

Other less direct ways of increasing the crop of marine resources could be more systematically investigated. When nutrients are limiting, fertilization by the addition of minerals to the sea may bring about higher productivities. Only this type of activity takes fishery management to a state much beyond the largely Mesolithic technology which, give or take a fossil-fuel-powered trawler or two, is still being used.

Aquaculture

The first stage away from a hunting and gathering economy is that of herding, and this is being used in, for example, Hong Kong, the Philippines and Japan. Frameworks are lowered into shallow offshore waters and allowed to colonize with sedentary molluscs like oysters and mussels. With some species, the individuals grow on ropes that hang clear of the bottom so that they are out of the reach of predators such as starfish. Although productive (Table 9.5), such systems are very vulnerable to contamination, and since the organisms filter large quantities of water their ability to concentrate substances toxic either to themselves or to consumers is very high. True aquaculture involves genetic manipulation of the chosen species by keeping them captive throughout their breeding cycle, a difficult though not impossible task. The requirements are unpolluted sea water and a suitable coastal site with adjoining land. Eastern England, for instance, would not suffice because of the degree of exposure, silt levels, low winter temperature and contaminations (C. E. Nash 1970a). The most efficient plant would be large and would require buildings, stores, hatcheries and covered tank complexes on the land, together with enclosed tidal areas and tanks, and ponds or lagoons in deeper water. For preference, use of all the water areas would be possible by housing together algae browsers such as abalone, pelagic herbivores like the grey mullet, and bottom-dwelling carnivores (C. E. Nash 1970b). The possibility of using waste heat to maintain constant water temperatures has been much discussed and tried, and in coastal temperate zones there exists the attractive possibility of raising tropical fish with a high productivity. Even the native species benefit from heated water, as experiments with plaice (*Pleuronectes platessa*) and sole (*Solea solea*) in Scotland have shown: most individuals attained a marketable size in 2 years, which is at least one year before the normal time for wild populations (C. E. Nash 1970b). More complex systems based on other waste products have been envisaged. For example, sewage and other eutrophicatory products might be used as the basis for algal production which forms the

TABLE 9.5   Aquacultural yields (fresh weight, without mollusc shells)

Location	Species	kg/ha/yr	tons/ac/yr
USA	Oysters		
	(national average	9	0·004
	(best yields)	5,000	2·00
France	Flat oyster		
	(national average)	400	0·16
	Portuguese oyster		
	(national average)	935	0·37
Australia	Oysters		
	(national average)	150	0·06
	(best yields)	540	2·20
Malaya	Cockles	12,500	5·00
France	Mussels	2,500	1·00
Singapore	Shrimp	1,250	0·50

Source: MacIntyre and Holmes 1971

food of oysters which then filter the water as well. The oyster droppings are eaten by worms which are the prey of bottom-living fish, whose nitrogenous excretions nourish water weeds which oxygenate the water. In another scheme, carbon dioxide from a power-station chimney is used to enhance production of algae which are fed to clams that then grow rapidly in the heated water which is also the output of the power station. Such designs are all too simple to be true and only limited operational success has so far been achieved.

A general disadvantage of aquaculture seems to be the considerable skill needed for success, and it is therefore yet another competitor in the LDCs for scarce, trained man-power. While we may assent to the principle of the Institute of Ecology's (1972) statement that money would be better invested in aquaculture than larger fishing fleets, the gloomier IWP (1970) statement, that even a five-fold increase in output from aquaculture by 1985 would be only marginal to the world situation (although perhaps being locally significant), seems closer to the reality of the near future.

The IWP on fisheries

The IWP accepts the idea of the oceans as providers of protein, but does not suggest any radical alteration in present trends, as can be seen from Table 9.6. For fish as food, the difference between the production objective and the probable reality in 1985 shows deficits for North America and the EEC countries, presumably as the result of strain upon fisheries of the north Atlantic and north Pacific. Fish for animal feed exhibit even greater deficits, partly for the same reason and partly because of diversion of exports by LDCs to their own use. However, any remaining notions of the seas as repositories of plenitude are dispelled by the generally negative balances for food in the LDCs, especially Asia, where population increase will outstrip virtually any improvements in harvesting. The increases in fodder predicted for Latin America and Africa depend upon the development of demand by indigenous livestock industries. To achieve the proposed rates of growth, the FAO suggests as main priorities the improvement of vessels, in particular the replacement of traditional craft by powered fleets, together with the development of improved ports and harbours with good storage and freezing facilities. As with agriculture, intensification is to be achieved by the extension of industrial technology, especially in the use of fossil fuels. More rational utilization of fish stocks is a third IWP priority.

In summary, the food resources of the sea can under the most optimal circumstances never be a panacea for all the nutritional problems of the world. Watt (1968) calculates that if we assume 100 g of marine food to contain 100 kcal of energy, and if the crop were to be multiplied 20 times, then about 9×10^8 people could be supported. With a population already at $3 \cdot 4 \times 10^9$ when he wrote, that meant only one-quarter of the present population could be thus fed. In some ways this is a misleading calculation, since the main use of marine food is for protein (9 per cent of the catch weight of fish may be edible protein), and the factor of 20 for future cropping is obviously too high. Estimates of potential yield and role vary but are of the same order, and that of Ricker (1969) seems to reflect a general view. His opinion is that in the next 40 years the 1968 catch can be increased by about 2·5 times, giving an eventual total of 150–160 million mt/yr, containing 20 per cent of usable protein. For a population of the order expected in AD 2000 this could supply about 30 per cent of the world's minimal protein requirements but only 3 per cent of its biological energy demands.

Over-uses of biological resources

The harvesting of marine biological resources is subject to the same constraints as any other wild crop if sustained yield is desired: the population must not be overcropped to the point that its reproduction no longer provides sufficient individuals to constitute a resource (Fig. 9.4). In view of the ecology of fish and sea mammals we might think that over-use

TABLE 9.6 Projected demand and supply of fish and fish products, 1975 and 1985 (million mt)

Region	Projected demand				Demand/ production objective balance	
	1975		1985		1985	
	Food	Feed	Food	Feed	Food	Feed
North America	3·8	4·4	4·6	4·7	−1·9	−3·4
EEC	2·7	6·0	3·2	7·5	−1·3	−7·4
North-west Europe	2·1	3·5	2·4	3·5	+0·5	−0·5
Southern Europe	2·4	1·4	3·0	2·1	+0·2	−2·0
Japan	6·5	3·0	7·4	3·7	+1·8	−2·9
Oceania	0·2	0·2	0·3	0·2	+0·3	−0·2
USSR	4·3	2·3	5·9	4·5	+7·6	−2·2
China	8·7	—	14·1	—		
Central Europe	0·8	2·3	1·0	3·3	+0·7	−2·9
Latin America	2·0	1·5	3·0	3·5	−0·2	+11·5
Africa south of Sahara	2·6	0·1	4·1	0·6	−0·7	+1·9
North-east, north-west Africa	0·6	0·3	1·0	0·6	−0·1	−0·4
Asia	10·3	1·0	18·2	2·8	−4·2	−2·6
World	47·6	26·4	69·0	37·5	+2·7	−9·5
(1968 = 64)	74·0		106·5			

Source: FAO *Indicative world plan for agriculture*, 1970, **1**

is not likely, but the gregarious nature of many fish, the large size of whales and seals, and the product desirability of mammals such as sea otters have caused great inroads to be made upon their populations.

Particularly favoured fish species have exhibited considerable declines, as for example the east Asian sardine, Californian sardine, north-west Pacific salmon, Atlanto-Scandian herring, the Barents Sea cod; and a number of others, including the Newfoundland cod, North Sea herring, British Columbia herring and yellowfin tuna, are showing signs of strain (Holt 1971). International regulatory measures are sometimes applied to such species, regulating catch and net size, but these measures are difficult to enforce and once a species has been overfished it may not be possible for it to regain its place in the energy pathways

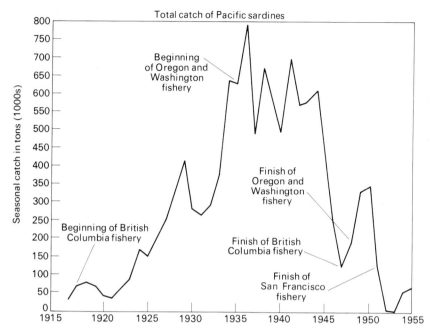

Fig. 9.4 At its height, the Pacific coast sardine fishery was the first-ranking fishery in North America in weight of fish landed, and third-ranking by value after tuna and salmon. The decline is attributed to over-fishing and there has been no recovery in 1955–70. Presumably the niche formerly occupied by the sardine has been taken over by another organism or the breeding stocks are too low to enable the population to gain in size.
Source: Dasmann 1972

of the ecosystem. The Pacific sardine (*Sardinops caerulea*) of the California current system was a major feeder on the zooplankton, and production of the fish aged 2 years and older was estimated at 4×10^6 mt/yr. It was overfished in the 1930s and replaced by a competitor, the anchovy *Engraulis mordox*. At the end of the 1950s the latter's biomass was similar to that of the sardine 30 years before and it has clearly ousted the former species, apparently irreversibly (Ehrlich and Ehrlich 1970).

The increasing number of incidents concerning fishing fleets in territorial waters and the desire of many countries (Peru and Iceland are notable instances) to extend their cropping hegemony to the edge of the continental shelf are obviously indicative of competition for the sea's protein resources. Such an attitude towards the use of the resource may promote ecologically sound harvesting of fish populations if the nation which is enforcing the fishery limit is a good manager, and if the extension of limits keeps out the overfishers, but there is no guarantee of such eventualities.

Sea mammals other than whales have often been the subject of over-exploitative cropping. The porpoise family (Delphinidae) appears to be in no danger, although little is known about its worldwide status: only local populations have been studied. Japan, for example, is taking about 20,000 porpoises per year and the arctic porpoise (white whale or beluga) is extensively used in some northern regions. Fur seals are better documented: the

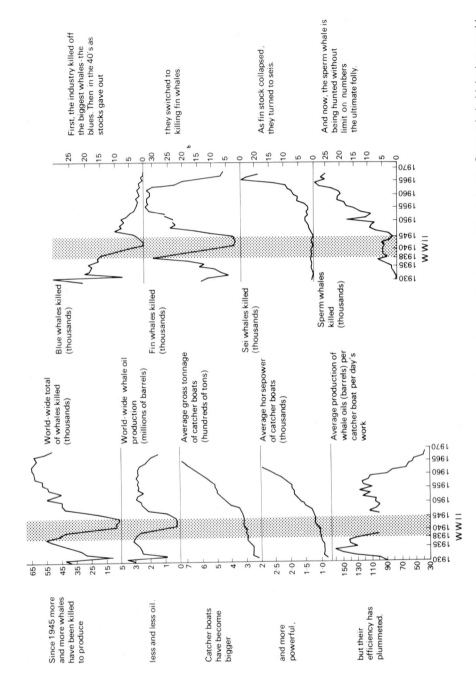

Fig. 9.5 A polemical view of the decline in whale numbers, related to the inputs of the industry. Some whale biologists would claim that the extinction of the blue whale has been averted and that most whales are now being cropped at a sustained-yield level.
Source: Ehrlich and Ehrlich 1970

Guadalupe fur seal was almost exterminated late in the nineteenth century, and the Northern or Pribilof fur seal was reduced from about one million individuals to 17,000 in 1910, since when careful management by the US Government has built the stock up to 1·5 million with a sustained yield of 80,000 animals per year. The true seals are also extensively killed, especially the harp seal of the north Atlantic. Canada, Norway and France share in this resource which, although the subject of controversy, is not in a great decline. The grey seal of the British Isles is also a controversial animal since it eats salmon, and some herds are culled in order to reduce its status as a competitor.

The most outstanding example of the over-use of marine populations is the history of whaling. The products of both baleen (plankton-consuming) and sperm (predatory, mainly on squids) whales have been highly valued in the past: oil, meat, blubber, skin and ambergris have all been used, although effective substitutes could now be found for most of them and whale products were forbidden in the USA in 1970. But a biologically depletive programme of whale cropping, mainly by Japan and the USSR, continues despite falling yields and obviously dwindling stocks. The decline of the whale resource is summarized in Table 9.7 and Fig. 9.5. The International Whaling Commission, which sets catch limits, is fully aware of the depletion of the whale stocks and has set out catch limits and preservation policies such as the complete protection of the Blue Whale (now numbering about 7,000) since 1965. Ehrlich and Ehrlich (1970) argue that exploitation to the point of extinction is occurring, whereas Gambell (1972) suggests that most stocks are stabilized at a sustained-yield level, with the exception of the overcropping of the antarctic and north Pacific fur whales. Such a stabilization is presumably much below the level that could have been achieved if rational management policies had been followed earlier.

TABLE 9.7   Diminution of whale catch

	1933	1966
Catch	28,907	57,891
Barrels of whale oil	2,606,201	1,546,904

Source: Ehrlich and Ehrlich 1972

Effects of contamination

Large as the oceans are, they are not immune from the end-products of man's resource processes. The input of materials into seas is both deliberate and accidental, and only recently has there been much concern about the use of the sea as a garbage can, so that quantitative studies are rare.

The nature and effects of individual contaminants of the biosphere are dealt with in Chapter 11 and here we will mention briefly only those which have been described as creating particular problems in the seas. They are: radio-isotopes, industrial effluents, oil, persistent pesticides, and eutrophication agents such as untreated sewage, fertilizer runoff and detergents. All of them affect coastal waters most markedly, but organochlorine

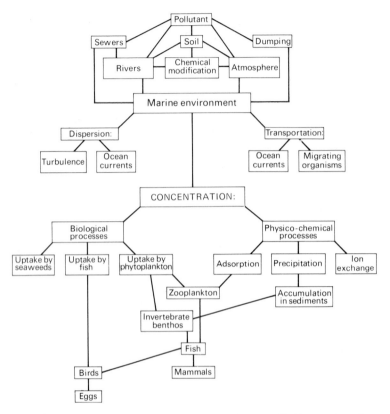

Fig. 9.6 A flow diagram of the pathways by which a contaminant can find its way into the oceans and the ways in which it can be concentrated, with various lethal and sublethal effects.
Source: MacIntyre and Holmes 1971

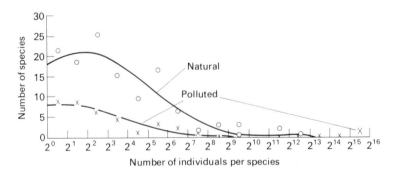

Fig. 9.7 The diversity of diatom communities in natural and polluted waters. While pollution of some kinds such as eutrophication may increase productivity (not shown here), it generally reduces diversity.
Source: MacIntyre and Holmes 1971

pesticides appear to be ubiquitous, having turned up in the fat of antarctic penguins and in the Bermuda petrel, which lands only on its nesting islets and is at the top of a long pelagic food chain. The way in which a marine pollutant is dispersed through the seas is shown in Fig. 9.6.

Pesticides such as DDT have been reported as causing a reduction in the photosynthetic rate of marine algae at very low (10–100 ppb) concentrations (Wurster 1968). Experimental findings such as these are difficult to extend to the oceans themselves, and so this effect of residual organic chemicals is as yet unproven. If reduced photosynthesis or the extermination of certain species were a result of organochlorine residues, then in shallow waters there would probably be floral imbalance and large-scale blooms, exacerbating the effects of eutrophication (Fig. 9.7). Reduced primary productivity must lead inevitably to a lowering of the net biomass of the sea. The effect of substances such as DDT and other marine contaminants is in reality difficult to measure, because the populations of the resident organisms are subject to wide fluctuations under natural conditions (Longhurst et al. 1972). It is thus easy to label a particular substance as a destroyer of sea life, only to be proved wrong and accused of crying wolf. The way is then opened for the complacent to do nothing about trying to discover the objective truth of the effects of contaminants in the oceans.

At a global scale, the effects of reduced rates of photosynthesis in the sea would be very severe, for the role of marine phytoplankton in regulating the CO_2/O_2 balance of the atmosphere appears to be critical. However, the concentrations required to effect any alteration appear to be unlikely to be attained in the open oceans, since the solubility of DDT in water is 1 ppb. If DDT were to be concentrated in a surface oil-film then it might reach levels toxic to plants. The possibilities still exist that DDT may be toxic to phytoplankton species as yet unchecked and that other organochlorines may be more poisonous than DDT and its breakdown products.

Using certain broad-scale assumptions, the 1970 Report of the Study of Critical Environmental Problems (SCEP) calculated that the surface waters of the ocean could accommodate a load of $7 \cdot 5 \times 10^7$ mt of DDT, i.e. about 10 times the total production to date, one-quarter of which is estimated to have entered the oceans. There is every indication that DDT is not uniformly distributed in the surface layers of the sea: it is likely to be concentrated in the surface film, which contains alcohols and fatty acids. From there it may enter the food chains via bacteria and phytoplankton or be absorbed into formerly airborne particles which sink through the water and are ingested by detritus feeders. In the case of the oceans approximately $0 \cdot 1$ per cent of the total output of the chemical has brought about considerable alterations in population structures, particularly of fish-eating birds. Since the rate of decay of the organochlorines in the sea is unknown, a reduction in the amounts reaching the sea would seem to be a wise precaution. Even the SCEP study, not given to alarmism, found that 'our prediction of the hazards may be vastly underestimated'.

A form of eutrophication peculiar to the seas is the dinoflagellate bloom, common under natural conditions where there is an upwelling of nutrient-rich water or disturbance of bottom sediments by tides. The microscopic dinoflagellates may secrete toxins which directly poison the water, may use up all the oxygen in the water if in a relatively confined space, or if filtered through molluscs may build up to high levels. Eating mussels after a 'red tide' allows ingestion of a poison which affects the human central nervous system and to which there is no known antidote. Some recent blooms have appeared in the waters off-shore from known sources of untreated sewage, as off north-east England in 1968 and Nova Scotia–New England in 1972, and although proof is lacking, there is a strong suspicion that human activities can initiate the onset of such phenomena. At any rate red tides put up the price of shrimps by 15 per cent in North America during 1972.

The future value of the oceans

Even under ideal institutional conditions the sea is neither an inexhaustible provider of food and mineral resources nor a bottomless sink for the end-products of resource processes. The ecology of the sea is inimical to the production of large quantities of organic matter per unit volume, as is the volume of water to harvesting of crop, and the sheer immensity of the quantity of water means again that mineral extraction is expensive. If minerals impose any constraints upon the primary productivity of much of the oceans, their removal for industrial purposes could possibly reduce marine harvests, a trend which is likely to be exacerbated by certain forms of pollution of the seas.

Man's 'ecological demand' upon the sea, as upon other biospheric systems, is increasing steadily. Over-use, particularly of fish, seems easy to attain: the adults are overfished and so reproduction is hindered and younger individuals are taken, reducing recruitment to the population. In turn, man's competitors for fish are perceived as pests and if possible their populations are reduced. The eventual effect is likely to be instability in the ocean systems, with large and unexpected outbreaks of 'pest' species and large fluctuations in fishing yields. These symptoms are likely to occur when yields of two to four times the present crop are achieved (Institute of Ecology 1972). Various estimates seem to agree, however, that the maximum world fish catch is 90–100 million mt/yr, out of a biological production of about 240 million mt/year, but do not say whether such a level is a sustainable yield. It is certainly unlikely to be reached if gross contamination of the seas by toxic substances takes place, since the coastal zones are especially vulnerable to pollution and from them come half the fish production and over half the money made on fishing as an occupation. Estuaries are especially fragile ecosystems and are much polluted and reclaimed, but are among the most productive ecosystems on earth, as well as often being important habitats for fish in their early stages of development. These seemingly barren places, haunts principally of wildfowlers and melancholic poets, therefore deserve special protection.

This all supposes rational exploitation of the marine resources, which regrettably does not happen. There are a relatively large number of international agreements about fishing rights and practices (such as the 1958 Geneva Convention on Fishing and Conservation of Living Resources of the High Seas), but loopholes are not difficult to find, and the nature of fisheries has been changing more rapidly than the machinery to deal with them. The International Whaling Convention frequently disregards the advice of its biologists and harvests well above maximum sustained-yield levels; pirate whaling outfits operate without regard to the IWC; Denmark refused to limit her oceanic catch of North Atlantic salmon in spite of the decline in its numbers. Numerous examples, some of them leading to inter-national incidents like the Peruvian seizure of US fishing boats and the British–Icelandic

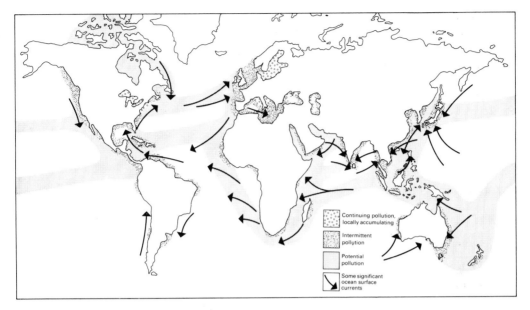

Fig. 9.8 Marine pollution around the world, both actual and potential. The latter refers especially to oil or noxious cargoes along the major shipping lines.
Source: M. Waldichuk and L. Andrèn, reprinted in *Ceres* **3** (3), 1970, 36–7

'cod war' of 1972–3, can be found. At an FAO Conference in 1972, one fish-management scientist was quoted by the press as saying, 'If we wrote a book about our profession, there would be 20 pages of introduction, one page of results and 180 pages of excuses.' The sea, as Garrett Hardin (1968) has pointed out, is a common where every extra exploited unit beyond the ecologically permissible limit is of benefit to the individual cropper but a significant loss to everyone else. New concepts of the 'ownership' of marine resources are probably needed for rational management: the alternatives (Holt 1971) seem to be international ownership or the unprecedented extension of appropriations by nation states. But even given substantial institutional agreement, no improvement in fisheries management is likely for at least 15 years. The first priority, however, is to reduce the already extensive pollution of the oceans (Fig. 9.8), towards which the 1972 agreements on dumping in the oceans was a first step. Thereafter long-term management of the exploitation of fisheries becomes an absolute necessity.

Further reading

CHRISTY, F. T. and SCOTT, A. 1967: *The common wealth in ocean fisheries.*
CLOUD, P. 1969: Mineral resources from the sea.
CRUTCHFIELD, J. A. (ed.) 1965: *The fisheries: problems in resource management.*
HOOD, D. W. (ed.) 1971: *Impingement of man on the oceans.*
INSTITUTE OF ECOLOGY 1972: *Man in his living environment.*
LOFTAS, T. 1972: *The last resource.*
MARX, W. 1967: *The frail ocean.*
RICKER, W. 1969: Food from the sea.

10

Energy and minerals

The energy and minerals dealt with here are from inanimate sources and hence differ in quality from the renewable materials so far discussed. They are often called 'stock' or 'non-renewable' resources, and in the case of minerals this is true to the extent that 'new' materials can only be extracted from the earth's crust once. But even in the transformed states in which they are used, they are not lost to the planet (if we except lunar module junkyards) and so are ideally available for re-use. Energy is somewhat different, since direct solar energy is certainly not cyclically renewable but there is for all practical purposes an unending supply. Stored solar energy as coal, oil and lignite is non-renewable, except on a time-scale of millions of years; in the case of wood the renewability is the same as any other use of a tree or shrub. The raw materials at present used to generate nuclear power are inorganic minerals, and only water power is truly renewable in the manner of an organic resource. Access to energy sources changes the whole of man's relationships to the planet and in particular the use of all kinds of resources, since their extraction, conversion and transport may depend upon the control of large quantities of energy. Access to stored energy sources is the basis of industrialization with all its concomitants in terms of the manipulation of ecosystems by mechanical and chemical means. It also permits penetration to nearly all parts of the planet, making possible such activities as recovering minerals from under the sea-bed or living permanently at the South Pole.

Together, energy and mineral use have also provided the means for man to escape from the surface of the planet and hence the chance to view it from outside, both personally as in the case of astronauts and vicariously as with remote sensing. The effects upon our perception of this planet have yet to be fully appreciated.

Energy

A context

All resource processes can be characterized by quantifying the flows of energy through them, and studies of energetics may be used to link their ecological and economic dimensions (H. T. Odum 1971, Garvey 1972). The increase in organizational complexity of the industrial nations is only made possible by the understanding and application of energy flows, and it is not without significance that the term 'power' is used for energy obtained for urban and industrial purposes. The actual quantities of energy used are measured by the

rate of flow of useful energy that can be made to do work; it is a one-way flow and degradation occurs, so that heat sinks are an inevitable consequence. Resource processes should
therefore consider the ecology and economics of the whole process, from the 'capturing' of
the energy source through to its dispersal into the ecosphere as heat. Table 10.1 shows the
increase in energy consumption from the basic metabolism of plants and men to the levels
needed to fuel a small car, a symbol of industrialization. The supply of energy to all resource
processes which yield a tangible product is so important, and the escalation of use so rapid,
that concern is being evinced over the relations between supply and demand both in the
near future and in the longer term, even if not in the time-scale of William Blake's dictum
that 'energy is eternal delight'. The various sources of power supply must therefore be
examined, with the understanding that this, along with mineral science, is one of the areas
where the development of technology may change the prognosis most rapidly, albeit on a
time-span of decades rather than years. This must be set against a world consumption of
energy that is currently doubling approximately every 17 years.

TABLE 10.1   Energy consumption (kcal/day)

Green plant covering 1 m² of ground	4,000
Human consuming food	3,000
Waterfall 10 m high, 10⁵ gal/day	9,100
Small car burning gasoline	900,000

Source: H. T. Odum 1971

Time-use of direct solar energy

The flows of present-day solar energy (Fig. 10.1) are well known from climatic studies.
Only 1 per cent or less of the incoming solar radiation is enmeshed in photosynthesis
(Woodwell 1970a), and interest has been shown in the direct industrial and domestic use
of solar radiation. Its input totals about 100,000 times the world's installed electric power
capacity and is virtually constant over long periods, in contrast to the fossil fuels to be
treated later. On a small scale, many practical uses can be made of it as in water and house
heating, cooking, distillation and photoelectric reactions. The possibility of providing electric
power on the same scale as modern generating plants is of a different order. In a solar-electric
station the maximum conversion efficiency would be about 10 per cent, so that a plant of
1,000 electrical megawatts capacity would require an input of 10,000 megawatts (MW). If
the average solar power at the earth's surface is 500 cal/cm²/day, then the area required to
collect 10^{10} watts of solar power would be 42 km², equivalent to a square 6·5 × 6·5 km
(Hubbert 1969), and while the whole process is no doubt feasible, its complexity, the cost of
the equipment and the effect upon land-use patterns bring into question the practicability of
the undertaking. In particular, LDCs short of large-scale energy supplies for industrialization would not be likely to benefit from this source. An improved technique might be to
orbit a lightweight panel of solar cells in a 35,880 km (22,300 mi) high orbit, collecting solar
radiation 24 hours a day. At a radiant energy collection efficiency of 15–20 per cent, a conversion to microwave energy efficiency of 85 per cent, and a conversion to electricity

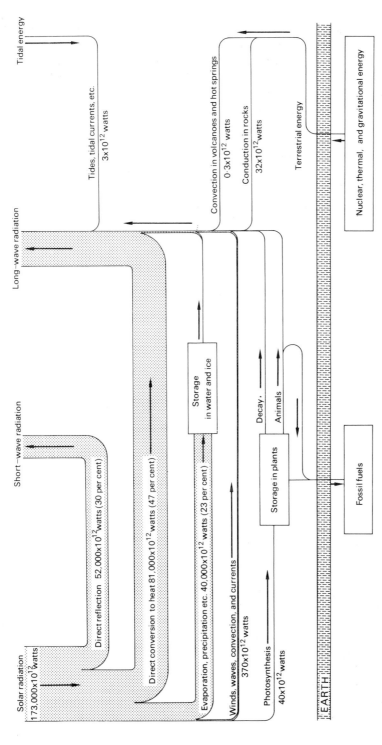

Fig. 10.1 The flow of energy to and from the earth. The overwhelming contribution of solar radiation can easily be seen, as can the small proportion of it which at present enters resource processes, especially via photosynthesis. The thin band leading to fossil fuels reflects their slow rate of accumulation.
Source: Hubbert 1971

efficiency of 70 per cent, then a panel 12·95 km² (5 mi²) with a ground antenna 15·5 km² (6 mi²) could produce the 10,000 MW required for New York City. The projected US demand of 2,500 Gigawatts (GW) for AD 2000 would need 250 such installations and the incremental demand until 2000 could be supplied with 125 of them (Summers 1971). The objections to ordinary solar plant apply to this project too, together with the added difficulties of increasing the density of large orbiting objects. At an early stage of experiment is one device for coupling chlorophyll to a zinc oxide semi-conductor, using the neutron-donating properties of the pigment as in photosynthesis but with an efficiency of 10 per cent. This process is estimated to be 100 times cheaper than orbiting solar cells ('Monitor' 1972). Solar collectors on the earth's surface would not add to the waste heat load; space collection systems would add less than nuclear or fossil sources of energy. Perhaps more feasible is the use of heat absorbed by the seas, to give electric power, fresh water and maricultural products (Othmer and Roels 1973).

Another ubiquitous commodity, though less constant in its presence, is wind, a climatic result of solar input. Again, local use for a specialized purpose is feasible, but production on an industrial scale so puny as to exclude it from serious consideration.

Hydro-electric power

Of the early sources of industrial energy only water remains important in the form of hydro-electric power. Its development since 1900 has been rapid wherever conditions are suitable, and plants of 1,000-MW capacity now exist. Stream-flow determines the upper limit, which for the USA has been estimated at 161,000 MW, installed capacity at present being 45,000 MW. On a world scale, the installed capacity in 1964 was 210,000 MW, about 7·5 per cent of its potential capacity. Table 10.2, for a slightly earlier date, shows the continental distribution of the water-power capacity of the world. A significant feature of these developments is the complementarity they exhibit with coal reserves (p. 253), for Africa and South America both have large HEP potential.

TABLE 10.2   World water-power capacity, early 1960s

Continent	Potential (10³ MW)	% of world total	Development (10³ MW)
North America	313	11	59
South America	577	20	5
Western Europe	158	6	47
Africa	780	27	2
Middle East	21	1	<0·5
South-east Asia	455	16	2
Far East	42	1	19
Australasia	45	2	2
USSR, China and satellites	466	16	16

Source: Hubbert 1962

Hubbert (1969) suggests that in the long term the full development of the world's hydropower potential would produce a quantity equivalent to the present-day total world consumption. If fossil fuels failed overnight, the world could exist at its present industrial level on hydropower, but there would be no scope for growth. Although hydropower is an apparently inexhaustible source of power, climatic shifts could cause regional variations in output and silting is a further detractor from efficiency. In fact, much hydropower potential is a considerable distance from any possible user and the capital required for yet other sites would preclude their development under most conditions.

Tidal and geothermal power

The source of tidal energy is the combined kinetic and potential energy of the sun–moon–earth system, and uses barrages which store up the potential energy of a high tide and then generate electricity upon its release. It shares the relatively benign ecological characteristics of river-generated power, but high tidal amplitudes are not so common that it can be thought of as having other than local future significance. The world potential is about 13,000 MW compared to 2,800,000 MW for conventional HEP—i.e. less than 1 per cent. The first major project is at La Rance in France, which dates from 1966 and has an annual output of 544×10^6 kilowatt hours (KWH) from a tidal range of 8·4 m. The Soviet Union plans to use the 7 m tidal range of Lumborskaya Bay (east of Murmansk) to generate 320,000 KW, while a larger plant on the Mezen Bay of the White Sea will use a 9 m range to produce 1·3 million KW (Pryde 1972). A project has been in the planning stage since the 1930s for Passamaquoddy Bay off the Bay of Fundy with an average tidal range of 5·52 m. An annual output of $1,318 \times 10^6$ KWH has been envisaged (Hubbert 1969).

Large geothermal energy plants have been constructed only in recent decades. Italy leads in this field with an installed capacity in 1970 of 362 MW at Larderel, followed by New Zealand (192 MW at Wairakei), USA (192 KW in northern California), Japan, Mexico and Iceland. The total world capacity was estimated at 752 MW in 1970 (Rex 1971). About 1 per cent of hydrothermal energy, usually in the form of superheated water or steam, can be converted into electricity. Estimates of world potential are difficult to achieve but are of the order of 60 times the present installed capacity. This amounts to about 20 per cent of the present total installed electric power of the USA. As with tidal power, it may be locally significant but can contribute only fractionally to world energy requirements (Cook 1971).

Fossil fuels

Table 10.3 shows that until AD 1800, man's access to energy was mostly limited to recently arrived solar radiation: the metabolism of human or animal food, the burning of wood, animal and vegetable oils, the tapping of moving air or falling water were used, and they possessed the disadvantage that they could not be economically transported nor their energy content transmitted any distance once released. Ecologically the effect of their utilization was usually quite local and small-scale, except where large quantities of wood were used

TABLE 10.3   Energy use during human cultural development (kcal/cap/day)

Emergent man	2,000	Assumes no control over fire
Primitive hunter with fire	4,000	
Primitive agriculturalist	12,000	
Advanced agriculturalist	24,000	Without fossil-fuel input
Industrial man	70,000	For example, 1850–70 period. In industrial regions of Europe and North America only
Technological man	230,000	This is the US figure

Based on Cook 1971

for smelting metals. The ecology of large parts of the Weald of south-east England was changed by iron smelting during medieval times, for example, as were parts of the remaining forests of Scotland in the eighteenth and nineteenth centuries; and nearly half the present wood production of the world is used for fuel, mainly in the LDCs. Use of peat changed vegetation locally, and its continued use for power generation in Ireland (Dwyer 1958) has altered the landscape of large areas, while the transport of 'sea-cole' into the Tudor cities of England foreshadowed later pollution problems. The full realization of the properties of coal led to its use for smelting metals, the development of the steam engine, steam locomotives and ships, and steam-electric power. Only about a century ago the even more malleable fuels, oil and natural gas, were discovered and led to diesel-electric power and the internal combustion engine in all its forms. Once the technology for discovery, recovery and utilization had been produced, use of these major energy sources grew rapidly. Coal was used in negligible amounts early in the nineteenth century, but by 1870 the production rate was 250 million mt/yr; in 1970 it was $2 \cdot 8 \times 10^9$ mt, rising currently at $3 \cdot 6$ per cent p.a. With crude oil, a negligible production in 1890 has risen to a present extraction rate of 12,000 million bbls/yr at a rise of 7 per cent p.a., i.e. doubling every 10 years (Hubbert 1971). Table 10.4 sets out the increases in consumption of the major sources of energy (excluding firewood, wind-power and other miscellaneous sources) during 1925–68. In 1968, the total consumption of 6,306 million mt coal equivalent came $36 \cdot 7$ per cent from solid fuels, $42 \cdot 8$ per cent from liquid fuels, $18 \cdot 3$ per cent from natural gas and $2 \cdot 1$ per cent from hydro-electricity. Nuclear power was less than $0 \cdot 1$ per cent of the total (Darmstadter 1971). Fig. 10.2 shows the absolute amounts of energy and its percentage

TABLE 10.4   World energy consumption in recent decades

	1925	1938	1950	1960	1968
Total consumption millions of mt coal equivalent	1,484	1,790	2,610	4,196	6,306
Per capita consumption kg coal equivalent	785	826	1,042	1,403	1,810

Source: Darmstadter 1971

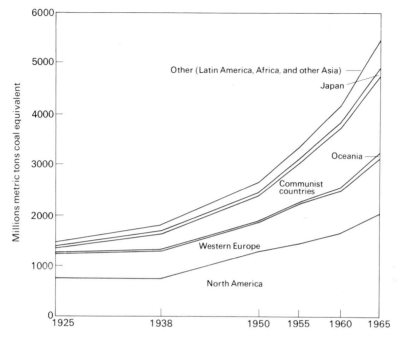

Fig. 10.2 World energy consumption by major regions 1925–65. The dominant position of North America has been maintained for the whole period, although its proportion of the whole has declined slightly. Source: Darmstadter 1971

distribution by regions up to 1968. These figures represent the culmination of annual rates of growth of 2·3 per cent in 1925–50, 5·1 per cent in 1950–65, and 4·8 per cent in 1965–8. The projected rate of growth of consumption 1965–80 for the world is 5·2 per cent p.a., and Table 10.5 shows some regional components of this average, along with the various shares in total consumption for the base and terminal years of the projection.

The consumption of energy is dominated by the USA, which, in any other set of units uses 2·2 million MW/yr out of an estimated total of 6·6 million MW/yr (Table 10.5). This means that much of the rest of the world uses energy barely above the food-intake level (about 100 W/day), compared with the daily per capita use of 10,000 W by each US citizen. If in 50 years' time a world population of 10,000 million were to use energy at contemporary US standards, the energy needed would amount to 110 million MW/yr (Brown *et al.* 1963).

Why worry?

The rates of present and projected consumption of energy sources have led to considerable discussion about the adequacy of coal, oil and natural gas for future industrial and domestic use, and the possibilities of substitution, especially with nuclear fuel. Agreed estimates of reserves are uncommon and most depend upon assumptions about economics, technology

TABLE 10.5   Regional growth rates and shares in total energy consumption 1965–80

Region	% of world total	Annual growth rate 1965–80, %	% of world total, projected, 1980
USA	34·2	3·5	26·8
Canada	2·9	5·5	3·0
Western Europe	20·0	4·0	16·8
Japan	3·3	7·9	4·9
Middle East	0·9	9·4	1·5
Other Asia	2·8	8·2	4·3
Oceania	1·2	4·8	1·1
Latin America	3·5	7·4	4·8
Africa	1·7	6·5	2·0
USSR	15·9	6·5	19·1
Communist eastern Europe	7·1	4·6	6·5
Communist Asia	6·5	7·6	9·1
World	100	4·7	100

Source: Darmstadter 1971

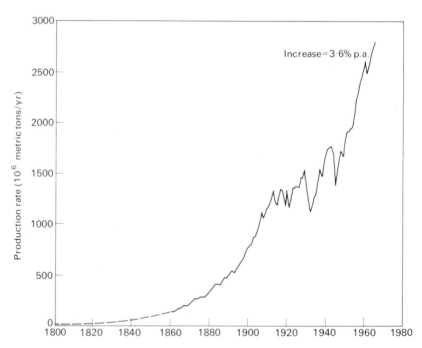

Fig. 10.3 World production of coal and lignite.
Source: Hubbert 1969

and politics that may undergo alteration during the periods about which prognoses are made. The following discussion relies heavily upon the estimations of Hubbert (1969) and Darmstadter (1971).

Coal

The distribution of coal is relatively well known because of the accuracy with which coal deposits can be mapped. The world's resources of minable coal (about 50 per cent of the coal present) are dominated by the USSR (Table 10.6) and the USA. Fig. 10.3 shows the rate of production for the world since AD 1800. Continued growth at 3·6 per cent p.a. is not feasible for much longer, for it would exhaust a minable reserve of $7·6 \times 10^{12}$ mt in about 30 years. More realistically, Hubbert (1969) calculates that the peak production of coal

TABLE 10.6   Minable coal and lignite (mt $\times$ 10⁹)

Region	Estimated resources	Established by mapping
USSR (including European part)	4,310	2,950
USA	1,486	710
Asia outside the USSR	681	225
North America outside the USA	601	70
Europe	377	280
Africa	109	35
Oceania	59	25
South and Central America	14	10
Total	$7·6 \times 10^{12}$	$4·3 \times 10^{12}$

Source: Hubbert 1969, Darmstadter 1971

will occur in AD 2220 and that 80 per cent of the reserves will be consumed between AD 2040 and 2380. Such calculations assume no great advances in technology which would make accessible currently unminable deposits, and also assume that no other major energy sources beyond those now known will be discovered. Given these premises, the order of magnitude of time during which coal can be expected to be a major contributor to industrial energy requirements on a world basis can be seen to last about 400 years. This forecast does not preclude the possibility of regional shortages.

The same type of calculation can be carried out for oil and natural gas. Whereas coal is all in the solid phase, this group covers a range from extremely viscous liquids found in tar sands (and the true solid, kerogen, found in oil shales) through the liquid gasolines to gaseous methane. The reserves of these resources are more difficult to calculate than coal because of the erratic manner in which accumulations of oil and gas are found underground. Gas is especially difficult to estimate for anywhere but the USA and calculations have to be based on the assumption that the ratio of natural gas to crude oil is the same as for the USA, and also that these products, often now wasted, will be utilized in future. Table 10.7

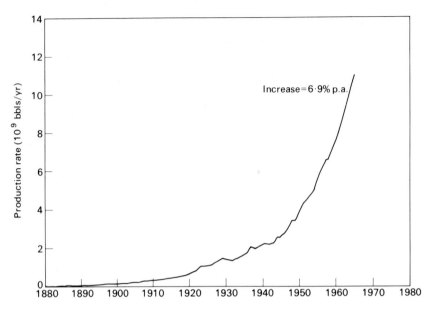

Fig. 10.4 World production of crude oil.
Source: Hubbert 1969

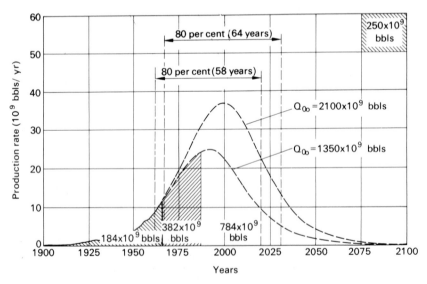

Fig. 10.5 A projection of the complete cycles of world crude oil production. $Q \infty$ represents the ultimate amount of the fuel recovered during the cycle and is given here for different estimates of the $Q \infty$ of crude oil. The difference between them makes little difference to the long-term situation. The quantities enumerated under the curve represent the amounts recovered during various time-segments of the recovery curve.
Source: Hubbert 1969

Plate 17 An oil refinery at Fawley, on Southampton Water in England, with a throughput of 20 million mt/yr. The size of the jetty and the installations underline the importance of fossil fuels to an industrial economy. A few remnants of estuarine marsh (cf. Plate 1) can be seen between the jetty and the plant area. *(Esso Petroleum Company Ltd, London)*

shows some world crude oil estimates which also give an approximate indication of the location of this resource; as Darmstadter (1971) shows, these estimates are conservative, and other calculations increase the ultimate reserve by 3·5 times. Petroleum products may also be extracted from oil shales, bituminous rocks and tar sands, and the world recoverable reserves have been evaluated at 190×10^9 bbls of crude oil, with an estimated ultimate recovery of 15×10^{12} bbls. Oil shales are widespread, especially in North and South America and to a lesser extent in Europe. These present special problems in refining and are not yet an attractive commercial proposition, and so are usually left out of estimates for the oil sector of energy sources. A refining plant exists on the tar sands of the Athabaska River in Alberta, Canada.

The world production of crude oil (Fig. 10.4) is, like that of coal, exponential in nature but has a relatively constant slope of 6·9 per cent p.a. from 1890 to the present, i.e.

doubling every 10 years. Given the accuracy of a projected total recoverable resource of 2,100 × 10⁹ bbls, then the peak production will be reached about AD 2000, with the middle 80 per cent of production being reached between AD 1968–2032 (Fig. 10.5). The estimates are of course subject to many assumptions about technology, but the order of magnitude is thought to be correct. Another set of estimates based on an even lower world resource of 1,350 × 10⁹ bbls puts peak production at 1,990 and the 80 per cent of cumulative production between 1961–2019 (Hubbert 1969). The time-span of the availability of oil and natural gas is thus quite limited, not only as a fuel but for the many other uses derived from its by-products, including pharmaceuticals and the use of hydrocarbons as a substrate for the growing of foods (Plate 17). The diversion of some crude-oil fractions to purposes other than energy generation seems likely some time before eventual exhaustion (Hubbert 1969). The middle 80 per cent of the petroleum family is likely to be gone in about 100

TABLE 10.7   World crude oil

Region	Proved reserves (1967) 10^9 bbls	Est. ultimate recovery (EUR) 1967 est.[1]
Europe	3·0	20
Africa	31·9	250
Middle East	273·7	600
Far East	15·1	200
Latin America	56·9	225
Canada	10·9	95
United States	113·4	200
USSR and China and satellite states	65·5	500
Total world	571·0	2,090

[1] EUR = produced + proved + probable + future discoveries.
Source: Hubbert 1969

years, but coal will last 300–400 years alongside them (Fig. 10.6), although only 100–200 years if it were to be the main energy source. Thus on a grand time-scale the age of the fossil fuels appears as a transitory phase, even if the most generous estimates of reserves are accepted.

Nuclear energy

Considerable attention has been given to nuclear reactions, since small quantities of raw materials yield very large quantities of energy: 1 g of uranium 235 when fissioned yields $8 \cdot 19 \times 10^{10}$ joules which is equivalent to 2·7 mt of coal or 13·7 bbls of crude oil. An electrical power plant of 1,000 MW capacity would consume U-235 at a rate of only 3 kg/day. Three types of reactor have been built to house the controlled chain reaction in which U-235 is fissioned by the capture of thermal neutrons. These are burner, converter and breeder reactors; the first will use only U-235, which is a relatively rare element, occurring in nature with an abundance of 0·711 per cent of total uranium compared with the

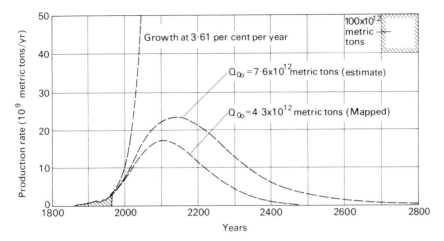

Fig. 10.6 A projection of two complete cycles of coal production for two different values of Q ∞ (see Fig. 10.5 for explanation). The effect upon the reserves of the current growth rate is also plotted. Compared with crude oil, a much longer availability is contemplated.
Source: Hubbert 1969

99·283 per cent of U-238. However, conversion and breeder reactors will use the fissile isotopes U-233, U-235, and plutonium (Pu) 239. U-238 and thorium 232, non-fissile, can be converted into fissile isotopes with an energy yield nearly the same as U-235. Since cheap uranium ores to supply U-235 for burner reactors are at a premium and likely to increase in price to the point of making atomic energy uneconomic in the short term, priority is being given to the development of the fast breeder reactor, or catalytic burner, using U-238 and Pu-239. In addition another breeder reactor using U-233 and thorium 232 is under development. This will allow the use of immense quantities of rock containing low amounts of uranium and thorium: within the USA the energy potentially obtainable from rocks occurring at minable depths containing at least 50 g/mt of combined uranium and thorium is hundreds or thousands of times larger than that of all the fossil fuels combined. One set of granites with a thorium concentration of 30 ppm would provide enough fuel for a world population of 2×10^{10} people using 20 KW/cap/yr for 200 years (Weinberg and Hammond 1971). Transition from burner and converter reactors to breeder types is therefore essential if the energy-producing potentialities are to be realized (Hubbert 1969, Singer 1971).

Atomic fusion may also be a source of energy: the fusion of deuterium and tritium (two isotopes of hydrogen) into helium, with the release of enormous quantities of energy, is called the hydrogen bomb. Regrettably for more peaceful purposes, the reaction cannot at present be controlled. Theoretically, two other reactions should be possible, the deuterium-deuterium fusion and the lithium-deuterium reaction. Using sea water as a source of raw materials in the first reaction, 1 m³ of sea water could yield $8·16 \times 10^{12}$ joules, equivalent to 269 mt of coal or 1,360 bbls of crude oil (Table 10.8). 1 km³ of sea water would then equate with $1,360 \times 10^9$ bbls of crude oil, which is the lower of two estimates of world resources of crude oil. The total volume of the oceans would yield energy equivalent to 500,000 times the world's initial supply of fossil fuels. In the second reaction, lithium 6 is in the shortest supply. On a world basis about 2.4×10^{23} joules could be extracted from known lithium 6 deposits, about equal to the world's initial supply of fossil fuels (Hubbert 1971). Given, therefore, the technology to achieve controlled reactions, immense amounts of energy can be forthcoming from nuclear fusion; but the use of energy to perform work is only one part of the resource process. The raw materials have to be garnered and processed, waste matter must be disposed of, and heat is the inevitable by-product. The possible ecological effects of these other sectors of the resource process cannot be overlooked, and their costs should be included in the accounting of the supply industry. Thus estimates like those of Weinberg (1968), that within about 15–20 years there will be inexhaustible and ubiquitous energy at a price something like one-third of the present price of nuclear-generated power, may have to be tempered by the addition of the true costs of the environmental impact of such profusion. Nuclear energy on such a scale also gives rise to numerous fears about the safety of the process, chiefly centred upon the disposal of the radioactive wastes from fission plants (see Chapter 11). Here we will note that proposals

TABLE 10.8   Summary of energy yields from nuclear sources

1. Deuterium-deuterium fusion per atom: yield is 4·96 Mev = 7.94×10^{-13} joules

   or 34·4 g D (1 m^3 of sea water) = 8.16×10^{12} joules = 269 mt coal = 1,360 bbls oil.
2. Lithium 6 per atom: yield is 22·4 Mev = 3.58×10^{-12} joules.
3. Uranium 235 per atom: yield is 200 Mev = 3.20×10^{-11} joules

   or 1 g U-235 = 8.19×10^{10} joules = 2·7 mt coal or 13·7 bbls oil.

Source: Hubbert 1969

have been made to site nuclear power stations offshore (Gwynne 1972) and underground (Rogers 1971) for reasons of safety and to avoid some land-use conflicts. Nevertheless, breeder reactors will involve large quantities of plutonium, only a few kilograms of which are necessary to produce an explosive device, and the possibilities of theft, sabotage, wrecking and threat rise with each additional generator; one company was unable to account for 6 per cent of the highly enriched uranium that it was supposed to possess. We might legitimately conclude that much of the enthusiasm about the future of energy supplies based on atomic power are predicated upon rather ideal social conditions. Even Dr Edward Teller, not exactly an opponent of nuclear power, has been quoted as saying in this context that sooner or later a fool will prove greater than the proof, even in a foolproof system.

Ecology of energy use

Any energy source has to be collected, or extracted, processed to a condition suitable for a particular use, transported or transmitted to its site of consumption and made to do work (Fig. 10.7). As a consequence of any of these stages waste products may be formed, and

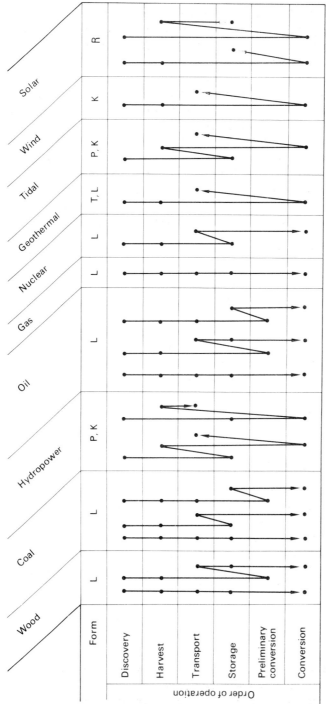

Fig. 10.7 The ecology of energy must also reflect the various stages in its recovery and use. Here the pathways of different energy sources of different forms (L = latent, P = potential, K = kinetic, T = thermal, R = radiant) through the sequence of operations between discovery and use is plotted, showing that alternatives exist for some and that the sequences vary.
Source: Luten 1971

heat is an inevitable result of the transfer of energy from a 'concentrated' to a 'dispersed' condition. Any of these stages may therefore exert their effects on the ecology of the biosphere at various scales. The magnitude of some of these effects is now such that the term 'pollution' is applied, and some will be discussed in greater detail in a later section.

The collection of energy sources is often an agent of ecological change: biota may be altered to capture particularly useful energy-rich organic matter as in agriculture; whole ecosystems may be drowned to provide a constant head of water for hydro-electric power plants. The destruction of large land areas for open-cast or strip-mining of coal and lignite is an analogous procedure. Restoration can take place, as it can for similar types of mineral extraction, but in countries like the USA control is a recent innovation and in Alberta, Canada, no conditions are imposed upon strip coal-mining works in the Rocky Mountain foothills. By contrast the restoration of agricultural land by the National Coal Board in Britain often provides better-drained farmland than previously existed. Although oil and natural gas from underground sources need only a well-head installation such as a derrick, a 'praying mantis' pump, or a simple capping installation, there is inevitably some ecological change in the vicinity of its installation unless, as in Los Angeles, the location is already suburban. In wildlands, however, forest clearance will be undertaken and the installation of the well-head equipment may involve road building and other forms of disturbance from which fragile environments are slow to recover.

Transportation and transmission of oil, natural gas and electricity are commonly by pipeline or overhead transmission lines. Although they can be partially landscaped, the latter share with the oilfield the opprobrium of being aesthetically unattractive, except perhaps to shareholders. Pipelines usually create only temporary disturbance if underground and only a visual intrusion if overground, but in the case of particularly fragile ecosystems certain types of pipeline create considerable problems. The example of the controversial 800-mile, 48-inch diameter (1280 km, 120 cm) pipeline from Prudhoe Bay to Valdez, Alaska, carrying oil across the tundra is possibly the most controversial case (Sage 1970). Oil exploration in the Arctic has shown how easy it is to damage the surface by using heavy equipment, thus compacting the surface layers and allowing increased solar penetration to the permafrost layer, and direct heating might produce similar conditions but more quickly. The Alaskan pipeline will carry 2 million barrels per day, would cross areas of seismic activity, and friction between the oil and the interior of the pipe would generate heat up to 60°C. With 11,000 barrels of oil in each mile (6,831 bbls/km), even perfect locks every 15 miles (24 km) might allow an efflux of 165,000 barrels in the event of a fracture. The construction would destroy arctic flora for 10–20 years even in minimally disturbed areas, use 80 million yd^3 of sand, gravel and crushed rock, and result in a bulk of thawed and muddy earth 6–9 m in diameter. Elsewhere in the USA there were 2,452 accidents in natural gas and liquid throughout pipelines during 1968–70, resulting in 80 deaths, 216 injuries and nearly $10 million of damage (Garvey 1972).

The processing and use of coal, oil, natural gas and nuclear fuels all create by-products of the combustion that is necessary to release their energy. In the case of nuclear energy, the waste products are radioactive and require special care. The other energy sources yield mostly waste gases, though with coal there is a great amount of solid matter which is piled into heaps, put back down disused shafts or dumped into the sea. The waste gases are dominated by CO_2, though SO_2 is another common constituent, and the effects of them and other wastes on both local and global scales are discussed in the section on pollution. The greatest waste product of all is heat. This is usually released directly into the atmosphere or into large quantities of water which have been used as a coolant in the industrial process (Singer 1970b). Such calefaction of water changes its ecology drastically but contains the potential for the culture of rapidly growing tropical or subtropical herbivorous fish, provided the water is not so contaminated as to be toxic to the fish or their food (Bienfang 1971).

New techniques may in time revolutionize power production. Electro-gas dynamics, still in the early 1970s at an experimental stage, converts heat energy directly into electricity with high efficiency by sweeping charged particles through an electric field in a stream of gas. The efficiency of EGD generators appears to be independent of size, and the continuous combustion employed would yield 'cleaner' exhaust gases than from internal combustion engines (Musgrove and Wilson 1970). Another useful development might be the direct use of nuclear power to produce hydrogen gas. The basic raw material is water, which is also the chief product of combustion. The hydrogen could be transported by pipeline and stored cryogenically, for both of which the technology is available. Its thermal output is less than that of natural gas, so that one year's supply of natural gas for the USA ($22 \cdot 5 \times 10^{12}$ ft^3/$0 \cdot 64 \times 10^{12}$ m^3) would have to be replaced by 70×10^{12} ft^3 ($1 \cdot 98 \times 10^{12}$ m^3) of hydrogen, and four times the electrical generating capacity would be necessary. Hydrogen should also be 70 per cent efficient in fuel cells. Certain flammability problems are associated with its use: for example, certain hydrogen–air mixtures can be ignited by static electricity, but D. P. Gregory (1973) argues that an economy based on hydrogen transmission has distinct advantages for an industrial nation. The process is in some ways analogous to the gasification of coal which produces methane, which may then be transported in gaseous or liquid form.

General remarks on energy

The indispensability of power supplies in the modern world needs little emphasis, for there is no substitute for them, only interchangeability between sources. The suppliers of the resources are therefore in a position to extract a maximum return for their efforts, a fact not overlooked by the governments of oil-producing LDCs. In Britain, the coal miners' strike of January–February 1972 produced such unlooked-for effects as a shortage of eggs, since battery-hen production relies on electric power for lighting and ventilation; a shortage of milk, because of the ubiquity of power milking; difficulties of water supply, due to electrically powered pumps and also pipes burst during surges after cut-offs; and pollution of rivers, because only those sewage works with fermentation plants producing methane had enough power to treat the incoming effluents.

The economic and social factors which surround energy production and use play a large part in determining the cost of energy at a given location and hence the mix of energy sources which is available at a particular time. In the West, for example, the contribution of oil and natural gas has been increasing relative to coal, and in the USA this process has

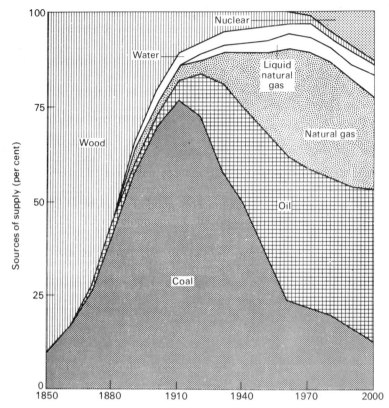

Fig. 10.8 A time sequence of the energy mix (in terms of the relative representation of different sources) for the USA. The rise and fall of coal is particularly noteworthy, although a renewed interest in it was evinced during 1972–3. Although nuclear power is much hailed as an important new source, its contribution to the overall mix is not expected to be particularly high. Resistance by citizen groups to the siting of nuclear power plants is one of the reasons for slow growth of this source.
Source: Singer 1970a

been taken much further (Fig. 10.8). Such shifts invariably cause different ecological effects according to the energy source: a shift to oil, for example, may mean less destructive strip-mining of coal but more oil pollution of marine waters. Because of their requirements for water as a coolant, atomic power stations need to be sited on the coast or beside large lakes, often thus creating conflicts with recreation and amenity values.

Whatever the mix, the trend in energy requirements is inexorably upwards at a world rate of about 4 per cent p.a. (Fig. 10.9). The main effects of this growth upon the ecosphere are in the substances released into the atmosphere as pollutants, and most important, heat. In 1970, the world energy use was $5 \cdot 7 \times 10^{12}$ W, compared with a solar input of $1 \cdot 76 \times 10^{17}$ W of which 50 per cent is absorbed at the earth's surface. Man's output of heat was therefore about one fifteen-thousandth (1/15,000) of the sun's contribution to the heating of the atmosphere (Brubaker 1972). At a rise of 4 per cent p.a. the human-induced proportion would be 1/100 in 130 years, 2 per cent in 148 years and equal to that of the sun in 250

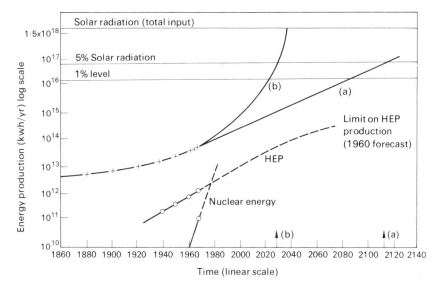

Fig. 10.9 A forecast of the increased heat emissions consequent upon rises in energy consumption. An equilibrium source producing no extra heat burden, such as HEP, is plotted along with a non-equilibrium source such as nuclear power. Curve (a) represents the current doubling time of 14 years; by AD 2028 heat emissions will have reached 1 per cent of the solar flux and by 2120 will be at the 5 per cent level. Curve (b) represents a compound growth law with a steadily decreasing doubling period for the growth rate.
Source: Chapman 1970

years. Pessimistic observers suggest that a 5 per cent level could give a global warming of 10°C which would bring about the melting of the polar ice-caps; Luten (1971) says that the 5 per cent level has indeed been reached over the 1,920 km² of the Los Angeles basin. Holding at or below the 5 per cent level is also suggested by Chapman (1970) since this is the order of temperature change involved in the Pleistocene climatic fluctuation. On the other hand, optimists such as Weinberg and Hammond (1971) calculate that 20×10^9 people consuming 20 KW/cap/yr (which is twice the current US usage) would add only 1/300 of the solar load and raise the global temperature by 0·25°C. The consumption figure may be a little low, since US consumption already appears headed for per capita figures several times the current level. As a perspective upon both points of view, we may note that, as Singer (1970) puts it, 'the atmospheric engine is subtle in its operation and delicate in its adjustments. Extra inputs of energy in particular places can have significant and far-reaching consequences.' Synergistic effects may also intervene; a rising carbon dioxide level (see Chapter 11) will presumably decrease heat loss, since CO_2 has strong absorption bands in the infra-red spectrum of outward-bound heat energy (Ehrlich and Holdren 1969). Shifts from fossil and nuclear sources of energy to 'equilibrium' sources such as solar radiation, tidal and HEP sources might be desirable to reduce risks of atmospheric instability, but their contributions to the totals envisaged by an industrializing world seem to be likely to be small. Acceptance, therefore, of a limit to the use of heat-generating energy requires a radical rethinking of the West's way of life since 1750.

Mineral resources

Stuff for things

The planet is, and has to be, self-sufficient in its sources of materials to make 'things'. Apart from a few kilograms of moon-dust, which has not entered commercial use, all minerals come from the earth's crust, and their transformation also requires a few elements from the atmosphere such as nitrogen, hydrogen and oxygen. The history of mineral use is also the history of man's material culture, dating from the first use of rock tools for killing and dismembering animals, and the origins of present machine-orientated cultures lie in the discovery of how to smelt metal ores. Copper was first, but was replaced eventually by the much harder iron. It was the much later discovery by Abraham Darby of Coalbrookdale that iron could be smelted using coke as a fuel that set up one of the foundation pillars of the industrial state; today's world can be said with some truth to be built upon a framework of steel.

Wealth from the earth

We demand a great variety of planetary inorganic materials. Chief among these are the ores which are used on a large scale to yield metals like iron, aluminium and copper. To them must be added elements which may not be needed in large quantities but which are indispensable in many modern industrial processes, as for example catalysts and hardeners: vanadium, tungsten and molybdenum are instances of this category. Finally there are non-metallic materials which are vital to industrialized nations such as sand and gravel, cement, fluxes, clay, salt, sulphur, diamonds, and the chemical by-products of petroleum refining.

The distribution of minerals in the earth's crust is characterized by discontinuity. There is, immediately, spatial discontinuity in which deposits rarely coincide with the boundaries of nation states that wish to use them. North America is well supplied with the ore of molybdenum, for example, whereas Asia is not; by way of compensation Asia is rich with tin, tungsten and manganese. Between them, Cuba and New Caledonia have half the world's reserves of nickel, and industrial diamonds are dominated by Zaïre. Such discontinuities are emphasized by temporal patterns of use: the older industrial countries such as the UK are running out of their ore reserves and coming to depend upon imports, and heavy users like the USA face similar problems; in both cases iron ore stands as a good example. The political ramifications are obvious. Another type of discontinuity is exemplified by the richness of an ore. A few metal ores show a more or less continuous grading from the richest ores (which are usually worked first and are cheapest to extract) to the poorest: iron and porphyry copper are examples. On the other hand some ores are either very rich or very poor or both. A simple extension of extraction and refining techniques learned from the rich ores down to the poorest may not thus be possible: a whole new dimension of technology may well be essential (Lovering 1968). In spite of any difficulties of supply and processing, the industrial nations of the world have come to be very large users of minerals of all kinds. Iron and its products are perhaps the most important, and are a good index of industrialization. From 1957 to 1967 the worldwide rate of increase in steel consumption per capita was 44 per cent, from 100kg/cap to 144 kg/cap. Japan, for example, rose by 270 per cent, the USA by 12 per cent (Fig. 10.10). In absolute amounts the USA uses most steel: 634 kg/cap in 1967; this is of course new steel to be added to that already in existence. Analyses of figures of production and of losses suggests that each US citizen is now supported by 9·4 mt of steel, mostly in the form of heavy structure, piling and galvanized sheet metal but about 8 per cent in cars, trucks and buses (H. Brown *et al.* 1963, L. R. Brown 1970).

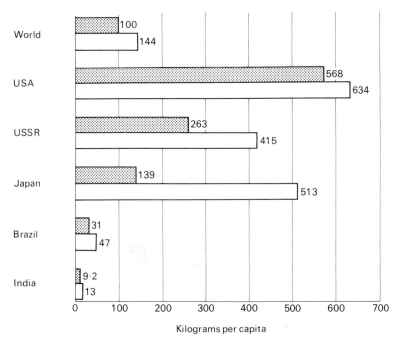

Fig. 10.10 World steel consumption 1957 (stippled) and 1967 (open). The rises were substantial but unevenly distributed, showing the continued dominance of already industrialized nations and the rapid consumption by countries like Japan which was experiencing a phase of fast economic growth. LDCs, by contrast, used little more.
Source: H. Brown 1970

The extension of these levels of use to other parts of the world would place some strain upon resources. To raise the present population of the world to such standards would require an annual increase in extraction of iron by 75 times, 100 times as much copper, 75 times for zinc and 250 times for tin. The iron (18·3 × 10⁹ mt) could theoretically be supplied, although a shortage of molybdenum for the iron–steel conversion process might be limiting; but for the others the quantities involved exceed all known or inferred reserves: 305 million mt of copper, 203 million mt of zinc and 30·5 million mt of tin (H. Brown *et al.* 1963). Although the LDCs cannot be expected to reach such levels quickly even if they desired, the limiting nature of these statistics in terms of eventual industrialization (sometimes proclaimed as a panacea for LDCs) is apparent. Even a level of 1–2 mt of steel per capita represents a formidable programme of capital investment and energy use. And all these calculations assume a static population which seems hardly to be the case. Although figures for the USA are somewhat atypical, they nevertheless represent a level of aspiration in many places. Apart from the steel requirement discussed above, the US citizen is also responsible for the yearly use of 7·25 kg of lead, 3·55 mt of stone, sand and gravel, 227 kg of cement, 91 kg of clay, and 91 kg of salt; in all representing about 20·32 mt of raw material to be extracted from the earth to support each individual (L. R. Brown 1970). Demands upon the planet's resources and space caused by extension of such demands to many nations would be staggering, but under the present system of economics are unlikely to occur.

Future use

Increasing population levels, together with higher per capita use, have led to concern about future supply. Very sober calculations of future reserves of critical materials have been

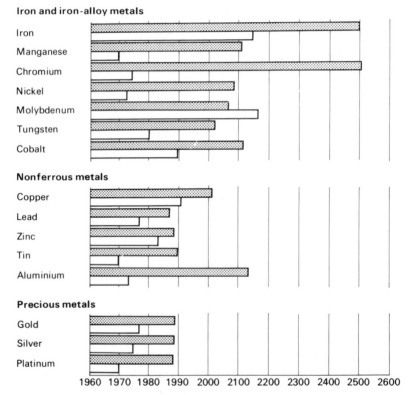

Fig. 10.11 Estimated lifetimes of useful reserves for the world (stippled) and for the USA (open). Assumptions include a rising demand created by both population growth and increased per capita use, and the discovery of new reserves. US demands are expected to increase four and a half times by AD 2000.
Source: H. Brown 1970

made, and the time-span over which such reserves appear to last is shown in Fig. 10.11. The relatively short periods of availability of reserves have thus caused many writers to emphasize the need for conservation of materials, especially metals, which in practice means recycling them after use. New reserves need then only be called upon to replace losses by processes such as friction. (The possible contribution of the seas and oceans is discussed in Chapter 9. Here it need only be repeated that costs will make recovering of all but the commonest minerals virtually prohibitive.) More optimistic views have appeared as well. The work of Lasky upon copper, which stated that as the grade of ore decreases arithmetically, so its abundance will increase geometrically until the average abundance in the earth's crust is reached, led to some euphoria about mineral supply. However, it is only applicable to ores with a continuously decreasing ratio of ore to gangue rock and fails to take into account the cost of energy in extracting the poor ores (Cloud 1968). Similarly, the presence of most mineral elements in common rocks such as granite has led to the suggestion (H. Brown 1954) that specialized deposits can eventually be abandoned and all necessities extracted in multi-metal plants based upon granite. Apart from environmental and storage difficulties (mined rock increases by some 40 per cent in volume), the idea is totally predicated upon unlimited cheap energy, the supply of which is not yet assured. Cloud (1968) sets the costs of high capital investment, power transmission, waste disposal and plant operation against the cheapness of extraction forecast by nuclear-power proponents, and suggests (Fig. 10.12) that increased application of energy does not proportionately increase production of minerals.

In the shorter term, some economists have postulated that since the costs of production of metal ores have been falling, the availability of future supplies cannot be in danger. Furthermore, the promises of technological breakthroughs in techniques of recovery and

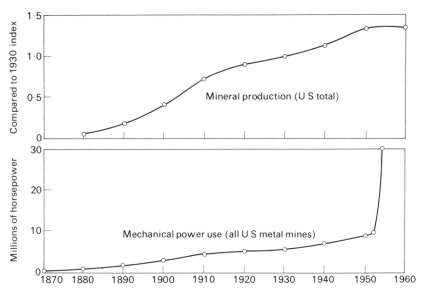

Fig. 10.12 Data produced by Lovering (1969) to suggest that increase in energy input into mining does not increase the output of minerals.

processing, and of substitution if price levels rise too high, are more likely to be kept in this field of endeavour than most; nevertheless Lovering (1968) disputes that unit costs of production of metal ores are declining, and suggests that conclusions such as those of Barnett and Morse (1963) that 'the progress of growth generates antidotes to a general increase in resource scarcity' are not sustainable except where short-term economics are the only factor in determining the resource processes involved. Granted that materials technology holds a great future, the cornucopian promise (Barnett and Morse 1963) that 'technological progress is automatic and self-reproducing in modern economies' is perhaps a little sweeping for most people, and does nothing for the LDCs which are deficient in technology.

A modification of the cornucopian view suggests that supplies will always be available, though at increasingly higher cost, but that the very fact of their ubiquity will pose serious threats to apparently inexhaustible resources such as air and water. It is possible therefore to believe in a continuity of mineral supply while advocating the overall strategy proposed by the neo-Malthusians.

Ecology of mineral use

As Flawn (1966) puts it,

> Man, like an earthworm, burrows into the earth and turns over its surface; like a bird, he brings material from elsewhere to build his nest; and like the pack rat he accumulates quantities of trash.

And most of these activities have side-effects of an ecological nature. Underground mining, for example, may include whole new towns among its surface installations: the San Manuel coppermine in Arizona necessitated 1,000 dwellings, 19 km of paved streets and three schools. Timber is cut in forested areas, often leading to soil erosion, and the tailings and mine-waste have to be discarded. Large-size solid wastes can be used as backfill or sold for aggregates, but tailings usually yield silt particles to wind and water and are often chemically unstable; the only suitable treatment appears to be to 'fix' them with vegetation. Mine waters are often heavily contaminated and have to be treated chemically and physically, or injected into 'safe' rock strata. Either method is expensive and the desire to forgo such outlays may overcome some mining operators, resulting in ecologically toxic effects. It is reported, for example, that the Bougainville mine in the Solomon Islands, extracting 0·48 per cent copper ore, was preceded by the removal of 40 million tons of overburden, including forest, and two-fifths of all material mined (over 400 million tons) will be dumped in a neighbouring valley. An oval basin 2·1 × 1·5 km will be an end result, as will the choking of the water courses and silting of the coastline. The lifetime of the project is estimated at 25–30 years and the profits to the developer at £20 million/yr (Counter Information Services n.d.).

Plate 18 (opposite) The skeleton of the industrial world is derived from iron ore. This pit in Minnesota, USA, exemplifies the attributes of mineral resource recovery in holes and heaps, high energy input, and a large land area for both the pit and its associated services and housing for workers. (Grant Heilman, Lititz, Pa)

Considered for the whole world, open-pit mining is more widespread than extraction by shaft; in the USA, for example, 80 per cent of metallic ores and 95 per cent of non-metallic minerals and rocks are extracted by this means (Plate 18). The technology has been facilitated by machines such as dumper trucks with a capacity of 137 mt, coal haulers of 245 mt capacity and draglines with 84 m booms. Thus the biggest operations can extract 101,600 mt (100,000 tons) of ore per day. Waste disposal becomes a major problem to which backfill is the obvious solution; if the topsoil is saved then restoration to agricultural or recreational use is often possible. Where dredging is concerned, disposal of spoil is the main difficulty, together with changes in the equilibrium systems of water bodies. The extraction of sand and gravel from bays has caused the erosion of beaches, and in river beds has increased the downstream erosive capacity of the stream. The extra sediment suspensions created may kill flora and fauna, as with oyster reefs along the Texas coast. The processes of concentration, beneficiation and refining may all create biological change if various products are released into nearby ecosystems. Washing yields sediment and slime-charged liquid wastes, leaching produces spent acids, flotation is a source of tailings and contaminated liquids, and smelting gives rise to slags and gases high in elements like sulphur or even fluorine. Devastated areas like the lower Swansea Valley of south Wales or Copper Hill in Tennessee are familiar examples. Nearly all these effluents can be treated or put to gainful use, usually at some extra cost, but they would be produced in unprecedented quantities if 'common rock' such as granite were to be used as a multi-mineral source, for the ratio of waste to usable rock would be 2,000 : 1. If underground leaching were adopted, large underground explosions would be needed to shatter the rock, followed by the drilling of input and recovery wells. Subsequent contamination of ground water with extractive chemicals would be difficult to avoid. One further aspect of mineral extraction and processing is the differential invasion of wild ecosystems where competition for other uses tends to be less and where processing is remote from concentrations of people who might be harmed. An example is the Canadian shield, a very heavily mineralized region, where the wild lands are highly valued for their unaltered state. Then controversy ensues, as with the constant pressure to open the Wilderness Areas of the USA to mining, or with the explorations for gold and copper reserves in the Snowdonia National Park in north Wales.

Each individual industrial plant, along with the energy use from which it is inseparable, produces local ecological change by placing a strain on the capacity of the systems of the biosphere to absorb the concentrations of elements which industrial processes create, and which economics dictate shall be discarded. Whether there is a worldwide capacity for wastes is difficult to assess, but monitoring of potentially toxic elements would seem to be a minimal step towards trying to avert any breakdown of the biogeochemical cycles of the planet on anything other than a restricted spatial scale.

Recycling

Increased recovery of mineral elements from scrap and waste is often advocated as a response to shortages and a way of minimizing the environmental impacts of the extraction of new materials. Success of the processes depends upon the quantities available in the recoverable unit (obsolete iron machinery has scrap value but not iron rods embedded in concrete foundations), and the resistance of the material to chemical and physical break-down. Costs of collection will be high from dispersed sources: thus lead from exhausted vehicle batteries can be reclaimed but not that from lead bullets, except perhaps in Texas.

TABLE 10.9   Scrap metal in the United States

Metal	Approximate annual recovery from scrap[1] (1 ton = 1·016 mt; 1 oz = 28·349 g)	Remarks
Iron	70–85 million tons[2]	In the iron cycle from mine to product to recovery, the loss of iron is 16–36 per cent. About half the feed for steel furnaces is scrap.
Copper	1 million tons	Secondary copper production from old and new scrap ranges from 900,000 to 1,000,000 tons per year, about half of which is old scrap. Old scrap reserve is estimated at 35 million tons in cartridge cases, pipe, wire, auto radiators, bearings, valves, screening, lithographers' plates.
Lead	0·5 million tons	Estimated reserve is 4 million tons of lead in batteries, cable coverings, railway car bearings, pipe, sheet lead, type metal.
Zinc	0·25–0·40 million tons	Zinc recovered from zinc, copper, aluminium, and magnesium-based alloys.
Tin	20,000–25,000 tons	Tin recovered from tin plate and tin-based alloys, 20 per cent; tin recovered from copper and lead-based alloys, 80 per cent.
Aluminium	0·3 million tons	Because aluminium is a comparatively new metal the old scrap pool is small, but it is growing rapidly.
Precious metals	gold = 1 million ounces silver = 30 million ounces	Precious metals including platinum are recovered from jewellery, watch cases, optical frames, photo labs, chemical plants. Because of the high value, recovery is high.
Mercury	10,520 flasks	Recovery is high. Nearly all mercury in mercury cells, boiler instruments and electrical apparatus is recovered when items are scrapped. Other sources are dental amalgams, battery scrap, oxide and acetate sludges.

[1] Includes old and new scrap. New scrap or 'home' scrap is produced in the metallurgical and manufacturing process; old scrap is 'in use'.
[2] Old and new scrap *consumed* rather than *recovered*.
Source: Flawn 1966

The costs of recycling must be set against those of new materials and at present the latter are generally less. Many of those who hold neo-Malthusian or 'environmentalist' views advocate a minerals tax which would increase the price of new material *vis-à-vis* recycled substances, forcing a shift towards greater employment of secondary sources. Some notion of the sources and quantities of metal recycling in the USA are given in Table 10.9.

Energy and minerals in the face of rising populations

Substances such as metals and concrete are for practical purposes limited in quantity, for only 0·1 per cent of the crust of the earth is accessible by any imaginable means. Clearly, new reserves will be found, new processes for refining lower-grade ores perfected and recyling more pervasively adopted, but such generalities must of necessity be resolved into specifics and the time taken to develop new processes may result in shortages. Again, the demands of an industrializing world may prove very hard to meet and it could be difficult to sustain the situation where nations like the USA with less than 10 per cent of the world's population are using some 30–40 per cent of its material resources.

The past 200 years has seen the development of a fossil-fuel-based foundation to the world economy, and only because of industrial processes can agriculture be intensified: the Green Revolution is essentially an outgrowth of the Industrial Revolution, for it depends upon synthesized fertilizers and pesticides, together with pumped water. The material benefits of energy-intensive industry are so apparent that people in the LDCs, informed by instant electronic communications and every Hollywood film of their desirability, are coming to want them too. Landsberg (1971) argues that energy consumption in the West is related less to population growth than affluence and that a reduction in incomes would be far more effective in slowing demand than zero population growth (ZPG). A Shell Oil Company (1972) report agrees, suggesting that immediate ZPG would reduce demand by only 3 per cent in the USA during 1972–85. Add to this the propensity of the people of the West to be gulled into demanding more than they need, and the basic energy–minerals problem is clear. Two basic attitudes, to be further discussed in Chapter 13, have evolved: a Malthusian attitude which considers that only a stable population practising re-use of all materials, preferably in a frugal way, can provide anything like a satisfactory solution in both material and environmental terms; and a cornucopian view which is predicated upon the discoveries of technology allied to the economics of a society in which expansion of production and consumption is an essential element, although even optimists like Weinberg say that energy abundance must be used to buy time in which to stabilize populations. Whether either of the extremes will turn out to be correct is not yet foreseeable, but we need to remind ourselves of the key role of energy not only in industry but in all resource processes, and the fact that there is no substitute for it, only different ways of harnessing it. It is easier to substitute for materials especially if energy is plentiful, e.g. hydrogen can be used to smelt iron, gasify coal or make a hydrogenated liquid fuel from coal; but the development of new techniques tends to be lengthy, the more so because of the inertia of vested capital in existing processes. Energy is so crucial that its costs (under any economic system) seem likely to be the main element of material costs, whether of mining new metal ore or recycling scrap. Energy availability and price therefore define what is and what is not a resource, and the basic currency of a world in resource stress, whether from shortages of minerals or food or both, is likely to be energy. But its production exists in the real world of a limited biosphere. Its use creates waste products, notably heat, which have to be dispersed, and the capacity of the atmosphere to absorb this without disturbing its balances may be limited. As with agriculture our capacity to increase qualities is, subject to certain overall limits, very great if we will the money and people to work on it, but more than ever the question must also be asked, 'What are the ecological consequences of such expansions of production and use?'

Further reading

BROWN, H. 1954: *The challenge of man's future.*
— 1970: Human materials production as a process in the biosphere.
DARMSTADTER, J. 1971: *Energy and the world economy.*
FLAWN, P. 1966: *Mineral resources.*
GARVEY, G. 1972: *Energy, ecology, economy.*
HAMMOND, A. L. *et al.* 1973: *Energy and the future.*
HUBBERT, M. KING 1969: Energy resources.
LEWIS, R. S. and SPINRAD, B. I. (eds.) 1972: *The energy crisis.*
ODUM, H. T. 1971: *Environment, power and society.*
SCHURR, S. H. (ed.) 1972: *Energy, economic growth and the environment.*
'SCIENTIFIC AMERICAN' 1971: Energy and power issue, **224** (3) (September).
THOMAS, T. M. 1973: World energy sources: survey and review.

11

Wastes and pollution

Everything touched by King Midas turned to gold. By a sort of inversion process, pretty well everything modern men touch, including themselves, turns to a waste product sooner or later. Exceptions are rare, and centre around such things as valued landscape views, and objects of 'high culture' such as Old Masters, priceless buildings and symphonies. Even Michelangelos will crumble some day, presumably, and fed through hi-fi technology Brahms may become noise pollution. In the sphere of material use, the creation of waste products is generally accepted as inevitable: food becomes sewage, automobiles become junked cars, while quarries and mines become derelict land. The ways in which some of the wastes arise in an industrial society are shown in Fig. 11.1.

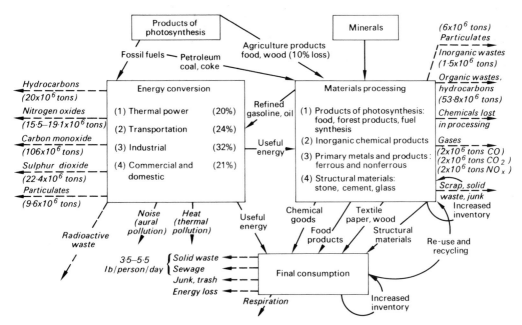

Fig. 11.1 A scheme of material flow through the resource processes of the USA, showing how inputs of energy and materials become converted to various kinds of wastes. Those from energy conversion in particular become contaminants of the atmosphere. Two attitudes to pollution are possible: one seeks to disperse the contaminants over a wide area and hence decrease their effect; the other wishes to increase the magnitude of the 're-use and recycling' loop and possibly erect other loops.
Source: O'Riordan 1971b

Wastes of all kinds may follow one of two paths when they become identified as such. They may be regarded as sources of raw materials (the resource process of re-use or recycling) or ignored as too costly or technically unsuitable to undergo such processing. In the first type of perception, sewage becomes a source of manure, junked cars a veritable treasure-heap of steel, and derelict land an opportunity to create new parkland or housing space. The second perception sees bagged fertilizer as cheaper than dried sludge, new steel as more convenient than reprocessing old cars, and agricultural land as easier to convert to housing than levelled tip heaps; and there is as yet no way of filtering out the organochlorine pesticides from the waters of the oceans. The strategy of re-use is thus heavily dependent upon the relative cost of re-used and new materials and hence of the type of technology used in each process, assuming that supplies *de novo* of the material are still plentiful. Global scarcity would change the relative costs quite strikingly.

Materials and waste heat from energy consumption which currently are not or cannot be re-used are led off into the environment as a means of disposal. Usually the wastes are not put back at the point of first extraction but as close as possible to the processing plant or the sites of use: wastes from coal extraction accumulate at the pit head, garbage in the dustbins of domestic consumers and then at the municipal rubbish dump; heat and gases are dispersed into the atmosphere (Plate 19). Food wastes are usually discarded into water, with or without processing. In fact, the use of flowing water or the ocean margins as sinks for all kinds of agricultural, urban and industrial wastes is the outstanding feature of the world's resource processes: the hydrological cycle ensures the steady movement of all kinds of wastes into the oceans, and the deeps are deliberately used for the dumping of radioactive material and spare barrels of chemical and biological warfare (CBW) agents. Most of the systems of the biosphere have some capacity for absorbing foreign substances, although quantities vary greatly (McGauhey 1968). But each has a threshold beyond which its functioning is altered. Sewage above certain concentrations drastically alters the level of available oxygen in fresh water and thus eliminates certain fauna, for example; likewise toxic fumes poured from an industrial plant may kill vegetation downwind from the point of effluence, and toxins may accumulate with lethal effects in the bodies of animals. When waste substances reach such a concentration that they exert measurable effects upon ecosystems then they are said to be pollutants. The term is also used for waste substances which impinge upon human life, where the threshold is cultural rather than biological. So the presence of high noise-levels near airports, for example, becomes labelled pollution. Similarly, an odour emitted from a pig farm or a chemical factory may be unacceptable, and called pollution, even though it is doing no detectable biological damage to the people. The two kinds of threshold interact. The death of songbirds from pesticide poisoning may not 'matter', since they are not an 'economic' resource and their niche in the ecosystem can be filled by another group, but their loss is culturally unacceptable to many people. There can be no doubt that acceptability of the pollutant by-products of economic activity varies with affluence: it is the already rich nations which are trying to grapple with pollution. Poor countries and the poorer regions of the industrialized nations are prepared to tolerate the effects of pollution if their living standard is raised by the operation of the earlier parts of the resource process: loss of wildlife through use of DDT brings little sorrow to Asians freed from malaria, and the cessation of pollution from pulp-mill waste is

Plate 19 Industrial and urban areas gather together materials and hence dispose of the wastes in a concentrated form. This steel works at Workington, Cumberland, England, can be seen to be emitting wastes into both the sea and the atmosphere. *(Aerofilms Ltd, London)*

little compensation to the workers of the shut-down plant in an isolated part of Newfoundland. Cultural thresholds are very difficult to quantify, since man possesses the ability to adapt to changing external circumstances and little is known about the way in which levels of tolerance are felt.

Classification of wastes and pollutants

A division of the various types of wastes for purposes of discussion is attempted in this chapter, on the basis of the type of material and its ecological effect when it reaches a concentration sufficient for it to be called a pollutant. This method is chosen in preference

TABLE 11.1   Major waste products and their receiving environments

Wastes	Air	Fresh water	Oceans	Land	Clinical effects of residues on humans?
Environments into which wastes are discharged: X					
Environments into which wastes get transferred: O					
Gases and associated particulate matter (e.g. SO_2, CO_2, CO, smoke, soot)	X	O	O	O	Yes
Photochemical compounds of exhaust gases	X	O	?	O	Yes
Urban/industrial solid wastes			X	X	No
Persistent inorganic residues, e.g. lead (Pb), mercury (Hg)	X	O	OX	X	Pb—disputed Hg—definitely
Persistent organic compounds:					
Oil			X	O	No
Organochlorine residues	O	XO	X	X	Disputed
Pharmaceutical wastes		X	O		Unknown
Short-life wastes:					
Sewage		X	X		Possible bacteria carrier
Fertilizer residues with N_2, P		O	O	X	Yes, especially N_2
Detergent with P		X	O		No
Radioactivity	X	O	X	O	Yes
Land dereliction				X	No
Heat	X	X			No
Noise	X				Yes
Deliberate wasting—CBW, e.g. defoliation		O	O	X	Yes

to the alternative way of classification by type of environment (air, land, sea, etc.) since it involves less repetition. A summary chart of waste material by environment type is presented in Table 11.1.

Gaseous and particulate wastes emitted into the atmosphere

Fossil fuels and water vapour

The gaseous composition of the atmosphere is more or less constant except for the amount of water vapour. By-products of a gaseous and finely divided particulate nature are emitted into it: some are gases already present in the 'natural' air, others are foreign (Schaefer 1970), and some particles such as dust from exposed soils are also present in uncontaminated air. Notably, most of the emissions into the atmosphere are by-products of the combustion of fossil fuels for energy use. (Table 11.2 shows the relative values of common pollutants for one year in the USA. Radioactive wastes are also produced during power generation by nuclear fission, but are dealt with separately below.) The biggest product of such oxidation reactions is water, but this is not usually regarded as a contaminant, possibly since the atmospheric content is normally variable between 1–3 per cent by volume and emissions do not radically change this figure at ground level. At higher altitudes, it may be noted in passing, some writers have suggested that water emissions from turbojet engines may form coalescent condensation trails along busy airlanes. The actual evidence for this eventuality is scanty, but Bryson and Wendland (1970) calculate that if 300 supersonic transports (SSTs) were travelling at 2,400 kph, and 1 per cent make contrails with an average duration of 25 hrs and the average width is 1·6 km (figures all derived from military supersonic aircraft), then permanent gloom from a man-made cirrus cloud would cover the area of operation. The SCEP (1970) study is more cautious but suggests that water-vapour injection in areas of dense traffic may increase by 60 per cent and that greater cloudiness in the stratosphere will be likely, though no estimates of the magnitude are made.

TABLE 11.2   Emissions of air pollutants (USA 1969, in millions of tons p.a.; 1 million tons = 1·016 mt)

Source	CO	Particu-lates	SO_2	HC	NO_x	Total	% change 1968–9
Transportation	111·5	0·8	1·1	19·8	11·2	144·4	− 1·0
Fuel combustion in stationary sources	1·8	7·2	24·4	0·9	10·0	44·3	+ 2·5
Industrial processes	12·0	14·4	7·5	5·5	0·2	39·6	+ 7·3
Solid waste disposal	7·9	1·4	0·2	2·0	0·4	11·9	− 1·0
Miscellaneous	18·2	11·4	0·2	9·2	2·0	41·0	+ 18·5
Total	151·4	35·2	33·4	37·4	23·8	281·2	+ 3·2

Source: US President's Council on Environmental Quality 1971

CO, CO_2, SO_2 and H_2S

These four gases comprise the biggest volume of wastes emitted into the atmosphere (Landau 1968, Stern 1968). Carbon monoxide, mainly from the internal combustion engine, is the largest of the three and in the USA its volume equals the sum of all the other industrial contaminants (about 100 million tons/yr). In cities its concentration is usually between 1 and 55 ppm with an average 10 ppm, but detectable clinical symptoms appear at 100 ppm (a level often achieved in Oxford Circus, London) and humans are killed at 1,000 ppm. Los Angeles has established alert levels for CO at 100, 200 and 300 ppm. Its effect often spreads into buildings, especially during the heating season when it is drawn into apartment blocks and offices by upward currents of warm air: in one office building in New York, permissible CO levels were exceeded for 47 per cent of the time during which the block was being heated. Although deleterious to humans because of its affinity for haemoglobin, thus depriving body tissues of their oxygen supply, CO is not cumulative, and removal of the pollutant source allows a rapid return to a normal level. At high concentrations, however, its effect appears to be synergistic. Its major effect therefore is as a human poison, rather than a factor of ecological change.

Carbon dioxide is normally present at a concentration of about 310 ppm. Since, however, it does not affect people until the level reached is about 5,000 ppm, it is rarely regarded as a pollutant on a local scale except where carbonate-containing rocks are common building materials. Since the early nineteenth century, global emissions of CO_2, mostly from the combustion of fossil fuels, have risen rapidly to the point where some 14 per cent of the CO_2 in the atmosphere is produced by industry, and by AD 2000 an estimated 50 per cent will have been produced in this way, at current rates of increase. Oxidation of all the remaining fossil fuels present in the earth's crust would increase the amount of atmospheric CO_2 by seventeen times. Concern over CO_2 levels is therefore mostly at a global scale and is dealt with below.

Although produced in smaller quantities by resource use than the two previous gases, sulphur dioxide is much more toxic. It comes from the combustion of coal and fuel oils, at sulphuric acid plants, and in the processing of metal ores containing sulphur. In the atmosphere it lasts an average of 43 days, being converted to SO_3 and reacting with water to produce an aerosol form of sulphuric acid which is toxic to plants at 0·2 ppm and is highly corrosive of iron, steel, copper and nickel, while building materials containing carbonates find these compounds replaced by soluble sulphates. Sulphur dioxide is produced in very large quantities in urban-industrial areas: New York City emits nearly 2 million tons/yr (2·2 million mt) from coal, and Great Britain 5·8 million tons (5·9 million mt). A concentration of 1–5 ppm usually produces a detectable physiological response in man, and in London's great smog of December 1952, 1·34 ppm was recorded; elsewhere, urban concentrations yp to 3·2 ppm have been noted. Plants are injured at such levels, and animals including man suffer from inflammation of the upper respiratory tract. Like CO, therefore, SO_2 is particularly a pollutant of urban areas, although downwind transport of H_2SO_4 from industrial Britain is claimed to be acidifying the fresh-water bodies of Scandinavia. Some sulphates have been claimed to be damaging to health at concentrations 30–40 times lower than, for example, the SO_2 levels set for the USA by the Clean Air Act of 1970.

Hydrogen sulphide and its related organic compounds, mercaptans, are sometimes by-products of petroleum processing, coking, rayon manufacture and the Kraft process for making paper pulp. Hydrogen sulphide is also present when anaerobic bacteria are found in considerable quantity, as in inadequately treated sewage. Both these sources are nuisances rather than dangers, their odour being detectable at concentrations of 0·03 ppb (mercaptans) and 0·035–0·10 ppm (H_2S).

Smog

The combustion of coal, oil or natural gas in power plants and the internal combustion engine both result in the emission of nitrous oxides into the atmosphere (Haagen-Smit and Wayne 1968). Of these sources, the incomplete combustion of the auto engine is by far the most important contributor by a factor of about 6. Because of its motorized life-style and inversion frequency, Los Angeles provides many of the data on nitrous oxides and their atmospheric fate. LA County produces about 0·15 kg of nitrous oxides/cap/day and concentrations of 0·02–0·9 ppm are typical, with an alert level at 3·00 ppm. The major constituent is NO_2 (nitrogen dioxide), which is a respiratory irritant. It also absorbs sunlight, especially in the blue wavelengths, and so appears as a yellow-brown gas in which a concentration of 8–10 ppm reduces visibility to one mile. Since it absorbs sunlight, it can undergo photolysis, at a rate of 2 ppm/hr. The chemical reactions are complex (Fig. 11.2),

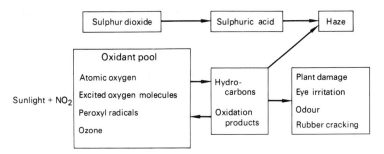

Fig. 11.2 A scheme of the reactions involved in photochemical air pollution.
Source: Landau 1968

but the products include ozone, formaldehyde and nitrous oxide (NO). This latter appears to be oxidized to NO_2, providing a further source of reactants. Numerous other substances are present in the ensuing 'photochemical smog' resulting either from atmospheric reactions or incomplete combustion in auto engines. They include other aldehydes, olefins, ethylene and peroxyacetyl nitrate (PAN) (Table 11.3). This somewhat heady brew bears little relation to laughing gas, and indeed lachrymation is one of the usual effects. Ozone concentrations of 1·25 ppm cause respiratory difficulties, and a series of smog-alert levels in Los Angeles and other North American and Japanese cities tell citizens, especially those with chronic respiratory ailments, of the potential dangers of smog levels. The effects of smog are not confined to people: damage to crops during the 1960s in California exceeded $8 million/yr, and on the eastern seaboard of the USA $18 million. The forests around the

Los Angeles basin, a vital reserve of recreation space, suffer from various forms of die-off due to atmospheric pollution and it is thought that ozone is probably the chief agent of biotic damage. Damage to materials is also prevalent, stretched rubber being one of the most vulnerable substances. Los Angeles, due to its geographical peculiarities, is the most quoted example of a smoggy city, and as such often used as a whipping-boy (whipping-girl would be more accurate, in view of its full name) by all opponents of the motor car. But practically all industrial cities suffer to some degree from photochemical smog, and any which are liable to air stagnation, usually in the form of inversions, are vulnerable to smog accumulation, like Toronto and New York in the summer of 1970; in large Japanese cities such as Kyoto and Tokyo, CO level readout panels are installed at some intersections and sometimes the traffic police wear masks as confirmation of the high levels of exhaust gases.

TABLE 11.3   Typical ranges of air contaminant levels in Los Angeles, smoggy and non-smoggy days

| Contaminant | Typical contaminant range, ppm | | Record maximum value, ppm |
	Smoggy day[1]	Non-smoggy day[2]	
Aldehydes	0·05–0·60	0·05–0·60	1·87
Carbon monoxide	8·00–60·00	5·00–50·00	72·00
Hydrocarbons	0·20–2·00	0·10–2·00	4·66
Oxides of nitrogen[3]	0·25–2·00	0·05–1·30	2·65
Oxidant	0·20–0·65	0·10–0·35	0·75
Ozone	0·20–0·65	0·05–0·30	0·90
Sulphur dioxide	0·15–0·70	0·15–0·70	2·49

[1] Defined as a day with severe eye irritation in central Los Angeles.
[2] Defined as a day with no eye irritation in central Los Angeles.
[3] $NO_x = (NO + NO_2)$.
Source: Stern 1968

Particulate matter

Industrial processes, auto exhausts, bare soil and backyard barbecues alike produce particulate matter, a conspicuous component of air pollution for many centuries. Dust comes from many sources including the gradual comminution of the debris which accumulates in cities and open spaces without vegetation. Soot consists of finely divided carbon and heavy hydrocarbons from combustion processes, and to this may be added finely particulate material from almost every urban-based resource process: ash, flour, rubber, glass, newspaper, lead and fluorides. The last-mentioned are produced in the manufacture of ceramics, bricks and phosphatic fertilizers and, especially in the form of hydrogen fluoride, can cause damage to plants, animals and man. Fluorosis, the mottling of teeth, occurs at concentrations of 20 ppm, but levels are usually less than 0·02 ppm except around poorly designed emission sites. Low levels of fluoride in drinking water are held to be beneficial to dental health and addition to the water supply is often practised, except where public opinion regards it as another unacceptable pollutant. Many other chemicals are present as particulates, but concentrations above 50 mg/1,000 m^3 air seem to be unusual.

The particulate materials have well-known effects. The reduction of visibility is obvious in most cities, soiling of paintwork, buildings and Monday's wash is commonplace, metals are corroded, and immense social and economic costs are incurred because of the aggravation of bronchial illnesses which takes place. Some writers also attribute carcinogenesis in people to one or more of the substances of this class of wastes. Their order of magnitude can be gauged by the fallout: in Great Britain large cities experience depositions of 500–2,000 tons/mi^2/yr (131·6–526·3 $\times$ 10^6 kg/ha) whereas small towns and rural areas receive 10–100 tons/mi^2/yr (2·6–26·0 $\times$ 10^6 kg/ha).

Effects at the global scale

All the effects so far discussed have been at a local or regional scale and apparent in a short period of time. But the dynamic nature of the atmosphere, its ability to provide reactants for chemical change, and its exchange processes with land and sea all ensure that many of the emissions are translocated far from their source, sometimes in a chemically altered form. Of the substances enumerated, most appear to have no global implications, although since monitoring is so recent and so fragmentary this should be regarded as an interim conclusion. Most of the sulphur compounds end up in the oceans as soluble sulphates with no known effects, for example; photochemical pollutants stabilize either as nitrates or as $CO_2 + H_2O$; the global emission of 33,528 mt/day of nitrous oxides means a yearly atmospheric increase of 2×10^{-6} ppm.

TABLE 11.4   Carbon dioxide production and accumulation

Year	Amount added from fossil fuel (mt/yr)	Cumulative amount added over previous decade	Concentration by volume (ppm)	Total in atmosphere (mt)
1950	6,700	52,200	306	2·39 $\times$ 10^6
1960	10,800	82,400	313	2·44 $\times$ 10^6

Source: SCEP 1971

Carbon dioxide is the waste which has excited most interest. Table 11.4 shows recent figures for the amount added to the atmosphere, and the quantity remaining there, which is about 51 per cent of the emissions (SCEP 1971). Thus the oceans and terrestrial biomes appear to be absorbing 49 per cent of the carbon dioxide, but their ability to continue to take the same proportion is unknown and in any case must be impaired by a diminution in photosynthetic rates such as is caused by large-scale clearance of forests. More serious is the accumulation of CO_2 in the atmosphere. The hypothetical result is to produce a 'greenhouse' effect in which the additional CO_2 allows the absorption of more solar radiation and hence the rise of global temperatures with subsequent ice-cap melting and shifting of climatic belts. Interacting with the CO_2 is the increase in atmospheric turbidity resulting from particulate emissions. By scattering radiation this might reduce global temperatures. Since these latter have in fact fallen since 1940, it is tempting to suggest that the particles are 'beating' the CO_2. As Murray Mitchell (1970) points out, there are complications because natural particulate emissions from volcanoes have until recently far exceeded even the highest estimates of human-induced output. Mitchell considers that although CO_2 is more efficient than particulate matter in influencing planetary temperatures, by AD 2000 the continuation of present doubling times of these contaminants will make man-made particles the most important inadvertent modifier of climate.

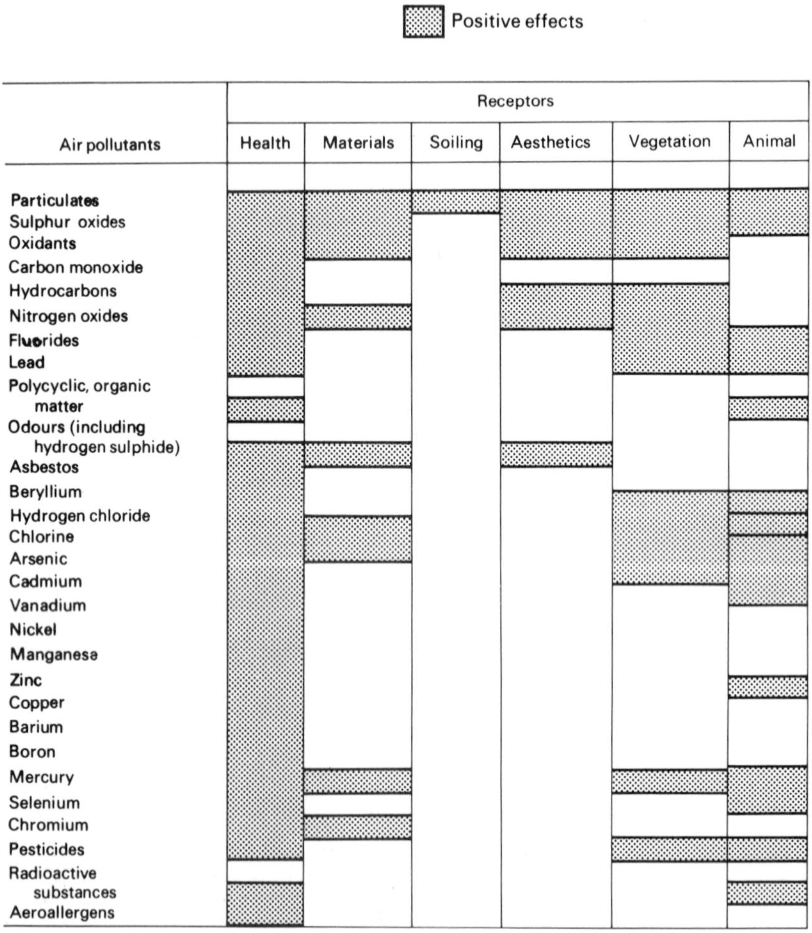

Fig. 11.3 The effects of air pollutants upon various receptors in the USA.
Source: US President's Council on Environmental Quality 1971

The deleterious effects to many people of this category of wastes are therefore seen at three scales. There is the point-source danger, as when a noxious gas is imperfectly controlled: an H_2S escape in Mexico in 1950 caused 22 deaths. Regionally, various pollutants doubtless exacerbate existing illnesses (especially respiratory troubles) and maybe induce them. In unusually severe episodes of smog or industrial pollution, premature death is caused. Many other substances are emitted in particulate form into the atmosphere, cause problems in terms of health, damage to materials and living matter, and are aesthetically unacceptable. A newspaper quoted a tentative estimate of the health costs of air pollution in the USA in 1968 as $\$6\cdot1 \times 10^9$. A table showing which contaminants cause, in qualitative terms, these difficulties is reproduced as Fig. 11.3. Measures are now being adopted in most industrial nations to reduce air pollution in cities, but less attention is generally given to substances which do not directly affect the human population. At a global scale, problems become more nebulous. The probability of direct changes in climate resulting from CO_2 emissions seem small this century, but the longer-term possibilities are so serious that efforts to learn about trends of climatic change and the fate of industrially produced CO_2 must claim a high priority.

Economic poisons

The elimination of competitors

In the course of resource processes such as agriculture, many poisons are applied to ecosystems in order to eliminate or diminish the effect of man's competitors for the crop. We also apply poisons to ourselves in order to kill viruses and bacteria which are inimical to our health, to our immediate surroundings to kill the vectors of disease such as the malaria-carrying mosquito, or to kill competitors for stored food such as the rat. All the substances used as poisons interfere with the metabolism of organisms and are effective in small doses. Ideally, the toxic substance breaks down into biologically insignificant compounds as soon as it has performed its work, so that dead organisms contain no residue of poison to be passed to scavengers, and soils would contain no active toxin to be washed off into streams or be available to organisms other than the targets. Some substances used as poisons do not possess this quality, and some are converted to an even more toxic form when they remain in the environment: collectively they are known as persistent toxins (Rudd 1963, Mellanby 1967, N. W. Moore 1967). Both short-lived and persistent poisons are rarely totally effective or completely harmless: application to any population of plants or animals elicits a spectrum of response from the organisms. The toxity of some substances is dependent upon environmental factors, especially in an aqueous medium. Thus temperature, oxygen content, pH and calcium level may all affect the efficacy of a particular poison. All but the most extreme poisons leave a few resistant individuals and if their immunity is genetically transmissible, and poisoning continues at a constant level, then resistant populations may develop. Examples are the bacterium *Staphylococcus* which is often unaffected by penicillin, and the mosquito *Anopheles* (a vector of malaria), some strains of which are immune to the effects of DDT. The toxin is unlikely to affect all the species in a habitat, so that another species may experience a population surge and itself become a weed or pest. Most important of all the unwanted effects of economic poisons is that caused by persistent residues when they undergo ecological amplification. Typically their concentration increases as they pass from one trophic level to another through a food web. The concentrations in successive organisms are cumulative to the point where lethal or sub-lethal effects upon an organism, often far removed in time and space from the target, are sometimes observed: precautions against sheep warble fly end up preventing the reproduction of golden eagles, for example, or anti-gnat measures cause the death of grebes. The longer the food chain the higher the probability of physiologically significant concentrations in the highest predator levels.

What follows is an examination of some of the most commonly used toxic substances (about 9,000 are commercially available in the USA) which are applied mainly to terrestrial habitats, occasionally to fresh waters. Residues inevitably pass through the runoff phase of the hydrological cycle, and if sufficiently long-lived they accumulate in the oceans. Some of the indirect effects of these compounds form the basis for the discussion, but most of them are poisonous to humans if large quantities are inhaled, ingested or absorbed cutaneously as a consequence of escapes during application; few of the toxins discussed here have not been the direct cause of human death. However, it is with the unintentional effects of residues that we are mainly concerned.

Herbicides

Chemicals such as copper sulphate (as Bordeaux mixture) have been used for hundreds of years against pests in orchards. Sodium chlorate is a well-known weedkiller, highly explosive and moderately persistent; sulphuric acid is still used for the destruction of potato haulms. These simple substances have largely been replaced by complex organic compounds, of which DNOC is a much-used member. It is very poisonous (but not persistent) and protective clothing must be worn for its application, typically by spray at 10 lb/ac (1·8 kg/ha). Accidents from spray drift have had unpleasant results. More popular still have been the contact hormone weedkillers which affect broadleaved plants only (thus leaving cereals and grasses, for example) and are said not to affect man. Their effect is to stimulate growth hormones to the point where the plant grows so fast it virtually dies of exhaustion. Two popular examples are 2,4-D (non-persistent) and 2,4,5-T (highly persistent). Both have been criticized because spray drift is an indiscriminate killer of vegetation, and there is coming to light an uncomfortable amount of evidence suggesting that teratogenicity of human foetuses can result from certain levels of exposure to any 2,4,5-T which contains the contaminant dioxin. Two types of systemic total herbicides have also been developed. The first group, typified by Simazine and Monuron, are persistent and prevent regrowth for periods of up to one year; the second group are short-lived: the effect of Dalapon lasts for 6–8 weeks, Paraquat has a life of a few hours only once it reaches the soil. Dalapon is especially suitable for aquatic weeds since there is little apparent effect upon animal life.

Fungicides

Compounds of two metals dominate this group of toxins. Residues of copper-based substances are likely to be toxic to animals but are overshadowed in importance by the use of
mercury. This is used as a seed dressing and, as discussed in the section on heavy metals
(p. 306), the effects can be severe. The withdrawal of methyl mercury compounds in favour
of phenylmercuric urea may have alleviating effects.

Insecticides

The success and adaptability of the insects has provoked a formidable battery of poisons.
There are three main kinds: inorganic compounds, botanicals based on natural substances, and synthetic organic compounds of two major subtypes, the organophosphorus
compounds and the chlorinated hydrocarbons. Outstanding among the inorganics is lead
arsenite, deployed against caterpillars on fruit trees. Since the combination of lead and
arsenic appears particularly frightening, it is comforting that in Britain the Food and
Drugs Act 1955 lays down that no food may have > 1 ppm arsenic or > 2 ppm lead
content. Lead arsenite is not applied later than 6 weeks before marketing. The botanicals
are dominated by powders derived from two plants: rotenone, from the roots of *Derris
elliptica*, is often called derris and is non-persistent, though deadly to fish if it drifts or is
spilled into water-courses. The flowers of *Chrysanthemum cinerariaefolium* yield Pyrethrum,
which paralyses insects but is non-persistent and non-toxic to most other groups. In some
ways it is an ideal insecticide but is expensive, so that ways of synthesizing it cheaply by
industrial methods are being sought, and by 1974 were showing signs of success.

Pesticides

From 1944 onwards organophosphorus pesticides, most of which are aimed at insects, became commonly used. Most of them are cholinesterase inhibitors which impede impulse
transmission in the nervous system so that respiratory failure ensues. Two of the commonest are Parathion and TEPP, both of which are very toxic beyond the target group
(1 oz (28·35 g) of TEPP will kill 500 people) but break down very rapidly. Both are
suspected of having killed non-target organisms locally, but proof is difficult because of
their rapid breakdown. Their close relative Malathion is safer, being much less toxic and
having also a rapid disintegration rate into non-toxic substances. In many instances it could
replace the persistent DDT but is much more costly to manufacture.
    The most widespread and heavily used group of pesticides are the organochlorines. The
most famous, DDT, was first synthesized in the nineteenth century but did not come
into widespread use until the war of 1939–45, when its efficacy against malarial mosquitoes became known; after 1945 its role in agriculture quickly came to exceed that of
medical applications. DDT shares some characteristics with several other commercially
available organochlorines. It is highly toxic to insects, though resistant strains can breed,
but is poisonous to many other groups as well, of which fresh-water fish are one of the most
vulnerable. The whole group is long-lived, with lives of at least 10–15 years. Thus they

TABLE 11.5   Quantities (in metric quintals) of poisons used by sample countries for

Country	DDT and related compounds	BHC and Lindane	Aldrin	Dieldrin	Organo-phosphorus compound
USA	148,564	—	—	—	—
Canada	8,314	362	1,964	27	10,205
Sweden	2,430	1,050	—	—	1,900
UAR	46,010	—	2,240	—	13,690
Japan	9,783	28,416	—	61	22,623

These figures generally refer to the active ingredient of the commercial preparation.
Source: FAO *Production Yearbook 23*, 1969

persist in food chains, causing both sub-lethal and lethal effects at various trophic levels. A great deal of investigation has been done on the effects of DDT residues, usually meta-bolites such as DDE and DDD which share its characteristics, although DDE is con-siderably less toxic to most organisms. DDT and its metabolites appear to be distributed over the whole surface of the globe, including the far oceans and the lower layers of the atmosphere: for example, African pesticides appear in Caribbean winds (Wurster 1969). Analyses of DDT concentration in water are perhaps misleading, since it is scarcely soluble in water (1·2 g/litre) but highly soluble in organic substances (e.g. 100 g/litre in lipids) so that it will always 'flow' from the inorganic world to the organic (Woodwell 1967a). This may account for its presence in the fat and viscera of fish and penguins in Antarctica, along with other chlorinated hydrocarbons such as BHC, dieldrin and heptachlor epoxide (Tatton and Ruzicka 1967). Its ability to build up in food chains is well documented in an example from estuaries on the east coast of the USA, where a concentration in water of 0·0005 ppm is accompanied by concentrations of 0·33 ppm in *Spartina* grass, 0·4 ppm in zooplankton, 2·07 ppm in needlefish, 3·57 ppm in herons, 22·8 ppm in fish-eating mergansers, and 75·5 ppm in gulls (Woodwell *et al.* 1967). The DDT present (about 70 per cent as DDE) is all residual. At Clear Lake in California DDD was deliberately applied to kill gnat larvae. The application rate resulted in a concentration of 1 part DDD to 50 million parts water; in fish, concentrations of 40–2,500 ppm were found and in the predaceous grebes up to 1,600 ppm, which was lethal to a large number of birds (Hunt and Bischoff 1960). Sub-lethal effects are also common: DDT appears to inhibit calcium carbonate deposition in the oviducts of certain birds (e.g. pelicans and the peregrine falcon) and thin-shelled eggs which rarely come to term are the result. The Bermuda petrel, living at the top of a long marine food chain but out of contact with inhabited areas, has accumulated levels of 6–7 ppm of DDT in its eggs and chicks (Wurster 1969). Breeding success declined by 3·25 per cent p.a. during 1958–68, and an extrapolation of the trend would bring about complete failure to reproduce by 1978. It should be added that some recent work suggests that the levels of residual pesticides in organisms are due more to the ability of a particular species to excrete the compounds than to biological magnification; this does not alter the significant effects upon biota which have been detected.

ngle year (1968)

rsenicals	Botanicals	Copper fungicides	Mercury fungicides	Herbicides
—	1,527	168,699	—	1,833,841
,265	9	799	9,208	121,494
—	—	60	2,150	54,270
30	580	2,090	—	1,880
,194	994	28,628	182	265,424

Particularly because of its effects upon wildlife, notably avian raptors, DDT has attracted a great deal of attention. Less well known, therefore, are other chlorinated hydrocarbons which are equally or more toxic in residual form. The most potent of these is BHC, a mixture of several isomers of which the highly active γ-BHC (Lindane) is lethal to many forms of life but fortunately is unpalatable to vertebrates when applied as a seed dressing. Other members of this family are dieldrin, aldrin, endrin, endosulphan and heptachlor. At least two of these are transformed in the soil to more stable compounds, aldrin into dieldrin, with a life of at least 10 years, and heptachlor into heptachlor epoxide which is more persistent and more toxic. Death of wildlife in Britain led during the 1960s to voluntary bans on certain of these substances, e.g. dieldrin as a spring wheat dressing and as a component of sheep dip (Table 11.5). The replacement of cheap and at one time universally efficacious agents like DDT is likely to be gradual and expensive: gradual because of the longer testing processes now considered essential before a biocide is introduced into the environment, and expensive because most substitutes are more costly to make. Metcalf (1972) quotes the costs of DDT in WHO anti-malaria campaigns as $0.185/lb ($0.084/kg) whereas Malathion cost $0.65/lb ($0.295/kg), Propoxur $1.60/lb ($0.725/kg) and Fenetrothion $0.73/lb ($0.331/kg); presumably the larger-scale production of third-generation pesticides found to be suitable might cause costs to fall.

The persistent organochlorines have attracted a good deal of opprobrium in recent years, though stoutly defended by those who point to the increased productivity and stability of agriculture gained by their use. Levels in human body fat are typically 12–16 ppm in DCs, so that in the USA most people are now legally unfit for human consumption. No adverse effects have as yet been noted, but since 1945 marks a zero datum line, no individual can yet have carried the current body burden through a normal life-span. Since newer and less persistent pesticides will be developed, together with non-chemical methods of biological control, it is to be hoped that heavy reliance upon persistent pesticides will soon cease, in view of their known dangers to man, animals and the general quality of the environment. In particular, synergistic effects may exert long-run changes in ecosystems which are impossible to predict (Sassi 1970).

Accidental contamination by organic substances

Oil

The dominant member of this category is crude oil. On one scale its loss during transport may be acutely dangerous to human life, the more so because of the inflammable nature of some of its constituents. More concern is generally expressed with its toxicity to plants and animals and with the aesthetic effects caused by spilt oil being washed up on beaches and shorelines (Zobell 1964). Fig. 11.4 sets out the toxicities of various fractions of crude oil over a broad spectrum of marine animals, from which it can be seen that the low-boiling aromatic hydrocarbons and non-hydrocarbons provide the greatest source of toxic materials: these are, however, the first to evaporate after a spill.

The scale of oil contamination of the biosphere is not accurately known. Most of it is found on the seas, in estuaries and large water bodies such as the Great Lakes, but oil-field spills along inland rivers are quite common. The total world oil production is of the order of 1.8×10^{15} g/yr; of this total 1.0×10^{15} g/yr is transported by sea, so that the marine emphasis in the list of sites of contamination is hardly surprising. (One quarter of the world's production passes through the English Channel.) The losses in transport through collisions, transfer leaks and explosions are estimated at 1×10^{12} g/yr, to which must be added tankwashing at sea, contrary to both law and shipowners' agreements, and the multitude of seepages from installations at transit points. These may together double the estimated total loss, and there is in addition a small background exudation from natural deposits (Hoult 1969). The refining processes of petrochemicals also produce wastes of the order of a Biological Oxygen Demand (BOD) of 100 lb/1,000 bbls (45·36 kg/1,000 bbls) processed. Hydrocarbon or oil wastes can be 3 per cent of the total treated, and in addition there are sulphur wastes like H_2S and mercaptans, alkalis, phenols, ammonia (some as basic

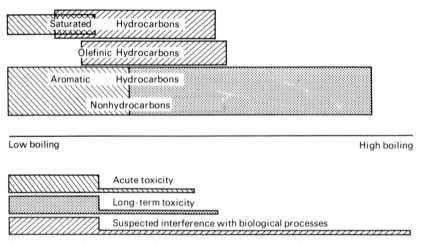

Fig. 11.4 A diagram of the toxicity to marine organisms with different fractions of crude oil. The low-boiling saturated hydrocarbons are the most poisonous but are the first to evaporate.
Source: Blumer 1969

nitrogenous compounds) and miscellaneous materials like chromate and phosphate corrosion inhibitors, tars and spent catalysts. Many of the compounds are not found in natural systems and in Kupchanko's (1970) words 'disposal is not always simple'.

Contamination by oil is largely a problem of marine ecosystems. Very little is known about the long-term cumulative effects of the fractions which have a long residence-time in the sea water, although some hydrocarbons can apparently be concentrated in food chains. The examples quoted are alkylated 4- and 5-ring aromatic hydrocarbons of the type which are known to induce carcinogenesis experimentally. They are likely to affect the flavour of sea food as well. Much more knowledge of the effects of oil on biota has accrued from large oil spills such as the wreck of the *Torrey Canyon* off Cornwall, England, in 1967 and the submarine seepage caused by drilling in the Santa Barbara Channel off California in 1969. Such incidents were treated very seriously and are well documented, but we may remember that incidents of the magnitude of the *Torrey Canyon* disaster (which carried 118,000 tons (119,888 mt) of oil) occur about once a week in the world as a whole. The seriousness of tanker incidents is exacerbated by the increasing size of vessels used: tankers of 210,000–250,000 tons are now used.

The effects of oil on marine biota vary considerably according to the initial composition of the oil, the rate of evaporation of various fractions, the species affected and, with littoral organisms, their place in the intertidal range. Emulsions of diesel oil at a concentration of 0·01–0·1 per cent cause the impairment of photosynthesis in kelp, and the more delicate red algae are very severely affected, probably because they often grow in pools where the oil can settle for long periods. The low-boiling saturated hydrocarbons are particularly toxic to invertebrates, but they often evaporate before reaching a shore (local wind and tide conditions are of course critical in such events), and this is thought to have happened at Santa Barbara, where the loss of mollusca, for example, was not particularly severe. The most obvious victims of large spills are seabirds, and many thousands usually perish. Birds which are rescued and cleaned often exhibit high mortality rates after release, but it is unknown whether this is due to pneumonia or a medium-term toxicity effect. In attempts to disperse the oil through the water rather than leaving it as a thick surface film, emulsifiers have sometimes been used as a clean-up agent. This has generally been disastrous for marine biota, especially mollusca. The detergents used are often more toxic to marine animals (Table 11.6) than is oil, but in any case the thinned oil can often penetrate the tightly closed valves of mollusca: thus limpets exhibit a mortality of 100 per cent if an emulsifier is used, but with oil alone they may survive. Emulsifier at a concentration of only 0·01 per cent caused 100 per cent mortality in cockles, and longer-term effects are hinted at by the reduction of photosynthesis in kelps at concentrations of 1–10 ppm. With both oil and emulsifier, separately or together, species at the ends of their littoral ranges exhibited greater losses. Partly this is caused by the long stay of oil in pools, partly because emulsifiers enable oil to penetrate deeper into pool water, and partly because the species are in any case under considerable stress at the extremes of their tolerances. Cleaning procedures using straw as at Santa Barbara, or chalk, appear to be more effective and less damaging to biota, and several techniques for physically dispersing or collecting the oil are now under development (Nelson-Smith 1970).

Apart from the concentrated oil spills which reach the public eye, there appears to be

TABLE 11.6   Toxicity of BP 1002 (detergent) to some sublittoral species at 12°C

Species	Common name	Concentration (ppm) needed to kill majority in 24 hrs	Notes
Coelenterata			
Calliactis parasitica	Sea anemone	25	Stay closed at 5 ppm
Crustacea			
Corystes cassivelaunus	Masked crab	10	
Portunus holsatus	Swimming crab	5	
Diogenes pugilator	Hermit crab	25	
Mollusca			
Nassarius reticulatus	Netted whelk	2·5	Some survived 2·5 ppm
Chlamys opercularis	Queen scallop	1	Affected at 0·5 ppm (tended to gape)
Laevicardium crassum	Smooth cockle	1	Affected at 0·5 ppm (tended to gape)
Spisula subtruncata	Smooth cockle	2	Affected at 1 ppm (tended to gape)
Ensis siliqua	Razor-shell	0·5	
Echinodermata			
Asterias rubens	Common starfish	25	Climbing stopped at 10 ppm
Ophiocomina nigra	Brittle-star	5	Affected at 2 ppm
Algae			
Delesseria sanguinea	Red seaweed	10	Took several days to change colour

Source: Ehrenfeld 1970

something of a universal distribution of small gobs of residual hydrocarbons. On his transatlantic voyage in the *Ra II*, Heyerdahl found lumps of oil residue throughout the voyage, while a survey ship in the Sargasso Sea reported that by volume they caught three times as much oil as Sargasso weed in their nets. Because oil is a valuable substance, and is getting costlier with time, the motivations to lose as little as possible are stronger than with unwanted residues of industrial or agricultural resource processes. But the costs are widely ramified, and include, besides the loss of natural resources, the loss of revenue to resort areas, and the costs of cleaning up by local government when the source of the spill cannot be traced. There are losses to the polluters if they are fined and even others incurred in investigating responsibility and in prosecution through the courts. The total of these can never be accurately assessed (Hawkes 1961). It will take a great deal of tough action by nation states along their shores to produce a noticeable decline in contaminated beaches (which although undesirable are probably in the long term the least important of the effects of oil pollution) and inshore pollution. The stopping of pollution on the open oceans requires international action of a scale not so far envisaged as practicable.

PCBs

Analogous to oil in some ways are a class of organic substances called polychlorinated biphenyls (PCBs) which are a by-product of the plastics, lubricants and rubber industries. These are long-lasting, insoluble in water but soluble in fat (N. W. Moore 1969). Their actual presence and their toxic effects are difficult to measure, but they appear to have been strongly implicated in the deaths of many seabirds and possibly of other biota too. They are also used in paper products and inks, and it has been feared that recycling paper may concentrate the PCBs which, being fat soluble, will migrate to foods packaged in the re-used materials. In some countries their chief manufacturer has seen fit either to withdraw these substances from the market or replace the most stable forms with more quickly biodegradable ones.

Derelict land

Creation of waste land

Many resource processes of an industrial kind produce land which is no longer valuable for any other purpose; the UK definition of derelict land, for example, is 'land so damaged by industrial or other development that it is incapable of beneficial use without treatment'. Mining of various kinds is the chief contributor of derelict land: open-pit mining produces a large hole together with dumped overburden and spoil, and the hole may fill with water. Machinery and buildings may with everything else be abandoned when extraction ceases after the average life of pits and quarries of 50 years. Shaft mining produces few holes, but tips of waste material are usual and subsidence may render unusable further areas of land. Surface mining is relatively cheap and over 50 minerals are produced in the USA by this means; costs are held down by the technological capacity now available to highly capitalized operators. Industrial processes such as smelting also create considerable quantities of waste, as do the armed forces, especially at war-training areas, and railways and waterways in periods of decline.

The actual amounts of derelict land in some industrial countries are very high. Measurement is difficult, since official definitions often include only land which is derelict and abandoned. Thus a tip heap still in use is not classified in the UK as derelict land, neither is land covered by any form of planning permission or restoration conditions, however impossible these may be to enforce. Thus in the West Riding of Yorkshire, England, there were officially 2,542 ha of derelict land in 1966, yet functionally derelict land was estimated from an aerial survey at 9,754 ha. Even using the official figures, England and Wales had 45,460 ha of derelict land in 1967, increasing at 1,417 ha/yr. The true amount is probably 101,250 ha; and most of it is a result of the extraction of some 406 million mt/yr of minerals which occurs in Great Britain: for instance, about one-fifth of the National Coal Board's land holdings are derelict land (Barr 1969). In the USA, an estimated 1,295 km² (5,000 mi²) of land were disturbed by surface mining at January 1965, with an annual increment of 61,956 ha: an amount equivalent to a rectangle 16 $\times$ 40 km. An additional 129,600 ha were or had been in use for roads and exploration activities. Coal dominated the picture, being responsible for 41 per cent of the disturbance, with sand and gravel 26 per cent (US Department of the Interior 1967, US President's Council on Recreation and Natural Beauty 1968, Weisz 1970).

Effects of derelict land

The effects of dereliction extend beyond the immediate sterilization of tracts of land. Open mining may contribute dust to the local atmosphere, and waste material, especially if unvegetated, is a considerable source of silt. On 40 per cent of derelict sites in the USA, soil erosion was taking place on the tips, and strip-mined lands in Kentucky yielded $7 \cdot 1 \times 10^9$ kg/ha of silt whereas undisturbed forest nearby yielded $6 \cdot 5 \times 10^6$ kg/ha. Thus in the USA, 9,280 km of streams and 1,175 ha of impoundments are affected by the operations of open-cast mining of coal (US Department of the Interior 1967). Chemical effects may also occur when water leaches through waste materials with soluble elements in them: sulphur-bearing tailings may well yield streams contaminated with sulphuric acid.

Restoration

Treatment and reclamation of derelict land are not technically impossible but currently appear expensive. In Lancashire, England, 15·5 ha of derelict land cost the local authority £3,700 to buy, but reclamation and landscape cost £15,000, and the usual cost of reclamation is £32–£284/ha. Nevertheless, authorities in England like Lancashire and Durham County Councils have Treasury-aided reclamation programmes of an ambitious nature. Since 1965 Durham has launched 80 reclamation schemes on land made derelict by coal extraction and has treated 81 ha at a gross cost of £2·5 million; ongoing programmes plan to reclaim 200–250 ha/yr, but even this is not keeping pace with colliery closures. England and Wales have been reclaiming a total of 800 ha/yr in recent years and restoration conditions are usually placed on planning permission to extend mineral extraction, but these are often difficult to enforce (Baker 1970). The attitudes of the industrial revolution are clearly changing with regard to derelict land: where there's muck there's brass, but there is also dirt, dust, rats and even large-scale death as at Aberfan in south Wales. The psychological effects are also important: authorities of such areas which seek to attract new industry have great difficulty in persuading managers to locate amid mountains of waste or lunar landscapes of dust and water. The use of derelict land as a resource for filling in holes, for making new sites for housing and industry and for creating marinas and nature reserves is a necessity in small countries with large populations, and a desirable aim for others (Karsch 1970).

Organic wastes

Concentration in runoff

Most of the substances considered here are not persistent as are, for instance, chlorinated hydrocarbon pesticides, but contain certain elements present and important in the biosphere (of which nitrogen and phosphorus are the most studied), which are concentrated by man in the course of their use and are then released back into the biosphere. The effects are those of providing a large quantity of an element which may well have been limiting, and of accelerating the natural cycle of that substance in the biosphere.

Sewage

Contamination of fresh waters and shallow offshore seas by sewage is a common occurrence. Sewage is about 99·9 per cent water and 0·02–0·04 per cent solids of which proteins and carbohydrates each comprise 40–50 per cent and fats 5–10 per cent. Water carriage of sewage from urban areas dates only from the 1840s, before which the contamination of water supplies led to epidemics of cholera, typhoid and dysentery. Such outbreaks are still common in LDCs and in pockets of poverty in the DCs such as in migrant labour camps (e.g. in Florida early in 1973) and in regions of colonization with many native people (e.g. the Mackenzie Delta of Canada in October 1972). Treatment of sewage to kill the agents of these diseases is an important part of sewage processing where this exists: chlorine is generally used. The wastes of any human population will also contain bacteria and viruses from other ill people and from healthy carriers, which reinforces the need for treatment of the water component of sewage. Contamination of water by untreated sewage is denoted by the presence of the bacterium *Escherichia coli* which is not itself infectious but is an indicator of the presence of the agents of typhoid and dysentery.

Further sewage treatment consists of the separation of the organic matter from the water and its conversion to a biologically inactive and aesthetically inoffensive state. The end-product is sludge, a valuable fertilizer but one which is currently more expensive than factory-produced material. However, many large cities in the West do not treat their sewage at all: in metropolitan Canada, for instance, 100 per cent of the sewage of Toronto gets a two-stage treatment, whereas practically all the production of the population of Montreal and Quebec is poured untreated into the St Lawrence River. In Canada as a whole, less than 40 per cent of the households are connected to a sanitary sewer and only 60 per cent of sewage gets any treatment (MacNeill 1971). A well-fed human excretes 14 g N_2 and 1·5 g P per day, of which 20–50 per cent is removed by waste treatment. In the USA the mixture of treatment and non-treatment means that an estimated 450–680 million kg of nitrogen and 91–250 million kg of phosphorus (Bartsch 1970) reach the surface waters of the continent every year (Fig. 11.5). Even tertiary treatment of municipal sewage will not eliminate the eutrophication of fresh water. Algal blooms can occur at phosphorus concentrations of < 0·1 mg/l and nitrogen concentrations of 0·01 mg/l if other essential elements are present (Lawson and Brisbin 1970). Tertiary treatment is therefore different from nutrient removal, which calls for the even more expensive process of the removal of inorganic and organic compounds from a stabilized sewage effluent.

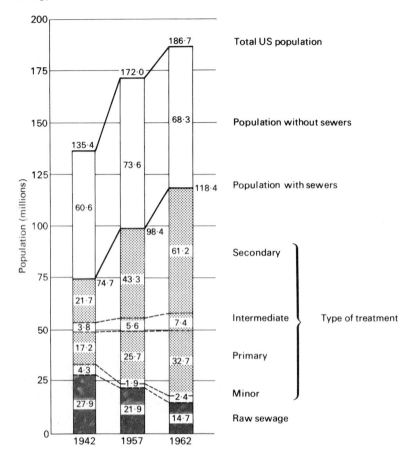

Fig. 11.5 Even in rich countries like the USA, sewerage may scarcely keep pace with the growth in population, although in 1957–62 it began to gain. Lack of sewers does not necessarily mean pollution if effective septic tanks and cesspools are used, but in the case of many large cities raw sewage is dumped into nearby water.
Source: A. Wolman 1965

Detergents

Phosphorus and nitrogen are the important elements in the contributions of fertilizer runoff to chemical changes in water bodies. More phosphorus is added from 'hard' synthetic detergents whose foaming reduces photosynthesis and inhibits oxygenation of the water. Concentrations of < 1 ppm may also inhibit oxygen uptake by organisms. 'Soft' or biodegradable detergents are now available and are replacing their forerunners, but both they and the organic cold-water detergents contain phosphorus: indeed 'enzyme' detergents are in fact phosphate pre-soaks (US Congress 1970).

Animal wastes

As a source of water contamination, the products of urban dwellers are globally less important than industry and agriculture. The volume of effluent from industry cannot even be estimated, but we may note that some 500,000 organic chemicals are synthesized, most of which are synthetically produced and whose effects on the biosphere are unknown. Agriculture produces the fertilizer runoffs already mentioned and also a great deal of solid residues. Crop residues in the USA amount to about 8 tons/family/yr and each year sees 58 million dead birds unfit for eating whose carcasses have to be dispersed. Intensive animal farming produces wastes analogous to a town: the volume of daily wastes from such operations are approximately 10 times those of humans. A poultry unit of 1 million chickens produces the same quantity of waste as 68,000 people, while each year the human population of the USA produces 153 million m³ of sludge and its domesticated animals 765 million m³ (Taiganides 1967). In New England dairy farms, each cow is responsible for a net loss to the environment of 119 kg/yr of nitrogen, 34 kg/yr of phosphorus and 53 kg/yr of potassium (Ashton 1970).

Eutrophication

The introduction of large quantities of nitrogen and phosphorus into water bodies is one of the major problems of wastes today (Sawyer 1966). Phosphorus is a scarce element in the

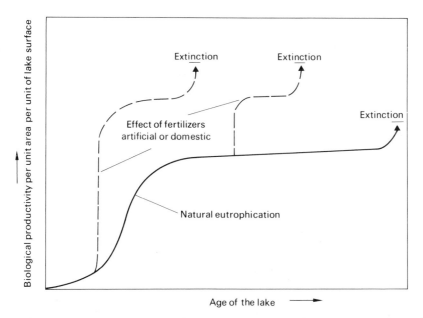

Fig. 11.6 The pathways through which a lake may become extinct. The solid line indicates the natural sequence, the pecked lines the effects of the addition of nutrients from fertilizers or sewage, i.e. eutrophication. The extinction of the lake then occurs far sooner than under natural conditions.
Source: Sawyer 1966

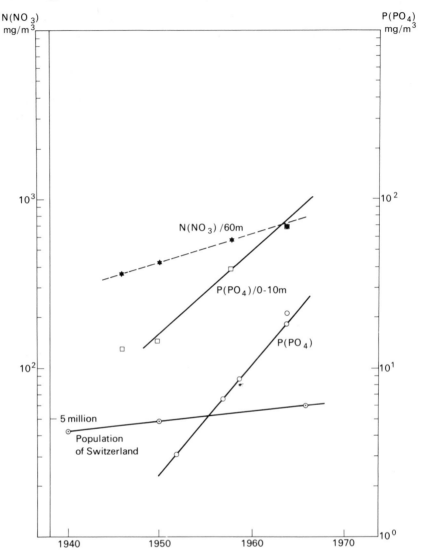

Fig. 11.7 Changes in nutrient concentrations as measured in the Zurichsee and Bodensee in Switzerland, compared with the rate of population growth. The cultural rather than metabolic reasons for eutrophication can be inferred.
Source: OECD 1970.

lithosphere and many ecosystems are adjusted to its scarcity: it is a limiting element in Liebig's sense (p. 42). The large quantities made available by human-induced concentrations lift such limits and 'blooms' result; nitrogen may then become the limiting factor and organisms such as blue-green algae take over from the plankton because they escape the nitrogen limits. 'Blooms' of such algae then follow. The additional nitrogen and phosphorus accelerate the ageing of lakes, themselves short-lived in geological terms, by nutrient enrichment or eutrophication (Fig. 11.6). Such a process happens naturally but is speeded up many times by human activities which result in large inputs of phosphorus and nitrogen (OECD 1970). Fig. 11.7 shows the build-up of nutrients in two European lakes which have undergone enrichment. Many other examples are known, of which the Great Lakes of North America are probably the best documented, especially Lakes Erie and Ontario (Charlier 1970, International Joint Commission 1970). The total dissolved solids in these two lakes have risen by 50 ppm in the last 50 years, for example, and the fish populations have changed almost completely (a situation complicated by the effects after 1945 of the parasitic sea-lamprey, which, however, cannot spawn in the tributaries of Lake Erie). The bottom fauna too has changed sweepingly, especially through increases in midge larvae and tubificid worms. In summer a serious depletion of dissolved oxygen occurs, *Cladophora* piles up in offensive heaps on the shores and blue-green algal scums are formed. The problem is complicated by the presence of pesticide residues: in 1969 a catch of 1,000 kg of coho salmon from Lake Michigan was destroyed because of the high concentration of DDT residues. Eutrophication is not confined to water: input–output studies of forested watersheds in New Hampshire showed that the aerially derived input of some mineral elements exceeded the loss by runoff. This suggests a gradual enrichment of this habitat, but the long-term effects are difficult to predict because of the considerable powers of nutrient absorption possessed by the forest flora.

One direct danger to humans has been detected. Nitrates can be converted in the digestive tract by certain bacteria to nitrites, and the same transition may occur in opened cans of food even if they are subsequently refrigerated. Nitrites react with haemoglobin, forming methemoglobin which will not take up oxygen. Laboured breathing and occasional suffocation results. The condition is most severe in human infants; in the central valley of California contamination of water supplies is such that only bottled water is often recommended for babies. Ehrlich and Ehrlich (1972) say that Elgin, Minnesota, was forced by nitrate pollution to find a new water supply. There is also the possibility that nitrites may react with creatinine (present in vertebrate muscles) to form nitrosarcosine, which can be carcinogenic.

The cessation of eutrophication of water bodies is clearly an immense task both technically and institutionally; but failure to achieve it will result in the loss not only of biologically significant elements of diversity but also in the diminution of an important element of environmental quality for humans.

Radioactive wastes

Effects of radiation (see Table 11.7 for a glossary of terms)

Natural radiation is emitted from a wide variety of sources such as X-rays and cosmic rays, but its level is such that a normal dose of 5 roentgens (5r) is accumulated over the first 30 years of life (a dental X-ray is 1r). In addition to this are certain man-made emissions which result from nuclear explosions in the atmosphere and underground and by the use of nuclear fission processes to generate energy. Nuclear testing in the atmosphere has been much reduced since the Test-Ban Treaty of 1967, although China and France have set off devices since then. Underground weapons testing has continued, especially by the USA and USSR, and there have been trials of nuclear explosions for non-military purposes as with the US Project Gasbuggy in 1967, when an attempt to improve natural gas yields was made by shattering a 'tight' reservoir rock beneath New Mexico. There has been a considerable rise since 1950 in the number of atomic power plants, and most writers foresee a much greater reliance upon atomic power in the future.

TABLE 11.7   Glossary of terms used in radiation studies

Roentgen (r)	The amount of X or gamma radiation produced in one cubic centimetre of standard dry air ionization equal to one electrostatic unit of charge. Describes the radiation field to which organisms may be exposed.
Curie (Ci)	One curie is the amount of any radioactive nuclide that undergoes 37 billion transformations per second.
Half-life	The average time required for half the atoms of an unstable nuclide to transform.
Dose	A measure of the energy actually absorbed in tissue by interactions with ionizing radiation.

Whenever energy is released by splitting atoms, so are potential contaminators of the ecosphere by the radioactive particles which are the products of the fission reaction. Atmospheric explosions yield numerous isotopes, some very short-lived, others like Sr-90 and Cs-137 having half-lives measured in decades. These are caught up in the atmospheric circulation and gradually come to the earth's surface as 'fallout'. Underground explosions release fewer particles but the chance of contaminating groundwater is always present, especially when the area used is highly faulted geologically.

The concern exhibited about radioactive wastes is caused by the deleterious effects of radiation upon people. Emissions are undetectable by human senses and ineradicable except by the processes of natural decay. A dose of 600r kills all exposed persons within 1 month, and 300r will kill 25 per cent of the exposed population and induce serious injury to 90 per cent of the remainder. Death from 300–600r doses may be from 'marrow death' as blood cells are not replaced, or from 'intestinal death' as the gut ceases to function; at 1,000r 'central nervous system death' occurs quite quickly: an employee at Los Alamos who received a multi-second exposure of 1,200r died within 36 hours. Irradiation of organs produces specific effects at lower doses: a dose of 50r will inhibit spermatogenesis for 1 week or will drop the lymphocyte count by 50 per cent for 1 week. 150r will cause retardation of bone growth in children (hence the 1950s concern about Sr-90 which is taken up by bone), and 250r will produce sterility in males for 1 year and defective genes thereafter, according to Schubert and Lapp (1957). There seems to be no threshold of radiation below which cancer, the shortening of life or genetic damage is not possible. At a dose of 1r per generation about 1 person in 8,000 will have severe genetic effects attributable to radiation, and the peaceful uses of atomic energy at the 1971 level make possible the production of about 5 mutations/100 million genes.

Radioactive material in food chains

Such concerns are exacerbated by the biological magnification of radioactive particles. Just as residues of persistent chemicals may accumulate in the biosphere far beyond the initial dose, so may long-lived isotopes. Clay minerals may selectively absorb and concentrate particles, for example, as with Sr-90, Cs-137, Co-60 and Ru-106. As might be expected, however, one of the most frequent processes is accumulation along food chains. Retention at the various stages depends upon many variables such as the differential uptake of various isotopes and their retention in different organs. In the total biomass, a major fraction of most of the radioactive isotopes is held in the primary production level, but this does not prevent large absolute amounts from reaching high trophic levels (Woodwell 1963, 1967b).

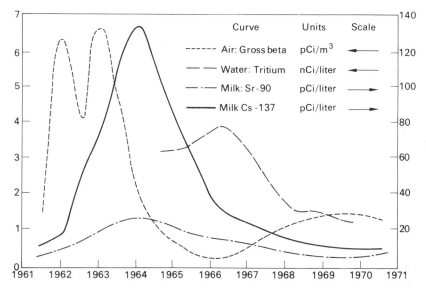

Fig. 11.8 Trends of selected radio-isotopes in the atmosphere, water and milk, as measured in the USA. The effects of the cessation of atmospheric nuclear weapons testing (except by France and China) is apparent.
Source: US President's Council on Environmental Quality 1971

Atmospheric nuclear testing produced very high rates of fallout in arctic regions, especially of Sr-90 and Cs-137. From the atmosphere the particles settle onto, and become incorporated in, the lichens of the tundra and taiga. Cs-137 is effectively retained in the upper parts of these organisms whereas Sr-90 is translocated through the whole plant, which grows very slowly, incorporating approximately 95 per cent of the fallout (half-lives 3–13 years) which settles on it. The lichens are important winter food for caribou which graze off them, especially the top parts, thus leading to high winter uptake levels of isotopes. Some native peoples depend largely upon caribou meat for food, though not usually in the winter, and adult males may eat 5–6 kg/week. Thus certain northern peoples of Alaska, Canada, Lapland and the USSR have body burdens of Cs-137 and Sr-90 which average 50–100 times higher than those of temperate-zone inhabitants (Hanson 1967a,

1967b). Cessation of atmospheric nuclear testing except by France and China has led to a diminution in fallout rates (Fig. 11.8).

Disposal of radionuclides

Caution has to be exercised over wastes from power plants because they may accumulate firstly in the fine silts and muds of estuaries and secondly in long marine food chains. Fluid wastes disposed of in solid rock may cause problems, as with the series of earthquakes triggered off around Denver, Colorado, by the pumping of liquid wastes into the rock beneath the Rocky Mountains arsenal of the US Army (Healy 1968). Radioactive particles were not present in this instance, but the events have served as a warning of the unsuitability of this method of disposal of wastes of any kind.

The generation of nuclear power creates large quantities of nuclear wastes. A 1 million KWe reactor will produce 72 million curies/yr of I-131, and 130,000 curies of tritium in its first year, somewhat less in subsequent years. No treatments yet proposed will remove these from the liquid or gaseous effluents of the reactors (Abrahamson 1972). At Windscale in Cumberland, England, the most significant radionuclide released into the sea is ruthenium-106 which is accumulated in marine algae. These include *Porphyra umbilicalis* which, as laver-bread, is eaten by Welshmen. Their appetite for laver-bread thus determines the level of radioactive waste discharged from the plant (Hedgpeth 1972). Most authorities connected with atomic power generation believe that their 'safe levels' are meaningful and that waste concentrations are held below these limits. More writers are now questioning this view, holding that since our knowledge of ecology is so thin, we cannot agree that it is safe to increase the radiation content of any part of the biosphere. There is also the question of accidents, against which considerable precautions are taken but against which insurance companies will not take a risk. In the USA, the Atomic Energy Commision described the possible effects of a major accident at a reactor which was small by today's standards; at worst, they thought that 3,400 deaths, 43,000 injuries, 7×10^9 property damage and crop damage over 150,000 mi^2 could occur (Abrahamson 1972).

The advent of very large-scale use of atomic energy by fission will produce 3×10^6 Ci/yr of tritium, along with other long-lived radionuclides (Table 11.8). Fusion of the high-level wastes, which are 1 per cent by volume but contain 90 per cent of the radioactivity, into ceramics and then burial in salt mines is the usual method advocated for disposition of these wastes. Weinberg and Hammond (1971) suggest that an installed capacity of 400,000 KW will require 78 km^2 of salt mine per year. Dangers are said to be low (Gordon 1970), though opponents of nuclear power are not slow to point out the various places where leakage could occur. Although some re-use of fissionable materials is possible (a plant in South Carolina is to be built to recycle spent fuels), the need to isolate such materials from the biosphere for about 250,000 years has led to the suggestion that containers of radioactive waste be placed every 10 km^2 on parts of the ice of Antarctica. They would sink under their own heat and weight, to rest at the rock-ice interface where they would be safe against all forms of natural disaster, and accidents would be impossible (Zeller *et al.* 1973). The Antarctic Treaty forbids the disposal of such wastes, but the signatories are among those likely to have to cope with perhaps a hundredfold increase in the quantity of high-level wastes in the period 1972–2000. Perhaps by the latter date nuclear fusion, which produces no radioactive wastes, will be a usable power source.

TABLE 11.8   Nuclear wastes as a function of power production, USA, 1970–2000

	1970	1980	2000
Installed nuclear capacity MW(e)	11,000	95,000	734,000
High-level liquid waste, annual production (gal/yr)	23,000	510,000	3,400,000
Accumulated volume (gal)	45,000	2,400,000	39,000,000
Accumulated fission products: megacuries			
Sr-90 (half-life 27·7 yrs)	15	750	10,800
Kr-85 (half-life 11·2 yrs)	1·2	90	1,160
H-3 (half-life 12·3 yrs)	0·04	3	36
Total for all fission products (gal)	1,200	44,000	860,000
Total for all fission products (tons)	16	388	5,350

1 US gallon = 3·785 litres; 1 ton = 1·016 mt
Source: SCEP 1970

Metals

Man's concentrations of natural elements

These elements are often essential to the metabolism of plants and animals but usually at very low concentrations. At high dosage levels they are frequently toxic to plants, animals and men and several of them are thought to be cumulative. They are of course part of the 'natural' environment but little is known about the development of tolerances, with the exception of the evolution of strains of certain plants, mainly grasses, able to withstand very high levels of, for example, lead and zinc, and thus grow on industrial waste tips formed at the sites of the smelting of these metals. But overall biological diversity is much reduced in such areas, and downstream from the tips at lead and copper mines, for example, their toxic effects are easily observable. The uses of metals are extremely widespread and, apart from the obvious and visible, include substances such as pesticides where 141 metals can be found in 112 compounds, and in additives like lead in petrol. Material concentrations in industrial areas are likely to be big pools of metals: sewage and urban solid wastes, for example, are high in their concentration of them. While in use, elements like lead, mercury, zinc, selenium, manganese, chromium, copper, cadmium and nickel are likely to be closely observed for toxicity, especially among workers handling them or consumers of products: hence the development of lead-free paints. However, their residual effects, as wastes and in unobservable forms like aerosols, are likely to escape notice until levels somewhere build up to a toxic concentration.

Lead

Among the toxic heavy metals, two which have come under the most scrutiny for possible pollutant effects from residues are lead and mercury. Lead is known to cause poisoning in most organisms, though tolerances vary. Some 180 kilotons (kt)/yr is estimated to be discharged into the oceans as a result of 'natural' processes, whereas about 2,000 kt/yr is mined (Lagerweff 1967). One of the newest (since 1923) and fastest-growing uses has been the addition of lead alkyls (commonly tetraethyl lead) to petrols as an 'anti-knock' additive (7,625 kt of leaded petrol sales in 1960, 14,010 in 1970). This results in an increase of lead in the atmosphere which eventually falls out, as the evidence collected by Murozumi *et al.* (1969) from cores of ice in Greenland shows (Fig. 11.9). Since the early 1970s, many countries have started to phase out the use of lead in this manner. Lead can enter drinking water from the atmosphere, from lead pipes if these are still used, and from the lead filler used in the joints of PVC pipes (Fig. 11.10).

Assessing the relationship between environmental (especially atmospheric) lead and lead levels in humans is a difficult matter (Bryce-Smith 1971, M. Williams 1971). Ingested and inhaled lead does not necessarily have a long residence time in the body as much of it is quickly excreted (Table 11.9). Tissue lead levels show, however, that there may be some accumulation in the body. Measurements in Manchester, England, revealed that a group of children had an average blood level of 0·309 ppm of lead, and that 4 per cent of them had

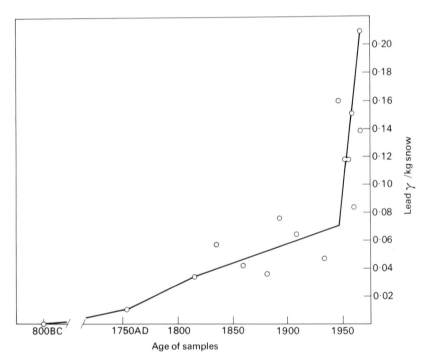

Fig. 11.9 The increase in the fallout of lead onto the snow of the Greenland ice-cap since 800 BC.
Source: Murozumi *et al.* 1969

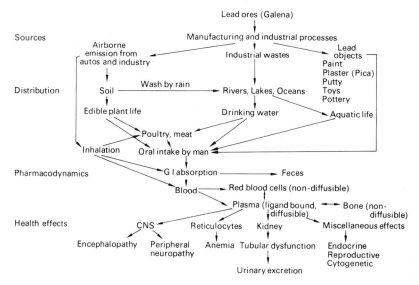

Fig. 11.10 A diagram of the pathways of lead in the biosphere and its effects on man. No mention is made of any natural flows of lead through the biosphere. GI = gastro-intestinal, CNS = central nervous system.
Source: Goyer and Chisholm 1972

levels above 0·8 ppm, a level which is associated with brain damage in children. The mean level in city-dwelling adults of the USA is 0·15–0·21 ppm, derived at least in part from an air level of 0·1–3·4 µg/m³. The USSR has tentatively set a maximum permissible level of 0·7 µg/m³ for the general atmosphere; in Britain the safety level for industrial workers in lead is 200 µg/m³ for a 40-hour week. Since air levels in cities are about 40 times less than this figure, there would seem to be little danger to humans, but the possibilities that

TABLE 11.9   Average daily intake of lead by a 'normal' person in the USA

Substance	Daily intake	Lead concentration in substance	Lead ingested per day (mg)	Fraction absorbed	Lead absorbed per day (mg)
Food	2 kg	0·17 ppm	330	0·05	17
Water	1 kg	0·01 ppm	10	0·1	1
Urban air	20 cubic metres (m³)	1·3 mg/m³*	26	0·4	10·4
Rural air	20 cubic metres (m³)	0·05 mg/m³*	1	0·4	0·4
Tobacco smoke	30 cigarettes	0·8 mg per cigarette	24	0·4	9·6

* Much of this is in the form of lead chloride and lead oxide.
Source: Walker 1971

the absorption rates of industrial lead and airborne lead are different, or that there might be synergistic results, should not be forgotten. Interestingly, imbibers of moonshine whiskey are at risk for lead poisoning, among other things (Goyer and Chisholm 1972).

Mercury

If there is some doubt about the status of lead as a toxic agent, then the case of mercury is much clearer. Mercury is used in industrial processes (its main use is in the production of chlorine and caustic soda in which there is a loss of 0·2 kg Hg per ton of the chlorine produced), and as an agricultural fungicide, so that it appears in industrial effluent and in runoff, both discharging frequently into lakes or at the coast (Table 11.10).

TABLE 11.10   Major uses of mercury in the USA, 1969

	kg
Electrolyte chlorine	71,300
Electrical apparatus	626,000
Paints	335,000
Agriculture	95,000
Pharmaceuticals	23,600
Paper industries	19,100

Source: Harriss 1971

The 'natural' level of mercury is of the order of a release of 5,000 mt/yr by chemical weathering, and human use adds about the same quantity (Harriss 1971). The pathways are shown in Fig. 11.11. Some is held in soils, but once in water it is rapidly absorbed by

TABLE 11.11   Mercury concentrations reported in environmental samples

Sample	Estimated natural levels	Concentrations measured in con-taminated samples
Air	2 μg/m³	2–20 μg/m³
Water:		
Sea water	0·00006–0·0003 ppm	0·0005–0·030 ppm
Fresh water	0·00006 ppm	0·0001–0·040 ppm
Soils[1]	0·04 ppm	0·08–40 ppm
Lake sediments[1]	0·06 ppm	0·08–1,800 ppm
Biological materials:		
Fish	0·02 ppm	0·5–17 ppm
Human blood	0·0008 ppm	0·001–0·013 ppm

[1] Mercury concentration is dependent on organic content.
Source: Harriss 1971

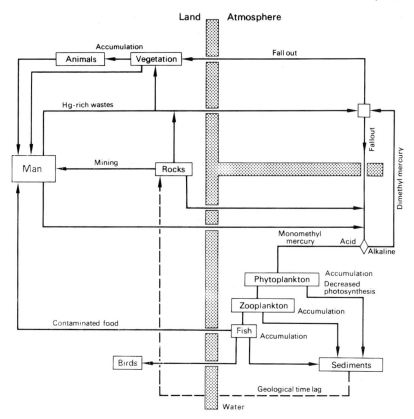

Fig. 11.11 A diagram of the pathways of mercury in the biosphere and man's position in them, both as a controller of some of the flows and the recipient of unwanted wastes.
After an original by Barbara Downey

particulate organic and inorganic material. Also, relatively innocuous inorganic or phenyl mercury is converted into toxic methyl or dimethyl compounds in sediments where bacteria are present. As with organochlorine pesticides, levels in organic matter are higher than in the surrounding water, and concentration in food chains is well established (Table 11.11). In organisms, mercury is concentrated in the liver, brain and kidneys, and alarm has been shown at the level of residues in foods such as tuna fish and swordfish, since the safe level suggested by the US Food and Drug Administration and WHO (0·5 ppm) has often been exceeded. Poisoning of humans from mercury-contaminated fish and shellfish has been established in Japan, where the symptoms of neural damage are known as Minamata disease after the town most strongly affected (Irukayama 1966). On the Manitoba–Ontario border in Canada, mercury levels in fish are 24 times the acceptable level in food of 0·5 ppm, and some of the Indians had body levels of 100–200 ppb (50 ppb is considered the safe upper limit). Eating of the fish is banned and no symptoms of mercury poisoning among the Ojibways have yet developed (Table 11.12).

TABLE 11.12   Concentration factors for mercury in some aquatic organisms

Algae	200–1,200
Large plants	4–2,400
Invertebrates	400–8,400
Fish (pike)	3,000

Source: Harris 1971

It has been shown that photosynthesis in some plants is inhibited by concentrations of 0·001 ppm of mercury, and that explosions of other populations and alterations in the structure of food webs are likely. Synergistic effects reported include an increased toxicity to crustacea of inorganic mercury and ethyl mercury chloride in the presence of low quantities of copper (US Geological Survey 1970). Public health standards in the USA and USSR of 0·005 ppm in drinking water have now been set and Japan will not permit > 0·01 ppm in industrial waste. Chlor-alkali plants in Canada may release no more than 0·005 lb of mercury per ton ($2·54 \times 10^{-4}$ kg/mt) of chlorine produced into rivers frequented by fish. These standards, however, ignore the long-term concentration and food-web effects and are perhaps insufficiently stringent, since at least 90 per cent of all mercury pollution in effluent can be eliminated without causing economic strain to the industries involved (Fimreite 1970). Agricultural residues are more difficult to deal with and withdrawal of mercuric pesticides, as happened in Sweden in 1966, seems the most logical step.

Solid wastes

Products of city metabolism

Urban areas concentrate materials greatly and there is a good deal of waste which has to be removed from the cities. Solid wastes are characterized by a great mixture of substances, including fine dust, cinder, metal and glass, paper and cardboard, textiles, putrescible vegetable material, and plastics. In addition, there is bulky waste such as old refrigerators, washing machines and autos (UK 1970, US President's Council 1971); in Britain these latter comprise 3–4 per cent of the total weight of refuse. The quantities of these materials are high: in the USA a year's solid wastes amount to 168 million mt (1965) or an average of 2 kg/cap/day or 907 kg/cap/yr. (The equivalent figure in 1920 was 1·25 kg/cap/day.) The high extremes of the distribution come from places like Los Angeles (2·59 kg/cap/day) and the San Francisco Bay area (3·62 kg/cap/day). Included in these totals are 48×10^9 cans (135/cap) bottles, together with 7 million junked autos. In the UK the number of discarded cars rose from 325,000 in 1967 to 600,000 in 1970 and is predicted to become 1,300,000 by 1980. The composition of the garbage is changing too: the last 10 years has seen a considerable rise in the proportion of plastics, paper and packaging materials, to the point

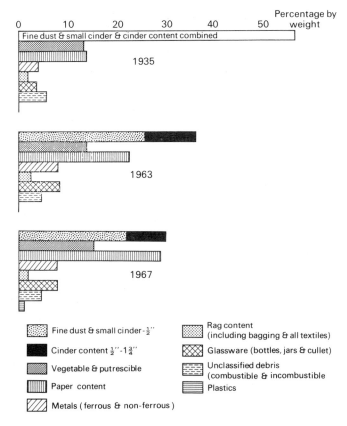

Fig. 11.12 The changing content of urban solid wastes in Britain 1935–67. The reduction of coal wastes, the late appearance of plastics and the increase in paper are the major features.
Source: United Kingdom 1970

where Chicago refuse is about 56 per cent paper. The proportion of fuel wastes has, however, fallen: in Britain, the average weekly weight of garbage fell from 16·8 to 12·7 kg between 1935–67, reflecting a fall from 9·70 to 5·46 kg of dust and cinder (Fig. 11.12).

Under the carpet?

Such quantities of unwanted material can cause serious disposal problems. The simplest method is crude tipping or open dumping: in 1965 the USA had 17,000–22,000 such places, and in the UK (1963) 115 local authorities still used this method. More satisfactory is controlled tipping or the sanitary landfill. A layer of about 6 ft of refuse is covered by at least 9 in of earth, ash or other inert material, up to the level of the hole chosen. The surface can then be used for housing or sports fields, for example. Before such filling, the wastes can be pulverized by machines to a uniform particle size: by this means the volume is reduced and thus the life of the tip extended, and some of the refuse is more quickly biodegraded. Again, pulverized material can be subjected to fermentation before dumping: the heat generated (65°C) helps to destroy bacteria and insect larvae. Incineration can be carried on inside cities, the residues used for civil engineering purposes, and power generated from combustible material, as at St Louis, where an electrical plant derives 15 per cent of its energy input from processed solid waste. Temperatures of 870–1,040°C (1,600–1,900°F) are commonly used, but unless electrostatic precipitators are used, air pollution is substituted for garbage problems; particulate matter from incinerators is estimated to constitute 10–15 per cent of New York City's airborne load. None of these methods is without its side-effects. Uncontrolled tipping contributes smells, windborne litter, dust, flies, rats and complete loss of amenity, and more seriously still, fire (used to consume the combustible components, it may smoulder inside the tip, breaking out sporadically), and contamination of ground water and streams by rainfall which has percolated through the tip. Controlled tipping is not immune to all these difficulties, and even wire fences will not control the airborne litter in a strong wind. Water percolation still occurs, and rats may find nesting places in hollow vessels or large objects which are not completely filled with the sealing material. Filler of earth or ash is often difficult to find, leading to delays in covering the tip or skimping of fill layers. Pulverization can create bad dust problems unless it is covered quickly; fermented material, like sewage sludge, could be sold, but it is expensive and is also very high in certain metals. One overall problem is the effect upon amenity, for although everybody wants their garbage taken away, nobody wants to live near the tip or the incinerator. There may also be a shortage of suitable sites within some jurisdictions and thus agreements with neighbours have to be made, or more often large cities have to exert pressures to gain space in outlying rural areas. Toronto, for example, in 1973 was prepared to pay $Can 6.50/ton to a railway company to haul and bury 400,000 tons/yr (out of a total solid waste production of 1·5 million tons) for at least 15 years. The residents of the intended receiving area were not thrilled by the prospect even when the company announced it would erect viewing platforms for the public to see the tipping and filling process. While the use of quarries and pits for such purposes is to some extent acceptable, the covering of wildlands such as mud flats and swamps is a much more serious loss in terms both of amenity and biological productivity.

Clearly, refuse is an immense potential source of raw materials, but steps towards re-use are very slow, with the exception of metals. Cars especially can now be virtually pelletized and the scrap sold to steel works. Paper can be recycled and many other materials re-used, but labour costs are very high and few people wish to do the work. Thus successful paper reclamation schemes like those of certain Canadian cities rely on subsidies from local taxes. In metropolitan Toronto, the borough of York spent $Can 687 to collect and ship 6 tons of waste paper for recycling which it sold for $Can 31. In 1970 the Greater London Council forecast that ferrous metal recovery was the only permanent salvage activity it could foresee in the future.

Solid wastes also include a variety of industrial materials, some of which are very toxic, like cyanide wastes. These can be neutralized, but unscrupulous industrialists pay truck drivers to dump the wastes by night onto open tips. A series of revelations of this practice in the English midlands in 1972 led to emergency legislation designed to prevent 'fly-tipping' of these materials. Probably only the tip of this particular iceberg has emerged (Dawe 1972).

Waste heat

Whenever energy performs work, heat is released which is radiated back into the atmosphere. Man concentrates this process spatially, and the resultant heating of air and water is called calefaction. In practical terms the commonest sources of concentrations of waste are power-generating plants. 1 KWH of energy generated from fossil fuels creates 6,000 BTU of heat; the same energy from nuclear fuels gives off 10,000 BTU. Nuclear plants in general produce about 50 per cent more heat than thermal plants. The demand for power has meant that in Canada, for example, waste heat from thermal power generation is predicted to rise 14 times in the period 1966–90, and by AD 2000 the amount of waste heat reaching Lake Ontario in January will be equivalent to 8 per cent of the solar energy input in that month (Cole 1969). Most of the heat is carried away as hot water and this produces distinct changes in biota. A body of water at 30–35°C is essentially a biological desert and many game fish require temperatures of $< 10°C$ for successful reproduction although they will survive above that temperature. A temperature rise of 10°C will double the rate of many chemical reactions and so the decay of organic matter, the rusting of iron and the solution rate of salts are all accelerated by calefaction. Since the rate of exchange of salts and organisms increases, any toxins are liable to exert greater effects, and temperature fluctuations are also likely to affect organisms. Calefaction is therefore likely to exert a disruptive effect upon aquatic ecosystems, although some ways of putting the waste heat to beneficial use have been suggested. Where power plants are near deep ocean waters, the very cold water at depth could be brought up for efficient cooling and then pumped at its raised temperature into tanks used for raising fish or algae. Experiments in Hawaii and in St Croix in the Virgin Islands have suggested that a 100 MW plant could service a pond volume of 10^5 m^3 and produce 70 mt dry weight of carnivorous (third trophic level) fish/yr. Such a plan would also obviate the disturbance of the aquatic littoral community (Bienfang 1971). Such local developments do not countermand the fact that energy production and use all contribute heat to the atmosphere. The possible global effects are discussed in Chapter 10.

Noise

Noise is primarily a feature of cities, as exemplified by J. Caesar's action in banning chariots from the streets of Rome by day, thus producing insomnia by night. Defined as 'sound without value' or 'any noise that is undesired by the recipient', noise is still largely encountered in cities and so is not a major concern of this book. Noise levels in many urban-industrialized situations are known to be deleterious to human health and efficiency, with effects on the sense organs, cardiovascular system, glandular and nervous systems, while physical pain results at a level of 140 perceived noise decibels (pNdB) (Table 11.13; Molitor 1968, US Federal Council 1968).

TABLE 11.13   Noise levels (pNdB)

Silence	0	Rock band	100
Average residence	40–50	Compressors and hammers on	
Dishwasher	65	construction work at 10 ft	110
Auto at 20 ft	70–80	Four-engine jet at 500 ft	118
Light truck	75	Hydraulic press at 3 ft	130
Light truck accelerating	85	Threshold of pain	140
Subway train at 20 ft	95		

Source: US Federal Council 1968

    Localized noise derived from sources such as traffic or pan-throwing neighbours may affect personal health but does not have any obvious ecological repercussions. Recreation areas may be affected by noise from motorboats, but environmental noise is particularly associated with aircraft, especially along flight-paths in the vicinity of airfields (Plate 20). Settlement location may need to be adjusted in such places with consequent ecological disruptions elsewhere. The sonic boom path associated with SST projects such as Concorde will produce noise of a very different order, in the form of sudden but repeated shock waves. These will cause disturbance to wild birds as well as domestic stock and buildings; if SSTs come into extensive use, subsonic flight over land seems to be a necessary condition.

Plate 20 The use of fossil fuel usually means noise. At this moment the Indian 'Palace in the Sky' is probably preferable to the Englishman's castle on the ground. *(Guardian, London)*

Chemical and biological warfare (CBW)

All effects so far discussed have been the unsought side-effects of resource processes, where ecosystems have been altered either unconsciously or because there were no apparent economic alternatives. With chemical and biological conflict (to which is added here the possibility of geophysical warfare), ecosystems are altered deliberately in order to produce military gain (R. Clarke 1968, Hersh 1968). Most CBW agents are aimed at people and thus ecological change would be indirect, but a few forms are aimed at ecological devastation.

With chemical warfare, for example, most of the potential agents are lethal to humans. From the use of arsenical smokes in the Sung Dynasty and sulphur fumes in the Peloponnesian Wars to the nerve gases like SE, GF, VE, and VX of which 70 mg inhaled or 1,250 mg cutaneously absorbed is fatal, the aim has been at other people; in addition the modern method of dispersal by aerosols would distribute such agents over wide areas. Modern nerve gases are cholinesterase inhibitors (thus the power to contract muscles is lost and death from asphixiation results quickly) and so are presumably effective against most animals. The chances therefore of eliminating a key animal in an ecosystem might be quite high. A misuse of biological resources occurs in the cultivation of disease organisms as a prelude to biological warfare. Numerous bacterial and viral diseases are suitable, especially those which have a high epidemicity. Anthrax, brucellosis, cholera, plague, tularemia, yellow fever and smallpox are all members of the gruesome list and several of them produce very high fatality rates. These again are aimed primarily at human populations, but several of them are diseases of wild and domesticated animals which might be expected thus to share in the general mortality accompanying any deliberate use, especially if the toxins were dispersed initially in aerosol form. Perhaps the most virulent of all these agents is the chemical toxin botulin, produced by the anaerobic bacterium *Clostridium botulinum*. A dose of 0·12 μg will produce 60–70 per cent mortality by inhalation or ingestion; treatment is difficult and there is no known antidote or vaccine. It decomposes after 12 hours in the air and so invaders could enter 24 hours after its use without danger. One ounce (28·35 g) of the 'A type' toxin is sufficient to kill 60 million people and 8 oz (226·8 g) should be enough for the entire population of the world. Dissemination by aerosols would be easy and the toxin is 1,000 times more effective when inhaled in spray droplets. It can be easily manufactured and stored indefinitely. Its use on a wide scale would undoubtedly produce respiratory paralysis of many animals other than those for which it was intended.

On a larger scale, man's planetary processes may be harnessable to harass an enemy. Several such activities are currently unpredictable in their effects or else not yet possible, but they do not appear to be far beyond the reach of technological developments (Calder 1968). Weather modification, for example, is usually employed to increase precipitation on a given area, as has been tried by the USA during the Vietnam War. If your enemy lives downwind he can be desiccated by the same method. Similarly the potential possibility of guiding a hurricane away from your own shores between guidelines of monomolecular films confers the equal possibility of guiding it onto an unfriendly shore. The upper layers of the atmosphere between 15–20 km altitude contain an ozone layer which absorbs most of the ultra-violet (UV) radiation from the sun; if a 'hole' could be created by chemical or physical action (e.g. UV radiation at 250 millimicrons wavelength decomposes O_3 atoms) then everything beneath would be burnt. At a crustal level, the strain energy present in large fault systems could be triggered off by underground nuclear explosions. At present the whereabouts of the resulting earthquakes cannot be foreseen (hence the worry over the large explosion under Amchitka Island in the Aleutians in November 1971), but improved knowledge of the behaviour of seismically unstable systems might tempt a dweller by the China Sea to have a jiggle at the San Andreas fault. On a larger scale altogether is the hypothetical possibility of setting off very large nuclear explosions at the base of ice-caps, especially in Antarctica, thus initiating outward sliding of the ice-sheet. The two results would be huge tsunamis that would wreck coastal developments even in the northern hemisphere, and greater ice accumulation owing to the changed albedo, thus bringing about a new 'glacial' period, with more temperate conditions in the tropics. Since only land-locked tropical states would benefit, the likelihood of an attempt seems as low as the likeli-hood that the sequence of geophysical events would actually follow the predicted path (MacDonald 1968).

The necessity of avoiding all the above eventualities has led to some measure of inter-national agreement about the banning of CBW. As with large-scale nuclear warfare, or even intensive conventional bombing as in Vietnam (Westing and Pfeiffer 1972), the effects of widespread dispersal of the agents would affect not only people but the structure and functioning of many ecosystems, and many irreversible changes might be produced. In Vietnam, where aerial spraying of 2,4-D and 2,4,5-T has been used by the USA to defoliate forests and devastate crops (Table 11.14), Tschirley estimates that although mangroves may recover in about 20 years' time, some sprayed areas of forest may become vegetated with bamboo, retarding regeneration of forest considerably. By March 1969, 189,782 ha of crops had been destroyed and 1·67 million ha of 'jungle' defoliated. It is impossible to estimate the amount of accidental damage by spray drifts, and load dumping may deposit 1,000 gal (3,785 litres) in 30 seconds instead of 4 minutes, an unprecedented concentration (Tschirley 1969, Orians and Pfeiffer 1970, Whiteside 1970, Lewallen 1971). Even though dioxin, a contaminant of 2,4,5-T, appears to be associated with foetal teratogenicity, the USA has not regarded this activity as being chemical or biological warfare, although cessation of the practice has accompanied the USA withdrawal. Perhaps Tacitus best sums it up: 'Ubi solitudinem faciunt: pacem appellant'.

The invasion of the biosphere

As Table 11.1 has shown, the various components of the biosphere act as temporary or permanent resting places for man-induced wastes. Many contaminants pass through the atmosphere, for example, but gases such as CO_2 which remain there, and finely divided particulate matter, provide the most likely agents of widespread change. The chemical balance of gases in the atmosphere is apparently the product of biological processes and can be changed by man with possible effects upon the global climate. By contrast, contamination of moving fresh water is primarily a local or regional problem, and if the offending inputs

TABLE 11.14   Defoliating agents used in Vietnam

Code-name	Ingredient of mixture	lb/gal (114 g/litre) acid equivalent	Use
Agent Orange	2,4-D 50 2,4,5-T 50	4·2 3·7	General defoliation of forest, brush and broad-leaved crops.
Agent Blue	2,4-D 50 2,4,5-T 30 2,4,5-T 20	4·2 2·2 1·5	Used interchangeably
Agent White	2,4-D 50 Picloram	2·0 0·54	Forest defoliation—for long-term results
Agent Blue	Sodium cacodylate 27·7% Cacodylic acid 4·8% Water, NaCl to 100%		Rapid, short-term defoliation of grass and rice

Source: Orians and Pfeiffer 1970

cease, then the biological processes and the hydrological cycle restore the water to a purer condition (Wolman 1971). This may of course take some time, as in the case of the River Rhine, where *inter alia* a German factory discharges wastes with a daily BOD equivalent to the sewage of 4·7 million people, and Alsatian potash mines discharge enough salt to raise the chlorine content of the river from 150 to 350 mg/litre in 30 years. As Coleridge remarked, 'What power divine / Shall henceforth wash the river Rhine?' Relatively rapid cleansing is not possible in large lakes where poisoning and eutrophication can bring about apparently irreversible biological death if they proceed too far; small lakes at an early stage of enrichment can be saved. Soils also can accumulate nutrients with as yet unknown effects. Many residual poisons in soils form the greatest magnitude of contamination having the most measurable ecological effect. The oceans inevitably form the main repository for contaminants from land, fresh water and atmosphere, although they lose some volatile substances to the last of these. Even if accumulation ceased now, the great water bodies would harbour residual pesticides for many years to come, along with numerous long-lived industrial, chemical and pharmaceutical compounds and oil effluent. Apart from their role as a food provider, the oceans play a significant part in the CO_2/O_2 balance of the planet, and the inhibition of photosynthesis by contaminants may seriously affect both. It is difficult to estimate which environment suffers the most contamination, but probably that of the oceans is most significant (MacIntyre and Holmes 1971). In 1972 an international convention to reduce the dumping of waste materials into the sea was signed by 80 countries whose fleets account for about 90 per cent of ocean pollution. It prohibits the dumping of radioactive wastes, CBW agents, oils, cadmium and mercury, and organohalogen compounds. A special clause allows some of these to be dumped if they are immediately hazardous to human health. A second list contains substances which may only be offloaded in specific locations and quantities with prior permission from a secretariat: arsenic, lead, copper, cyanides and fluorides are included. The accord closely follows the terms of the Oslo Agreement for the North Sea (also of 1972) but includes large maritime nations such as the USA, USSR, Liberia, Japan and Greece. It is impossible so far to see what effect such conventions may have.

On the land, poisoning of animals and plants by various air- and water-borne effluents is a daily occurrence in industrialized countries and cumulative toxins build up steadily, although radioactive fallout has fortunately continued to decline. Mortality among predators at the tops of food chains has been accompanied by sub-lethal effects in these and other animals at lower trophic levels.

Inevitably the possible effects of all these wastes upon man has been the subject of most concern. Apart from direct poisoning during toxin application, mortality from waste products is not apparently very high, though deaths from contaminated drinking water or sewage-laden sea-water off resorts are doubtless not publicized by the communities in which they occur. Directly traceable incidents like Minamata disease are generally rare, and features like smog perhaps exacerbate existing ailments rather than induce new ones. But the increased volume and incidence of pollutants is so recent that no adult has yet gone through a life-span carrying for example the body-burden of DDT now common. Not until those born after 1950 have gone through a normal twentieth-century Western urban existence without showing significant damage can we say that the present levels of contamination are harmless.

More important than considerations of the personal health of individuals is the 'health' of the systems of the biosphere, for man is inextricably bound up in the webs of these systems and cannot exist apart from them. It is notable therefore that the effects of the various forms of pollution upon ecosystems can be generalized and indeed predicted. Putting together the evidence from ecological change caused by radioactivity, eutrophication, toxins, defoliation and deforestation, Woodwell (1970b) summarizes his findings that

> pollution operates on the time scale of succession, not of evolution, and we cannot look to evolution to cure this set of problems. The loss of structure involves a shift away from complex arrangements of specialized species toward the generalists; away from forest, toward hardy shrubs and herbs; away from those phytoplankton of the open ocean that Wurster proved so very sensitive to DDT, towards those algae of the sewage plants that are unaffected by almost everything including DDT and most fish; away from diversity in birds, plants and fish toward monotony; away from tight nutrient cycles toward very loose ones with terrestrial systems becoming overloaded; away from stability toward instability especially with regard to sizes of populations of small rapidly producing organisms such as insects and rodents that compete with man; away from a world that runs itself through a self-augmentive, slowly moving evolution, to one that requires constant tinkering to patch it up, a tinkering that is malignant in that each act of repair generates a need for further repairs to avert problems generated at compound interest.

To which may be added that all these shifts represent a movement away from systems which are highly valued in aesthetic and other non-economic terms to those of lower acceptability and value: in other words, a lowering of what we choose to call environmental quality.

The solution to the ecological downgrading caused by contamination can only be multi-dimensional. A suitable technology is an obvious starting place and may indeed be the easiest phase to achieve. Efficacious methods of material 'sieving' to prevent contamination of biospheric systems are available for many resource processes, although in some cases they merely transfer the site of the disposal problem. But nevertheless, sewage can be treated and smokes can be scrubbed, mine wastes can be reburied along with atomic wastes, and non-residual third-generation pesticides will replace the chlorinated hydrocarbons. But some contaminations are beyond the reach of technology: as long as industry persists, carbon dioxide and heat will be generated and led off into the atmosphere, and no technique for sieving out the DDT and related substances now in the oceans has been, or is likely to be, invented. So while recovery of many wastes is technically possible, there are some contaminant-caused problems to which no technological solution is at all likely. Movement towards greater sifting of the by-products of resource processes is likely to be accelerated by a shortage of the initial supply of the material. Current economic and social values dictate that the proper response to a materials shortage is to develop a new process which will render hitherto inaccessible sources usable or to achieve substitution by another material. The complexity of contemporary technology means however that long 'lead times' are inevitable for new processes, so that the time-scale of problem accumulation is much slower than the time-scale of finding solutions. Substitution may not always be possible because of scale factors: water is the obvious example here. Recycling of materials is, therefore, not popular in the DCs at present but is likely to become more applicable because of cost factors and because of public concern, for example over disposable but non-returnable articles like plastic bottles and paper products. This movement may gain impetus if ways of accounting are devised that include the full social costs of environmental contamination in its various forms; 'making the polluter pay' is unpopular in DCs because of the fear that industrial firms will become less competitive in world markets. But even though an estimated 287×10^9 must be spent in the USA on meeting air and water quality standards in the period 1971–80, this will only lower the rate of growth of GNP by 0·1 per cent; without such controls it would be 4·8 per cent p.a., with them, 4·7 per cent p.a. (Anon 1972). The loss of environmental quality due to insidious degradation is scarcely likely, however, to be susceptible to such analysis and will likely be ignored. Another institutional difficulty is the low status and satisfaction in working at materials recovery with present technology. A basic change in human values that puts healthy ecosystems before an unending supply of new materials would be ideal but seems destined to remain a low priority.

The atmosphere and the deep oceans are also a commons in Hardin's (1968) sense, and so international agreement is necessary for any of the clean-up processes to be effective. The scale and magnitude of the agreements necessary, for example to lower nitrogen and phosphorus levels in estuaries or to prevent untreated sewage reaching the seas, are immense and less capable of solution than the development of new technology. The guidelines issuing from the UN 1972 Stockholm conference make general references to pollution but offer no suggestions for implementing technological solutions on an international basis. 'The just struggle of the people of all countries against pollution should be supported' is not a blueprint for environmental cleanliness.

Finally, we must remember that pollution and contamination exist as the end-parts of resource processes and cannot sensibly be viewed outside this context; attempts to 'cure' pollution without considering the whole of the relevant resource process are as useful as trying to cure lung cancer with aspirins. Hence the primary importance of recycling wastes as sources of raw materials. The magnitude of the processes is inevitably linked to the ever-increasing rates of production of material goods and hence to population levels. People are not pollution, as some slogans aver, but there is little doubt that they are the cause of it, particularly the affluent ones; the example of China in reclaiming every possible material from every waste output is both a precept and a probable portent (Unger 1971). Pessimists tend to take as symbolic the story (only slightly embroidered from LaMore 1971) of the rich Texan who was buried in a king-size grave propped up in the front seat of a Cadillac convertible with the FM radio playing and the air-conditioning full on. One mourner was heard to say to another, 'Man, that's livin'.'

Further reading

CALDER, N. (ed.) 1968: *Unless peace comes.*
HODGES, L. 1973: *Environmental pollution.*
MARX, L. 1971: *Waste.*
MOORE, N. W. 1967: A synopsis of the pesticide problem.
MURDOCH, W. W. (ed.) 1971: *Environment,* 189–366.
SINGER, S. F. 1970: *Global effects of environmental pollution.*
STERN, A. C. (ed.) 1968: *Air pollution.*
STUDY OF CRITICAL ENVIRONMENTAL PROBLEMS (SCEP) 1970: *Man's impact on the global environment: assessment and recommendations for action.*
STUDY OF MAN'S IMPACT ON CLIMATE (SMIC) 1971: *Inadvertent climatic modification.*
WOODWELL, G. M. 1970: Effects of pollution on the structure and physiology of ecosystems.

Part III
The perception of limits

12

Resources and population

This section opens with a discussion of the growth of and future prospects for man's numbers. This leads into a consideration of some of the spatial and social consequences of the interaction of population and resources, and an evaluation of the developing concepts of resource and environmental management especially as enunciated in the DCs.

Population

Historical perspectives

Many general references have been made to population growth and its relationship to resource use. Since it is people who use materials and environments, both as metabolic requirements and cultural accessories, an examination of the past, present and probable future numbers of people and their distribution is considered at this point. There are numerous specialized works on demography and population geography (e.g. J. I. Clarke 1965, Zelinsky 1966, Bogue 1969, Petersen 1969, Trewartha 1969, Zelinsky, Kosinki and Prothero 1970), and only their general conclusions are presented here.

Estimates of the world's population before about AD 1650 are, as a UN publication sharply puts it, 'vague reconstructions', although perhaps the stage when the totals were one and two is reasonably well documented. Estimates for prehistoric times and for the first 1600 years AD are generally based on calculations of culture area by population density, where the latter is inferred from values for present-day examples of such economies as hunting and gathering or shifting agriculture. The taking of censuses began in 1655 and is now common, although many of them are probably not very reliable; on a world basis we may, however, expect a degree of cancellation of errors. The estimated numbers up to the present can be seen in Fig. 12.1, and Table 12.1 gives Deevey's (1960) estimates of population total and density for various periods.

Though the data are scanty before AD 1650 they give a consistent picture of a population with a very slow rate of growth (Fig. 12.1). High infant mortality rates and low longevity meant that rates of increase were small; in Roman times the average life expectation for men was about 30 years, and this was not altered significantly until the coming of scientific medicine in Europe. The replotting of the curve for total world population upon a logarithmic basis reveals a number of surges in population (Fig. 12.2), the first of which was coincident with the Neolithic revolution and the advent of agriculture, when population increased 25-fold due to increase in the means of subsistence. Once agriculture had become

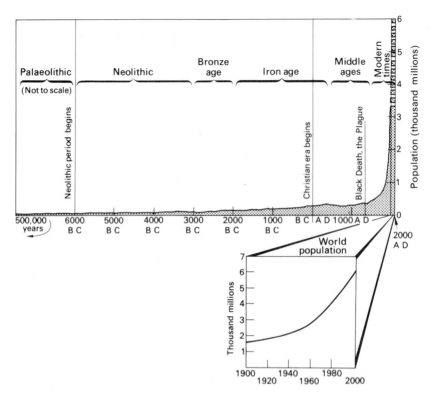

Fig. 12.1 The growth of the world's human population since the Palaeolithic, and projected at current rates of increase to AD 2000. Catastrophes like the Black Death had remarkably little long-term effect. Source: Trewartha 1969

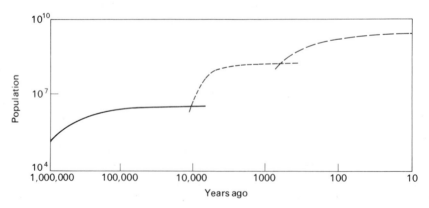

Fig. 12.2 A logarithmic plot of the population curve: surges in population are inferentially connected by Deevey (1960) with the invention of tool making (solid line), the agricultural revolution of the Neolithic (short dashes) and the scientific-industrial revolution (long dashes). Other writers (e.g. Durand 1967) interpret the latest surge as originating before the scientific-industrial revolution. Source: Deevey 1960

TABLE 12.1   Population growth

Years ago (base-date = 1960)	Cultural stage	Area populated	Assumed density per km²	Total population (millions)
1,000,000	Lower Palaeolithic (hunting–gathering)	Africa	0·00425	0·125
300,000	Middle Palaeolithic (hunting-gathering)	Africa and Eurasia	0·012	1·0
25,000	Upper Palaeolithic (hunting–gathering)	Africa and Eurasia	0·04	3·34
10,000	Mesolithic (hunting–gathering)	All continents	0·04	5·32
6,000	Village farming and early urban	Old World / New World	1·0 } 0·04 }	86·5
2,000	Village farming and urban	All continents	1·0	133
310 (1650)	Farming and industrial	All continents	3·7	545
210 (1750)	Farming and industrial	All continents	4·9	728
160 (1800)	Farming and industrial	All continents	6·2	906
60 (1900)	Farming and industrial	All continents	11·0	1,610
10 (1950)	Farming and industrial	All continents	16·4	2,400

Source: Deevey 1960

firmly established (4000–3000 BC) three main zones of occupance existed: high-density areas of agriculture and gathering around the agricultural hearths and diffusion areas; areas with thinly spread gathering and hunting cultures; and unoccupied areas. By about 2000 BC the agricultural occupance of much of Eurasia and the northern half of Africa is postulated. Beyond this core lay the food gatherers and hunters, and the uninhabited areas were still considerable, though reduced in size. Within the agricultural areas densities were higher in favoured places and highest of all where cities had developed. At the time of the Classical world, 200 BC–AD 200, the populations of the world are dominated by empires. The Indian subcontinent held 100–140 million and mainland China 71 million; Imperial Rome under Augustus had some 54 million people who constituted a quarter to a fifth of the world's population. Between AD 1000–1600 a steady but slow growth is seen on most continents (Table 12.2) in spite of intermittent checks imposed by famine and plague. The exception is the Americas, where the colonists and conquistadors were responsible for reducing the aboriginal populations to fractional levels through warfare and disease, although it has been argued that a group like the Maya were on the verge of collapse, having outrun their resource base.

A population of 470–545 million in AD 1650 seems very large by comparison with the figures for BC/AD 0 or 4000 BC, but becomes small in the context of the accelerated growth after AD 1650. The magnitude of the subsequent growth is widely agreed upon with some relatively minor variations according to the sources used (Table 12.3). The major components of the growth 1750–1950,-continent by continent, are shown in Table 12.4, using

TABLE 12.2 Approximate population (millions) of the world and its subdivisions, AD 1000–1600

Year	World	Europe	Asiatic Russia	South-east Asia	India	China Major[1]	Japan	South-east Asia, Oceania	Africa	The Americas
1000	275	42	5	32	48	70	4	11	50	13
1100	306	48	6	33	50	79	5	12	55	17
1200	348	61	7	34	51	89	8	14	61	23
1300	384	73	8	33	50	99	11	15	67	28
1400	373	45	9	27	46	112	14	16	74	30
1500	446	69	11	29	54	125	16	19	82	41
1600	486	89	13	30	68	140	20	21	90	15

[1] China proper, plus Manchuria and Korea, Outer Mongolia, Sinkiang and Formosa.
Source: Desmond 1965

TABLE 12.3 Estimates of world population (millions)

	1650	1750	1800	1850	1900
Wilcox	470	694	919	1,091	1,571
Carr-Saunders	545	728	906	1,171	1,608
Durand	not estimated	791	978	1,262	1,650

Source: Durand 1967

TABLE 12.4 Estimates of population growth 1750–1950 (millions)

Areas	1750	1800	1850	1900	1950
World	791	978	1,262	1,650	2,515
Asia (exc. USSR)	498	630	801	925	1,381
Africa	106	107	111	133	222
Europe (exc. USSR)	125	152	208	296	527
USSR	42	56	76	134	180
North America	2	7	26	82	166
South and Central America	16	24	38	74	162
Oceania	2	2	2	6	13

Figures in italics are those which lack a firm foundation.
Source: Durand 1967

Durand's (1967) work, to which reference should be made for discussion of the reasons for the growth in each individual continent. The major point of interest is the phase of accelerated population growth which has lasted to the present. Its inception varies from place to place and is prior to 1750 in Europe, Russia and America and probably before 1650 in China. The absolute numbers would of course rise quite steeply even with a constant rate of population growth, but as Table 12.5 shows, the actual rate itself has undergone acceleration, except in twentieth-century Europe and the USSR. The more accurate figures

TABLE 12.5   Annual rate of increase (per cent)

Areas	1750– 1800	1800– 1850	1850– 1900	1900– 1950
World	0·4	0·5	0·5	0·8
Asia (exc. USSR)	0·5	0·5	0·3	0·8
Africa	0·0	0·1	0·4	0·7
Europe (exc. USSR)	0·4	0·6	0·7	0·6
USSR	0·6	0·6	1·1	0·6
North America	—	2·7	2·3	1·4
South and Central America	0·8	0·9	1·3	1·6
Oceania	—	—	—	1·6

Figures in italics are those which lack a firm foundation.
Source: Durand 1967

TABLE 12.6   World annual rate of increase

Decade	%
1900–1920	0·6
1920–30	1·1
1930–40	1·0
1940–50	1·0
1950–60	1·8

Source: Durand 1967

of decadal rates for the twentieth century in Table 12.6 exhibit the same trend: the 1950–60 period shows an even greater jump in the rate. Close inspection of estimates of growth for individual nations has revealed little relationship between the development of industrialization and the expansion of population. Why there should then have been a simultaneous upturn in rates of growth in the eighteenth and early nineteenth centuries is not known. No simple explanation of causality is acceptable and Durand's (1967) hypothesis seems more plausible: he suggests that the stimulus of agricultural improvement in the sixteenth and seventeenth centuries provided the potential for considerable population expansion but that this was held back by the transmission of diseases which followed exploration and trade in the same period. By the eighteenth century sufficient resistance to imported infections had built up for the population potential to be realized. At the end of the nineteenth century the dichotomy of demographic process between industrial and less developed countries was apparent: the former had death control (giving lower rates of infant mortality and greater longevity) and a measure of birth control, but the latter had experienced only the initial impact of the death control techniques which are dominated by modern medical practices such as antisepsis, immunization, disease vector control and pharmaceutical improvements, together with a knowledge of nutrition science.

Present numbers, distribution and density

Estimates by the United Nations of the populations of the continents are given in Table 12.7, and the percentage contributions of the various areas shown in Table 12.8. These are summarized in the map of population density, Fig. 12.3. Such statements of distribution reveal that Europe and Asia together contain over three-quarters of mankind, and that Asia has more than half, whereas less than 10 per cent live in the southern hemisphere. Between 20°N–60°N in the Old World are found four-fifths of the population, in a zone which includes also most of the great deserts of the Old World, along with the Alpine and Himalayan mountain systems. Within this zone are two great concentrations of man: south-east Asia, where approximately one-half of the world's people live on one-tenth of the habitable area, and Europe (including European Russia) where one-fifth of the global population occupy less than one-twentieth of its ecumene. There are in addition secondary

TABLE 12.7   Estimated world population, mid-1973 (millions)

World	3,860	Latin America	308
Africa	374	Europe	472
Asia	2,204	USSR	250
North America	233	Oceania	21

Source: Population Reference Bureau 1973

TABLE 12.8   Continental percentages of world population, 1920–73

	1920	1960	1973
Africa	7·9	8·5	9·7
Asia	53·3	56·1	57·2
North America	6·5	6·6	6·0
Latin America	5·0	6·9	7·9
Europe	18·1	14·2	12·2
USSR	8·7	7·1	6·4
Oceania	0·5	0·5	0·5

Source: Population Reference Bureau 1969 and 1973

Fig. 12.3 World population density: only in regions of unfavourable climate are low densities found, but high densities are seen both in urban-industrial regions of the world and in rural-agricultural regions, especially in Asia.
Source: Trewartha 1969

Inhabitants per square

Mile	Km
Over 250	Over 100
125-250	50-100
25-125	10-50
2-25	1-10
Under 2	Under 1

concentrations in the eastern half of North America, California, coastal Brazil, the Plate estuary, the valley of the Nile, west Africa, south-east Africa and south-east Australia. Looked at politically, six states (China, India, Pakistan, Bangladesh, Japan and Indonesia) have nearly half the world's population and, contrarywise, some pocket populations like Gambia (0·4 million in 1972) and Iceland (0·2 million in 1972) continue to exist. Considerable variations in density are revealed by Fig. 12.3. The environmentally inhospitable parts of the globe are principally those too cold, too dry or too high for mass settlement and at concentrations of < 1/km² contrast with the favoured agricultural areas like the valley of the Ganges and maritime east Asia, and with intensely used industrial and agricultural zones, such as west and central Europe, both at 100/km². The inner cores of Western cities have traditionally held the densest agglomerations of people, but migration to suburbs is lessening the populousness of such places.

Future growth and numbers

Interest in the growth rates of populations and the consequent future numbers centres around the avilability of resources for them and also their effects upon the biosphere, especially that of the wastes they produce. But just as the reasons for population growth in the past can never all be known, so future growth cannot be predicted without making certain assumptions about demographic variables and the way in which these are affected by social and economic conditions. Some projections therefore assume constant fertility while others may assume that a form of demographic transition to lower birth rates will occur as nations become industrial, as happened in nineteenth-century Europe. Both of these assumptions may turn out to be untrue.

The simplest measure of population growth is the annual percentage increase which relates easily to doubling times (Table 12.9). The best estimate of the present world rate (1973) is 2 per cent p.a., which gives a doubling time of about 35 years. This average rate is composed of a multitude of national rates of greater or lesser accuracy of estimation, most of which are within the range 1–2·5 per cent but with extreme variants (Table 12.10). By continents, Europe appears to have the lowest rate of growth and Latin America the

TABLE 12.9   Growth rates and doubling times

Increase % p.a.	Years to double population
0·1	693
0·5	139
1·0	70
1·5	47
2·0	35
2·5	28
3·0	23
3·5	20
4·0	18

Source: Hardin 1969

TABLE 12.10   Population growth rates 1969 and 1972 (per cent per annum)

	Mean 1969	1972	Highest 1969	Highest 1972	Lowest 1969	1972	Individual countries 1972
World	1·9	2·0					
Africa	2·4	2·6	3·6	3·4	0·9	0·8	
Asia	2·0	2·3	7·6[1]	8·2[1]	1·1	1·2	
North America	1·1	1·1	2·0	1·7	1·0	1·0	Canada and USA only
Latin America	2·9	2·8	3·8	3·4	0·9	0·8	
Europe	0·8	0·7	2·7	2·8	0·1	0·0	
USSR	1·0	0·9					
Oceania	1·8	2·0					Australia and New Zealand only are listed

[1] For Kuwait: exaggerated by immigration from a (1972) natural increase of 3·6 per cent p.a.
Source: Population Reference Bureau 1969 and 1972

highest; East Germany has the lowest national rate of growth and Kuwait the highest, largely because of immigration. (For the purposes of this discussion migration has been ignored; although significant nationally, as in Lebanon, it is not relevant at the global scale.) Demographically two main groups exist, those with a birth-rate (BR) over 35/1,000 and those whose BR is < 35. The first group comprises most of the LDCs and has two subgroups, the first of which has BR < 35 and death rate (DR) > 15/1,000. This is best represented in Africa and Asia, where DRs remain high at present but are falling under the impact of modern medicine. The second subgroup has DRs < 15 and is responsible for the very high growth-rates of Latin America, since BR remains high but DRs have fallen substantially. A BR of < 35 is characteristic of the DCs and a few LDCs which have low absolute populations. A subdivision can be made on the basis of BR = 20; above this level are a few DCs whose birth rates seem bound to fall and thus bring them into a typical DC position where BR < 20. These countries have gone through a demographic transition to low birth rate and low death rate.

The different demographic types can be linked to variations in family characteristics, as detailed by Petersen (1969). These types are conceptualized in terms of the demographic transition in Europe but may have a relevance elsewhere to populations whose cultural characteristics are changing. In medieval times there was a traditional pre-industrial family where late marriage and non-marriage helped to depress birth rates. Guilds permitted marriage of their apprentices only when their service was complete, and younger children who would not inherit their father's farm, for example, might well enter the Church, whose clergy were supposed to be celibate. This family type was succeeded during the industrial revolution by the proletarian family in which early marriage was favoured by the availability of work within the factory system. There were few institutional barriers to sexual relations and illegitimacy was high, since in some countries the mother could force support from the putative father. Additionally, enough bastard children put out to work at an early age could ensure a comfortable living for the mother. The third type may be called the rational family and was coincident with the rise of a middle class. A sense of parental responsibility for limiting family size arose which was helped by the availability of contraceptive methods, and the age of marriage also began to rise.

All such generalizations are of course abstractions from a multitude of cultures, and as Zelinsky (1966) points out, it is easy to forget that all demographic characteristics are a result of cultural practices: the adoption of modern medicine is merely one of these. Any real understanding of population growth must therefore start with an assessment of the cultural variables involved, which naturally includes the peoples' perception of themselves and their physical and social environments.

Population projections

The pitfalls inherent in making forecasts of population levels beyond the immediate future are considerable (Dorn 1965). For example, it is often assumed that as the LDCs industrialize they will undergo the same type of demographic transition to low BR and low DR as did Europe in the nineteenth century. Yet there is no certainty of this since very different cultures are involved, apart from the assumption of the inevitability of industrialization in the poorer countries.

The assumptions underlying projections must therefore be clear if the estimates of future numbers are to have any usefulness. Two types of assumptions are most often used:

(1) constant fertility projections, in which the recent growth rate is projected into the future, i.e. a simple extrapolation of present trends; and

(2) changed fertility projections, in which assumptions are made about the socio-economic conditions affecting natural increase and migration, principally the former.

The uncertainties are so great that the UN projections, for example, employ three variants (high, medium and low) based on differing assumptions about the impact of medical and contraceptive programmes and of nutrition standards in various parts of the world. The high variant assumes that fertility will remain constant until 2000; the medium projection assumes that it will decline after 1975 at rates previously observed in some areas; the low variant posits an immediate decline in fertility which then remains continuously at low levels until 2000. Since the low variant is somewhat unlikely, the medium and high projections are most often quoted. Table 12.11 compares the 1969 figures with two of the projections for AD 2000. We can note two salient features of these projections: first, that the medium variant involves a virtual doubling of world population by 2000; second, that a large proportion of the additional people will be Asians: they above all others will be the most numerous. Frejka (1973) forecasts that the present ratio of 30 : 70 between the rich and the poor nations will inevitably become 20 : 80 and perhaps even 10 : 90, during the next few decades. Making certain assumptions about the coming of a demographic transition to the LDCs, he suggests that a virtually stable world population of 8,400 million is likely to be achieved by about AD 2100. This will probably be held in many quarters as a somewhat optimistic estimate.

TABLE 12.11   World and continental population projections (millions)

	World	Africa	Asia	North America	Latin America	Europe	Oceania	USSR
Mid-1969	3,551	344	1,990	225	276	456	19	241
2000—UN projection, constant fertility based on 1969	7,522	860	4,513	388	756	571	33	402
2000—UN projection, medium variant based on 1969	6,130	768	3,458	354	638	527	32	353
2000—UN projection, medium variant based on 1972	6,494	818	3,777	333	652	568	35	330

Source: Population Reference Bureau 1969 and 1972

The 2 per cent p.a. rise in world population does not seem particularly large unless the characteristics of an exponential curve with this increment are considered carefully. At present the doubling time for the population is 35 years, and at 2 per cent p.a. it will go on doubling at that interval no matter what the absolute level of population. The projection of this rate of growth unchanged into the future quickly brings very high absolute figures. A population of 3,000 million in 1960 rising at 2 per cent p.a. becomes 1×10^{15} in AD 2600. Each person will then have 5 ft² (approximately 0·5 m²) of room: this stage has thus been called SRO (Standing Room Only) day. Still at 2 per cent p.a., the year AD 4000 or thereabouts would see the earth as a mass of humanity expanding outwards at the speed of light. The types of life which such increased populations would enjoy (*sic*) have been explored by Fremlin (1964). In 890 years' time, for example, the present population, increasing at 2 per cent p.a., will be $60,000 \times 10^{12}$. To cope with such numbers the entire planet would be covered with a 2,000-storey building. Occupying 1,000 of these floors, each person would have 7·5 m² of floor space, while the rest of the building would be devoted to food-producing and refrigerating machinery. Life would be nearly sessile, but travel over a few hundred metres in any direction might be permissible so that each individual could then choose his friends out of some 10 million others. The limiting condition of this way of life would be the technological ability to radiate into space all the heat produced by the people and their machines, for the outer skin temperature of the 2,000-storey building would have to be at 1,000°C.

The possibility of shipping off excess population to other planets has been suggested from time to time. Even if the planets were hospitable environments, able to support human life, the economics are rather startling. At present the daily increment of people in the world is about 125,000. At present prices, to remove one day's increment to a hypothetical planet would cost $US369,000 million. If therefore the USA cut down its standard of living to 18 per cent of its present level, in one year it could set aside sufficient capital to finance the export of one day's additional people. As Hardin (1959) remarks,

'Such a philanthropic desire to share the wealth may be judged noble in intent but hardly in effect.'

These apparent fantasies of huge numbers and SF-type technologies have one serious purpose: to make us aware that absolute limits exist. If there were not the nutrition limit set by photosynthesis or even photosynthesis plus 'unconventional' foods, then there are the space limits and the heat limits. Therefore let nobody be persuaded that the earth has some infinite capacity for people.

Population control

Attempts to vary rates of increase have a long history (Benedict 1970). Most of our knowledge (and a great deal of folklore) has been concerned with efforts to increase fecundity, particularly in pre-industrial societies with high rates of infant mortality. Modern medicine is also a death-control mechanism, particularly as it affects longevity and infant mortality. Death control is usually more acceptable than birth control, although there is considerable evidence for the latter in pre-industrial groups, especially if we include abortion and infanticide as methods of reducing increase. Modern concern to limit birth stems from two types of motivation. The first is concern with the physical and economic health of an individual family, or a particular woman, where hardship occurs if too many children are born too quickly. However, the spacing of children does not necessarily mean a small number of births and medicine in many places enhances their chance of survival. A second reason for advocating birth control is the economic, social and ecological health of an entire community or nation, especially where resources are scarce or where the rate of growth is placing great strains on the ability of the community services to cope with it. Observation of the areas of fastest growth will often reveal a certain coincidence of rapid increase with poorly developed social infrastructures. The response to a desire for a slower growth rate comes in two phases. The first of these may be called the family planning phase, in which the efforts of government or private programmes are directed at individuals and families. Emphasis is placed on the advantages both to parents and to children of smaller or well-spaced families. Sterilization and contraceptive techniques are widely offered. However, abortion, usually illegal, is probably of more significance than any of the physical and hormonal contraceptives. Likewise, late marriage is a very effective factor in limiting births, as has been shown in China. The targets for family planning programmes usually aim at slowing a growth rate (e.g. by 1 per cent p.a.) in LDCs (Plate 21) or at eliminating 'unplanned' births in the DCs. The adoption of family planning programmes may, according to Davis (1967), have very limited results in terms of decelerating population expansion since, by offering only the means for couples to control fertility, such programmes neglect the means for society to do so. The very features that make family planning acceptable render it ineffective for the second phase, which is population control. This is linked to the circumstances of the community rather than the individual and envisages either a specific target population to be achieved by a slower rate of growth or a stabilization level with zero growth or even a diminution in absolute size. The persuaders aim at replacement level only, i.e. a maximum of two children per family (Fig. 12.4). Again, sterilization and contraception are the most widely offered

Plate 21 Jumbo-sized population increases need commensurate communications media. How many loops would an Air India Boeing 747 (see Plate 20) have bought? *(Camera Press Ltd, London)*

means, although the popularity of legal abortion is growing. No country has yet adopted a distinct control policy with announced targets in terms of absolute numbers, but some of the governments of the richer DCs are under strong pressure from neo-Malthusian pressure groups to do so. The US Commission on Population Growth and the American Future (1972) reported that no substantial benefits would appear to accrue from the continued growth of the nation's population, and recommended (with a few Commissioners dissenting) that the USA welcome the idea of and plan for a stabilized population; no positive steps to this end had emerged from the government by mid-1973. Opposition to both family planning and population control has often been strong, and the number of countries which have official and semi-official programmes is perhaps surprisingly high (IPPF 1972). An emphasis in Asian countries is noteworthy, especially where ethnic Chinese are concerned, and it is interesting that Singapore has announced its intention to cut social welfare programmes to people with more than two children.

A common theme of most opponents of population control is the right of the individual family to decide on its size: their procreative activities are no concern of the community. This is becoming less acceptable as it is more widely realized that every new individual requires resources which have significance to a wider group: the community, the nation or even the whole world. In hunting societies, where the limits of the environment are

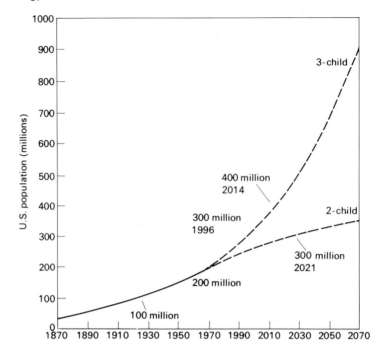

Fig. 12.4 The projected effects upon the US population of two-child and three-child families. Source: US President's Council on Environmental Quality 1971

closely perceived, population control appeared to be adjusted to the needs of the community, but the coming of agriculture seems to have put the onus on the family. First agriculture and then industrialization have allowed environmental limits to be perceived as virtually infinite. The advent of modern ecology has brought back into focus the limits to the carrying capacity of the planet, and the realization of an upper limit to the number of people that the earth can support. In the face of this fact the options appear to be twofold. If the population exceeds the carrying capacity then the natural checks of famine, disease and war will probably operate: the latter can now produce some very large-scale oscillations indeed; or we can bring to bear all the knowledge of science, values and communication that we possess in an effort to level off the exponential curve. Very few countries in the Third World, according to Notestein (1970), would at present find the aim of zero population growth acceptable and so far only in a few of the faster-growing populations has family planning begun to reduce birth rates. Hong Kong, Japan, Taiwan, Korea, Singapore, Fiji, Mauritius, Seychelles and Reunion are the countries where the BR has declined owing to family planning programmes (Nortman 1971, IPPF 1972). On the other hand, some countries are actively concerned that their population is not high enough and give pronatal financial inducements; notable among this group are the USSR and other Socialist republics of eastern Europe. Government inducements to breed in France, for example, having been less than successful, it may be wondered if this may not be the cheapest way to bring about declines in fertility.

A major problem is that although the problems caused by a rapidly increasing population can be identified on a world scale, their solution must inevitably be national. This produces a growing fear in the LDCs and among minority groups that 'they' are trying to subjugate 'us' by controlling 'our' numbers. As far as the LDCs are concerned, no power on earth can now stop them far exceeding the DCs numerically, but since concern over the global population–resources–environment balance comes mainly from the DCs it would seem prudent for them to practise what they preach in terms of population control.

Summary

The complex factors of demography boil down to one or two salient features as far as we are concerned here:

(1) Demographic history shows a rapid expansion of population after the seventeenth century, following thousands of years of very slow growth.

(2) The world population, currently (1971) at 3,600 million, has very uneven distribution, with a particular concentration in Asia.

(3) A world growth rate of approximately 2 per cent p.a. gives a doubling time of 35 years, irrespective of the absolute numbers.

(4) There is general discrepancy between the high rates of increase in the LDCs and a low rate (nearing stability in Sweden, for example) in the DCs.

(5) A rapid rate of urbanization prevails in both DCs and LDCs.

(6) Despite the widespread acceptance of family planning programmes, they have generally failed so far to reduce birth rates significantly outside the DCs, except perhaps in the highly urbanized or specially aided parts of Asia, together with mainland China.

Population–resource relationships

Growth

As populations have grown, so have the magnitudes of those resource processes which supply materials, so that the graph of population growth also describes in general terms the use of energy or the consumption of food. The important exception is that, worldwide, some resource processes are increasing in volume even faster than the population, i.e. per capita use is also going up: energy and water use are examples. This situation is most striking in the DCs, where access to technology creates a different kind of access to resources beyond those which are necessary to sustain life. In the LDCs, cultural consumption is by no means absent (particularly in those with a well-developed social stratification), but there is much greater emphasis on the provision of necessities such as food, shelter and employment. The contrast between the population–resource relationships of different types of countries allows the construction of a regional classification of the type put forward by Zelinsky (1966) and which appears as Fig. 12.5.

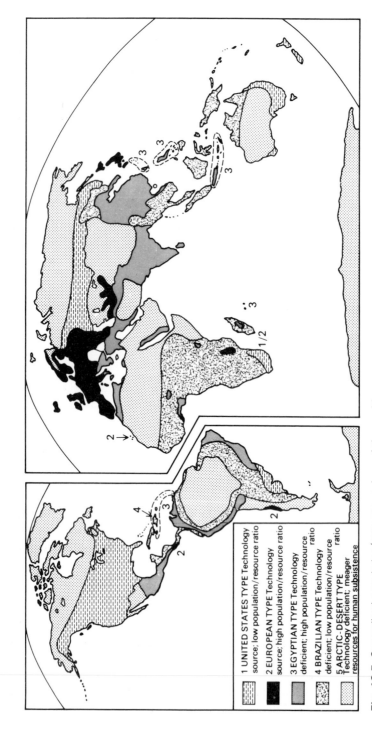

Fig. 12.5 Generalized population/resource regions of the world.
Source: Zelinsky 1966

1 UNITED STATES TYPE Technology source: low population/resource ratio

2 EUROPEAN TYPE Technology source: high population/resource ratio

3 EGYPTIAN TYPE Technology deficient: high population/resource ratio

4 BRAZILIAN TYPE Technology deficient: low population/resource ratio

5 ARCTIC-DESERT TYPE Technology deficient: meager resources for human subsistence

A diagnostic feature of these regions is the role of technology as part of the culture. The degree of application of mechanical and electronic technology, backed by expert knowledge, has been seen to alter the perception of available resources and hence lead to prosperity. Inherent in the role of technology as a creator of resources is its power to destroy them, either by misapplication or by means of the waste products which it creates; in addition it may have little to do with the long-term ecological stability of a resource process. Thus, while cognizant of the vital role of technology as a means of gaining access to environmental resources, we must not be so blinded as to fail to recognize its spin-off effects, not the least of which are its use for its own sake and the economic constraints created by the expensive machinery which is now widespread (Galbraith 1967). On the other hand, technology increases the chances of averting or minimizing economic and ecological disasters through the ingenuity it confers. Other factors must be considered when designating resource–population regions. The role of external enterprise and capital in creating resources (among which oil is the outstanding example) helps to emphasize that most of the regions are not self-contained in their resource processes: the way in which the DCs gather up resources from all over the world is an obvious example. Again, the use of money means that, outside subsistence economies, individuals do not gain their materials from their immediate surroundings.

Type A regions constitute technological source areas, where invention, research and development are at a high level. This is combined with a large land area which is well stocked with available and potential resources and has a low or moderately sized population relative to its size and to other nations. The high level of technology means that the people have access to the resources and also create the effective demand to ensure their use; prosperity allows the purchase from other countries of what they lack. The high levels of material wealth have been gained at the price of widespread environmental damage during phases of very rapid development and exploitation, and it is not surprising that the strongest public pressures for high-quality environments and 'environmentalist' crusading have come from the epitome of this group, the USA. In these countries, economic growth (i.e. the expansion of the magnitude of material-using resource processes) is in general a publicly espoused aim and its measures are seen as measures of the general welfare of the people. In the wealthiest, there may be some questioning of the purpose of such growth, particularly since the desired rates of expansion are very difficult to achieve in energy- and machine-intensive economies. This type of population–resource situation may be labelled 'the US type', but it also includes Canada, Australia, New Zealand, the USSR, part of Argentina and, with qualifications, Uruguay, south Brazil, South Africa and Rhodesia.

Type B may be categorized as 'the European type'. This is also a technology source area but differs from the US type because the population is high in both absolute numbers and density, the countries smaller and their heritage of resources less abundant and more fragmentary than those of larger nation-states. There is less room for trial and error than with type A and so a more 'conservative' attitude towards land and water resources has developed which is less profligate and damaging than the US type, although the number of people makes considerable environmental manipulation inevitable. Many of the man-made ecosystems, such as European agriculture, are essentially very stable, but the margin of stability is not very wide. Economically, an elaborate system of international exchange has to develop in order to ensure material supplies for the urban-industrial base. Thus trade with LDCs is widespread, partly as a historical result of colonialism, and international blocs (of which the EEC is the latest and largest) are commonplace. Again, economic growth is an explicitly stated goal of public policy, often being said to be necessary in order to clear up the legacy of a long history of industrial impact upon the environment and upon people. However, the value of growth is being questioned to some extent, as is shown by the

Plate 22 Immigration and natural increase, along with a small land base, produce squatter settlements like these in Hong Kong. Although its economy is perhaps closest to the European type, this colony's problems are exacerbated by its isolated location. *(World Council of Churches, Geneva)*

intention of Japan to develop an index of social welfare to replace GNP as an indicator of the performance of the economy. We may expect nations with a very slowly growing population and a culture capable of accepting changes in social aims, such as Sweden, to revise their attitudes towards growth in the near future. As would be expected, the European countries themselves provide type-specimens of this category, along with nations like Japan and Israel. In transit to this group are nations like Chile, together with Hong Kong (Plate 22) and the island of Puerto Rico; aspiring candidates who have passed some of the examinations would appear to be Mexico and Libya.

Type C envisages countries with large resource bases but which are deficient in technology. Their populations are relatively low, so that there is very little sense of pressure upon resources, except perhaps in the urban areas, but material standards are low as well. Their status is not permanent: increased technological development will allow them to move into the European category, but absence of such development if combined with rapid population growth may well depress them into type D countries. Such nations much desire economic growth and may even want population growth in order to try and achieve it faster. But they are hindered by economic factors such as the control of many of their exportable resources by outside interests or dependence upon world prices which may not move in their favour. This group may be labelled 'the Brazilian type' and is concentrated in three main areas: Indochina-Malaya (but excluding North Vietnam, Java and the north and central Philippines), tropical Africa, and South America. Standards of resource management vary widely and are critical in determining the movement of nations out of this category.

Type D is the most unfortunate group. Not only is there a deficiency of appropriate technology but the population presses hard upon the resources and is generally growing at 2 per cent p.a. or more. The capacity to deal with population–resource imbalances is frequently lacking, so that both the means of subsistence and the means of employment are deficient. Institutional factors may exacerbate the troubles of such nations. Small size of territory may impinge harshly upon a growing population, as may for example the activities of a landowning class who occupy all the productive land and grow cash crops for export upon it. This forces the peasants onto marginal lands which may erode quickly, depriving them of basic nutrition at the same time as their population levels far outrun any animal protein supply. Development programmes are most likely to misfire in such areas, not only because the limitations of the environment may be misunderstood and prediction of ecological side-effects inaccurate, but because of institutional factors centring around resistance to change on the part of the entrenched rich as well as the bewildered poor. This type can be labelled 'the Egyptian type' and includes part of southern Europe as well as classic LDCs in Africa like Ruanda-Burundi, Latin American and Caribbean areas like Haiti, Jamaica, Central America and the Andean highlands, India, Pakistan, Bangladesh, Sri Lanka, Syria and the islands of the Pacific and Indian Oceans. Escape from this category has been limited: Japan and probably China are outstanding examples.

Type E territories possess low resource bases because of the constraints of physical geography, and their populations are low, consisting either of people living on subsistence economies or those engaged in developing resources like minerals and oil. This 'arctic-desert' type also encompasses the oceans, only the fringes of which are subject to any form of inhabitation.

Controlling growth

The achievement of the economic growth espoused by most Western countries has usually been the result of private entrepreneurial ventures either aided or resisted by government. In centrally planned economies, the state has made all the running. But during the period since 1920 resource development has been increasingly subject to attempts to achieve an orderly, programmed rate of development, rather than submit to the irregular pyrotechnics of unfettered free enterprise. The first stage is usually termed *resource management*. Attempts are made to optimize yields from a particular resource process by exerting governmental control or influence upon part of the resource process. Such influence may be used to bring about regional development, as in the New Deal period of the USA, or to realize the maximum use of a potential resource, as with water-impoundment schemes which supply water for irrigation, urban-industrial purposes, recreation, and for the generation of hydro-electric power. A feature of resource-management philosophies in recent years has been to try to minimize the impact of economic development upon people and ecosystems not directly parts of the particular resource process. At a simple level this may mean building fish ladders alongside dams to enable migratory salmonids to reach their spawning grounds, or screening a new electricity-generating plant with mounds of earth and tree-plantings. More complex, and usually expensive, ameliorative measures include the whole battery of technological devices for removing toxic or harmful contaminants from industrial wastes, or the construction of new sewage-treatment schemes for large urban areas. The underlying values behind the abstraction labelled resource management are clear. They are devoted to development and change rather than preservation of the natural state, and to expansive growth of the scale of economic activity. Since exponential growth has for so long been the norm, it accepts the values of such a phase as correct, even when admitting that there may be deleterious side-effects. Above all, the concept acknowledges no upper asymptote to development, either because it cannot contemplate the reality of such a feature or because it believes that technological and social change will make the idea redundant. This set of values leads inevitably to problems in the balance of population and resources which have two dimensions, each with spatial implications. The first of these is the identification of problems, which can be viewed at a global scale, since certain manifestations are worldwide, as with the raising of expectations due to the ubiquity of electronic communications, and the global dispersal of certain by-products of technology such as carbon dioxide and pesticide residues like DDT. The second dimension is the solution of problems which at present can scarcely be contemplated other than in the framework of the national state. World government is scarcely a foreseeable reality, and even world gatherings for identification of problems (like the UN 1972 conference in Stockholm) ran into political difficulties.

The heightened awareness of the inter-relationships of biota and their inanimate surroundings has made possible the further step of identifying the wider concept of *environmental management*. It is recognized that it is the bioenvironmental systems of the planet which provide resources and that any resource process must be rationally managed in order to ensure a sustained yield—preferably one which is capable of due increase, but in which the existence of limits is recognized. In addition the deployment of an individual resource process must not be inimical to the operation of others with which it may share space or identical ecosystems. It is realized that the environment has simultaneously to be useful as a provider of materials, to be beautiful as a provider of recreation, wildlife and valued landscapes, and to be life-supporting as a provider of space, food and essential biological systems such as those which produce oxygen and carbon dioxide (O'Riordan 1971a). All things to all men, in fact, in which varying types of society exhibit different attitudes

(Table 12.12) and determine their own orders of priority. It would be unreal to pretend that environmental management is at present much more than a concept except in the relatively simple situation of Antarctica, but the formation of Ministries and Departments of the Environment in some countries may encourage integrative planning. If, however, we consider process-response situations such as the avoidance of flood hazard (O'Riordan 1971b) as environmental management, then the number of instances may be increased.

TABLE 12.12   Attitudes in environmental management

Purpose of environmental management	Resource-population type			
	USA	European	Brazilian	Egyptian
Useful, i.e. for materials	Dominant aim but decreasing emphasis	Dominant but decreasing; imports always significant	Dominant as industrializa- tion proceeds	Basic develop- ment often for export to USA and European types
Life-supporting, i.e. food and ecological stability, gaseous exchange	Increasing realiza- tion of wider implications	Importance only recently real- ized; too densely populated to achieve 'natural' stability	Food important, otherwise environment not much valued, although knowledge of implications sometimes present	Struggle for food often domi- nant, know- ledge of other processes discounted
Beauty	Strong motiva- tion for pre- servation as reaction to over-use	Always a feature of culture; now getting stronger in face of increased impact	Residual or marginal land may thus be employed	Wildlife on residual land may hold interest, otherwise little valued

The purpose of environmental management is to produce resources but simultaneously to retain a sanative, life-supporting environment. There is, therefore, an attempt to recon- cile the demands of socio-economic systems with the constraints of the biosphere. To this end, long-term strategies are essential and are based on two aims: the first is to reduce stress on ecosystems from contamination or over-use; the second is to pursue short-term strategies that are sufficiently flexible to preserve long-term options: no resource processes should be developed which bring about irreversible environmental changes. As a set of values, environmental management is ambivalent towards economic growth. It recognizes that there is an absolute limit to the materials and surface of the planet but sees no reason to prevent the use of the resources up to that limit provided that some ecological stability can be maintained, whether by preserving the natural systems or by increasing man- directed inputs of energy, matter and information.

Frameworks of resource management in developed countries

Within the United States and European types of resource–population relationships, the purposes of resource management differ between the free-market economies and the planned economies, i.e. between capitalist and socialist nations. In the free-market countries resource management comprises multiple aims: the provision of the material needs of the community by encouraging individuals to invest money and time and hence realize personal profits; the provision of environments for recreation and wildlife by protecting land from certain kinds of resource process; and the permitting of certain places to be used for waste disposal. Woven throughout the pattern are the roles of various levels of government: encouraging here, discouraging there and preventing everywhere. In principle, governments aim at maximizing the general good of the community, although they are often criticized for adopting the values of only one section of the population, and hence often will provide resources which individuals cannot profitably develop, such as nature conservation and countryside recreation. But the overall aim is economic growth, usually as measured by increases in GNP per capita. In this aim, there is little significant difference between free-market economies and Socialist centrally planned ones. In the latter, the government acts as sole entrepreneur and 'profits' are to be distributed over the entire population. Theoretically, integrated resource and even environmental management should occur, but the evidence seems to indicate that the USSR, for example, experiences problems of environmental contamination just as severely as the West (Gerasimov *et al.* 1971, Goldman 1971, Pryde 1972) and the writer's own experience of, for example, river pollution in Czechoslovakia bear out such reports. More thorough Communism, as practised in the People's Republic of China, may diminish contamination problems (Unger 1971), although we should note that large concentrations of heavy industry are not yet widespread in that country.

Along with citizen groups, most governments have tried to mitigate the impacts of resource development (especially industry) by a variety of measures, while retaining the general aim of an expanding economy. Such activities are often referred to as 'conserva-tion', although they fall well short of the integrative approach to man–environmental relationships which perhaps better deserves that label. Another name for tidying-up activities is 'the search for environmental quality' and a general attention to the landscape effects of industrialization and transportation is often a key element. Thus highway signs are regulated or eliminated, factories landscaped, and auto junkyards screened with trees. A wider concern with the protection of valued landscapes and open space may also be part of the same movement, so that green belts around cities may be created, as around the major cities of Britain. Alternatively, urban growth may be directed along particular axes, with 'green wedges' in between them; ideally this brings undeveloped land close into the city centre. In many European countries, the motivation to set aside valued landscapes is part of the 'conservation' movement: the 'Naturparken' of Denmark and West Germany and the National Parks of England and Wales are examples. Along with such movements often goes the desire to provide more open space and access to resources for outdoor recreation, which can frequently be combined with landscape protection. Here again, the protagonists are often called 'conservationists'. Many of the State Parks of the USA, the

Provincial Parks of Canada, and local arrangements such as the East Bay Regional Park District in California or the parks of the Metropolitan Toronto and Region Conservation Authority, are part of the same resource process. Much of the current effort in nature protection is also carried on in order to save biota and habitats from encroachment because of their national or regional significance in aesthetic or educational terms, rather than for their part in the stability of the biosphere on a global scale. The encouragement of a rare predator or wader to breed successfully on the margins of its range will elicit devotion and money that no unspectacular alga suffering from biocide toxicity can hope to receive.

The strongest of all these drives in the DCs is for pollution control. Many environmental contaminants are not only aesthetically undesirable but can be shown to be directly damaging to humans, and so in the industrial nations considerable legislation is being passed (and sometimes enforced) to control wastes. Water Quality Acts, such as those of the USA, set standards for the concentration of various effluents of a toxic or unaesthetic character. In the UK a standing Royal Commission on Environmental Pollution has been set up and all the water authorities are expected to deal with offences against the pollution laws. Noise is another area in which attempts to control levels are being made, in particular from aircraft and heavy vehicles. Few would deny that anti-pollution moves bring about improvements in the environmental quality for many people. However, the clamour is directed against one phase only of the resource process (the last) and does not consider the magnitude of and necessity for the earlier parts of the process. To this extent pollution abatement, like the other operations discussed in this section, is truly cosmetic. It improves the surface, but if the ecology of the resource process is unstable then it will not be corrective. Indeed, it may hide the need for more radical re-orientations of resource processes and can thus be used as camouflage by entrepreneurs and politicians. An example of the cosmetic approach can be seen in the declaration by the European Conservation Conference, meeting in 1970 (Council of Europe 1971). The human rights proposed are those of having air and water 'reasonably free from pollution', freedom from noise, and access to coast and countryside. Member nations are urged to combat pollution and, somewhat vaguely, to ensure the conservation of the European environment. Individuals, states article 30, should be ready to pay the costs of conservation. The other provisions largely concern planning for 'rational' use of resources and the reduction of pollution, especially the unwanted effects of the internal combustion engine, jet aircraft and chemicals such as pesticides, fertilizers and detergents. The aims and desirability of population and industrial growth are nowhere mentioned and the whole document is clearly an acceptance of current trends, subject to some improvements in national and regional planning and cleaning up of the more serious pollutants.

The next step beyond cosmetic procedures is to try to assess the ecological impact of a proposed development before it is put into effect. If the percussive effect of the change is deemed unacceptable (by standards that are not usually defined objectively but emerge empirically from public quasi-judicial proceedings) then another site is sought. Indeed, any enquiry may be specifically directed to choose between limited possibilities, as was the Roskill Commission of 1971 on the site of London's third airport. Symbolically, however, this Commission was not allowed to investigate whether London ought to have another major airfield, merely where it should be, so that only one phase of the resource process was considered. In the USA the 1969 Environmental Protection Act sets forth environmental policies for the nation which go beyond the loosely formulated suggestions of the European Declaration quoted above. For example, one of the objectives for the USA is to 'achieve a balance between population and resource use which will permit high standards of living and a wide sharing of life's amenities'. As far as actions by the Federal Government are concerned, it must 'utilize a systematic, interdisciplinary approach which will insure the integrated use of the natural and social sciences and the environmental design acts in planning and decision-making which may have an effect upon man's environment'. Any legislation or other Federal action which affects the quality of the human environment has to be investigated for its environmental impact and any adverse effects pointed out, along with alternatives to the proposed action; the relations between local and short-term uses of the environment and the maintenance of long-term productivity must be stated too. This Act tries therefore to impose limitations on the magnitude of resource processes if there are environmentally detrimental effects (Caldwell 1971).

Nations with well-established Socialist governments such as those of the USSR and eastern Europe have theoretically an institutional structure which will enable them to avoid the environmentally stressful features of free-market economics. Yet in performance they rarely seem any better and sometimes manifestly worse. A variety of reasons seems to account for such a position. Firstly, although integrated control of a resource process should exist, *de facto* it often does not. Secondly, resource managers are as keen as any capitalist to dispose of their wastes as cheaply as possible and thus externalize the costs. Because there is an ideological attachment to industrial and general economic growth, this cannot be slowed down because of difficulties over aesthetics or contamination. Lastly, because Marxism is held to be so superior to capitalism, it is hard to admit that the end-product may be the same and that Marxist-Leninist fish are as dead as capitalist fish.
Socialist governments may well outshine the Western nations at tasks like pollution control when they have decided to undertake the job; in fields like nature conservation their record is excellent. We may surmise nevertheless that Socialist nations will find it harder than most to deviate from goals of perpetual economic growth, particularly while they feel militarily threatened.

Resource management in Brazilian and Egyptian categories

The purposes of the development of resources in these two groups are twofold. Firstly, they are used for regional and national purposes in order to produce metabolic and cultural materials such as food, housing and roads, and also to provide jobs and create wealth to be used as capital for further development. Secondly, many bioenvironmental resources are developed for export to European and US type countries. Oil is an obvious instance, but many metal ores and crops like cocoa, coffee and rubber also enter this category. Such use brings income to the supplier, but it also brings dependence upon demand in the DCs; where the product is dispensable or subject to fashion or is overproduced, then the fortunes of the producers (as happens with cocoa and coffee) are fickle indeed; on the other hand where the product is so important, as with oil, that the industrial nations are virtually dependent upon the supplies, then the LDCs force up the price and nationalize expensive plants virtually with impunity.

The desire of the countries of the Third World to be masters of their own destinies leads them into the process of 'development', undertaken with substantial assistance from the richer nations. This is usually undertaken in response to particular exigencies such as under- or malnutrition or a chronic lack of employment or shelter, or to ensure the occupational survival of a political leader. As Caldwell (1971) points out, the process of development proceeds from a set of assumptions about the relationship of man and nature which were developed in the West during the phase of the industrial revolution and few if any of which (particularly those about the long-term effects on the stability of ecosystems of constantly increasing impacts of a technology based on fossil fuels) are verified by scientific evidence. Indeed, some writers aver that development is primarily for the benefit of the industrial nations and that this economic imperialism is mostly designed to secure large quantities of cheap raw materials at an immense profit for the industrialists, at the same time making the area safe for further penetrations by such entrepreneurial enterprise. Woodis (1971) says that in one of its operations in an African country, a rubber company takes home three times as much profit as the nation's entire revenue; that 28 per cent of UK overseas aid goes to pay back interest on former aid; and that the drop of 15 per cent in export prices of raw materials from tropical Africa in 1955–9 entailed a loss of twice the annual amount of foreign aid. Many large multi-national companies have annual economies many times the size of some small newly independent nations; it has even been rumoured that one corporation thought about buying one such country and running it as a tourist enterprise, having renamed it Tarzania.

Given that even the most exploitive resource-development programme will leave a residue of investment capital, or that disinterested aid from an international agency has been granted, development is not without hazard. The assumptions referred to above ensure the dominance of technical and economic factors in evaluating priorities at the expense of behavioural and ecological considerations. In the desire to transform simple agrarian societies into more complex industrially based economies, it may be forgotten that both traditional systems and natural ecosystems have passed the evolutionary tests of selection for survival but that the new ecosystems and new cultural values are not guaranteed to share such properties. The more interference with the old order, the greater the chance of unpredictable synergistic effects, and the success of a practice in one place may encourage unwarranted optimism about its potential in another. The hazards of the imposition of cultural complexes based on high-energy societies upon those accustomed to the flow of only solar energy, or for example the development on small islands of mining by techniques usually employed on large continents, may be disastrous: Taghi Farvar and Milton (1972) bring together a large number of unhappy case-histories; and in the same volume Caldwell considers that there are six barriers to success in 'development', only one of which is ecological, the others being derived from various parts of the cultural milieu, including the political. Development thus provides us with an example of a situation where, within the ecological envelope of facts, the cultural world of values is all-important and cannot in the least be ignored, a conclusion of significance when considering any alterations in the nineteenth-century assumptions which underlie so much of our thinking about man and nature. In the meantime many millions of individual people live far below their full potential as humans.

The area in which outside ideas can claim a little success is nature conservation, especially where this is a source of revenue from tourism. More wide-ranging environmental protection is virtually absent, with the possible exception of forest reserves established to prevent the denudation of steep hillsides or to safeguard a supply of wood for construction and fuel. Long-run ecological stability with no visible benefits is therefore, and understandably so, subordinate to economic growth in the short-term.

Growth and progress

It seems pertinent to remind ourselves that growth of economies and populations on the scale to which we are accustomed is a feature of the last 150 years only. But expansion rates of 5 per cent p.a. and above have come to be the normal situation for resource managers, their mentors, and of those who laid down the ground rules for both of them. Because growth has been a normal situation and because it appears to offer solutions to most problems, including those it has itself created, it has become almost everywhere a desirable goal and indeed equated to a large extent with the concept of 'progress'. Earlier in this century some questioning of the equivalence was heard, albeit faintly: one character in Aldous Huxley's *Point Counter Point* (1928) explodes, 'Progress! You politicians are always talking about it. As though it were going to last. Indefinitely. More motors, more babies, more food, more advertising, more everything, for ever. . . . What do you propose to do about phosphorus for example?' Although most of our present concern has shifted from the supply of that element to its disposal, the rest of Huxley's ideas have a contemporary air. Whether, where and how far the expansion of the magnitudes of resource processes can follow their present trajectories into the future is the subject of the last chapter of this book.

Further reading

ALLISON, A. (ed.) 1970: *Population control.*

BARR, H. M. *et. al.* (eds.) 1972: *Population, resources and the future: non-Malthusian per-spectives.*

DAVIS, W. H. (ed.) 1971: *Readings in human population ecology.*

DURAND, J. D. 1967: The modern expansion of world population.

GORDEN, M. and GORDEN, M. (eds.) 1972: *Environmental management.*

HABAKKUK, H. J. 1972: *Population growth and economic development since 1750.*

HINRICHS, N. (ed.) 1971: *Population, environment and people.*

O'RIORDAN, T. 1971: *Perspectives on resource management.*

PEACH, W. N. and CONSTANTIN, J. A. 1972: *Zimmermann's World Resources and Industries.* 3rd edn.

PRYDE, P. R. 1972: *Conservation in the Soviet Union.*

RIDKER, R. G. 1972: Population and pollution in the United States.

TAGHI FARVAR, M. and MILTON, J. P. (eds.) 1972: *The careless technology: ecology and inter-national development.*

US COMMISSION ON POPULATION GROWTH AND THE AMERICAN FUTURE 1972: *Population and the American future.*

ZELINSKY, W. 1966: *A prologue to population geography.*

13

An environmental revolution?

The last section of this book first examines the extension of the present patterns of resource processes, in particular the environmental and social problems which are created, and then moves to consider two main sets of reactions to the disharmonies which are evident. The first of these is the argument that technological development will eventually provide solutions; the second, by contrast, advocates a radically different approach to the relations of man and nature. The book ends with a consideration of alternative models of the future based largely upon these two types of reaction.

Impacts upon the environment

There is no doubt that an increasing disharmony between man and nature is becoming apparent, especially in phenomena such as malnutrition, soil erosion, gross pollution, and the attrition of the aesthetic qualities of parts of the environment which are valued in several cultures. One of the major concerns is that the increasing magnitude of resource processes is creating a set of environmental problems which in turn may impair not only the usefulness of the environment but also its life-supporting capability, its ability to absorb wastes and its beauty. The environmental problems created by more people using more materials can be divided into those with an environmental linkage, and those with a largely social linkage (Russell and Landsberg 1971). The former group in turn comprises regional problems such as sewage, sulphur dioxide fallout, the habitat requirements of migratory birds, or particular geographical entities such as the Rhine or the Nile and the uses made of them. Much stronger anxiety, however, has been expressed about global problems such as food supply and the consequences of agricultural intensification, residual pesticides, the effects of the contamination of the oceans by oil, and the alteration of atmospheric processes by increased loads of carbon dioxide and particulates. The most vivid statement of this view is Ehrlich's (1971) scenario for 'ecocatastrophe' in which poisoning of the oceans by organochlorine pesticides reduces food supplies to Asia at the same time as biocide-resistant strains of pest virtually eliminate the land-based food supplies. The demand for food of a very high and rapidly growing population is the trigger-factor of a worldwide nuclear war which he predicts will take place by 1979. A more penetrating analysis which emphasizes the role of population growth in creating environmental disharmony is given by Ehrlich and Holdren (1971). They suggest that the increases in human numbers have caused a totally disproportionate impact on environment. For example, the provision of minerals and fossil fuels to an expanding population even at fixed levels of consumption requires that as the nearest and richest ores are worked out, then the use of lower-grade ores, deeper drilling and extended supply networks all increase the per capita use of energy and hence the per capita impact on the environment (Table 13.1). Similarly, the environmental impact of supplying water needs rises dramatically when the local supply is outrun: ecological, aesthetic and economic costs are incurred in diverting

TABLE 13.1   World per capita use of selected resources per year

	Petroleum (bbls)	Natural gas (ft³)	Copper (lb)	Phosphate rock (lb)	Potash (lbK₂O)
1910	0·19	—	1·15	7·1	—
1930	0·70	1,060	1·70	12·8	2·48
1950	1·52	2,780	2·80	20·1	4·5
1960	2·62	5,700	3·76	30·2	7·1

1 bbl = 159 l; 1 ft³ = 0·0283 m³; 1 lb = 0·4536 kg
Source: McHale 1972

TABLE 13.2   World increases in agricultural activity 1955–65

Increase	%
Food production	34
Tractors used	63
Phosphates used	75
Nitrates	146
Pesticides	120

This table does not show the amounts of water and energy, for example, needed to manufacture the fertilizers and pesticides.
Source: SCEP 1970

supplies to the growing region. Increase of food production likewise requires energy uses disproportionate to the population fed because of the need to obtain and distribute water, fertilizer and pesticides (see pp. 219–20). Some indication of the environmental consequences may be inferred from Table 13.2.

The role of population density is also relevant, since some proponents of growth argue that countries with a low density can afford high rates of growth. Density is not necessarily a good criterion for the effect of populations upon the biosphere: industrial nations, for example, gather in resources from a very wide area. The Netherlands is often quoted as an example of a very dense but wealthy population, but it is the second largest importer of protein in the world and also imports the equivalent of 27 million mt/yr of coal. In addition, many environmental problems are independent of the distribution of population, especially those involving contamination of the oceans and atmosphere.

A cooler, more detailed view is taken by the authors of the SCEP (Study of Critical Environmental Problems) group (1970), who conclude that the current 'ecological demand' (i.e. the stress put upon planetary bioenvironmental systems by man's demands upon them) is not yet sufficiently great to cause a breakdown. Nevertheless, they point out the rapid rises in demands for materials, energy and space, some of which are set out in Table 13.3, and by considering Gross Domestic Product (GDP) minus services as an index of 'ecological demand', they calculate that it has been increasing at 5–6 per cent p.a., doubling in the 13·5 yrs after 1950, so that the next doubling of population (in 35 yrs at 2 per cent p.a.) will increase the environmental impact sixfold. These rates explain why environmental

TABLE 13.3   World average annual rates of increase in economic activity, 1951–66 (based on constant dollars)

Activity	% annual increase	Doubling time (yrs)
Agricultural production	3	23
Industry based on farm products	6	11
Mineral production	5	14
Industry based on mineral production	9	7
Construction and transport	6	11
Commerce	5	14

Source: SCEP 1970

problems appear to have erupted so suddenly and why many students fear that the future will bring more problems than exist at present to the point where a few more doublings of population will bring about the likelihood of the breakdown of the systems of the biosphere.

The differences between Ehrlich and SCEP, therefore, is only one of time: they agree that the planet cannot for much longer go on supplying the demands made on it for the supply of materials and the provision of valued environments, while absorbing the impact of the disposal of wastes, all within the framework of a human population doubling every 35 years.

The role of population growth in creating environmental problems has been closely examined by Commoner (1972a, 1972b), who suggests that the misapplication of technology is the most important factor in the growth of environmental disharmony. In the United States, for example, crop yield in Illinois increased 10–15 per cent in 1962–8 while the quantity of nitrogenous fertilizer doubled; similarly for detergents and non-returnable bottles Commoner calculates that it is the technology that creates the difficulties, not the rise in the numbers using it. While there is no doubt that 'ecologically faulty' technology exists, it seems that none of these arguments meet those of Ehrlich and Holdren (1971) quoted above, and they manifestly do not apply to those parts of the world where technology is distinctly lacking; to some extent Commoner appears to be lacking a wider perspective beyond the particular situation of the USA.

Thus while not every environmental ill can immediately be laid at the door of population growth, there emerges a strong suggestion that nowhere does the latter bring any benefits. To LDCs it brings medical and social problems; to DCs it may bring environmental problems beyond those of aesthetics; and in both groups, high densities of population add their own special difficulties.

Social values

The environmental disharmonies caused by rises in the scale of resource processes are paralleled by some negations of the social benefits which the growth has brought to most people. Economic growth expressed as GDP and Gross National Product (GNP) appears not to solve social problems, even of privileged areas. In the USA, evidence of primary malnutrition may be found among the poorer people; in less specific terms economic growth does little to narrow the gap between rich and poor in technologically based societies. If real net income rises by 10 per cent for the entire population, then the differences between the well-off and the deprived remain exactly the same as before; furthermore, the hard core of the poor do not share in economic growth and are dependent upon handouts from those whose benefit is direct. In DCs, economic growth is not really necessary to remove the very poor from their predicament: a minor redistribution of wealth (e.g. the reduction of the military budget by 25 per cent for the UK) would achieve the desired end (Mishan 1971). Indeed, some economic growth which goes into military expenditure might well be employed in a more useful fashion: one atomic submarine and its missiles would pay for $150 million in technical aid and one aircraft carrier could be replaced by 12,000 secondary schools (McHale 1972).

Another social argument advanced in favour of economic growth is that it produces more goods so that individuals and societies have more choice, which contributes to greater economic welfare. Such enhanced freedom tends to be illusory because there is constant replacement of models: one cannot choose a car from all the types ever made, only from those currently on the market, and the difference between alternative makes at the same price is more or less negligible. The proliferation of choice may bring forward harmful products which commercial interests have not properly evaluated, and much of it is not necessary: a choice between 50 makes of transistor radios at roughly the same cost is scarcely essential. Lastly, satisfaction with earnings may depend more upon an individual's place within the income structure than with his absolute level of wealth. This was exhibited during the miners' strikes of 1972 and 1974 in Britain, where one of the workers' chief sources of dissatisfaction was their fall in the 'league table' of industrial earnings.

The greatest externality of economic growth as measured now is its failure to take account of its environmental impact, largely because a money value can not be placed on environmental values lost. This book has chronicled numerous side-effects of economic growth, none of which will feature in the balance-sheets of those who caused them. Some measures of total goods and services such as GDP actually count deleterious impacts as components of the growth: if because of industrial emissions more people become ill, then the costs of extra hospital building and medical equipment adds to the GDP; if they die as a result of the same factor then presumably the undertaker's fees are added too. Such methods of accounting also omit the hidden costs of loss of earnings due to environmentally related illness, which can be no negligible sum as shown by Table 13.4. As was said in Part I, Boulding (1971) points out that GNP is simply a measure of decay (of food, clothing, gadgets and gasoline, as they are used), and the bigger the economic system the more it decays and the more that has to be produced simply to maintain it.

TABLE 13.4   Costs of diseases associated with air pollution, USA, 1958 ($ US million)

Respiratory cancer	680	
Chronic bronchitis	159·7	The categories of cost included
Acute bronchitis	6·2	are premature death, mor-
Common cold	331	bidity, treatment and preven-
Pneumonia	490	tion.
Emphysema	64	
Asthma	259	

Source: Newbould 1971b

Since economic growth depends upon the extension of the use of machines, many humanitarian writers have stressed that technology provides its own imperatives, some of which lead to attrition of the quality of human relations; electronic means of communication are probably the most sinister of these since, for example, 'the boss' can be isolated entirely from 'the worker' when audiovisual links are effected. Similarly the social worker may never have actually to see or to smell the derelict, and the doctor will be able to diagnose his patient from a safe distance. Paradoxically, the same media could bring about a sense of closeness on a world scale, the 'global village' to which McLuhan refers. The large size of organizations needed to control resource processes inevitably means impersonality and alienation, and the flexing of corporate power (of the 50 largest economic entities in the world 13 are corporations; in a recent year General Motors grossed more money than the total economy of Italy and of 73 other members of the UN) as in the case of a company which offered large rewards to anybody who could prevent the election of a particular politician in a LDC. More strictly relevant to our present theme is the rapid obsolescence which is associated with the products of machine technology. The social consequences are obvious since people will spend time and energy trying to possess the latest model, either willingly or at the behest of advertising. Probably more important is the heavy demand upon resources which such changes make, especially in an open-flow resource process without any recycling. Planned obsolescence is therefore a development which, although perhaps making sense (and a good deal of money for somebody) in terms of contemporary economics, is inimical to rational resource and environmental management.

Social consequences of size

Economic growth is very largely industrial growth, since advanced agriculture is an outgrowth of industry, dependent upon it for chemical inputs and for power supply, and industrial activity is largely carried on in cities and conurbations. The role of the city and its life-styles cannot therefore be overlooked in any consideration of the future of resource processes.

The major externality of industrial growth is its environmental effect, already discussed. But there are other effects which, assessed in social terms, are part of the unrest which causes the seeking of alternative ways of living. Behind the anxieties lies the thought that the transition to an urban-industrial life-style, after spending 90 per cent of his evolutionary history as a hunter, may set up psychic strains in man. Many of the traits which conferred a selective advantage in the hunting stage are now of distinctly less value, especially since population densities are so high in cities: aggressiveness is one such characteristic. Many of the biological mechanisms of adaptation to environmental struggles and stresses are now useless, and this is posing its own threat because there are insufficient challenges in bland surroundings which require little effort and thus provide few outlets for traits like aggression except in ritualized forms such as spectator sports. Personality structure breaks down if sensory stimuli are removed and indeed the intestinal tract fails to develop normally if conditions are totally germ-free (Dubos 1967). On the face of it, man appears to be a very adaptable species, for the overall health and survival rates of the inhabitants of Western cities are very good even though the people are isolated from nature. The price of such successful biological adaptability is, according to Dubos (1967), paid in social terms: people no longer mind ugliness, exhaust fumes and other contaminants, and even regard such conditions as normal. Since man could survive and reproduce in underground shelters or similarly confined conditions, the lower common denominators of existence become accepted for the sake of a grey and anonymous peace and tranquillity. Existence of these ideas suggests that because so many industrial and urban conditions do not immediately threaten biological survival, then we can give up perceiving the objective reality of their true effects, both in terms of environmental impact and in living conditions for man which are, to say the least, sub-optimal. Fortunately, our adaptability is cultural as well as biological and so it seeks to encompass the future as well as acknowledge the limits of the past. Thus arises the army of those engaged in trying to better the human condition.

Since the growth in economies and populations today leads inexorably to a rise in the size of cities, the observed behaviour of man in these agglomerations is now the subject of considerable concern, especially among US workers, whose cities seem to be experiencing forms of social change rather more rapidly than elsewhere in the West. As with much ethological study, experimental animals provide the first steps in research and the work of Calhoun (1962) is well known. His rats were provided with ample subsistence and adult mortality was so low that 5,000 adults might have been expected at the end of a 27-month period, yet the population had stabilized at 150 adults. Even 150 adults exerted considerable social stresses. Behavioural sinks developed in which a pathological 'togetherness' of 60–80 female rats tended to disrupt the sequences of activity necessary for mating, home-building and the rearing of young, and infant mortality ran as high as 96 per cent among

Plate 23 The negative qualities of city life can be exemplified by the famous *Oshiya* (pushing boys) of the Tokyo subway during rush-hours. *(Keystone Ltd, London)*

such disorientated females. Males also developed aberrant behaviour, among which pansexuality and total withdrawal were most noticeable, along with a group that was hyperactive, homosexual and cannibalistic, and which set upon females in oestrus. To extrapolate the results of such investigations to human populations in cities would be facile, but both Leyhausen (1965) and Calhoun (1971) have argued that the urban way of life exerts particular influences upon human behaviour patterns. They suggest that the size and population density of cities cause individuals to lose their place among the social-spatial order, thus developing psychic stress and other disorders. The possession of individual territory may serve as a secure, defensible base which enables the person to tolerate the socio-environmental insults, so that high-rise flats may be the antithesis of what is required for healthy living. Certainly, high rates of neurosis and delinquency are often associated with high-rise developments, although the evidence linking them is only circumstantial. More easily accepted perhaps is Milgram's (1970) analysis, largely concerned with a comparison of New York City with other metropolises and smaller settlements. He concludes that the modern city produces an overload in sensory input, so that social relations become superficial, anonymous and transitory, and low-priority inputs (such as other people in trouble) are disregarded. In transactions, boundaries are redrawn so as to offload responsibility, and individuals block themselves off by means of receptionists, hall porters and unlisted or disconnected telephones. Further screening devices and specialized institutions emphasize the anonymity of the individual, and thus reinforce the aggressiveness which is necessary in the competition for facilities as in rush-hour transport and lunch-hour ingestion (Plate 23). Some degree of anonymity is also a redeeming feature of the city. Minorities are much less stigmatized than in rural areas or small towns, and innovative behaviour can flourish instead of being smothered, as in the more normative situation of a group whose individuals are known to all the members. The role of absolute

TABLE 13.5   Crime in public housing in New York (felonies per thousand families, 1969)

	Three-floor walkups	Mid-rise (6–7 floors)	High-rise (13–30 floors)
Interior public spaces	5·3	16·5	37·3
Outside grounds	12·7	10·0	16·2
Inside apartments	12·0	14·5	14·5

Source: *Toronto Globe and Mail*, 30 October 1972

TABLE 13.6   US urban crime rates per 100,000 population, 1957

	Crime	> 250,000	Size of city 50,000– 100,000	< 10,000
Criminal homicide	Murder, non-negligent Manslaughter, manslaughter by negligence	5·5	4·2	2·7
		4·4	3·7	1·3
Rape		23·7	9·3	7·0
Robbery		108·0	36·9	16·4
Aggravated assault		130·8	78·5	34·0

Source: Parsons 1971

size in providing the settings for certain types of behaviour is demonstrated by figures from the USA set out in Table 13.6. While individual differences between the categories of city size might not be statistically significant, the upward trends in crime rates are impressively similar—although once again it is essential to exercise caution about extrapolating such figures to other cultural contexts. The types of building are probably significant as components of the US situation: again, large buildings have higher crime rates (Table 13.5), possibly because of their lack of 'defensible space', in the large interior areas which belong to and are surveyed by no one, whereas in smaller apartment blocks the interior public space becomes an extension of the home.

One incontrovertible drawback of cities is their ecological instability, dependent as they are upon inputs of food, water and power, and upon having their wastes removed (Table 13.7). Weiner (1950) points out that disconnection of the water supply to New York City for six hours is reflected in the death rate, while power disconnections cause hypothermia among the old and enhanced pregnancy rates in the fertile. In such a sense cities appear parasitic, but many dwellers in rural areas are similarly dependent upon supplies bought by money: the farmers and smallholders who might survive a real famine would be over-run by urban hordes long before harvest time, whatever the crop, so that in reality the two are interdependent. The city is therefore ecologically difficult (and, on the whole, anathema to ecologists) because it masses demands for all types of resources, and generates others external to it, such as countryside recreation. It concentrates wastes, the disposal of which may create high levels of contamination of ecosystems (Table 13.7). But probably

TABLE 13.7   Magnitude of city metabolism (daily flows in tons (= 1,016 kg) of a city of 1 million population, USA)

	Input				Output		
Water			625,000		Sewage		500,000
	Coal	3,000			Refuse		2,000
	Oil	2,800					
Fuels			9,500	BECOMES	Air	CO	450
	Nat. gas	2,700			pollutants	SO_2	150
	Motor	1,000				Particulates	150
						NO_x	100
Food			2,000			Hydrocarbons	100

Source: McHale 1972

none of these problems is intractable, and a fruitful field for technological development exists in the neutralization of the deleterious processes. Socially the city is ambivalent, with some evidence that very large agglomerations may enhance socially undesirable be-haviour. The city is, however, a centre of innovative thought and hence is in the vanguard of the study of both its own deficiencies and those of the economic growth which caused it to arise; many of the new approaches to man-environment relations have their origins in the cultural and intellectual ferment of urban conglomerations.

The ethical infeed

A further aspect of the feedback from our social and environmental situation is the failure of man's use of the earth to measure up to certain ethical principles which have been principally formulated, in this context, in the West. The first of these may be summarized as the 'duty to posterity' argument. Its basis is the exhortation to pass on the inheritance of one generation in an unimpaired condition to the next. In terms of resource processes this means the avoidance of foreclosing options for the future by making irreversible changes in the present. Obedience to such a dictum would appear to be ecologically sound as well, since it would have the effect of retaining maximum biological diversity. The difficulty comes with acknowledgement of the effects of increasing technological capability, which often removes the closure imposed at an earlier time or, by creating substitutes, throws the whole resource process into irrelevance. So it has been argued that since we cannot know what the future will hold, we automatically do the best for future generations by maximizing present benefits since this will build up capital in terms of wealth and knowledge which will enable future problems to be tackled successfully. Both versions are perhaps rather too exclusively economic in their orientation to find much favour with either ecologists or the promoters of ethics, who tend to be rather puritan by nature (Boulding 1970).

A second ethical theme is the idea of each generation of men as stewards of the earth who hold it for only a limited period and who are obliged to account for their tenure. This is basically a theistic idea, although a demythologized version seems to have a fairly wide secular appeal. One of its statements is in Aldo Leopold's (1949) 'land ethic' in which men are adjured to respect the qualities of the earth and to gain their living from it without damaging the chances of fruitful yield in the future. Although the formulation of his ex-position derives rather strongly from its origin in erosion and flooding problems in north-central North America, the general idea could be applied to resource processes as a whole, except that the criteria for what constitutes acceptable environmental manipulation as distinct from damage are left undefined. An elaboration of a similar theme is presented by Black (1970), who traces the notion of stewardship in those Judaic and Christian scriptures whose influence upon the contemporary world-view held by the West is acknowledged to be strong. He finds numerous examples of the concept of a man who is merely a temporary guardian of a resource and who is expected not merely to protect it against harm but to enhance its value. The earth must therefore be replenished as well as subdued. Since Black is a biologist, the way in which the ethical behaviour he advocates is seen to be consonant with sound scientific principles of environmental management is of considerable interest. Boulding (1971) also concludes that a shift in ethics towards man as a steward is a necessary part of the reconciliation between ecological and economic imperatives. A more specifically Christian formulation of similar principles is given by Montefiore (1970), who regards the totality of planetary systems as objects for the disinterested love which Christians are enjoined to profess. A similar view was taken by the Churches' Board of Social Responsibility document for European Conservation Year, 1970. Toynbee (1972) has even gone so far as to suggest that monotheistic religions encourage environmental exploitation and that only a reversion to pantheism and the religions of the East will suffice to alter present values. Unless instant conversions are made, we may harbour a suspicion that, even if efficacious, the time-span involved would be too long to alleviate some of the most pressing difficulties. In so far as the social costs of industrialization have been ignored in both capitalist and socialist countries, the so-called 'work ethic' has been a contributory factor, and as Bruhn (1972) suggests, it is time for ethics and science to unite to produce a guide to individual and collective behaviour which will stress the quality of life rather than the mere production of goods in the DCs; inevitably, the importance of 'work' (which many might suspect to have been strongly implanted by Protestant capitalism in the nineteenth century) would require radical re-evaluation.

Summary

The social difficulties created by continued expansion of present-day processes in the DCs are concisely summarized by Wagar (1970). In the first place we cannot be certain that present arrangements will go on, since neither free-market nor centrally planned economies have as yet developed systems capable of rapid effective response to environmental attrition; rather resource management by crisis has been the rule. Technological unemployment threatens domestic tranquility and there is a reliance upon defence industries for growth which might not be sustained. Again, the levels of organization are so complex that chain reactions of failure are very easy; and lastly growth can be sustained only by disproportionate inputs of energy and materials whose environmental impact has become clear.

Responses to the problems discussed so far in this section may be classified into two groups. The first allows that problems exist but predicates its answer upon continued economic growth; it is often divided about the role of population increase; the second requires a radical reorientation of material use and an immediate move towards stable population levels. The first approach will be called 'the technological fix'; the second the 'environmentalist' viewpoint.

The technological fix

This set of ideas admits that there are significant problems in the relations of population, resources and environment, but suggests that the difficulties are correctable by only relatively minor alterations in technology and institutions. Prognostications of ecological instability are discounted, and to Maddox (1972b), the state of mind of the catastrophists is more dangerous than what they predict.

The importance of population growth as a factor in problems of imbalance is subject to close scrutiny. An eventual levelling-off is regarded as desirable (and often as a by-product of other processes such as economic development), but the components of growth may be viewed differentially: for some regions a drastic retardation is required, for others no particular action seems necessary. Notably, the argument that the DCs should come quickly to zero growth because they dominate such a large proportion of the world's resource processes is not admitted as valid, since it is their growth which brings benefits for everybody else in its wake. In the DCs it is pointed out that many environmental problems are caused less by population growth than by the misapplication of technology by those in search of quick and high profits, such as the manufacturers of detergents, pesticides, chemical fertilizers, large overpowered automobiles, flip-top beer cans and electric carving knives. Commoner's (1972a) argument, that the ecologically unsound developments of the past two decades would have created severe trouble even if the population had been stable, is usually quoted, although it is apparent that, once launched, such developments can be fuelled by higher levels of population.

Reliance upon economic development to alleviate resource-related difficulties is especially strong in the LDCs, with obvious cause. Some also see higher populations as an eventual strength rather than a problem and may rely on political change to bring about better material conditions. In a wider perspective, they are not willing to be the environmental saviours of the DCs by acting as reservoirs of oxygen-producing plants or picturesquely backward tourist spots (Castro 1972). Many see reduced rates of population and economic growth in the DCs as deleterious (Wolfers 1971), since demand for their raw materials is thereby lessened; it seems, however, a curious world in which the rich must consume ever more to support the poor, and the implications of the political thralldom such linkages bring are not lost in many LDCs.

Economists who are also optimists point out that scarcity of any material resource will enforce substitution for it, but they note too that alleviation of shortages may be slow, and the ability of the price mechanism to give adequate forewarnings of the need for the development of substitutes in the face of the rapidity and magnitude of the doublings of demand now taking place has not yet been tested. Once a shortage is evident and there is an expectation that prices will rise faster than the rate of interest, then it pays a resource manager to stop production altogether, bringing about an unstable situation. Another improvement which can be made possible by economics is the internalizing of costs, particularly in the case of pollution control, and free-market economists incline to the view that if the costs are fully accounted then pollution becomes uneconomic; more intervention-minded writers (Brubaker 1972) ask if the contaminator can then purchase an unbounded right to pollute, and thus end up in favour of the concurrent imposition of governmental regulations.

Improvement of institutions is a hardy perennial in this field and nobody can deny its need; in particular, the closing of the commons is seen as a useful step: presumably nations might bid for the oceans, but the atmosphere is more difficult to apportion in view of its restless nature. Redistribution of food might help, along with an international larder to help the Mother Hubbard states over hard times in the short run; and no doubt the channelling of capital to the LDCs is not without its turbulent stretches.

Most important of all to those who advocate increased development, albeit directed to different places and sometimes to new ends, is the faith that technology will eventually provide answers. At a simple level of appeal, an energy-resource supplier will say at his annual shareholders' meeting, 'Why can't the environmentalists go away and leave us alone: something will turn up'; in a much more elaborate version, Eastlund and Gough (1969) envision the day when an ultra-high-temperature plasma acts as a fusion torch to reduce any material to its elements for separation so that on a large scale urban sewage could be processed, all solid waste recycled, electricity produced through fuel cells, and water desalted, all using only heavy hydrogen from sea water as a basic material and producing as a 'waste' only helium which will itself be quite valuable. (Waste heat will of course be produced too.) As always, science is a two-edged weapon, and believers in technology share with environmentalists a concern over what criteria would be used to decide what was to be produced from such a horn of plenty, and who would decide which buttons to press.

Another kind of world

As a reaction both to those who foresee imminent and inevitable doom and to those who see solutions mainly in terms of continued technological development, a set of views which emphasize the biological and physical limitations of the planet as a home for man have been put forward. Their answer lies in the adoption of a totally different strategy of man–environment relations, which is characterized largely by steady states of everything pertaining to man, be it population levels or economic activity.

The envelope of the alternative is clear. This is the objective knowledge about the ecosphere and its functioning which modern science is beginning to provide. As ecology, for example, becomes more sophisticated, its level of contribution will increase: Boulding (1966a) did not get into much trouble when he described ecologists as 'a lot of bird-watchers'. Indeed, ecology's major contribution so far has been to provide a holistic conceptual framework for thinking about the ecosphere rather than detailed, accurate and predicative data about the way it will behave in any given circumstances, although improvements will no doubt be brought about as a result of current research. One major general contribution of ecology has been the knowledge of limits. Since ecosystems function within the wider limits of finite solar radiation and finite cycling times of scarce mineral elements, we become aware of a set of finite limits to food production and of a finite boundary even to a population supported by continuously recycled materials. Terrestrial space is clearly finite and cannot be created, give or take a polder or two. Wastes may also produce limits, especially heat where there are probably not only safe limits beyond which atmospheric systems may be unpredictably altered, but absolute limits beyond which the transport out into space cannot take place at a sufficiently fast rate. The thresholds at which these limits might be expected to operate, other than at local scales, and the rates of activity which might bring them down upon us are uncertain, but no amount of technology or wishful thinking can make them go away, since they are inescapable parts of the physical constitution of the planet. An additional set of limits may be produced by the breakdown of the behaviour patterns of humans under conditions of high density. The evidence, as discussed above, is not conclusive, but since there is clearly a cultural dimension to tolerance of crowding, then expressions of aversion to particular conditions are probably significant. Thus if people feel that Britain, for example, is overcrowded, then perhaps it is overcrowded and action needs to be taken to stabilize and possibly reduce the population.

Within the envelope of the limits just discussed, a conception of an alternative man–environment relationship has grown up. Although deriving its fundamental thesis from the observations of biology, it has been given added impetus by inputs such as the NASA pictures of this fragile but fertile planet spinning alone in an infinity of hostile space. Thus the outstanding articulator of the idea, K. E. Boulding (1966c), has called it the 'spaceship earth economy'. He contrasts it with our present economy, which he calls the 'cowboy economy', being characterized by flamboyance, waste and a taste for burning candles at both ends; if we book a passage on the *Titanic*, there is no point in going steerage.

Basic principles of the 'spaceship earth' concept

The purpose of this alternative model is to establish a dynamic equilibrium. Populations are stable, or oscillate with only a small amplitude around a constant level. All materials are conserved by undergoing recycling. There is thus an end to exponential growth on a world scale, although individual parts may exhibit growth within the overall limits. The idea is thus analogous to preferred limits of population in hunting societies, as distinct from populations which necessitate the use of all the food resources of the group's territory.

Although the basic concept is simple, the specific conditions for its possible success need more detailed examination, and we must begin with the search for ecological understanding. At the traditional scales of ecological research, work is still essential to secure the fundamental understanding of how ecosystems work and, indeed, whether the ecological model of the functioning of nature is a correct one. In particular, more knowledge of the predictability of ecosystem response to various natural and anthropogenic stimuli is required, as is a deeper understanding of the nature of ecological stability and the conditions under which it can be expected (Woodwell and Smith 1969). Knowledge of the complete system of 'man and his total environment' is required, as Egler (1970) has stressed. Although the working of component parts of this ecosphere need to be better understood, a feeling for the whole is essential, especially for the repercussions of unwanted changes in unexpected places. In general, a determination to regard the phenomena of both physical and cultural systems holistically is necessary, unpopular though this is with 'pure' scientists who see an invasion of their carefully guarded swimming pools by the unwashed hordes from across the tracks. The integrated view is characteristic of geography as an intellectual discipline, and geography deals with the cultural dimension as well as the ecological, but geographers have shown few signs of wishing to put their feet into the turbulent waters of environmental debate, with certain honourable exceptions (Burton and Kates 1964, Zelinsky 1970, Eyre 1971). The development of schools of study, let alone administrative structures, at the integrative level of man and his total environment is slow in coming and subject to considerable opposition and general inertia.

In practical terms, the 'spaceship' economy is predicated upon the attainment of a stable population at a world scale. Growth of world population must clearly stop at some time, and the equilibrium approach prefers an all-out effort to bring this about by cultural and technical means rather than leave it to the alternatives. These latter are likely to be either psychological, with stress causing spontaneous abortion, inadequate parental care of infants or possibly enhanced rates of foetal re-absorption, or directly Malthusian, through famine, war and disease. Even if measures such as those of Fremlin were adopted there is still a limit to the number of people supportable on this planet. In bringing about population stability, priority needs to be given to the DCs and the Egyptian type of LDC. The importance of the European-US-type nations is twofold. Firstly, they are the dominant users of resources and producers of contaminants. Statistics for almost any part of a global resource process will show the USA itself in the lead for per capita use, followed closely by other nations of the US type, and hotly pursued by the European-type countries. A further reduction of the already slow rate of increase of population would help to remove the fundamental cause of their need for resources, although cultural demands would doubtless keep consumption levels high and the actual reduction of usage rates would have to be a cultural decision of a different kind from agreeing to attempt to stabilize population. Secondly, Western material culture is the object of aspirations in many LDCs who think that population control is basically an imperialist gambit to keep the Third World in its 'proper' place. It is essential therefore to practise what is preached, and to make it clear that population stabilization by the rich ought ultimately to be for the greater benefit of the poor.

The need for population control in resource-poor and technology-poor nations is self-evident. It is probably their only way of moving away from the precarious balance between adequacy and insufficiency, whether of food or employment. Intensified and more productive agriculture may improve living standards, but it inevitably causes a wholesale drift to the cities, where industrialization rarely proceeds fast enough to provide jobs for the influx, partly because capital accumulation per capita is low at times of rapid population growth. Furthermore, the basic resources for the industrial development of many of the populous LDCs are lacking: cheap energy, in particular, is likely to be difficult to acquire. Additionally, their rapid rates of population growth (often in excess of 2 per cent p.a.) impose strains upon their social structures, especially in the cases of newly independent nations lacking political stability. Not the least problem is the high proportion of young people in a rapidly growing population, many of whom will have material and educational aspirations on a scale undreamed of by their parents. Urgency is less marked in nations of the Brazilian character, since they can for a time contain their people by developing hitherto unattractive areas, witness the Brazilian plans for the Amazon Basin. But there can be no question of their freedom from eventual limits, and prudence would seem to dictate a halt to growth before their population-resources imbalances become national rather than local or regional. The fragility of many of the biomes in these countries, especially those in the tropics, serves to underline the virtues of leaving a wide margin of safety which is not dependent upon technology, an implement which is still generally lacking in such places and sometimes unwisely used where present.

Apart from cultural change, a large investment of money is needed to bring about population stabilization, and since fertility control is the most acceptable method, we may reflect that it is probably money better spent than on prestigious projects like a national airline or on developments which merely postpone decision-making, like some large dams. But one major difficulty is the time factor: another doubling of the world's population seems inevitable following the passage through the demographic structure of those already born. Thereafter, present campaigns for fertility control may show some effect on absolute numbers if they have been successful. To judge by present declines in fertility in LDCs, the highly urbanized societies and those with numerous ethnic Chinese people are showing the greatest response, as in Hong Kong, Taiwan and Singapore; there is also the example of Japan in the post-1945 period: it looks as if urbanization in the Third World may be a useful trend as far as reducing birth rates is concerned; however, there are indications that some techniques for 'selling' contraception are meeting with resistance, and the attachment of family planning to medicine and consequent association with illness may reduce acceptability.

But an equilibrium economy requires not only the attainment of a stable population but also its maintenance. If this is to be achieved, it will fundamentally require the acceptance of the notion that the maximum size of an individual's family is for society to decide, and not for the parents alone. In effect the situation will have been brought back to the condition of 'primitive' hunting groups which limited their populations to the number sustainable on a preferred food source rather than let it expand to the boundary of the entire supply of nutrition. A fairly drastic social adjustment consisting of the yielding up of an individual choice is therefore indicated. Those who argue the unacceptability of such a change must be asked to consider the other choices which will become unavailable in a condition of a serious imbalance of population, resources and environment. Even if the theses of Parsons (1971) are not all accepted, few of the developments of technology which some believe will avert any 'environmental crisis' seem to propose increased personal liberty and choice as their concomitants, let alone their immediate purposes.

The cycling of materials

This necessary condition is based on the premise that some materials, e.g. metals, will be in short supply because of the demands of increased populations wishing to share in the benefits of an industrial way of life. In addition, the environmental alterations inevitably associated with the extraction of lower qualities of materials will be diminished if supplies can be re-used. Relatively few materials are actually destroyed in the course of their use, so that given the appropriate technology and cost structure, recycling becomes a feasibility for many items: those containing metals and wood products (Plate 24) are obvious examples, but the idea can be applied to many diverse materials, including water, sewage and textiles. Some losses are unavoidable, as for example the escape of metals through friction; new sources would be used only to make up such losses, but additions to the total stock would presumably be made only after satisfaction of the strictest criteria. Probably the critical feature of the recycling economy would be the availability of energy to power the recycling processes, and in view of present attitudes towards the future costs of energy, Berry (1972) has suggested that the production and recycling of goods be evaluated from the point of view of energy economies. Using as measures the loss of thermodynamic potential involved in the manufacture of a new car and its subsequent recycling, he observes that, given increased demand for cars and present technology, recycling is a questionable process compared with extending the life of the machine, which would diminish by two to three times the energy used, since fewer new cars would be needed. Even bigger savings could be achieved by improvements in the technology of the basic recovery and fabrication processes of metals, where thermodynamic savings of five to ten times the present expenditure could be made. So, economies of energy use brought out by recycling are small compared with extended lifetimes of goods and smaller still compared with a technology which loses less energy; yet since recycling is more economically feasible it would be a useful start (a saving of 1,000 KWH/vehicle in the USA is equivalent to eight to ten generating stations) towards a policy of thrift. Industrialization of the LDCs, adds Berry, may only be achievable if policies of thermodynamic thrift are brought into effect.

Re-use has the further advantage that all wastes become important sources of raw materials and thus environmental contamination is reduced, except for the non-re-usable

Plate 24 Things to come? A recycling centre run by voluntary labour in Berkeley, California. Here, bottles are sorted into various kinds and the truck behind serves as a temporary repository for old newspapers. *(I. G. Simmons)*

substances, to which pollution-control measures will have to be applied. Pollution control *per se*, although useful and necessary at an early stage of moving to a closed-cycle economy, now becomes only a last-ditch treatment of intractable wastes.

Moving towards a recycling of materials will be difficult economically. Theoretically the price of recycled materials should make them more attractive as supplies from fresh sources become more expensive; but because of the nature of exponential curves, the limits of supply may be suddenly upon us before the price mechanism has had time to react so as to show the need for research and development into recycling technology and the accompanying changes in social patterns. Additionally, the external costs of pollution are not now levied upon the producer but upon society at large (Crocker and Rogers 1971, Davis and Kamien 1972). Effective legislation and taxation to internalize pollution costs and governmental inputs into recycling technology to prime the pump are therefore urgent priorities now.

Ecosystem balance

The ideas of overall economic and ecological stability embodied in the spaceship earth economy have to be translated into quantities of various types of ecosystem. Because the world cannot return to a pre-agricultural economy, the ecosystems of man's creation must also be included. A valuable start on the analysis needed to provide the criteria for balance between different types of ecosystems has been provided by E. P. Odum (1969). He emphasizes that nature is a mosaic of ecosystems at different levels of succession, some of them 'young' with low inherent stability and diversity but high productivity; by contrast, mature ecosystems have high stability and diversity but their productivity may be lower. Globally, the major ecosystems of the natural world exhibit a developed state of internal symbiosis, good nutrient conservation, high resistance to external perturbation, and low entropy. On the other hand, as Odum puts it,

> Man has generally been preoccupied with obtaining as much 'production' from the land as possible, by developing and maintaining early successional types of ecosystems, usually monocultures. But, of course, man does not live by food and fibre alone; he also needs a balanced CO_2–O_2 atmosphere, the climatic buffer provided by oceans and masses of vegetation, and clean (that is, unproductive) water for cultural and industrial uses. Many essential life-cycle resources, not to mention recreational and esthetic needs, are best provided man by the less 'productive' landscapes.

Different types of ecosystems must therefore form a balanced pattern. As in nature there is a mix of mature, stable systems with immature, unstable ones, so in the man-manipulated world there must be an intercalation of man-dominated simple systems alongside complex natural ecosystems. Four types of ecosystems may be distinguished:

(1) Non-vital systems, or the 'built environment' of urban and industrial areas. These are in fact dependent upon imports from outside, e.g. of oxygen and water, for their continued existence; in the natural state the nearest analogy is probably a volcano, for it too emits sulphur dioxide, carbon dioxide and particulate matter into the atmosphere. Other non-vital systems of the natural world might include ice-caps (which, however, act as reservoirs of water and affect climate) and the most barren deserts, to which cities are not infrequently compared by writers with bucolic yearnings, although perhaps cities are morphologically more akin to karst terrain.

(2) Intensively used biotic systems with high productivity and capacity for high yield to man. Like natural systems at an early stage of succession, man-directed systems such as agriculture have a low diversity of species and are unstable. However, they are easily exploitable and hence highly valued in economic terms. As in comparable natural situations, the growth qualities of the plants and animals selected for rapidity, and quantity of production is valued above quality.

(3) Compromise areas, such as those devoted to multiple-use management of forests, or intermixtures of forest, agriculture and grazing or other wild land, are analogous to natural ecosystems approaching, but not yet at, maturity. They are characterized by higher diversity than the earlier stages of succession and by the development of complex

webs of interdependence between organisms, in contradistinction to the linear chains, dominated by grazing, of earlier stages.

(4) The mature wild systems, i.e. areas of 'climax' vegetation which are basically unaltered by man. In addition to being important reservoirs of biotic diversity, they are vital agents in gaseous interchange, and provide a source of recreational and aesthetic pleasure. Their metabolism is diametrically different from that of early successional phases since it is a highly bound network of food webs with high internal conservation of nutrients by cycling, and has very high resistance to external perturbation. The characteristics of such ecosystems, compared with those in early stages of succession, are set out in Table 13.8. These natural systems play a role far beyond the value which conventional economics accords them. They are the 'anchormen' of total global stability, and perform a function

TABLE 13.8   Trends in the development of ecosystems

Ecosystem attributes	Developmental stages	Mature stages
Food chains	Linear, predominantly grazing	Weblike, predominantly detritus
Biomass supported/unit energy flow	Low	High
Total organic matter	Small	Large
Species diversity-variety component	Low	High
Size of organism	Small	Large
Life cycles	Short, simple	Long, complex
Mineral cycles	Open	Closed
Nutrient exchange rate between organisms and environment	Rapid	Slow
Internal symbiosis	Undeveloped	Developed
Nutrient conservation	Poor	Good
Stability	Poor	Good
Entropy	High	Low

Source: E. P. Odum 1969

which is 'protective' rather than 'productive' but no less vital. If the oceans are included as mature systems, we may note the suggestions quoted by Odum that the oceans are the governor (in the mechanical sense) of the biosphere, slowing down and controlling the rate of decomposition and nutrient regeneration, thereby creating and maintaining the highly aerobic terrestrial atmosphere to which the higher forms of life, ourselves included, are adapted.

Nature has a mosaic of these four types: so must man, if long-term stability of the biosphere is to be attained. The model elaborated is capable of simulation by computer to work out national limits for the size and capacity of each type of system, and the flows between it and the others. The next task seems to be to translate this functional-dynamic model into spatial terms, and using a per capita approach at US levels of consumption, Odum and Odum (1972) conclude that about 5 ac/cap (2·025 ha/cap) is needed by men for all purposes, of which two-fifths should be devoted to natural environments. Whether this proportion should be different in, for example, more fragile environments, what is the particular role of the oceans, and what effect cultural difference might have, are not discussed. The minimum scale at which the ratios become effective needs also to be explored by simulation. The strategy for balance between different kinds of ecosystem confirms yet again the importance of limits, for it is implicit that the now vital and highly productive ecosystems can only expand to certain limits, beyond which the protective systems cannot balance them.

Social and economic adjustments

The primary and ineluctable requirement for the implementation of the closed-cycle economy is population control, which must be aimed at producing a stable world population, with the initial priorities of achieving stable or even declining populations in the US and European types of resource–population situation, and stability in the UAR group. The Brazilian type can possibly be allowed to grow a little more, but not for long.

The basis of value of environmental resources will also undergo change in a recycling economy. Whereas present economic systems value throughput and high turnover allows low prices, the opposite is likely to occur in a revised system. Because of the need to conserve materials, articles which have a long life, preferably free of losses through wear, are likely to be relatively less expensive than those requiring frequent trips through the recycling process. Thus the Chippendale chair ought to cost less than the cardboard one, and the tough dress that lasts their whole adult lives will be easier on the ladies' fashion budget than the frilly number lasting only a few parties. (Such an equation ought to bring home the truly revolutionary nature of the spaceship earth concept.) The same argument, *mutatis mutandis*, will apply to more costly material possessions like vehicles, and the current idea of building disposable towns will be seen as an evanescent efflorescence of an age that denied its own limitations. The final disappearance of the goal of unlimited growth may also be a signal for a major redistribution of incomes. The gap between rich and poor should diminish, partly because less growth will provide fewer opportunities for rapidly gained entrepreneurial profits, and partly because a more coherently planned economy may well value more highly the present poor. A lessened emphasis on the quantity of industrial production will reverse the present trend to energy-intensive production in favour of labour-intensive outputs. This should encourage production of quality goods and services and perhaps restore to the manual workers some of the dignity and job-satisfaction which mass-production has taken away from them. Since labour is likely to be in shorter supply in a stable population, unemployment might reasonably be expected to diminish, and re-evaluation of those currently rejected as too old (rather than incapable) for particular tasks is likely to occur.

The role of industry must change. Nobody advocates a return to some pastoral condition where factories are unheard of and the cross-stitching on the shepherds' smocks is sullied only by the spots of blood from their inevitable tuberculosis, but certain shifts in industrial policy are advocated. Most important is the abandonment of the 'technological fix' as an article of faith, acknowledging that in many respects natural systems are much more efficient than those which are man-made. Next in priority is a realization that for some of the difficult problems caused by population growth, there are no simple (or even complex) technological panaceas worth having (Ehrlich and Holdren 1969). The disparate time-scales upon which population growth and technological development operate, and the complexity of man–environment relations outside the narrowly conceived context of food production, are all taken to suggest that present technology will not suffice to maintain the expected populations of the world, even given optimistic assumptions. Rather is it the case that technology will only become effective and life-enhancing in a stable economy, when the possibility of applying several technological schemes along a broad front (instead of the current piecemeal approach which usually creates several difficulties for each one it removes) becomes more feasible.

Given the abandonment of the ideology of growth, the redirection of technological effort becomes possible and its contribution to a harmonious relation of man and nature immense. New criteria of success will be essential, especially with regard to the environmental consequences and in the discarding of those material uses which are totally ephemeral and add nothing to the quality of anybody's life. Beyond such a stage it is possible that the kind of 'de-development' proposed by Ehrlich and Harriman (1971) may be essential in the European and US groups of nations. Here the control of 'needs' induced by advertising, the freeing of industrial policy from the hands of a few individuals unaccountable to the society which supports them, the enhancement of private affluence at the expense of public squalor, and all the excrescences of the 'disposable society' will have to be firmly controlled without undue delay, as requisites of the closed-cycle economy. Adaptation to a new type of economy, together with the many unsolved problems of the LDCs, will ensure a series of challenges to industry of an unprecedented nature. There is no desire to abandon technology, but neither should there be any intention to allow the big corporations (and their Socialist equivalents) to dominate the resource processes of the biosphere; control of the harmful technology described by Commoner (1972a, b) is necessary but is only a first step.

Brief, if insufficient, mention must be made of some of the institutional adjustments which would be necessary to the success of an equilibrium economy. At a global scale, international agreement on certain movements towards stability will be necessary, especially where the prohibition of poisoning or over-use of commons like the oceans is concerned. Moves towards lessening nuclear testing underground and towards the elimination of nuclear weapons altogether would also be a useful adjunct. Co-ordination of the programmes of nation states and economic groups like the EEC as they alter their goals would be a function of the UN, but a tighter global control is probably an unrealistic prognosis. The main effort would have to come from independent states and the blocs to which they have given over some of their sovereignty: it is they who would lead their people through the difficult task of reorientating their way of life.

It is of course possible that a different type of process might occur: that the changed consciousness of individuals may itself work towards a life-style which is consonant with long-term ecological stability. Thus whole populations may become 'greened', as Reich (1971) has postulated of American youth. Whether or not the contradictions of that book render its main thesis invalid, the revolution of outlook which he describes appears to be confined to the young, and to only a proportion of them. Whether we then have time to wait and see if their world-view persists into middle age, whether it is adopted by their children, and whether they are sufficiently numerous to infect the whole population with their different values, is a luxury we may not be permitted. Like it or not, the political process will have to be the lane down which change is pursued, albeit one lined with thorn hedges. We may parenthetically note that a stable population will have a higher proportion of elderly people in it than a growing one, so that a state of gerontocracy will presumably be even more likely than in the days of the simultaneous reigns of de Gaulle, Adenauer and Macmillan. Some conflict with the aspirations of the young may confidently be predicted.

A journey of a thousand miles

At the time of writing, the negative inputs to the search for new attitudes to the relationship of population, resources and environment have been dominant, whether in the form of 'doom-mongering' or in the more muted form of eloquent writers such as Dubos and Mumford. Positive responses like the setting-out of the spaceship earth concept have attracted less attention because they can spell out the future in less detail than can the forecasters of gloom who merely have to assume the continuation of present trends. More elaborate plans for a stabilized economy have appeared, which not only set out the conceptual framework in more detail but also formulate plans for the introduction of certain transitional stages at appropriate times, i.e. the 'orchestration' of change. The most pioneering of such documents is the 'Blueprint for Survival' (Goldsmith, Allen et al. 1972), produced in semi-popular form. After an analysis of the present trends in the growth of population and economies, and their impact upon the environment, it turns to specific remedies of the kind discussed above, and the co-ordination of their introduction. Its core is the assertion that exponential growth is unsustainable for long periods and that conscious measures to bring about an upper asymptote are better than the free operation of the market and Malthusian checks. It can be criticized in detail, as can all such syntheses, but its basic propositions are consonant with the concept of an equilibrium economy.

The type of measures needed to forestall collapse of ecological and economic systems are also set out by Meadows et al. (1972). Here, complex modelling by computer of several variables in the planetary system (population, industrial output, food production, level of pollution, resources) is used to predict the outcome both of continuing present trends and of altering singly or in concert the variables (Fig. 13.1). Needless to say, continued exponential growth leads to breakdown, and alternatives are explored. The authors conclude that at present very little can be said about the practical day-to-day steps that can be taken to realize the goal of equilibrium, since the models are too lacking in detail to enable all the implications of the transition from growth to equilibrium to be understood. They emphasize, however, that the greatest possible impediment to any sort of stability, or to a more just utilization of the world's resources, is population growth. If stability is the only alternative to the difficulties caused by growth, it also offers numerous advantages, as they argue

equilibrium would require trading certain human freedoms, such as producing unlimited numbers of children, or consuming uncontrolled amounts of resources, for other

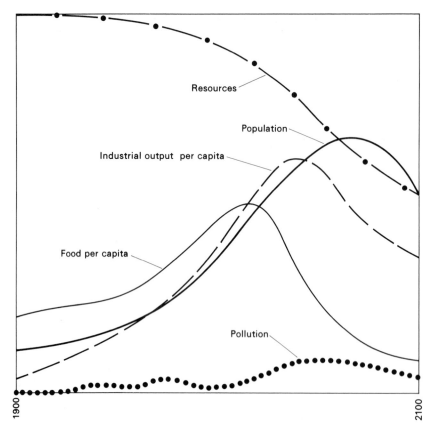

Fig. 13.1 A world model with 'unlimited' resources and pollution controls. Pollution generation per unit of output is reduced to 25 per cent of its 1970 value, but resource availability is doubled by cheap nuclear power, which also makes extensive recycling possible. Population and industry then grow until the limit of arable land is reached; food per capita declines and industrial growth is slowed as capital is devoted to food production.
Source: Meadows *et al.* 1972

freedoms, such as relief from pollution and crowding, and the threat of collapse of the world system.

It is possible that new freedoms might also arise—universal and unlimited education, leisure for creativity and inventiveness, and, most important of all, the freedom from hunger and poverty enjoyed by such a small fraction of the world's people today.

This work and that of Forrester (1971) have been subject to considerable criticism, principally by economists who argued that the assumptions are too simplistic. Others argue that because of the multiplier effects in the model, the alteration of one or two rates by 1 per cent may produce totally different conclusions from those reached in the study quoted. These antagonisms are not particularly relevant, for the importance of the complex modelling is in its demonstration of a technique which can be further refined as our knowledge of natural and social processes becomes more accurate.

Adjudication: limits of all kinds

If the human species is to continue to depend upon the natural systems of the biosphere for life-support, for materials, for valued surroundings and for waste disposal, then it must acknowledge the existence of limits.

The most obvious of these are the ecological limits of which numerous examples have been given in this work, outstanding among which is the SCEP (1970) calculation that every doubling of population increases the 'ecological demand' by six times. Within these limits, a new linkage is needed in which the socio-economic systems realize the importance of the protective systems and reflect this value in their economies. This will contrast with the present situation where wild-lands are usually regarded as raw materials which acquire value only if transformed to something else.

Politicians must also realize that these limits prevent them from promising unlimited 'growth' to their constituents. More realistically, those leaders might well work towards a condition in which all people had a 'right' to life-support from the planet. A fundamental flaw in the world's legal systems allows individuals to appropriate portions of the complex cycles upon which we all depend. They may contaminate part of the water cycle or the air, or may clear protective forest in order to enhance short-term gain from exploitive agriculture. The ownership of land and water must not therefore confer the right to remove it from the life-support systems, and those who wilfully release wastes which disorder those systems must be made to desist: a process which is beginning to take effect.

If limits are to be culturally accepted, then the poor have to be reassured that the rich are not merely pulling up the ladder behind them, having achieved their desired level of material prosperity. This applies both to rich and poor in industrial nations, and to rich and poor countries collectively. In industrial countries with clearly differentiated social strata most of the pressures both for cosmetic conservation and 'environmentalism' come from the 'middle class' and are often denounced on that account. There is often truth in the idea that cosmetic acts merely impose middle-class values upon the whole of the society and use up wealth which might be better spent upon necessities for the poor. Wider concepts of the closed-cycle equilibrium type, however, are basically advantageous to the less privileged groups in society. At present, the poor have a smaller share in the proceeds of economic growth, for example; the industrial workers suffer most from pollution both at work and in their homes, for the better-off can always move house to the cleaner suburbs and handle nothing more contaminating than the latest issue of *Playboy*. The much vaunted example of London's clearer air following smoke abatement programmes has merely transferred the pollution from London to the areas around the coking plants, and to Scandinavia. Some LDCs may forgo the energy-intensive economies of the West and opt for intermediate technology aimed at improving rural life, but those where industry has been made the basis of economic development will wish to attract more capital. Such LDCs can scarcely be expected to stabilize their economies at the present stage, but many will

presumably follow the examples of the DCs as they have over the benefits of industrialization; the relationship between the two groups at a time when DCs were stabilizing
economies but LDCs still expanding is a difficult and complex issue which needs a great
deal of study.

Admission of limits to the carrying capacity of the planet need not carry with it the
automatic connotation of doom if all expansion of flows through resource processes is not
stopped immediately. It is possible that the choice of chaos or survival currently postulated
is a false one. There may be two kinds of limits in the capacity of the earth. The first of

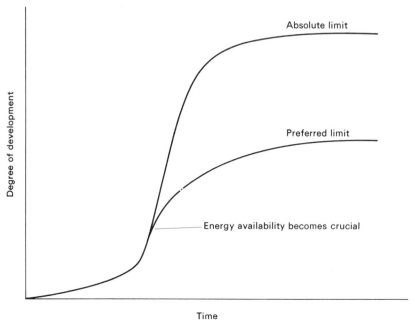

Fig. 13.2 A scheme of two alternative limits to world development: the absolute limit involves replacement of natural life-support systems by man-made processes, the preferred limit does not. The availability
of cheap and safe energy is crucial to the pursuit of the absolute limit.

these is the *absolute limit* in which a man-made stability replaces that of natural systems.
A first stage might be the conversion of the earth largely to a food–man monoculture, but
later the immense technological contribution of the type envisaged by Fremlin (1964)
would be mandatory. The human populations that could be supported would be huge, but
there would be little room for other than technological life-support systems. The alternative
might be a *preferred limit,* in which the natural systems continue to be crucial for our survival and in which they are valued accordingly. A diversity of habitat and culture would
remain (unlikely to happen in the absolute-limit alternative) but the supportable population
would be lower than in the technology-dependent world; this latter alternative is of course
identical with Boulding's spaceship earth concept. The two limits are depicted in Fig. 13.2.
There may be a third alternative in which the intensive use of cheap energy means that

all man's needs can be produced in industrial plant which is as much as possible isolated from the biosphere. Man's material needs would be supplied by an economic system parallel to but in minimal interaction with natural systems. Plans for underground and offshore nuclear power stations could presumably be extended to all kinds of manufacturing and processing installations so that, given adequate technology and favourable geology, even food could be produced from atomic and molecular building blocks in underground and submersible factories, or even in space, leaving the biosphere relatively free of human impact, although many people would still want to live on the earth's surface. In spite of its apparent reasonableness, this alternative has an air of science fiction about it. But both it and the system which depends upon the supersession of natural systems depend upon the provision of a cheap, clean and ubiquitous energy supply whose waste heat can be safely radiated into space without a major disturbance of atmospheric patterns. And so attention to developments such as controlled fusion reactions, alternative methods of energy conversion, more locally autonomous power sources of a non-fossil and non-nuclear type, more efficient technology which will effectively utilize energy inputs (few steam plants today operate beyond an efficiency of 45 per cent), and energy-conservative buildings, domestic heating systems and transport networks, are all vital and pressing needs. Without them only the environmentalist model offers hope of any quality of life.

If there is a choice between these alternatives, what criteria are to be used in making decisions? There is no doubt that the preferred limit is safer: it gives much wider margins for error, and forecloses fewer options than the absolute limit. It also offers a greater diversity of all kinds to individual people: of different employments, different places to visit and different cultures to exist alongside. But it is a world in which growth is no longer equated with progress; it is analogous to the condition of men in hunting societies who limited their populations to those who could be fed by a preferred food supply such as meat, rather than an absolute food supply which included rodents and roots.

The outlook of those who wish to advocate the preferred limit is essentially optimistic. Those who propose totally technological solutions are seeking to avoid dangers, but the spaceship earth proponents see a different kind of world. They do not wish to return to some forgotten Eden without machines (indeed they want more technology, not less, but applied in a different manner), but to create a world of stability in which the resources are used equitably by an adequately nourished population which does not poison its own habitat with the wastes. They see it as the most hopeful way of coming to grips with what Caldwell (1971) views as man's most fearsome problems: the containment of population growth, the management of energy flows, the development of stable ecological and political orders, and the formulation of a coherent political and ethical doctrine for human behaviour in relation to natural systems, and furthermore one which neither attempts the unforeseeable nor commits the irrevocable. Bringing this about is a task of immense difficulty, because it can only be made meaningful to diverse groups of men in terms of the lineaments of their own culture: success is unlikely if new ways are imposed internationally or by foreign-educated governors. But because of the accelerating rush to instability brought about by the exponential growth of numbers of people, consuming materials and energy, and subsequently discharging waste, all men should recognize that ecological instability is their common enemy, one which will not distinguish between rich and poor, black, white or brown, PhDs and peasant farmers. The alternatives are clear: to try to develop to an absolute limit in one of its forms, to aim for a preferred limit, or to adopt no overall strategy and allow present-day institutions to respond to individual problems as they arise. As was said at the beginning of this book, man is a material-using animal. He must also make moral choices.

Further reading

BECKERMANN, W. 1973: Growthmania revisited.

BLACK, J. 1970: *The dominion of man.*

BOYD, R. 1972: World dynamics: a note.

BOULDING, K. E. 1966: The economics of the coming spaceship earth.

CALDWELL, L. K. 1971: *Environment: a challenge to modern society.*

COLE, H. S. D. *et al.* (eds.) 1973: *Thinking about the future.*

COMMONER, B. 1972: *The closing circle.*

DETWYLER, T. R. and MARCUS, M. G. 1972: *Urbanization and environment.*

EHRLICH, P. R. and HOLDREN, J. P. 1969: Population and panaceas: a technological perspective.

— 1971: Impact of population growth.

ELLUL, J. 1964: *The technological society.*

GOLDSMITH, E. *et al.* 1972: Blueprint for survival.

HARDIN, G. 1973: *Exploring new ethics for survival. The voyage of the spaceship Beagle.*

MCHALE, J. 1969: *The future of the future.*

MADDOX, J. 1972: *The doomsday syndrome.*

MEADOWS, D. L. *et al.* 1973: *The limits to growth.*

MISHAN, E. J. 1967: *The costs of economic growth.*

MONTEFIORE, H. 1970: *Can man survive?*

MONCRIEF, L. W. 1970: The cultural basis for our environmental crisis.

ODUM, E. P. 1969: The strategy of ecosystem development.

STUDY OF CRITICAL ENVIRONMENTAL PROBLEMS (SCEP) 1970: *Man's impact on the global environment: assessment and recommendations for action.*

SPILHAUS, A. 1972: Ecolibrium.

WAGAR, J. A. 1970: Growth versus the quality of life.

WARD, B. and DUBOS, R. 1972: *Only one earth.*

Appendix

The slow pace of the production of a book (mostly the fault of the author) contrasts with the fast pace of events in the field of resources. These last remarks are therefore intended to update some of the trends described in the main chapters of the book, where recent developments have made them look unduly aged. Not all the numerous happenings can be considered, so emphasis will be put upon developments in attitudes towards resources and environment.

Energy

A 'crisis'

The Arab-Israeli war of October 1973 precipitated a situation which had been looming for some time, namely that oil production would be held at current rates or even reduced, and at the same time its price raised substantially. The shortages hit hardest at Europe, Japan and, although not nearly so dependent upon Arab oil, the USA. Oil landings in Europe and Japan fell to some 80 per cent of the previous year's totals and provoked numerous effects, some of which are described in the next section. The difficult question posed is whether that particular situation is the first taste of a real shortage caused by the depletion of the crude oil resource, or whether it is largely political and economic. Placed against Hubbert King's estimates in Chapter 10, the latter answer seems the more convincing. The key element, it would seem, is price. The sudden cessation of the supply of a cheap fuel will no doubt induce many kinds of short-term adjustments in industrial countries, but the high price on world markets may well lead eventually to an increased rate of recovery, so that the middle 80 per cent will probably be extracted on schedule. Indeed the 'conspiracy' theory of the oil crisis has the international oil companies withholding supplies in order to create shortages so that governments can be panicked into allowing oil prices, and hence company profits, to rise markedly. Some US Congress hearings on the oil industry held early in 1974 provided a few embarrassing moments for senior oil company executives.

Effects

Most noticeable to the average citizen has been the extra cost of oil and petroleum products for all uses, including domestic heating and motoring as well as industry. Shortages have also been evident in queues for gasoline in the USA and Britain, in restrictions on pleasure motoring in most of Europe, and reductions on deliveries of heating oil. At the time of writing, the extra costs of energy had not worked their way through the industrial system and so were not adding greatly to the inflation rampant in the West. The penetration of energy use into all facets of the industrial way of life has, however, been brought home to most people and even some governments. The rush for solutions has meant a re-evaluation of some fuels and grades of fuel which were becoming unpopular because of their pollutant qualities (high sulphur content coal and oil, for example); the introduction of emission standards for various parts of the USA was put back by the Environmental Protection Agency, and some existing controls were relaxed: the influence of environmental consciousness in government seems to have been rather easily eradicated.

Medium-term solutions

Immediate responses from industrial nations have been to accelerate the discovery and extraction of oil and natural gas, particularly where the sources are under the control of the consuming nation. Thus the years of controversy over the Alaska pipeline were speedily ended by the US Congress with only the most token of oppositions from environmentalist groups. The offshore oil recovery programme of Britain was accelerated by all possible means, and until the dissolution of Parliament in February 1974 a Bill to nationalize land needed for the oil industry's operations was proceeding through legislative process. Its effect would have been to bypass most of the cumbersome democracy whereby people who opposed such changes were allowed to argue their case publicly and at length. Another move was the re-evaluation of coal. The large reserves in the USA, for example, and the discovery of thick seams in Yorkshire, England, raised hopes that this source might again be the major underpinner of industrial economies. Token gestures in the direction of the problems of the environmental impact of surface mining and of pollution from combustion of low-grade coals were often made, but more promising were the technologically based suggestions that the processing of coal might make its use more flexible. The most promising of these products seems to be methanol, whose emission characteristics are superior to gasoline, which can be produced by the gasification of coal (Reed and Lerner 1973, Valéry 1974), and which could possibly be done underground. Inevitably, there are difficulties such as the lower kilometres per litre achieved, but it seems superior to hydrogen, for example, where storage-weight factors are prohibitive for small plant and moving vehicles: the equivalent of a 10-gallon (45-litre) petrol tank would be 16 gas cylinders weighing 1·25 tons (1,270 kg).

The consumption side of the balance sheet has also been under consideration and strong pleas made against unnecessary use of energy. One area where the use of energy is particularly excessive is packaging, especially where plastics are used. The energy costs of extra packaging, transporting the weight, and collecting and disposing of the resulting garbage have not been detailed but must be enormous. Domestic premises designed to be heated with cheap oil, with thin walls and large areas of glass, are probably due for review too. The realization of the high energy costs of the 'consumer society', together with shortages of some materials, have put new life into the recycling idea, although actual practice is lagging behind both the technology and the ideas. The conservatism of industries which might recycle waste, and of the collecting agencies in towns and cities, may yet be changed by the rapidly altering economics of materials supply, and intervention by governments ought theoretically to speed up the transition to a waste-using economy. Yet more conservative of energy might be the stipulation that most durable goods must last longer.

Longer-term solutions

The introduction of greater reliance upon nuclear power seems a virtual certainty in industrial nations, using atomic fission immediately and atomic fusion in the more distant future. The expansion of nuclear fission plants has been marked by considerable controversy over the safety of the present choice of the atomic energy authorities of the USA and, because they wish to purchase American reactors of that particular type, the UK. The highly technical arguments centre on the probabilities of certain classes of accident and on the disposal of large quantities of highly dangerous waste. Although these reactors are stoutly defended by their manufacturers and by government agencies already committed to them, there remains the thought that safety is too important to be left to the experts, and notably the 1972 Pugwash Conference thought it was unwise to embark on nuclear fission programmes as a major energy source. Such developments are being seen as Faustian compacts with society, in particular the next generation of breeder reactors whose production of plutonium raises the spectre of its promiscuous use for hostile acts. Opinion varies about whether it can inexpensively be rendered unsuitable for such use.

Beyond lies nuclear fusion, still in its infancy, although the major engineering problems seem along the road to solution, especially in the USSR. The use of lasers in a combined fusion-fission reaction (in which a deuterium-tritium fusion would then split boron nuclei) is also under development. Estimates suggest a commercial introduction of fusion power in 30–40 years' time, but few argue that the energy will be cheap.

Increased interest is also being shown in other energy sources, such as solar power, wind power, geothermal power, and the heat of the earth's core. Large-scale development seems a long way off (with the possible exception of solar-heated buildings), but they are all equilibrium sources, i.e. they do not impose an additional heat burden upon the atmosphere, and so may avoid the heat-limit problems associated with fossil fuel and nuclear power. By contrast, energy is now seen to be so intertwined with the Western way of life that proposals for 'democratizing' its use are emerging from radical thinkers such as Ivan D. Illich (1974).

Other shortages

Materials

Imbalance between supply and demand of some materials has developed, most noticeably in paper and metals, with resulting increases in price. In the case of the former, the explosive rises in demand caused by higher standards of living in terms of literacy and, above all, packaging, have outstripped the growth of the trees. Re-use is often practicable, but substitution seems a more likely development. With metals the picture is less clear since financial speculation in metals' futures has raised their price and kept them off the market. Nevertheless an upsurge of consortia aiming at exploiting the sea-bed has been seen, with recovery of manganese, copper, nickel and cobalt as the prime targets.

Food

Famine has again been widespread, especially in drought-prone regions like the Sahel and Ethiopia, and in other places the growth of population seems to be about to engulf even the achievements of the green revolution. Late in 1973, for example, FAO predicted a 9 million mt shortfall in wheat, Thailand banned rice sales abroad, the Philippines put all cereals under military control, and floods in Pakistan caused widespread destruction of crops. An international grain reserve has been called for several times, but the potential donor nations are having difficulties with, for example, fertilizer supplies: one estimate suggested that the US production of feed grains would drop by 20 million tons in 1973–4. An unknown factor is the consequence of the higher price of fossil fuels. Blaxter (1974) calculates that in the UK the energy input-output ratio for potatoes is 0·87, so that the input of fossil fuels is greater than the solar energy trapped; for wheat the same ratio is 2·2, milk 0·3 and eggs 0·16, these last two presumably being acceptable because of their protein content. Given such relationships, the ability of Western farmers to contribute to a world food larder may be considerably diminished.

Resources and environment

The MIT computer-based studies supported by the Club of Rome and published by Meadows *et al.* (1972) attracted more attention than the treatment in this book would indicate. Numerous arguments reached the pages of most journals and newspapers, the anti-limits critics producing evidence that the parameters were too aggregated, that the outcomes were especially sensitive to very small alterations in the rates of certain variables, and that important cultural feedback mechanisms were omitted. Defenders, on the other hand, pointed to the use of 'the intricate defensive' and thought that none of the detailed criticisms invalidated the main conclusion, which was that material-based economic growth could not go on for ever. True to the Anglo-Saxon mind, various compromises have been put forward, most of which hinge on the question of economic development in the LDCs. Almost all the developments cited so far in this Appendix are likely to prove inimical to the improvement of their lot, unless a two-tier price structure for oil were to be promulgated. At $8/bbl (a conservative estimate) the oil bill for the LDCs of Asia, Africa and South America will rise from $5,200 × 10^6 in 1973 to $27,000 × 10^6 by 1980. Such direct effects, which cancel out, for example, India's hope of self-sufficiency in foreign exchange by 1979, and turn Kenya's forecast growth rate of 7·4 per cent into a negative figure within 18 months, are paralleled by backlash effects from the DCs who may wish or be forced to cut back production which involves primary materials from the Third World. Especially vulnerable will be countries which rely on industries based on semi-manufactured products like plastics and synthetic fibres, such as Singapore, Hong Kong, Korea and even, perhaps, China. One response may be to follow the Arabs' example and exercise monopoly power: copper, tin, bauxite and cocoa are possible cases for OPEC-type treatment. But in the face of falling demand they might not achieve more than stabilization of incomes.

A small but growing body of opinion in the LDCs may wish to abandon the industrial path to sufficiency and opt for an intermediate-technology, low-energy-using route, which concentrates on rural improvements first. If successful such an economy might have much to teach the West, but it is difficult to see how it might succeed in the face of populations growing at 2–3 per cent per annum. So 1974, being World Population Year, is clearly a time for renewed efforts to reduce fertility in the LDCs (countered by news of India's large cuts in government finance of family planning), even if not yet to the barely replacement levels of parts of Europe and of the USA.

No changes of any significance in the balance and attitudes of cornucopians and environmentalists seem to have taken place, although new champions of both seem to be emerging. Perhaps 1972 was the high-water mark of intense public concern over population, resources and environment: now it is time for cooler appraisals, long-term strategies and fundamental questions of purpose.

Bibliography

ABERG, B. and HUNGATE, F. P. (eds.) 1967: *Radioecological concentration processes*. New York and London: Academic Press.

ABRAHAMSON, D. E. 1972: Ecological hazards from nuclear power plants. In M. Taghi Farvar and J. P. Milton (eds.), 795–811.

ADAMS, A. B. (ed.) 1964: *First World Conference on National Parks*. Washington, DC: US Government Printing Office.

ADAMS, W. P. and HELLEINER, F. M. (eds.) 1972: *International geography*. Toronto: University of Toronto Press.

AITKEN, P. L. 1963: Hydroelectric power generation. In Institute of Civil Engineers, 34–42.

ALLISON, A. (ed.) 1970: *Population control*. Harmondsworth: Pelican.

ALTSCHUL, A. M. and ROSENFELD, D. 1970: Protein supplementation: satisfying man's food needs. *Progress* **54**, 76–84.

ALVERSON, D. L., LONGHURST, A. R. and GULLAND, J. A. 1970: How much food from the sea? *Science* **168**, 503–5.

AMERICAN SOCIETY OF RANGE MANAGEMENT 1964: *A glossary of terms used in range management*. Portland, Oregon: American Society of Range Management.

AMIDON, E. and GOULD, E. M. 1962: *The possible impact of recreation development on timber production in three California National Forests*. Berkeley: US Forest Service Pacific SW Experimental Station Technical Paper **68**.

ANDREWARTHA, H. A. and BIRCH, L. C. 1954: *The distribution and abundance of animals*. Chicago: University of Chicago Press.

ANON 1972: Environmental cleanup—a $287 billion project. *Pollution Abstr.* **3** (6), 4–9.

ARBEJDSMINISTERIET DANMARKS 1968: *Arbejdstid og Ferie*. Copenhagen: Labour Ministry of Denmark.

ARKCOLL, D. B. 1971: Agronomic aspects of leaf protein production. In N. W. Pirie (ed.), 9–18.

ASHTON, M. D. 1970: *The relationship of agriculture to soil and water pollution*. Report on the 1970 Cornell Agricultural Waste Management Conference. Washington, DC: Reports of the UK Scientific Mission in North America, UKSM **70/12**.

BADGLEY, P. C. and VEST, W. L. 1966: Orbital remote sensing and natural resources. *Photogram. Engineering* **32**, 780–90.

BAKER, F. C. 1970: *Derelict land*. 'The Countryside in 1970', 3rd Conference, Report **18**. London: HMSO.

BAKUZIS, E. V. 1969: Forestry viewed in an ecosystem concept. In G. M. Van Dyne (ed.), 189–258.

BALIKCI, A. 1968: The Netsilik Eskimos: adaptive processes. In R. B. Lee and I. De Vore (eds.), 1968a, 78–82.

BARNARD, C. (ed.) 1964: *Grasses and grasslands*. London and Melbourne: Macmillan.

BARNARD, C. and FRANKEL, O. H. 1964: Grass, grazing animals and man in historic perspective. In C. Barnard (ed.), 1–12.

BARNETT, H. J. 1967: The myth of our vanishing natural resources. *TRANS-action* **4** (7), 6–10; text reprinted in R. Revelle *et al.* (eds.), 180–86; and in W. H. Davis (ed.), 201–4, with the original photographs.

BARNETT, H. J. and MORSE, C. 1963: *Scarcity and growth*. Baltimore: Johns Hopkins Press for RFF.

BARR, H. M., CHADWICK, B. A. and THOMAS, D. L. (eds.) 1972: *Population resources and the future: non-Malthusian perspectives*. Provo, Utah: Brigham Young University Press.

BARR, J. 1969: *Derelict Britain*. Harmondsworth: Pelican.

— (ed.) 1971: *The environmental handbook*. New York: Ballantine/London: Friends of the Earth.

BARRY, R. G. 1969: The world hydrological cycle. In R. J. Chorley (ed.), 11–29.

BARTSCH, A. F. 1970: Accelerated eutrophication of lakes in the United States: ecological response to human activities. *Environmental Pollution* **1**, 133–40.

BAUMHOFF, M. A. 1963: *Ecological determinants of aboriginal California populations*. University of California Publications in Archaeology and Ethnology **49** (2). Berkeley and Los Angeles: University of California Press.

BAYFIELD, N. 1971. Some effects of walking and skiing on vegetation at Cairngorm. In E. Duffey and A. S. Watt (eds.), 469–84.

BEAUMONT, P. 1968: Quanats on the Varamin Plain, Iran. *Trans. Inst. Brit. Geogr.* **45**, 169–79.

BECKERMANN, W. 1973: Growthmania revisited. *New Statesman* (19 October), 550–52.

BECKINSALE, R. P. 1969a: Human use of open channels. In R. J. Chorley (ed.), 331–43.

— 1969b: Human responses to river regimes. In R. J. Chorley (ed.), 487–509.

BENEDICT, B. 1970: Population control in primitive societies. In A. Allison (ed.), 165–80.

BERKOWITZ, D. A. and SQUIRES, A. M. (eds.) 1971: *Power generation and environmental change*. Cambridge, Mass.: MIT Press.

BERRY, R. 1972: Recycling, thermodynamics and environmental thrift. *Bull. Atom. Sci.* **28** (5), 8–15.

BIENFANG, P. 1971: Taking the pollution out of waste heat. *New Sci.* **51**, 456–7.

BIRDSELL, J. B. 1968: Some predictions for the Pleistocene based upon equilibrium systems among recent hunter-gatherers. In R. B. Lee and I. De Vore (eds.), 1968a, 229–40.

BJERKE, S. 1967: Landscape planning and nature parks. Copenhagen: Naturfrednings-foringen (mimeo).

BLACK, J. 1970: *The dominion of man*. Edinburgh: Edinburgh University Press.

BLAXTER, K. 1974: Power and agricultural revolution. *New Sci.* **61**, 400–403.

BLUMER, M. 1969: Oil pollution of the ocean. In D. P. Hoult (ed.), 5–13.

BOARD, C., CHORLEY, R. J., HAGGETT, P. and STODDART, D. R. (eds.) 1971: *Progress in geography* **3**. London: Edward Arnold.

BOGUE, D. J. 1969: *Principles of demography*. New York: Wiley.

BORGSTROM, G. 1965: *The hungry planet*. New York: Macmillan.

BORMANN, F. H. and LIKENS, G. E. 1969: The watershed-ecosystem concept and studies of nutrient cycles. In G. M. Van Dyne (ed.), 49–76.

BORMANN, F. H., LIKENS, G. E. and EATON, J. S. 1969: Biotic regulation of particulate and solution losses from a forest ecosystem. *Bioscience* **19**, 600–610.

BORMANN, F. H., LIKENS, G. E., FISHER, D. W. and PIERCE, R. S. 1968: Nutrient loss accelerated by clear-cutting of a forest ecosystem. *Science* **159**, 882–4.

BOUGHEY, A. S. 1968: *Ecology of populations.* New York: Macmillan.

BOULDING, K. E. 1962: *A reconstruction of economics.* New York: Science Edition.

— 1966a: Discussions in: F. Fraser Darling and J. P. Milton (eds.), 291–2.

— 1966b: Ecology and economics. In F. Fraser Darling and J. P. Milton (eds.), 225–34.

— 1966c: The economics of the coming spaceship earth. In H. Jarrett (ed.), 3–14.

— 1970: Fun and games with the Gross National Product: the role of misleading indicators in social policy. In H. W. Helfrich (ed.), 157–70.

— 1971: Environment and economics. In W. W. Murdoch (ed.), 359–67.

BOURNE, H. K. 1970: Preservation versus use of the American National Parks and other scenic and recreation areas. Washington, DC: Reports of the UK Scientific Mission in North America, UKSM **70/1**.

BOX, T. W. and PERRY, R. A. 1971: Rangeland management in Australia. *J. Range Management* **24**, 167–71.

BOYD, R. 1972: World dynamics: a note. *Science* **177**, 516–19.

BRACEY, H. C. 1970: *People and the countryside.* London: Routledge and Kegan Paul.

BRADY, N. C. (ed.) 1967: *Agriculture and the quality of our environment.* Washington, DC: Publication **85**, AAAS.

BRAIDWOOD, R. 1970: The agricultural revolution. In J. Janick (ed.), 4–12.

BRITISH TRAVEL ASSOCIATION-KEELE UNIVERSITY 1967: *The pilot national recreation survey, Report* **1**. London: BTA.

BROWN, H. 1954: *The challenge of man's future.* New York: Viking Press.

— 1970: Human materials production as a process in the biosphere. In *Scientific American* (ed.), 115–24.

BROWN, H., BONNER, J. and WEIR, J. 1963: *The next hundred years.* New York: Viking Press.

BROWN, L. H. 1971: The biology of pastoral man as a factor in conservation. *Biol. Cons.* **3**, 93–100.

BROWN, L. R. 1970: Human food production as a process in the biosphere. In *Scientific American* (ed.), 95–103.

BROWN, L. R. and FINSTERBUSCH, G. 1971: Man, food and environment. In W. W. Murdoch (ed.), 53–69.

—1972: *Food.* London and New York: Harper and Row.

BRUBAKER, S. 1972: *To live on earth.* Baltimore: Johns Hopkins Press for RFF/New York: Mentor Books.

BRUHN, J. G. 1972: The ecological crisis and the work ethic. *Int. J. Environ. Studs.* **3**, 43–7.

BRYAN, R. 1973: *Much is taken, much remains.* Belmont, Calif.: Wadsworth.

BRYCE-SMITH, D. 1971: Lead pollution and mental health. *Biologist* **18**, 52–8.

BRYSON, R. A. and WENDLAND, W. M. 1970: Climatic effects of atmospheric pollution. In S. F. Singer (ed.), 1970a, 130–38.

BURTON, I. and KATES, R. W. 1964: Slaying the Malthusian dragon: a review. *Econ. Geogr.* **40**, 82–9.

— (eds.) 1965: *Readings in resource management and conservation*. Chicago: University of Chicago Press.

BURTON, I., KATES, R. W. and SNEAD, R. E. 1969: *The human ecology of coastal flood hazard in Megalopolis*. Chicago: University of Chicago, Department of Geography Research Paper **115**.

BUSH, R. 1973: *The National Parks of England and Wales*. London: Dent.

BUTZER, K. 1964: *Environment and archaeology: an introduction to Pleistocene geography*. Chicago: Aldine Press.

CAHN, R. 1968: *Will success spoil the National Parks?* Boston: Christian Science Monitor Reprints.

CALDER, N. 1967: *The environment game*. London: Secker and Warburg.

— (ed.) 1968: *Unless peace comes*. Harmondsworth: Pelican.

CALDWELL, L. K. 1971: *Environment: a challenge to modern society*. New York: Doubleday Anchor Books.

— 1972: An ecological approach to international development: problems of policy and administration. In M. Taghi Farvar and J. P. Milton (eds.), 927–47.

CALDWELL, M. 1971: World resources and the limits of man. In P. H. G. Hettena and G. N. Syer (eds.), 15–37.

CALHOUN, J. B. 1962: Population density and social pathology. *Sci. Amer.* **206** (2), 139–48.

— 1971: Psycho-ecological aspects of population. In P. Shepard and D. McKinley (eds.), 111–33.

CANTLON, J. E. 1969: The stability of natural populations and their sensitivity to technology. In G. M. Woodwell and H. H. Smith (eds.), 197–205.

CARPENTER, K. J. 1969: Man's dietary needs. In J. Hutchinson (ed.), 61–74.

CARSON, R. 1963: *Silent spring*. Boston: Houghton Mifflin.

CASSIDY, N. G. and PAHALAD, S. D. 1953: The maintenance of soil fertility in Fiji. *Fiji Agric. J.* **24**, 82–6.

CASTRO, J. A. DE A. 1972: Environment and development: the case of the developing countries. In D. A. Kay and E. B. Skolnikoff (eds.), 237–52.

CHAMPAGNAT, A. 1965: Protein from petroleum. *Sci. Amer.* **213** (4), 13–17.

CHAPMAN, P. F. 1970: Energy production—a world limit? *New Sci.* **47**, 634–6.

CHARLIER, R. H. 1970: Crisis year for the Great Lakes. *New Sci.* **44**, 593–6.

CHORLEY, R. J. (ed.) 1969: *Water, earth and man*. London: Methuen.

CHRISTY, F. T. and SCOTT, A. 1967: *The common wealth in ocean fisheries*. Baltimore: Johns Hopkins Press.

CIRIACY WANTRUP, S. V. 1938: Soil conservation in European farm management. *J. Farm Econ.* **20**, 86–101.

CIRIACY WANTRUP, S. V. and PARSONS, J. J. (eds.) 1967: *Natural resources: quality and quantity*. Berkeley and Los Angeles: University of California Press.

CIVIC TRUST, 1964: *A Lee Valley Regional Park*. London: The Civic Trust.

CLARK, J. G. D. 1954: *Excavations at Starr Carr*. Cambridge: Cambridge University Press.

CLARKE, C. 1967: *Land use and population growth*. London: Macmillan.

CLARKE, J. I. 1965: *Population geography*. Oxford: Pergamon Press.

CLARKE, R. 1968: *We all fall down.* Harmondsworth: Pelican.

CLAWSON, M. 1963: *Land and water for recreation.* Chicago: Rand McNally.

CLAWSON, M. and KNETSCH, J. L. 1966: *Economics of outdoor recreation.* Baltimore: Johns Hopkins Press for RFF.

CLAWSON, M., LANDSBERG, H. H. and ALEXANDER, L. T. 1969: Desalted water for agriculture: is it economic? *Science* **164**, 1141–8.

CLOUD, P. 1968: Realities of mineral distribution. *Texas Quarterly* **11**, 103–26.
1969: Minerals from the sea. In NAS/NRC, 135–55.

COLE, H. S. D., FREEMAN, C., JAHODA, M. and PAVITT, K. L. R. (eds.) 1973: *Thinking about the future.* London: Chatto and Windus for Sussex University Press/New York: Universe Books (as *Models of Doom*).

COLE, L. C. 1969: Thermal pollution. *Bioscience* **19**, 989–92.

COLES, J. M. and HIGGS, E. S. 1969: *The archaeology of early man.* London: Faber and Faber.

COLWELL, R. N. 1968: Remote sensing of natural resources. *Sci. Amer.* **218** (1), 54–69.

COMMONER, B. 1972a: *The closing circle.* London: Cape.

— 1972b: The environmental costs of economic growth. In R. Dorfman and N. S. Dorfman (eds.), 261–83.

CONKLIN, H. 1954: An ethnoecological approach to shifting agriculture. *Trans. N.Y. Acad. Sci.*, Ser. II, **17**, 133–42.

— 1957: *Hanunoo agriculture in the Philippines.* Rome: FAO Forestry Development Paper **12**.

COOK, E. 1971: The flow of energy in an industrial society. *Sci. Amer.* **224** (3), 135–44.

COSTIN, A. B. 1964: Grasses and grasslands in relation to soil conservation. In C. Barnard (ed.), 236–58.

— 1971: Water. In A. B. Costin and H. J. Frith (eds.), 71–103.

COSTIN, A. B. and FRITH, H. J. (eds.) 1971: *Conservation.* Ringwood, Victoria: Penguin.

COSTIN, L. N. 1970: Range management in the developing countries. *J. Range Management* **23**, 322–4.

COULSON, J. C. 1972: Grey seals on the Farnes: kindness kills. *New Sci.* **54**, 142–5.

COUNCIL OF EUROPE 1971: *The management of the environment in tomorrow's Europe.* Strasbourg: European Information Centre for Nature Conservation.

COUNTER INFORMATION SERVICES, n.d.: *The Rio Tinto-Zinc Corporation Limited Anti-Report.* London: CIS.

COUNTRYSIDE COMMISSION: *Annual reports.* London: HMSO.

COX, G. W. (ed.) 1969: *Readings in conservation ecology.* New York: Appleton-Century-Crofts.

CRISP, D. J. (ed.) 1964: *Grazing in terrestrial and marine environments.* Oxford: Blackwell.

CRISP, D. T. 1966: Input and output of minerals for an area of Pennine moorland: the importance of precipitation, drainage, peat erosion and animals. *J. Appl. Ecol.* **3**, 327–48.

CROCKER, T. D. and ROGERS, A. J. 1971: *Environmental economics.* Hinsdale, Illinois: Dryden Press.

CROSLAND, C. A. R. 1971: *A Social Democratic Britain.* London: Fabian Society Tract **404**.

CRUTCHFIELD, J. A. (ed.) 1965: *The fisheries: problems in resource management.* Seattle: University of Washington Press.

DARBY, H. C. 1963: Britain's National Parks. *Advmt. Sci.* **20**, 307–18.

DARMSTADTER, J. (with TEITELBAUM, P. D. and POLACH, J. G.) 1971: *Energy in the world economy*. Baltimore: Johns Hopkins for RFF.

DASMANN, R. F. 1964a: *African game ranching*. Oxford: Pergamon Press.

— 1964b: *Wildlife biology*. New York: Wiley.

— 1968: *A different kind of country*. London: Macmillan.

— 1972: *Environmental conservation*. 3rd edn. New York and London: Wiley.

DASMANN, R. F., MILTON, J. P. and FREEMAN, P. H. 1973: *Ecological principles for economic development*. London: Wiley.

DAVIS, K. 1967: Population policy: will current programs succeed? *Science* **158**, 730–39.

— 1968: Review of C. Clark, 1967. *Sci. Amer.* **217** (4), 133–8.

DAVIS, O. A. and KAMIEN, M, I. 1972: Externalities, information and alternative collective action. In R. Dorfman and N. S. Dorfman (eds.), 69–87.

DAVIS, W. H. (ed.) 1971: *Readings in human population ecology*. Englewood Cliffs, NJ: Prentice-Hall.

DAWE, Q. 1972: Chaos that leads to killer dumps. London: *Sunday Times*, 16 January 1972.

DEEVEY, E. S. 1960: The human population. *Sci. Amer.* **203** (9), 195–204.

— 1968: Pleistocene family planning. In R. B. Lee and I. De Vore (eds.), 1968a, 248–9.

— 1970: Mineral cycles. In *Scientific American* (ed.), 83–92.

— 1971: The chemistry of wealth. *Bull. Ecol. Soc. America* **52**, 3–8.

DELWICHE, C. C. 1970: The nitrogen cycle. In *Scientific American* (ed.), 71–80.

DESHLER, W. W. 1965: Native cattle keeping in eastern Africa. In A. Leeds and A. P. Vayda (eds.), 153–68.

DESMOND, A. 1965: How many people ever lived on earth? In L. K. Y. Ng and S. Mudd (eds.), 20–38.

DETWYLER, T. R. (ed.) 1971: *Man's impact on environment*. New York: McGraw-Hill.

DIMBLEBY, G. W. 1962: *The development of British heathlands and their soils*. Oxford Forestry Memoir **23**.

DORFMAN, R. and DORFMAN, N. S. (eds.) 1972: *Economics of the environment*. New York: Norton.

DORN, H. F. 1965: Pitfalls in population forecasts and projections. In I. Burton and R. W. Kates (eds.), 21–37.

DORST, J. 1970: *Before nature dies*. London: Collins.

DOWNS, J. F. and EKVALL, R. B. 1965: Animals and social types in the exploitation of the Tibetan plateau. In A. Leeds and A. P. Vayda (eds.), 169–84.

DUBOS, R. 1967: *Man adapting*. New Haven and London: Yale University Press.

DUCKHAM, A. N. and MASEFIELD, G. B. 1970: *Farming systems of the world*. London: Chatto and Windus.

DUFFEY, E. (ed.) 1967: *The biotic effects of public pressure on the environment*. Monk's Wood Experimental Station Symposium 3. Great Britain: The Nature Conservancy.

DUFFEY, E. and WATT, A. S. (eds.) 1971: *The scientific management of animal and plant communities for conservation*. Oxford: Blackwell.

DUNN, F. L. 1968: Epidemiological factors: health and disease in hunter-gatherers. In R. B. Lee and I. De Vore (eds.), 1968a, 221–8.

DURAND, J. D. 1967: The modern expansion of world population. *Proc. Amer. Philos. Soc.* **111**, 136–59.

DUVIGNÉAUD, P. (ed.) 1971: *Productivity of forest ecosystems.* Paris: UNESCO.

DUVIGNÉAUD, P. and DENAEYER-DE SMET, S. 1970: Biological cycling of minerals in temperate deciduous forests. In D. Reichle (ed.), 199–229.

DWYER, D. J. 1958: Utilization of the Irish peat bogs. *Geogr. Rev.* **48**, 572–3.

EASTLUND, B. J. and GOUGH, W. C. 1969: *The fusion torch. Closing the cycle from use to re-use.* Washington, DC: US Atomic Energy Commission.

EGGELING, W. J. 1964: A nature reserve management plan for the island of Rhum, Inner Hebrides. *J. Appl. Ecol.* **1**, 405–19.

EGLER, F. E. 1970: *The way of science: a philosophy of ecology for the layman.* New York: Hafner.

EHRENFELD, D. W. 1970: *Biological conservation.* New York: Holt, Rinehart and Winston.

EHRLICH, P. 1968: *The population bomb.* New York: Ballantine.

— 1971: Ecocatastrophe! In J. Barr (ed.), 205–13.

EHRLICH, P. and EHRLICH, A. 1970: *Population resources environment. Issues in human ecology.* 2nd edn. San Francisco: Freeman.

EHRLICH, P. and HARRIMAN, R. L. 1971: *How to be a survivor.* New York: Ballantine/Friends of the Earth.

EHRLICH, P. and HOLDREN, J. P. 1969: Population and panaceas: a technological perspective. *Bioscience* **19**, 1065–71.

— 1971: Impact of population growth. *Science* **171**, 1212–17.

EHRLICH, P., HOLDREN, J. P. and HOLM, R. W. (eds.) 1971: *Man and the ecosphere.* San Francisco: Freeman.

ELLUL, J. 1964: *The technological society.* New York: Vintage Books.

ELTON, C. S. 1958: *The ecology of invasions by animals and plants.* London: Methuen.

— 1966: *The pattern of animal communities.* London: Methuen.

ENGLAND, R. E. and DE VOS, A. 1969: Influence of animals on pristine conditions in the Canadian grasslands. *J. Range Management* **22**, 87–93.

EYRE, S. R. 1971: Population, production and pessimism. In *Presidential addresses delivered at the Swansea meeting, 1971*, British Association for the Advancement of Science.

FAIR, G. M. 1961: Pollution abatement in the Ruhr district. In H. Jarrett (ed.), 171–89.

FARIS, G. T. M. A. 1966: *A contribution to the economic geography of present day forestry and forest products in the Sudan.* University of Durham, MA thesis.

FARMER, B. H. 1969: Available food supplies. In J. Hutchinson (ed.). 75–95.

FIMREITE, N. 1970: Mercury uses in Canada and their possible hazardous sources of mercury contamination. *Env. Polln.* **1**, 119–31.

FIREY, W. J. 1960: *Man, mind and land.* Glencoe, Illinois: Free Press.

FISHER, J., SIMON, N. and VINCENT, J. 1969: *Wildlife in danger.* London: Collins.

FITTER, R. S. R. 1963: *Wildlife in Britain.* Harmondsworth: Pelican.

FLAWN, P. 1966: *Mineral resources.* Chicago: Rand McNally.

FOOD AND AGRICULTURE ORGANIZATION (annually): *Yearbook of fishery statistics.* Rome: FAO.

— (annually): *Yearbook of forest products.* Rome: FAO.

— (annually): *Production Yearbook.* Rome: FAO.

— 1953: *Grazing and forest economy.* Rome: FAO.

— 1963: *World forest inventory.* Rome: FAO.

— 1967: *Wood: world trends and prospects.* Rome: FAO.

— 1970: *Indicative world plan for agriculture,* 2 vols. Rome: FAO.

FORD, E. D. 1971: The potential production of forest crops. In P. F. Wareing and J. P. Cooper (eds.). 172–85.

FORRESTER, J. 1971: *World dynamics.* Cambridge: Wright-Allen Press.

FRANKEL, O. 1969: Genetic dangers in the green revolution. *Ceres* **2** (5), 35–7.

FRASER DARLING, F. 1955: Pastoralism in relation to the populations of men and animals. In N. Pirie and J. B. Cragg (eds.), 121–8.

— 1956: Man's ecological dominance through domesticated animals on wild lands. In W. L. Thomas (ed.), 778–87.

— 1960: Wildlife husbandry in Africa. *Sci. Amer.* **203** (5), 123–34.

— 1963: The unity of ecology. *Advmt. Sci.* **20**, 297–306.

FRASER DARLING, F. and EICHORN, N. 1967: *Man and nature in the National Parks: reflections on policy.* Washington, DC: Double Dot Press for the Conservation Foundation.

FRASER DARLING, F. and FARVAR, M. A. 1972: Ecological consequences of sedentarization of nomads. In M. Taghi Farvar and J. P. Milton (eds.), 671–82.

FRASER DARLING, F. and MILTON, J. P. (eds.) 1966: *Future environments of North America.* New York: Natural History Press.

FREJKA, T. 1973: The prospects for a stationary world population. *Sci. Amer.* **228** (3), 15–23.

FREMLIN, J. H. 1964: How many people can the world support? *New Sci.* **24**, 285–7.

FROME, M. 1962: *Whose woods these are.* New York: Natural History Press.

FULLER, W. A. and KEVAN, P. G. 1970: *Productivity and conservation in northern circumpolar lands.* IUCN Pubs. New Series **16**. Morges: IUCN.

GABOR, D. 1963: *Inventing the future.* Harmondsworth: Pelican.

GALBRAITH, J. K. 1967: *The new industrial state.* Boston: Houghton Mifflin.

GALSTON, A. 1971: Crops without chemicals. *New Sci.* **50**, 577–9.

GAMBELL, R. 1972: Why all the fuss about whales? *New Sci.* **54**, 674–6.

GARVEY, G. 1972: *Energy, ecology, economy.* New York: Norton.

GATES, D. M. 1971: The flow of energy in the biosphere. *Sci. Amer.* **224** (3), 88–100.

GEERTZ, C. 1963: *Agricultural involution: the processes of ecological change in Indonesia.* Berkeley and Los Angeles: University of California Press.

GEORGE, C. J. 1972: The role of the Aswan High Dam in changing the fisheries of the southeastern Mediterranean. In M. Taghi Farvar and J. P. Milton (eds.), 159–78.

GERASIMOV, I. P., ARMAND, D. L. and YEFRON, K. M. (eds) 1971: *Natural resources of the Soviet Union: their use and renewal.* San Francisco: Freeman.

GIBBENS, R. P. and HEADY, H. F. 1964: *The influence of modern man on the vegetation of Yosemite Valley.* Berkeley: University of California Agricultural Experiment Station Manual **36**.

GLACKEN, C. J. 1967: *Traces on the Rhodian shore.* Berkeley and Los Angeles: University of California Press.

GOLDMAN, M. I. 1971: Environmental disruption in the Soviet Union. In T. R. Detwyler (ed.), 61–75.

GOLDSMITH, E., ALLEN, D. *et al.* 1972: Blueprint for survival. *The Ecologist* **2** (1), 2–43. Reprinted 1973, Harmondsworth: Pelican.

GORDEN, M. and GORDEN, M. (eds.) 1972: *Environmental management.* Boston: Allyn and Bacon.

GORDON, J. 1970: Nuclear power production and problems in the disposal of atomic wastes. In A. J. Van Tassel (ed.), 135–64.

GOUROU, P. 1966: *The tropical world.* 4th edn. London: Wiley.

GOYER, R. A. and CHISHOLM, J. J. 1972: Lead. In D. H. K. Lee (ed.), 57–95.

GREENWOOD, N. and EDWARDS, J. M. B. 1973: *Human environments and natural systems.* North Scituate, Mass.: Duxbury Press.

GREGORY, D. P. 1973: The hydrogen economy. *Sci. Amer.* **228** (1), 13–21.

GREGORY, R. 1971: *The price of amenity.* London: Macmillan.

GRIGG, J. 1970: *The harsh lands.* London: Macmillan

GULLAND, J. A. 1970: The development of the resources of the Antarctic seas. In M. W. Holdgate (ed.), Vol. 1, 217–23.

GWYNNE, P. 1972: Nuclear power goes to sea. *New Sci.* **55**, 474–6.

HAAGEN-SMIT, A. J. and WAYNE, L. G. 1968: Atmospheric reactions and scavenging processes. In A. C. Stern (ed.), Vol. 1, 149–86.

HABAKKUK, H. J. 1972: *Population growth and economic development since 1750.* Leicester: Leicester University Press.

HADEN-GUEST, S. (ed.) 1956: *A world geography of forest resources.* American Geographical Society Special Pub. 33. New York: Ronald Press.

HAMMOND, A. L., METZ, W. D. and MAUGH, T. H. 1973: *Energy and the future.* Washington, DC: AAAS.

HANSON, W. C. 1967a: Radioecological concentration processes characterizing Arctic ecosystems. In B. Aberg and F. P. Hungate (eds.), 183–91.

— 1967b: Caesium-137 in Alaskan lichens, caribou and eskimos. *Health Physics* **13**, 383–9.

HARDIN, G. 1959: Interstellar migration and the population problem. *J. Hered.* **50**, 68–70.

— 1968: The tragedy of the commons. *Science* **162**, 1243–8.

— (ed.) 1969: *Population, evolution and birth control.* 2nd edn. San Francisco: Freeman.

— 1973: *Exploring: new ethics for survival. The voyage of the spaceship Beagle.* Harmondsworth: Penguin.

HARRAR, J. G. and WORTMAN, S. 1969: Expanding food production in hungry nations: the promise, the problems. In C. M. Hardin (ed.), *Overcoming world hunger.* The American Assembly, 1969. New York: Prentice-Hall, 89–135.

HARRISS, R. C. 1971: Ecological implications of mercury pollution in aquatic systems. *Biol. Cons.* **3**, 279–83.

HARTE, J. A. and SOCOLOW, R. H. (eds.) 1971a: *The patient earth.* New York: Holt, Rinehart and Winston.

HARTE, J. A. and SOCOLOW, R. H. 1971b: The Everglades: wilderness versus rampant land development in south Florida. In J. A. Harte and R. H. Socolow (eds.), 181–202.

HAUSLE, E. A. 1972: Potential economic values of weather modification on Great Plains grasslands. *J. Range Management* **25**, 92–5.

HAWKES, A. L. 1961: A review of the nature and extent of damage caused by oil pollution at sea. *Trans 26th North American Wildlife Conference*, 343–55.

HEADY, H. F. 1972: Ecological consequences of Bedouin settlement in Saudi Arabia. In M. Taghi Farvar and J. P. Milton (eds.), 683–93.

HEALY, J. H. 1968: The Denver earthquakes. *Science* **161**, 1301–8.

HEATHERTON, T. (ed.) 1965: *Antarctica*. London: Methuen for the New Zealand Antarctic Society.

HEDGPETH, J. W. 1972: Atomic waste disposal in the sea: an ecological dilemma? In M. Taghi Farvar and J. P. Milton (eds.), 812–28.

HELFRICH, H. W. (ed.) 1970: *The environmental crisis*. New Haven and London: Yale University Press.

HENDRICKS, S. B. 1969: Food from the land. In NAS/NRC, 65–85.

HERSH, S. M. 1968: *Chemical and biological warfare*. New York: Doubleday Anchor Books.

HETTENA, P. H. G. and SYER, G. N. (eds.) 1971: *Decade of decision*. London: Academic Press for the Conservation Society.

HICKLING, C. F. 1970: Estuarine fish farming. *Adv. Marine Biol.* **8**, 119–213.

HIJSZELER, C. C. W. J. 1957: Late-glacial human cultures in the Netherlands. *Geol. en Mijnbouw* **19**, 288–302.

HILL, A. R. 1972: Ecosystem stability and man: a research focus in biogeography. In W. P. Adams and F. M. Helleiner (eds.), 255–7.

HINRICHS, N. (ed.) 1971: *Population, environment and people*. New York: McGraw-Hill.

HODGES, L. 1973: *Environmental pollution*. New York: Holt, Rhinehart and Winston.

HOLDGATE, M. W. (ed.) 1970: *Antarctic ecology*. 2 vols. London and New York: Academic Press.

HOLDRIDGE, L. R. 1959: Ecological indications of the need for a new approach to tropical land use. *Econ. Bot.* **13**, 271–80.

HOLLING, C. S. 1969: Stability in ecological and social systems. In G. M. Woodwell and H. H. Smith (eds.), 128–41.

HOLM, L. G., WELDON, L. W. and BLACKBURN, R. D. 1969: Aquatic weeds. *Science* **166**, 699–709.

HOLT, S. J. 1971: The food resources of the ocean. In P. Ehrlich, J. P. Holdren and R. W. Holm (eds.), 84–96.

HOLZ, R. (ed.) 1973: *The surveillant science*. Boston: Houghton Mifflin.

HOOD, D. W. (ed.) 1971: *Impingement of man on the oceans*. New York: Wiley.

HOPKINS, W. H. and SINCLAIR, J. D. 1960: Watershed management in action in the Pacific southwest. *Proc. Soc. Amer. For.*, 184–6.

HORSFALL, J. G. 1970: The green revolution: agriculture in the face of the population explosion. In H. W. Helfrich (ed.)., 85–98.

HOULT, D. P. (ed.) 1969: *Oil on the sea*. New York and London: Plenum Press.

HOWARD, N. J. 1964: Introduced browsing animals and habitat stability in New Zealand. *J. Wildlife Management* **28**, 421–9.

HUBBERT, M. KING 1962: *Energy resources: a report to the NAS/NRC*. Washington, DC: NAS/NRC Pubn. **1000D**.

— 1969: Energy resources. In NAS/NRC, 157–242.

HUBBERT, M. KING 1971: The energy resources of the earth. *Sci. Amer.* **224** (3), 61–70.

HUNT, E. G. and BISCHOFF, A. I. 1960: Inimical effects on wildlife of periodic DDD applications to Clear Lake. *California Fish and Game* **46**, 91–106.

HUNT, G. M. 1956: The forest products industries of the world. In S. Haden-Guest (ed.), 83–111.

HUNTER, J. M. 1966: Ascertaining population carrying capacity under traditional systems of agriculture in developing countries: notes on a method employed in Ghana. *Prof. Geogr.* **18**, 151–4.

HURD, L. E., MELLINGER, M. V., WOLF, L. L. and McNAUGHTON, S. J. 1972: Stability and diversity at three trophic levels in terrestrial successional ecosystems. *Science* **173**, 1134–6.

HUTCHINSON, G. E. 1970: The biosphere. In *Scientific American* (ed.), 1–11.

HUTCHINSON, J. (ed.) 1969: *Population and food supply.* Cambridge: Cambridge University Press.

HUXLEY, J. S. 1961: *The conservation of wildlife and natural habitats in central and east Africa.* Paris: UNESCO.

ILLICH, I. D. 1974: *Energy and equity.* London: Calder and Boyars.

INSTITUTE OF CIVIL ENGINEERS 1963: *Conservation of water resources in the United Kingdom.* London: ICE.

INSTITUTE OF ECOLOGY 1972: *Man in his living environment.* Madison: University of Wisconsin Press.

INTERNATIONAL JOINT COMMISSION, CANADA AND THE USA 1970: *Pollution of Lake Erie, Lake Ontario and the international section of the St Lawrence River.* Ottawa: Information Canada.

INTERNATIONAL PLANNED PARENTHOOD FEDERATION (annually): *Family planning in five continents.* London: IPPF.

IRUKAYAMA, K. 1966: The pollution of Minamata Bay and Minamata disease. *Adv. Wat. Polln. Res.* **3**, 153–80.

IUCN 1969: *Red data book.* 2 vols. Morges: IUCN.

— 1970: *United Nations list of National Parks and equivalent reserves.* Brussels: Hayez.

JACOBSEN, T. and ADAMS, R. M. 1958: Salt and silt in ancient Mesopotamian agriculture. *Science* **128**, 1251–8.

JANICK, J. (ed.) 1970: *Plant Agriculture.* San Francisco: Freeman/*Scientific American.*

JARRETT, H. (ed.) 1961: *Comparisons in resource management.* Lincoln, Nebraska: Bison Books.

— 1966: *Environmental quality in a growing economy.* Baltimore: Johns Hopkins Press for RFF.

JENNY, H. 1961: Derivation of state factor equations of soils and ecosystems. *Soil Sci. Am. Proc.* **25**, 385–8.

JEWELL, P. A. 1969: Wild mammals and their potential for new domestications. In P. J. Ucko and G. W. Dimbleby (eds.), 101–9.

JOHNSON, P. L. 1971: Remote sensing as a tool for study and management of ecosystems. In E. P. Odum, 468–83.

KALININ G. P. and BYKOV, V. D. 1969: The world's water resources, present and future. *Impact of Science on Society* **19** (2), 135–50.

KARSCH, R. F. 1970: The social costs of surface mined coal. In A. J. Van Tassel (ed.), 269–90.

KASSAS, M. 1972: Impact of river control schemes on the shoreline of the Nile delta. In M. Taghi Farvar and J. P. Milton (eds.), 179–88.

KATES, R. W. 1962: *Hazard and choice perception in flood plain management.* Chicago: University of Chicago, Department of Geography Research Paper **78**.

KAY, D. A. and SKOLNIKOFF, E. B. 1972: *World eco-crisis: international organizations in response.* Madison: University of Wisconsin Press.

KEMP, W. B. 1970: The flow of energy in a hunting society. *Sci. Amer.* **224** (3), 104–15.

KLAPP, E. 1964: Features of a grassland theory. *J. Range Management* **17**, 309–22.

KLEIN, D. R. 1970: Tundra ranges north of the boreal forest. *J. Range Management* **23**, 8–14.

KNETSCH, J. and CLAWSON, M. 1967: *Economics of outdoor recreation.* Baltimore: Johns Hopkins Press for RFF.

KOK, L. T. 1972: Toxicity of insecticides used for Asiatic rice borer control to tropical fish in rice paddies. In M. Taghi Farvar and J. P. Milton (eds.), 489–98.

KOVDA, V. 1970: Contemporary scientific concepts relating to the biosphere. In UNESCO, 13–29.

KRUTILLA, J. V. (ed.) 1972: *Natural environments.* Baltimore: Johns Hopkins Press for RFF.

KUCERA, C. L., DAHLMANN, R. C. and KRELLING, M. R. 1967: Total net productivity and turnover on an energy basis for tall grass prairie. *Ecology* **48**, 536–41.

KUPCHANKO, E. E. 1970: Petrochemical waste disposal. In M. A. Ward (ed.), 53–65.

LACK, D. 1966: *Population studies of birds.* Oxford: Clarendon Press.

LADEJINSKY, W. 1970: Ironies of India's green revolution. *Foreign Affairs* **48**, 758–68.

LAGERWEFF, J. V. 1967: Heavy metal contamination of soils. In N. C. Brady (ed.), 343–364.

LAGLER, K. F. 1971: Ecological effects of hydroelectric dams. In D. A. Berkowitz and A. M. Squires (eds.), 133–57.

LAMBRECHT, F. L. 1972: The tsetse fly: a blessing or a curse? In M. Taghi Farvar and J. P. Milton (eds.), 726–41.

LAMORE, G. E. 1971: At last—a revolution that unites. In M. A. Strobbe (ed.), 126–32.

LANDAU, R. (ed.) 1968: *Air conservation.* Washington, DC: AAAS Publication **50**.

LANDSBERG, H. H. 1971: Energy consumption and optimum population. In S. F. Singer (ed.), 1971, 62–71.

LAUT, P. 1968: *Agricultural geography.* 2 vols. Sydney: Nelson.

LAWSON, P. D. and BRISBIN, K. J. 1970: Pollution from municipal sources. In M. A. Ward (ed.), 67–76.

LEE, D. H. K. (ed.) 1972: *Metallic contaminants and human health.* London and New York: Academic Press.

LEE, R. B. 1968: What hunters do for a living, or how to make out on scarce resources. In R. B. Lee and I. De Vore (eds.), 1968a, 30–43.

— 1969: !Kung Bushman subsistence: an input:output analysis. In A. P. Vayda (ed.), 47–49.

LEE, R. B. and DE VORE, I. (eds.) 1968a: *Man the hunter*. Chicago: Aldine Press.

— 1968b: Problems in the study of hunters and gatherers. In R. B. Lee and I. De Vore (eds.), 1968a, 3–12.

LEEDS, A. and VAYDA, A. P. (eds.) 1965: *Man, culture and animals*. Washington, DC: AAAS Publication **78**.

LEITH, H. 1965: Versuch einer kartographischen Darstellung der Productivitat der Pflanzendecke auf die Erde. *Geographisches Taschenbuch 1964/5*, 72–80.

— 1972: Modelling the primary productivity of the world. *Nature and Resources* **8** (2), 5–10.

LEOPOLD, A. 1949: *Sand County almanac*. New York: Oxford University Press.

LEOPOLD, A. S. 1963: Study of wildlife problems in National Parks. *Trans. 28th North American Wildlife Conference*, 28–45.

LEWALLEN, J. 1971: *Ecology of devastation: Indochina*. Baltimore: Penguin.

LEWIS, G. M. 1969: Range management viewed in the ecosystem framework. In G. M. Van Dyne (ed.), 97–187.

LEWIS, R. S. and SPINRAD, B. I. (eds.) 1972: *The energy crisis*. Chicago: Educational Foundation for Nuclear Science.

LEYHAUSEN, P. 1965: The sane community—a density problem? *Discovery* **26**, 27–33, 51.

LIKENS, G. E. and BORMANN, F. H. 1971: Mineral cycling in ecosystems. In J. A. Wiens (ed.), 25–67.

LINDEMANN, R. L. 1942: The trophic-dynamic aspect of ecology. *Ecology* **23**, 399–418.

LOFTAS, T. 1972: *The last resource*. Harmondsworth: Penguin.

LONGHURST, A., COLEBROOK, M., GULLAND, J., LE BRASSEUR, R., LORENZEN, C. and SMITH, P. 1972: The instability of ocean populations. *New Sci.* **54**, 500–502.

LOVERING, T. S. 1968: Non-fuel mineral resources in the next century. *Texas Quarterly* **11**, 127–47.

— 1969: Mineral resources from the land. In NAS/NRC, 109–34.

LOWE, V. P. W. 1971: Some effects of a change in estate management on a deer population. In E. Duffey and A. S. Watt (eds.), 437–56.

LUCAS, R. C. 1964: Wilderness perception and use: the example of the boundary waters canoe area. *Nat. Res. J.* **3**, 384–411.

— 1965: Recreational capacity of the Quetico-Superior area. St Paul, Minn.: US Forest Service Lakes States Research Paper **LS–15**.

LUTEN, D. B. 1971: The economic geography of energy. *Sci. Amer.* **224** (3), 165–75.

MACARTHUR, R. H. 1955: Fluctuations of animal populations, and a measure of community stability. *Ecology* **36**, 533–6.

MACDONALD, G. J. F. 1968: How to wreck the environment. In N. Calder (ed.), 191–213.

MACFADYEN, A. 1964: Energy flow in ecosystems and its exploitation by grazing. In D. J. Crisp (ed.), 3–20.

McGAUHEY, P. 1968: Earth's tolerance for wastes. *Texas Quarterly* **11**, 36–42.

McHALE, J. 1969: *The future of the future*. New York: Ballantine.

— 1972: *World facts and trends*. 2nd edn. New York: Macmillan.

MACINTOSH, N. A. 1970: Whales and krill in the twentieth century. In M. W. Holdgate (ed.), Vol. 1, 195–212.

MACINTYRE, F. and HOLMES, R. W. 1971: Ocean pollution. In W. W. Murdoch (ed.), 230–53.

MACNEILL, J. W. 1971: *Environmental management*. Ottawa: Information Canada.

MCVEAN, D. N. and LOCKIE, J. D. 1969: *Ecology and land use in upland Scotland*. Edinburgh: Edinburgh University Press.

MADDOX, J. 1972a: The case against hysteria. *Nature* **235**, 63–5.

— 1972b: *The doomsday syndrome*. London: Macmillan.

MARGALEF, R. 1968: *Perspectives in ecological theory*. Chicago: University of Chicago Press.

MARKS, P. L. and BORMANN, F. H. 1972: Revegetation following forest cutting: mechanisms for return to steady-state nutrient cycling. *Science* **176**, 914–15.

MARSH, G. P. 1864: *Man and nature, or Physical geography as modified by human action*. Reprinted 1965, Harvard: Belknap Press (D. Lowenthal, ed.).

MARTINELLI, W. 1964: *Watershed management in the Rocky Mountain alpine and subalpine zones*. Fort Collins, Colo.: US Forest Service Rocky Mountain Research Station Research Note **RM-36**.

MARX, W. 1967: *The frail ocean*. New York: Sierra Club/Ballantine.

— 1971: *Waste*. New York and London: Harper and Row.

MATELES, R. I., BARUAH, J. N. and TANNENBAUM, S. R. 1967: Growth of microbial cells on hydrocarbons: a new source of single cell protein. *Science* **157**, 1322–3.

MATELES, R. I. and TANNENBAUM, S. R. (eds.) 1968: *Single cell protein*. Cambridge, Mass.: MIT Press.

MEADOWS, D. H., MEADOWS, D. L., RANDERS, J. and BEHRENS, W. W. 1972: *The limits to growth*. London: Earth Island Press.

MEGGERS, B. J., AYENSU, E. S. and DUCKWORTH, W. D. (eds.) 1973: *Tropical forest ecosystems in Africa and South America: a comparative review*. Washington, DC: Smithsonian Institution Press.

MEIER, R. L. 1969: The social impact of a nuplex. *Bull. Atom. Sci.* **26**, 16–21.

MELLANBY, K. 1967: *Pesticides and pollution*. London: Collins.

METCALF, R. L. 1972: DDT substitutes. *CRC Critical Reviews in Environmental Control* **3** (1), 25–59.

MICKLIN, P. P. 1969: Soviet plans to reverse the flow of rivers: the Kama-Vychegda-Pechora project. *Canad. Geogr.* **13**, 199–215.

MIKOLA, P. 1970: Forests and forestry in subarctic regions. In UNESCO, *Ecology of the subarctic regions*. Paris: UNESCO, 295–302.

MILGRAM, S. 1970: The experience of living in cities. *Science* **167**, 1461–8.

MISHAN, E. J. 1967: *The costs of economic growth*. London: Staples Press.

— 1971: *Twenty-one popular economic fallacies*. Harmondsworth: Pelican.

MITCHELL, J. M. 1970: A preliminary evaluation of atmospheric pollution as a cause of the global temperature fluctuation of the past century. In S. F. Singer (ed.), 1970a, 139–55.

MOISEEV, P. A. 1970: Some aspects of the commercial use of the krill resources of the antarctic seas. In M. W. Holdgate (ed.), Vol. 1, 213–16.

MOLITOR, L. 1968: *Effects of noise on health*. Council of Europe Public Health Committee Report **CESP (68)**. Strasbourg: Council of Europe.

MONCRIEF, L. W. 1970: The cultural basis for our environmental crisis. *Science* **170**, 508–12.

'MONITOR' 1972: Power to the people from leaves of grass. *New Sci.* **55**, 228.

MONTAGUE, A. (ed.) 1962: *Culture and the evolution of man*. New York: Oxford University Press.

MONTEFIORE, H. 1970: *Can man survive?* London: Fontana.

MOORE, C. W. E. 1964: Distribution of grasslands. In C. Barnard (ed.), 185–205.

MOORE, N. W. 1967: A synopsis of the pesticide problem. *Adv. Ecol. Res.* **4**, 75–129.

— 1969: The significance of the persistent organochlorine insecticides and the polychlorinated biphenyls. *Biologist* **16**, 157–62.

MOORE, R. M. and BUDDISCOMBE, E. F. 1964: The effects of grazing on grasslands. In C. Barnard (ed.), 221–35.

MORE, R. J. 1969: The basin hydrological cycle. In R. J. Chorley (ed.), 65–76.

MORGAN, W. T. W. (ed.) 1972: *East Africa: its peoples and resources*. 2nd edn. Nairobi: Oxford University Press.

MORLEY, S. G. 1956: *The ancient Maya*. Stanford: Stanford University Press.

MURDOCH, W. W. (ed.) 1971: *Environment*. Stamford, Conn.: Sinauer.

MURDOCK, G. P. 1968: The current status of the world's hunting and gathering peoples. In R. B. Lee and I. De Vore (eds.), 1968a, 13–20.

MUROZUMI, M., CHOW, T. J. and PATTERSON, C. 1969: Chemical concentrations of pollutant lead aerosols, terrestrial dusts and sea salts in Greenland and Antarctic snow strata. *Geochimica et Cosmochimica Acta* **33**, 1247–94.

MURRA, J. V. 1965: Herds and herders in the Inca state. In A. Leeds and A. P. Vayda (eds.), 185–215.

MUSGROVE, P. J. and WILSON, A. D. 1970: Power without pollution. *New Sci.* **45**, 457–9.

NACE, R. L. 1969: Human use of ground water. In R. J. Chorley (ed.), 285–94.

NASH, C. E. 1970a: Marine fish farming. Part 1. *Marine Pollution Bull.* **1**, 5–6.

— 1970b: Marine fish farming. Part 2. *Marine Pollution Bull.* **1**, 28–30.

NASH, R. 1967: *Wilderness and the American mind*. New Haven: Yale University Press.

NAS/NRC 1969: *Resources and man*. London and San Francisco: Freeman.

NELSON, J. G. and SCACE, R. C. (eds.) 1969: *The Canadian National Parks: today and tomorrow*. Calgary: University of Calgary Studies in Land Use History and Landscape Change National Park Series **3**. 2 vols.

NELSON-SMITH, A. 1970: The problem of oil pollution of the sea. *Adv. Mar. Biol.* **8**, 215–306.

NEWBOULD, P. J. 1971a: Comparative production of ecosystems. In P. F. Wareing and J. P. Cooper (eds.), 228–38.

— 1971b: The cost of a good environment. In P. H. G. Hettena and G. N. Syer (eds.), 91–103.

NEW ZEALAND FOREST SERVICE 1970: *Conservation policy and practice*. Wellington: New Zealand Forest Service.

NG, L. K. Y. and MUDD, S. (eds.) 1965: *The population crisis*. Bloomington: Indiana University Press.

NGUYEN-VAN-HIEP, 1971: Rapport sur la situation de la conservation au Vietnam en 1969. In *The National Park Situation in S. Asia*, IUCN 11th Technical Meeting (New Delhi, 1969), IUCN Publications New Ser. **19**, Vol. 3. Morges: IUCN, 54–62.

NORTMAN, D. 1971: *Programmes de population et de planning familial: un tour d'horizon*. 2nd edn. New York: Population Council Bulletins de démographie et de planning familial **2**.

NOTESTEIN, F. W. 1970: Zero population growth: what is it? *Family Planning Perspectives* **2** (3), 20–24; reprinted in W. H. Davis (ed.), 1971, 107–11.

OBERLE, M. 1969: Forest fires: suppression policy has its drawbacks. *Science* **165**, 568–71.

O'CONNOR, F. B. 1964: Energy flow and population metabolism. *Sci. Progr.* **52**, 406–14.

ODUM, E. P. 1959: *Fundamentals of ecology*. 2nd edn. Philadelphia: Saunders.

— 1969: The strategy of ecosystem development. *Science* **164**, 262–70.

— 1971: *Fundamentals of ecology*. 3rd edn. Philadelphia: Saunders.

ODUM, E. P. and ODUM, H. T. 1972: Natural areas as necessary components of man's total environment. *Trans. 37th North American Wildlife and Natural Resources Conference*, 178–89.

ODUM, H. T. 1957: Trophic structure and productivity of Silver Springs, Florida. *Ecol. Monog.* **27**, 55–112.

— 1971: *Environment, power and society*. London and New York: Wiley.

OECD 1970: *Scientific fundamentals of the eutrophication of lakes and flowing waters, with particular reference to nitrogen and phosphorus as factors in eutrophication*. Prepared by A. Vollenweider. Paris: OECD.

OORT, A. H. 1970: The energy cycle of the earth. In *Scientific American* (ed.), 13–23.

OPENSHAW, K. 1974: Wood fuels the developing world. *New Sci.* **61**, 271–2.

ORIANS, G. H. and PFEIFFER, E. W. 1970: Ecological effects of the war in Vietnam. *Science* **168**, 544–54.

O'RIORDAN, T. 1971a: Environmental management. In C. Board *et al.* (eds.), 173–231.

— 1971b: *Perspectives on resource management*. London: Pion Press.

O'RIORDAN, T. and MORE, R. J. 1969: Choice in water use. In R. J. Chorley (ed.), 547–73.

ORRRC 1962a: *Recreation for America*. Washington, DC: US Government Printing Office.

— 1962b: *Report 23, Projections to the Years 1976 and 2000*. Washington DC: US Government Printing Office.

OTHMER, D. F. and ROELS, O. A. 1973: Power, fresh water, and food from cold, deep sea water. *Science* **182**, 121–5.

OVINGTON, J. D. 1957: Dry matter production by *Pinus sylvestris* L. *Ann. Bot.* **21**, 287–314.

— 1962: Quantitative ecology and the woodland ecosystem concept. *Adv. Ecol. Res.* **1**, 103–92.

— 1965: *Woodlands*. London: English Universities Press.

OVINGTON, J. D., HEITKAMP, D. and LAWRENCE, D. B. 1963: Plant biomass and productivity of prairie grassland, savanna, oakwood and maize field ecosystems in central Minnesota. *Ecology* **44**, 52–63.

PADDOCK, W. C. 1971: Agriculture as a force in determining the United States' optimum population size. In S. F. Singer (ed.), 1971, 89–95.

PADDOCK, W. C. and PADDOCK, M. 1967: *Famine 1975!* Boston: Little, Brown.

PAINE, R. T. 1969: A note on trophic complexity and community stability. *Amer. Nat.* **103**, 91–3.

PARKER, B. C. (ed.) 1972: *Conservation problems in Antarctica*. Blacksburg, Va.: Virginia Polytechnic.

PARKER, I. S. C. and GRAHAM, A. D. 1971: The ecological and economic basis for game ranching in Africa. In E. Duffey and A. S. Watt (eds.), 393–404.

PARSONS, J. 1971: *Population versus liberty*. London: Pemberton Books.

PATMORE, J. A. 1971: *Land and leisure in England and Wales*. Newton Abbott: David and Charles.

PAYNE, P. and WHEELER, E. 1971: What protein gap? *New Sci.* **50**, 148–50.

PEACH, W. N. and CONSTANTIN, J. A. 1972: *Zimmermann's World Resources and Industries*. 3rd edn. London: Harper and Row.

PEARSALL, W. H. 1957: *Report on an ecological survey of the Serengeti National Park, Tanganyika, November and December 1956*. London: Fauna Preservation Society.

PEARSON, F. A. and HARPER, F. A. 1945: *The world's hunger*. Cornell: Cornell University Press.

PETERSON, W. 1969: *Population*. 2nd edn. London: Macmillan.

PIGOTT, C. D. 1956: The vegetation of Upper Teesdale in the North Pennines. *J. Ecol.* **44**, 545–86.

PIPER, A. M. 1965: *Has the US enough water?* US Geological Survey Water Supply Paper **1797**. Washington, DC: US Government Printing Office.

PIRIE, N. and CRAGG, J. B. (eds.) 1955: *The numbers of men and animals*. Inst. Biol. Symp. **4**. Edinburgh and London: Oliver and Boyd.

PIRIE, N. W. 1969: *Food resources: conventional and novel*. Harmondsworth: Penguin.

— 1970: Orthodox and unorthodox methods of meeting world food needs. In J. Janick (ed.), 223–31.

— (ed.) 1971: Leaf protein: its agronomy, preparation, quality and use. *IBP Handbook* **20**. Oxford: Blackwell.

POLSTER, H. 1961: *Neuere Ergebnisse auf dem Gebiet der Standortsokologischen Assimilations- und Transpirations Forschung an Forstgewechse*. Berlin: Sitzber. Deut. Akad. Landwirtschaftwiss. **10**, 1.

POMEROY, L. R. 1970: The strategy of mineral cycling. *Ann. Rev. Ecology and Systematics* **1**, 171–90.

POPULATION REFERENCE BUREAU (annually): *World population data sheet*. New York: PRB.

PRICKETT, C. N. 1963: Use of water in agriculture. In Institute of Civil Engineers, 15–29.

PRIESTLEY, J. B. and HAWKES, J. 1955: *Journey down a rainbow*. London: Cressett Press.

PROVINCE OF ALBERTA 1968: *Water diversion proposals of North America*. Edmonton: Department of Agriculture Water Resources Division.

— 1969: *Prime: Alberta's blueprint for water development*. Edmonton: Department of Agriculture Water Resources Division.

PRYDE, P. R. 1972: *Conservation in the Soviet Union*. Cambridge: Cambridge University Press.

PUGH, N. J. 1963: Water supply. In Institute of Civil Engineers, 9–14.

PYKE, M. 1970a: *Man and food*. London: Weidenfeld and Nicolson.

— 1970b: *Synthetic food*. London: Murray.

— 1971: Novel sources of energy and protein. In P. F. Wareing and J. P. Cooper (eds.), 202–12.

RANDERSON, P. F. and BURDEN, R. F. 1972: Quantitative studies of the effect of human trampling on vegetation as an aid to the management of semi-natural areas. *J. Appl. Ecol.* **9**, 439–57.

RAPPAPORT, R. A. 1971: The flow of energy in an agricultural society. *Sci. Amer.* **224** (3), 116–32.

READER'S DIGEST PUBLICATIONS 1970: *The living world of animals.* London: Reader's Digest Assn.

REED, C. A. 1969: The pattern of animal domestication in the prehistoric Near East. In P. J. Ucko and G. W. Dimbleby (eds.), 361–80.

REED, T. B. and LERNER, R. M. 1973: Methanol: a versatile fuel for immediate use. *Science* **182**, 1299–1304.

REICH, C. 1971: *The greening of America.* Harmondsworth: Penguin.

REICHLE, D. (ed.) 1970: *Analysis of temperate forest ecosystems.* London: Chapman and Hall.

RENNIE, P. J. 1955: The uptake of nutrients by mature forest growth. *Plant and Soil 7*, 49–95.

REVELLE, R. 1967: Outdoor recreation in a hyper-productive society. *Daedalus* **96**, 1172–91.

REVELLE, R., KHOSLA, A. and VINOVSKIS, M. (eds.) 1971: *The survival equation: man, resources and his environment.* Boston: Houghton Mifflin.

REX, R. W. 1971: Geothermal energy—the neglected energy option. *Bull. Atom. Sci.* **27** (8), 52–6.

RICHARDS, P. 1952: *The tropical rain forest.* Cambridge: Cambridge University Press.

RICHARDSON, S. D. 1971: The end of forestry in Great Britain. *Advmt Sci.* **27**, 153–63.

RICKER, W. 1969: Food from the sea. In NAS/NRC, 87–108.

RIDKER, R. G. 1972: Population and pollution in the United States. *Science* **176**, 1085–90.

— 1973: To grow or not to grow: that's not the relevant question. *Science* **182**, 1315–18.

ROBERTS, B. 1965: Wildlife conservation in the Antarctic. *Oryx* **8**, 237–44.

RODIN, L. E. and BAZILEVIC, N. I. 1966: The biological production of the main vegetation types in the northern hemisphere of the old world. *For. Abstr.* **27**, 369–72.

ROGERS, F. C. 1971: Underground power plants. *Bull. Atom. Sci.* **27** (8), 38–41, 51.

ROHMER, R. 1973: *The arctic imperative.* Toronto: McClelland and Stewart.

ROTHE, J. P. 1968: Fill a dam, start an earthquake. *New Sci.* **39**, 75–8.

RUBINOFF, I. 1968: Central American sea-level canal: possible biological effects. *Science* **161**, 857–61.

RUDD, R. L. 1963: *Pesticides and the living landscape.* Madison: University of Wisconsin Press.

RUSSELL, C. S. and LANDSBERG, H. H. 1971: International environmental problems—a taxonomy. *Science* **172**, 1307–14.

RYTHER, J. 1969: Photosynthesis and fish production in the sea. *Science* **166**, 72–6.

SAARINEN, T. F. 1966: *Perception of the drought hazard on the Great Plains.* Chicago: University of Chicago Department of Geography Research Papers **106**.

— 1969: *Perception of environment.* Washington, DC: AAG Resource Paper **5**.

SABLOFF, J. A. 1971: The collapse of classic Maya civilization. In J. A. Harte and R. H. Socolow (eds.), 16–27.

SAGE, B. L. 1970: Oil and Alaskan ecology. *New Sci.* **46**, 175–7.

SAN PIETRO, A., GREER, F. and ARMY, T. J. (eds.) 1967: *Harvesting the sun*. London and New York: Academic Press.

SARGENT, F. 1969: A dangerous game: taming the weather. In G. W. Cox (ed.), 569–82.

SASKATCHEWAN-NELSON BASIN BOARD 1972: *Water supply for the Saskatchewan-Nelson Basin: a summary report*. Ottawa: Information Canada.

SASSI, T. 1970: The harmful side effects of pesticide use. In A. J. Van Tassel (ed.), 361–95.

SATER, J. E., RONHOVE, A. G. and VAN ALLEN, L. C. 1972: *Arctic environments and resources*. Washington, DC: Arctic Institute of North America.

SAUER, C. O. 1952: *Agricultural origins and dispersals*. New York: American Geographical Society (reprinted 1969, MIT Press).

— 1961: Fire and early man. *Paideuma* 7, 399–407; reprinted in J. Leighley (ed.), 1963, *Land and life*. Berkeley and Los Angeles: University of California Press, 288–99.

SAWYER, C. N. 1966: Basic concepts of eutrophication. *J. Wat. Polln. Control Fedn.* **38**, 737–44.

SCHAEFER, V. J. 1970: The inadvertent modification of the atmosphere by air pollution. In S. F. Singer (ED.), 1970a, 158–74.

SCHEIDER, E. V. 1962: The meaning of leisure in an industrial society. In *Recreation in wildland management*, University of California Extra-mural Forestry Field School report. Berkeley: University of California School of Forestry.

SCHUBERT, J. and LAPP, R. E. 1957: *Radiation*. New York: Viking Press.

SCHULTZ, A. M. 1964: The nutrient-recovery hypothesis for arctic microtine cycles. 2: Ecosystem variables in relation to arctic microtine cycles. In D. J. Crisp (ed.), 57–68.

— 1967: The ecosystem as a conceptual tool in the management of natural resources. In S. V. Ciriacy Wantrup and J. J. Parsons (eds.), 139–61.

SCHURR, S. H. (ed.) 1972: *Energy, economic growth and the environment*. Baltimore: Johns Hopkins Press for RFF.

'SCIENTIFIC AMERICAN' (ed.) 1970: *The biosphere*. San Francisco and London: Freeman.

SCOTTER, G. W. 1970: Reindeer husbandry as a land use in northern Canada. In W. A. Fuller and P. G. Kevan (eds.), 159–69.

SCRIMSHAW, N. 1970: Food. In J. Janick (ed.), 206–14.

SEARS, P. B. 1956: The importance of forests to man. In S. Haden-Guest (ed.), 3–12.

SEHLIN, H. 1966: The importance of open-air recreation. In *First International Congress on Leisure and Tourism*, Theme **1**, Report **1**. Rotterdam: Alliance Internationale de Tourisme.

SEMPLE, A. T. 1971: Grassland improvement in Africa. *Biol. Cons.* **3**, 173–80.

SENGE, T. 1969: The planning of national parks in Japan and other parts of Asia. In J. G. Nelson and R. C. Scace (eds.), 706–21.

SEWELL, W. R. D. and BURTON, I. 1971: *Perceptions and attitudes in resource management*. Canadian Department of Energy, Mines and Resources Resource Paper **2**. Ottawa: Information Canada.

SHACKLADY, C. A. 1969: The production and evaluation of protein derived from organisms grown on hydrocarbon residues. *Proc. Nutrition Soc.* **28**, 91–7.

SHAPLEY, D. 1973: Sorghum: 'miracle' grain for the world protein shortage. *Science* **182**, 147–8.

SHELL OIL COMPANY 1972: *The national energy position.* (?) Houston: Shell Oil Co.

SHEPARD, P. and MCKINLEY, D. 1971: *Environ/mental: essays on the planet as a home.* Boston: Houghton Mifflin.

SIMMONS, I. G. 1966: Wilderness in the mid-20th century USA. *Town Planning Rev.* **36**, 249–56.

— 1967: How do we plan for change? *Landscape* **17**, 22–4.

— 1971: *Sequoia sempervirens*: conflicts over conservation. *Advmt. Sci.* **27**, 301–3.

— 1973: The protection of ecosystems and landscapes in Hokkaido, Japan. *Biol. Cons.* **5**, 281–9.

SIMONS, M. 1969: Long term trends in water use. In R. J. Chorley (ed.), 535–44.

SINDEN, J. A. and SINDEN, L. B. 1964: A forest recreation survey: implications for future development. *Scottish Forestry* **18**, 120–27.

SINGER, S. F. (ed.) 1970a: *Global effects of environmental pollution.* Dordrecht: Reidel.

— 1970b: Human energy production as a process in the biosphere. In Scientific American (ed.), 105–13.

— (ed.) 1971: *Is there an optimum level of population?* New York: McGraw-Hill.

SMITH, K. 1972: *Water in Britain.* London: Macmillan.

SOLOMON, M. E. 1969: *Population dynamics.* London: Edward Arnold.

SONNENFELD, J. 1966: Variable values in space landscape: an enquiry into the nature of environmental necessity. *J. Social Issues* **22**, 71–82.

SPENCER, J. E. 1966: *Shifting cultivation in SE Asia.* Berkeley and Los Angeles: University of California Press.

SPILHAUS, A. 1972: Ecolibrium. *Science* **175**, 711–15.

STAATSBOSBEHEER (NETHERLANDS) 1966: *The task of the State Forest Service in the Netherlands.* Utrecht: SBB.

STAMP, L. D. 1969: *Nature conservation in Britain.* London: Collins.

STARK, N. 1972: Nutrient cycling pathways and litter fungi. *Bioscience* **22**, 355–60.

STATHAM, D. C. 1971: Development of the Yorkshire potash industry. *Town Planning Rev.* **42**, 361–76.

STERN, A. C. (ed.) 1968: *Air pollution.* 2 vols. 2nd edn. London and New York: Academic Press.

STEWART, C. M. 1970: Family limitation programmes in various countries. In A. Allison (ed.), 204–21.

STODDART, D. R. 1968: The Aldabra affair. *Biol. Cons.* **1**, 63–70.

STODDART, D. R. and WRIGHT, C. A. 1967: Ecology of Aldabra atoll. *Nature, Lond.* **213**, 1173–7.

STOTT, D. H. 1962: Checks on population growth. In A. Montague (ed.), 355–76.

STREETER, D. C. 1971: The effects of public pressure on the vegetation of chalk downland at Box Hill, Surrey. In E. Duffey and A. S. Watt (eds.), 459–68.

STROBBE, M. A. (ed.) 1971: *Understanding environmental pollution.* St Louis: Mosby.

STUDY OF CRITICAL ENVIRONMENTAL PROBLEMS 1970: *Man's impact on the global environment: assessment and recommendation for action.* Cambridge, Mass.: MIT Press.

STUDY OF MAN'S IMPACT ON CLIMATE 1971: *Inadvertent climate modification.* Cambridge, Mass.: MIT Press.

SUMMERS, C. 1971: The conversion of energy. *Sci. Amer.* **224** (3), 149–60.

SWANK, W. G. 1972: Wildlife management in Masailand, east Africa. *Trans. 37th North American Wildlife and Natural Resources Conference,* 278–87.

SWEET, L. E. 1965: Camel pastoralism in N. Arabia and the minimal camping unit. In A. Leeds and A. P. Vayda (eds.), 129–52.

TAGHI FARVAR, M. and MILTON, J. P. (eds.) 1972: *The careless technology: ecology and international development.* New York: Natural History Press.

TAIGANIDES, E. P. 1967: The animal waste disposal problem. In N. C. Brady (ed.), 385–394.

TALBOT, L. M. 1966: *Wild animals as a source of food.* US Department of the Interior Bureau of Sport, Fisheries and Wildlife Special Scientific Report—Wildlife **98**. Washington, DC.

— 1972: Ecological consequences of rangeland development in Masailand, east Africa. In M. Taghi Farvar and J. P. Milton (eds.), 694–711.

TALBOT, L. M. and TALBOT, M. H. 1963: The high biomass of wild ungulates on east African savanna. *Trans. 28th North Amer. Wildlife Conf.,* 465–76.

— (eds.) 1968: *Conservation in tropical south east Asia.* IUCN Publications New Series **10**. Morges: IUCN.

TANSLEY, A. G. 1935: The use and abuse of vegetational concepts and terms. *Ecology* **16**, 284–307.

TATTON, J. O'G. and RUZICKA, J. H. A. 1967: Organochlorine pesticides in Antarctica. *Nature, Lond.* **215**, 346–8.

THOMAS, T. M. 1973: World energy sources: survey and review. *Geogr. Rev.* **63**, 246–58.

THOMAS, W. L. (ed.) 1956: *Man's role in changing the face of the earth.* Chicago: University of Chicago Press.

THORSTEINSSON, I., OLAFSSON, G. and VAN DYNE, G. M. 1971: Range resources of Iceland. *J. Range Management* **24**, 86–93.

TOYNBEE, A. 1972: The religious background of the present environmental crisis. *Int. J. Environ. Studs.* **3**, 141–6.

TREWARTHA, G. T. 1969: *A geography of population: world patterns.* London: Wiley.

TSCHIRLEY, F. H. 1969: Defoliation in Vietnam. *Science* **163**, 779–86.

TUAN, YI FU 1968: Discrepancies between environmental attitude and behaviour: examples from Europe and China. *Canad. Geogr.* **13**, 176–91.

TURNER, J. 1962: The *Tilia* decline: an anthropogenic interpretation. *New Phytol.* **61**, 328–41.

UCKO, P. J. and DIMBLEBY, G. W. (eds.) 1969: *The domestication and exploitation of plants and animals.* London: Duckworth.

UNESCO 1970: *Use and conservation of the biosphere.* Paris: UNESCO Natural Resources Research **X**.

UNGER, J. 1971: Profits from waste. *Far Eastern Economic Review* **73**, 51–2.

UNITED KINGDOM 1970: 'The Countryside in 1970', 3rd Conference, Report **4**: *Refuse disposal.* London: HMSO.

UNITED NATIONS (annually): *Demographic yearbook.* New York: UNO.

— (annually): *Statistical yearbook.* New York: UNO.

DEPARTMENT OF SOCIAL AFFAIRS 1953: *The determinants and consequences of population trends.* New York: UN Population Study **17**.

DEPARTMENT OF ECONOMIC AND SOCIAL AFFAIRS 1958: *The future growth of world population.* New York: UN Population Study **28**.

— 1964: *World population prospects as assessed in 1963.* New York: UN Population Study **41**.

US COMMISSION ON POPULATION GROWTH AND THE AMERICAN FUTURE 1972: *Population and the American future.* Washington, DC: US Government Printing Office/New York: New American Library.

US CONGRESS 1970: *Phosphates in detergents and the eutrophication of America's waters.* Washington, DC: House of Representatives Report **91–1004**.

US DEPARTMENT OF AGRICULTURE 1955: *Water.* Yearbook of agriculture 1955. Washington, DC: US Government Printing Office.

US DEPARTMENT OF THE INTERIOR 1967: *Surface mining and our environment.* Report of the Strip and Surface Mine Study Policy Committee. Washington, DC: US Government Printing Office.

US FEDERAL COUNCIL FOR SCIENCE AND TECHNOLOGY, COMMITTEE ON ENVIRONMENTAL QUALITY 1968: *Noise-sound without value.* Washington, DC: US Government Printing Office.

US GEOLOGICAL SURVEY 1970: *Mercury in the environment.* Washington, DC: USGS Professional Paper **713**.

US NATIONAL PARKS SERVICE 1967: *Administrative policies for natural areas of the National Park system.* Washington, DC: US Government Printing Office.

US PRESIDENT'S COUNCIL ON ENVIRONMENTAL QUALITY 1971: *Environmental quality 1971.* Washington, DC: US Government Printing Office.

US PRESIDENT'S COUNCIL ON RECREATION AND NATURAL BEAUTY 1968: *From sea to shining sea.* Washington, DC: US Government Printing Office.

US PRESIDENT'S SCIENCE ADVISORY COMMITTEE 1967a: Losses and protection of food. In *The world food problem.* Washington, DC: US Government Printing Office; abridged version reprinted in R. Revelle *et al.* (eds.), 257–72.

— 1967b: Agricultural-technical and resource opportunities. In *The world food problem.* Washington, DC: US Government Printing Office; abridged version reprinted in R. Revelle *et al.* (eds.), 242–9.

VALÉRY, N. 1974: The best substitute for petrol may be petrol. *New Sci.* **61**, 203–5.

VAN DER SCHALIE, H. 1972: WHO project Egypt 10: a case history of a schistosomiasis control project. In M. Taghi Farvar and J. P. Milton (eds.), 116–36.

VAN DYNE, G. M. (ed.) 1969: *The ecosystem concept in resource management.* London and New York: Academic Press.

VAN HYLCKAMA, T. E. A. 1971: Water resources. In W. W. Murdoch (ed.), 148–52.

VAN RENSBURG, H. J. 1969: *Management and utilization of pastures in east Africa (Kenya, Tanzania, Uganda).* FAO Pasture and Fodder Crop Series **3**. Rome: FAO.

VAN TASSEL, A. J. (ed.) 1970: *Environmental side effects of rising industrial output.* Lexington, Mass.: Heath Lexington.

VAYDA, A. P. (ed.) 1969: *Environment and cultural behavior.* New York: Natural History Press.

VERNEY, R. B. 1972: *Sinews for survival: a report on the management of natural resources.* London: HMSO for the Department of the Environment.

VICKERY, P. J. 1972: Grazing and net primary production of a temperate grassland. *J. Appl. Ecol.* **9**, 307–14.

WADE, N. 1973: World food situation: pessimism comes back into vogue. *Science* **181**, 634–8.

WAGAR, J. A. 1970: Growth versus the quality of life. *Science* **168**, 1179–84.

WALFORD, L. A. 1958: *Living resources of the sea.* New York: Ronald Press.

WALKER, C. 1971: *Environmental pollution by chemicals.* London: Hutchinson.

WARD, B. and DUBOS, R. 1972: *Only one earth.* Harmondsworth: Penguin.

WARD, M. A. (ed.) 1970: *Man and his environment.* Part 1. Oxford: Pergamon Press.

WAREING, P. F. and COOPER, J. P. (eds.) 1971: *Potential crop production.* London: Heinemann.

WATER RESOURCES BOARD 1966: *Water supplies in SE England.* London: HMSO.

— 1969: *Planning our future water supply.* London: HMSO.

— 1970: *Water resources in the north.* London: HMSO.

WATT, K. E. F. 1965: Community stability and the strategy of biological control. *Canad. Entomol.* **97**, 887–95.

— 1968: *Ecology and resource management: a quantitative approach.* New York: McGraw-Hill.

— 1973: *Principles of environmental science.* New York: McGraw-Hill.

WATTERS, R. F. 1960: The nature of shifting cultivation: a review of recent research. *Pacific Viewpoint* **1**, 59–99.

WATTS, D. 1971: *Principles of biogeography.* London: McGraw-Hill.

WECK, J. and WIEBECKE, C. 1961: *Weltwirtschaft und Deutschlands Forst- und Holzwirtschaft.* Munich: Bayerischer Landwirtschaftsverlag.

WEINBERG, A. M. 1968: Raw materials unlimited. *Texas Quarterly* **11**, 92–102.

WEINBERG, A. M. and HAMMOND, R. P. 1971: Limits to the use of energy. In S. F. Singer (ed.), 42–56.

WEINER, N. 1950: *The human use of human beings.* Boston: Houghton Mifflin.

WEISZ, J. A. 1970: The environmental effects of surface mining and mineral waste generation. In A. J. Van Tassel (ed.), 291–312.

WEST, O. 1972: The ecological impact of the introduction of domestic cattle into wild life and tsetse areas of Rhodesia. In M. Taghi Farvar and J. P. Milton (eds.), 712–25.

WESTHOFF, V. 1970: New criteria for nature reserves. *New Sci.* **46**, 108–13.

WESTING, A. H. and PFEIFFER, E. W. 1972: The cratering of Indochina. *Sci. Amer.* **226** (5), 21–9.

WESTOBY, J. C. 1963: The role of forest industries in the attack on economic underdevelopment. *Unasylva* **16**, 168–201.

WHARTON, C. R. 1969: The green revolution: cornucopia or Pandora's box? *Foreign Affairs* (April), 464–76.

WHITE, G. F. (ed.) 1964: *Choice of adjustment to floods.* Chicago: University of Chicago Department of Geography Research Paper **93**.

— 1966: *Alternatives in water management.* Washington, DC: NAS/NRC Publication 1408.

WHITESIDE, T. 1970: *Defoliation.* New York: Ballantine/Friends of the Earth.

WIENS, J. A. (ed.) 1971: *Ecosystem structure and function.* Corvallis: Oregon State UP.

WILLARD, B. E. and MARR, J. W. 1970: Effects of human activities on alpine tundra ecosystems in Rocky Mountain National Park, Colorado. *Biol. Cons.* **2**, 257–65.

WILLIAMS, M. 1971: Lead pollution on trial. *New Sci.* **51**, 578–80.

WILLIAMS, W. A. 1966: Range improvement as related to net productivity, energy flow and foliage configuration. *J. Range Management* **19**, 29–34.

WOLFERS, D. 1971: The case against zero growth. *Intern. J. Env. Studs.* **1**, 227–32.

WOLLMAN, N. 1960: *A preliminary report on the supply of and demand for water in the US as estimated for 1980 and 2000.* Washington, DC: US Senate Select Committee on Water Resources 86th Congress 2nd Session, Committee Report **32**.

WOLMAN, A. 1965: The metabolism of cities. *Sci. Amer.* **218** (9), 179–90.

WOLMAN, M. G. 1971: The nation's rivers. *Science* **174**, 905–18.

WOODBURN, J. 1968: An introduction to Hadza ecology. In R. B. Lee and I. De Vore (eds.), 1968a, 49–55.

WOODIS, J. 1971: An introduction to neo-colonialism. In R. Revelle *et al.* (eds.), 303–12.

WOODWELL, G. M. 1963: The ecological effects of radiation. *Sci. Amer.* **208** (6), 2–11.

— 1967a: Toxic substances and ecological cycles. *Sci. Amer.* **216** (3), 24–31.

— 1967b: Radiation and the pattern of nature. *Science* **156**, 461–70.

— 1970a: The energy cycle of the biosphere. In *Scientific American* (ed.), 25–35.

— 1970b: Effects of pollution on the structure and physiology of ecosystems. *Science* **168**, 429–33.

WOODWELL, G. M., CRAIG, P. P. and JOHNSON, H. A. 1971: DDT in the biosphere: where does it go? *Science* **174**, 1101–7.

WOODWELL, G. M. and SMITH, H. H. (eds.) 1969: *Diversity and stability in ecological systems.* Upton, NY: Brookhaven Symp. Biol. **22**.

WOODWELL, G. M., WURSTER, C. F. and ISAACSON, P. A. 1967: DDT residues in an east coast estuary. *Science* **156**, 821–4.

WURSTER, C. F. 1968: DDT reduces photosynthesis by marine phytoplankton. *Science* **159**, 1474–5.

— 1969: Chlorinated hydrocarbon insecticides and the world ecosystem. *Biol. Cons.* **1**, 123–9.

WYNNE-EDWARDS, V. C. 1962: *Animal dispersal in relation to social behavior.* New York: Hafner.

YOUNG, G. 1973: *Tourism: blessing or blight?* Harmondsworth: Penguin.

ZELINSKY, W. 1966: *A prologue to population geography.* New York: Prentice-Hall.

— 1970: Beyond the exponentials: the role of geography in the great transition. *Econ. Geogr.* **46**, 498–535.

ZELINSKY, W., KOSINSKI, L. A. and PROTHERO, R. M. (eds.) 1970: *Geography and a crowding world.* New York: Oxford University Press.

ZELLER, E. J., SAUNDERS, D. F. and ANGINO, E. E. 1973: Putting radioactive wastes on ice: a proposal for an international radionuclide depository in Antarctica. *Bull. Atom. Sci.* **29** (1), 4–9, 50–52.

ZEUNER, F. E. 1964: *A history of domesticated animals.* London: Methuen.

ZOBELL, C. E. 1964: The occurrence, effects and fate of oil polluting the sea. *Adv. Water Polln. Res.* **3**, 85–109.

ZU LOWENSTEIN, H. 1969: The story of a sophisticated breed. *Ceres* **2** (1), 44–6.

Index

Prepared by Brenda Hall, MA, Registered Indexer of the Society of Indexers